Gulliver's Travels

by

Jonathan Swift

The Echo Library 2011

Published by

The Echo Library

Echo Library
Unit 22
Horcott Industrial Estate
Horcott Road
Fairford
Glos. GL7 4BX

www.echo-library.com

Please report serious faults in the text to complaints@echo-library.com

ISBN 978-1-4480-1909-0

CONTENTS

THE PUBLISHER TO THE READER.

[As given in the original edition.]

The author of these Travels, Mr. Lemuel Gulliver, is my ancient and intimate friend; there is likewise some relation between us on the mother's side. About three years ago, Mr. Gulliver growing weary of the concourse of curious people coming to him at his house in Redriff, made a small purchase of land, with a convenient house, near Newark, in Nottinghamshire, his native country; where he now lives retired, yet in good esteem among his neighbours.

Although Mr. Gulliver was born in Nottinghamshire, where his father dwelt, yet I have heard him say his family came from Oxfordshire; to confirm which, I have observed in the churchyard at Banbury in that county, several tombs and monuments of the Gullivers.

Before he quitted Redriff, he left the custody of the following papers in my hands, with the liberty to dispose of them as I should think fit. I have carefully perused them three times. The style is very plain and simple; and the only fault I find is, that the author, after the manner of travellers, is a little too circumstantial. There is an air of truth apparent through the whole; and indeed the author was so distinguished for his veracity, that it became a sort of proverb among his neighbours at Redriff, when any one affirmed a thing, to say, it was as true as if Mr. Gulliver had spoken it.

By the advice of several worthy persons, to whom, with the author's permission, I communicated these papers, I now venture to send them into the world, hoping they may be, at least for some time, a better entertainment to our young noblemen, than the common scribbles of politics and party.

This volume would have been at least twice as large, if I had not made bold to strike out innumerable passages relating to the winds and tides, as well as to the variations and bearings in the several voyages, together with the minute descriptions of the management of the ship in storms, in the style of sailors; likewise the account of longitudes and latitudes; wherein I have reason to apprehend, that Mr. Gulliver may be a little dissatisfied. But I was resolved to fit the work as much as possible to the general capacity of readers. However, if my own ignorance in sea affairs shall have led me to commit some mistakes, I alone am answerable for them. And if any traveller hath a curiosity to see the whole work at large, as it came from the hands of the author, I will be ready to gratify him.

As for any further particulars relating to the author, the reader will receive satisfaction from the first pages of the book.

RICHARD SYMPSON.

A LETTER FROM CAPTAIN GULLIVER TO HIS COUSIN SYMPSON.

WRITTEN IN THE YEAR 1727.

I hope you will be ready to own publicly, whenever you shall be called to it, that by your great and frequent urgency you prevailed on me to publish a very loose and uncorrect account of my travels, with directions to hire some young gentleman of either university to put them in order, and correct the style, as my cousin Dampier did, by my advice, in his book called "A Voyage round the world." But I do not remember I gave you power to consent that any thing should be omitted, and much less that any thing should be inserted; therefore, as to the latter, I do here renounce every thing of that kind; particularly a paragraph about her majesty Queen Anne, of most pious and glorious memory; although I did reverence and esteem her more than any of human species. But you, or your interpolator, ought to have considered, that it was not my inclination, so was it not decent to praise any animal of our composition before my master Houyhnhnm: And besides, the fact was altogether false; for to my knowledge, being in England during some part of her majesty's reign, she did govern by a chief minister; nay even by two successively, the first whereof was the lord of Godolphin, and the second the lord of Oxford; so that you have made me say the thing that was not. Likewise in the account of the academy of projectors, and several passages of my discourse to my master Houyhnhnm, you have either omitted some material circumstances, or minced or changed them in such a manner, that I do hardly know my own work. When I formerly hinted to you something of this in a letter, you were pleased to answer that you were afraid of giving offence; that people in power were very watchful over the press, and apt not only to interpret, but to punish every thing which looked like an innuendo (as I think you call it). But, pray how could that which I spoke so many years ago, and at about five thousand leagues distance, in another reign, be applied to any of the Yahoos, who now are said to govern the herd; especially at a time when I little thought, or feared, the unhappiness of living under them? Have not I the most reason to complain, when I see these very Yahoos carried by Houyhnhnms in a vehicle, as if they were brutes, and those the rational creatures? And indeed to avoid so monstrous and detestable a sight was one principal motive of my retirement hither.

Thus much I thought proper to tell you in relation to yourself, and to the trust I reposed in you.

I do, in the next place, complain of my own great want of judgment, in being prevailed upon by the entreaties and false reasoning of you and some others, very much against my own opinion, to suffer my travels to be published. Pray bring to your mind how often I desired you to consider, when you insisted on the motive of public good, that the Yahoos were a species of animals utterly incapable of amendment by precept or example: and so it has proved; for, instead of seeing a full stop put to all abuses and corruptions, at least in this little island, as I had reason to expect; behold, after above six months warning, I cannot learn that my book has produced one single effect according to my intentions. I desired you would let me know, by a letter, when party and faction were extinguished; judges learned and upright; pleaders honest and modest, with some tincture of common sense, and Smithfield blazing with pyramids of law books; the young nobility's education entirely changed; the physicians banished; the female Yahoos abounding in virtue, honour, truth, and good sense; courts and levees of great ministers thoroughly weeded and swept; wit, merit, and learning rewarded; all disgracers of the press in prose and verse condemned to eat nothing but their own cotton, and quench their thirst with their own ink. These, and a thousand other reformations, I firmly counted upon by your encouragement; as indeed they were plainly deducible from the precepts delivered in my book. And it must be owned, that seven months were a sufficient time to correct every vice and folly to which Yahoos are subject, if their natures had been capable of the least disposition to virtue or wisdom. Yet, so far have you been from answering my expectation in any of your letters; that on the contrary you are loading our carrier every week with libels, and keys, and reflections, and memoirs, and second parts; wherein I see myself accused of reflecting upon great state folk; of degrading human nature (for so they have still the confidence to style it), and of abusing the female sex. I find likewise that the writers of those bundles are not agreed among themselves; for some of them will not allow me to be the author of my own travels; and others make me author of books to which I am wholly a stranger.

I find likewise that your printer has been so careless as to confound the times, and mistake the dates, of my several voyages and returns; neither assigning the true year, nor the true month, nor day of the month: and I hear the original manuscript is all destroyed since the publication of my book; neither have I any copy left: however, I have sent you some corrections, which you may insert, if ever there should be a second edition: and yet I cannot stand to them; but shall leave that matter to my judicious and candid readers to adjust it as they please.

I hear some of our sea Yahoos find fault with my sea-language, as not proper in many parts, nor now in use. I cannot help it. In my first voyages, while I was young, I was instructed by the oldest mariners, and learned to speak as they did. But I have since found that the sea Yahoos are apt, like the land ones, to become new- fangled in their words, which the latter change every year; insomuch, as I remember upon each return to my own country their old dialect was so altered, that I could hardly understand the new. And I observe, when any Yahoo comes from London out of curiosity to visit me at my house, we neither of us are able to deliver our conceptions in a manner intelligible to the other.

If the censure of the Yahoos could any way affect me, I should have great reason to complain, that some of them are so bold as to think my book of travels a mere fiction out of mine own brain, and have gone so far as to drop hints, that the Houyhnhnms and Yahoos have no more existence than the inhabitants of Utopia.

Indeed I must confess, that as to the people of Lilliput, Brobdingrag (for so the word should have been spelt, and not erroneously Brobdingnag), and Laputa, I have never yet heard of any Yahoo so presumptuous as to dispute their being, or the facts I have related concerning them; because the truth immediately strikes every reader with conviction. And is there less probability in my account of the Houyhnhnms or Yahoos, when it is manifest as to the latter, there are so many thousands even in this country, who only differ from their brother brutes in Houyhnhnmland, because they use a sort of jabber, and do not go naked? I wrote for their amendment, and not their approbation. The united praise of the whole race would be of less consequence to me, than the neighing of those two degenerate Houyhnhnms I keep in my stable; because from these, degenerate as they are, I still improve in some virtues without any mixture of vice.

Do these miserable animals presume to think, that I am so degenerated as to defend my veracity? Yahoo as I am, it is well known through all Houyhnhnmland, that, by the instructions and example of my illustrious master, I was able in the compass of two years (although I confess with the utmost difficulty) to remove that infernal habit of lying, shuffling, deceiving, and equivocating, so deeply rooted in the very souls of all my species; especially the Europeans.

I have other complaints to make upon this vexatious occasion; but I forbear troubling myself or you any further. I must freely confess, that since my last return, some corruptions of my Yahoo nature have revived in me by conversing with a few of your species, and particularly those of my own family, by an unavoidable necessity; else I should never have attempted so absurd a project as that of reforming the Yahoo race in this kingdom: But I have now done with all such visionary schemes for ever.

April 2, 1727

PART I—A VOYAGE TO LILLIPUT.

CHAPTER I.

[The author gives some account of himself and family. His first inducements to travel. He is shipwrecked, and swims for his life. Gets safe on shore in the country of Lilliput; is made a prisoner, and carried up the country.]

My father had a small estate in Nottinghamshire: I was the third of five sons. He sent me to Emanuel College in Cambridge at fourteen years old, where I resided three years, and applied myself close to my studies; but the charge of maintaining me, although I had a very scanty allowance, being too great for a narrow fortune, I was bound apprentice to Mr. James Bates, an eminent surgeon in London, with whom I continued four years. My father now and then sending me small sums of money, I laid them out in learning navigation, and other parts of the mathematics, useful to those who intend to travel, as I always believed it would be, some time or other, my fortune to do. When I left Mr. Bates, I went down to my father: where, by the assistance of him and my uncle John, and some other relations, I got forty pounds, and a promise of thirty pounds a year to maintain me at Leyden: there I studied physic two years and seven months, knowing it would be useful in long voyages.

Soon after my return from Leyden, I was recommended by my good master, Mr. Bates, to be surgeon to the Swallow, Captain Abraham Pannel, commander; with whom I continued three years and a half, making a voyage or two into the Levant, and some other parts. When I came back I resolved to settle in London; to which Mr. Bates, my master, encouraged me, and by him I was recommended to several patients. I took part of a small house in the Old Jewry; and being advised to alter my condition, I married Mrs. Mary Burton, second daughter to Mr. Edmund Burton, hosier, in Newgate-street, with whom I received four hundred pounds for a portion.

But my good master Bates dying in two years after, and I having few friends, my business began to fail; for my conscience would not suffer me to imitate the bad practice of too many among my brethren. Having therefore consulted with my wife, and some of my acquaintance, I determined to go again to sea. I was surgeon successively in two ships, and made several voyages, for six years, to the East and West Indies, by which I got some addition to my fortune. My hours of leisure I spent in reading the best authors, ancient and modern, being always provided with a good number of books; and when I was ashore, in observing the manners and dispositions of the people, as well as learning their language; wherein I had a great facility, by the strength of my memory.

The last of these voyages not proving very fortunate, I grew weary of the sea, and intended to stay at home with my wife and family. I removed from the Old Jewry to Fetter Lane, and from thence to Wapping, hoping to get business among the sailors; but it would not turn to account. After three years expectation that things would mend, I accepted an advantageous offer from

Captain William Prichard, master of the Antelope, who was making a voyage to the South Sea. We set sail from Bristol, May 4, 1699, and our voyage was at first very prosperous.

It would not be proper, for some reasons, to trouble the reader with the particulars of our adventures in those seas; let it suffice to inform him, that in our passage from thence to the East Indies, we were driven by a violent storm to the north-west of Van Diemen's Land. By an observation, we found ourselves in the latitude of 30 degrees 2 minutes south. Twelve of our crew were dead by immoderate labour and ill food; the rest were in a very weak condition. On the 5th of November, which was the beginning of summer in those parts, the weather being very hazy, the seamen spied a rock within half a cable's length of the ship; but the wind was so strong, that we were driven directly upon it, and immediately split. Six of the crew, of whom I was one, having let down the boat into the sea, made a shift to get clear of the ship and the rock. We rowed, by my computation, about three leagues, till we were able to work no longer, being already spent with labour while we were in the ship. We therefore trusted ourselves to the mercy of the waves, and in about half an hour the boat was overset by a sudden flurry from the north. What became of my companions in the boat, as well as of those who escaped on the rock, or were left in the vessel, I cannot tell; but conclude they were all lost. For my own part, I swam as fortune directed me, and was pushed forward by wind and tide. I often let my legs drop, and could feel no bottom; but when I was almost gone, and able to struggle no longer, I found myself within my depth; and by this time the storm was much abated. The declivity was so small, that I walked near a mile before I got to the shore, which I conjectured was about eight o'clock in the evening. I then advanced forward near half a mile, but could not discover any sign of houses or inhabitants; at least I was in so weak a condition, that I did not observe them. I was extremely tired, and with that, and the heat of the weather, and about half a pint of brandy that I drank as I left the ship, I found myself much inclined to sleep. I lay down on the grass, which was very short and soft, where I slept sounder than ever I remembered to have done in my life, and, as I reckoned, about nine hours; for when I awaked, it was just day-light. I attempted to rise, but was not able to stir: for, as I happened to lie on my back, I found my arms and legs were strongly fastened on each side to the ground; and my hair, which was long and thick, tied down in the same manner. I likewise felt several slender ligatures across my body, from my arm-pits to my thighs. I could only look upwards; the sun began to grow hot, and the light offended my eyes. I heard a confused noise about me; but in the posture I lay, could see nothing except the sky. In a little time I felt something alive moving on my left leg, which advancing gently forward over my breast, came almost up to my chin; when, bending my eyes downwards as much as I could, I perceived it to be a human creature not six inches high, with a bow and arrow in his hands, and a quiver at his back. In the mean time, I felt at least forty more of the same kind (as I conjectured) following the first. I was in the utmost astonishment, and roared so loud, that they all ran back in a fright; and some of them, as I was afterwards told, were hurt with the falls they got by leaping from my sides upon the ground. However, they soon returned, and one of them, who ventured so far as to get a full sight of my face, lifting up his hands and eyes by way of admiration, cried out in a shrill but distinct voice, Hekinah degul: the others repeated the same words several times, but then I knew not what they meant. I lay all this while, as the reader may believe, in great uneasiness. At length, struggling to get loose, I had the fortune to break the strings, and wrench out the pegs that fastened my left arm to the ground; for, by lifting it up to my face, I discovered the methods they had taken to bind me, and at the same time with a violent pull, which gave me excessive pain, I a little loosened the strings that tied down my hair on the left side, so that I was just able to turn my head about two inches. But the creatures ran off a second time, before I could seize them; whereupon there was a great shout in a very shrill accent, and after it ceased I heard one of them cry aloud Tolgo phonac; when in an instant I felt above a hundred arrows discharged on my left hand, which, pricked me like so many needles; and besides, they shot another flight into the air, as we do bombs in Europe, whereof many, I suppose, fell on my body, (though I felt them not), and some on my face, which I immediately covered with my left hand. When this shower of arrows was over, I fell a groaning with grief and pain; and then striving again to get loose, they discharged another volley larger than the first, and some of them attempted with spears to stick me in the sides; but by good luck I had on a buff jerkin, which they could not pierce. I thought it the most prudent method to lie still, and my design was to continue so till night, when, my left hand being already loose, I could easily free myself: and as for the inhabitants, I had reason to believe I might be a match for the greatest army they could bring against me, if they were all of the same size with him that I saw. But fortune disposed otherwise of me. When the people observed I was quiet, they discharged no more arrows; but, by the noise I heard, I knew their numbers increased; and about four yards from me, over against my right ear, I heard a knocking for above an hour, like that of people at work; when turning my head that way, as well as the pegs and strings would permit me, I saw a stage erected about a foot and a half from the ground, capable of holding four of the inhabitants, with two or three ladders to mount it: from whence one of them, who seemed to be a person of quality, made me a long speech, whereof I understood not one syllable. But I should have mentioned, that before the principal person began his oration, he cried out three times, Langro dehul san (these words and the former were afterwards repeated and explained to me); whereupon, immediately, about fifty of the inhabitants came and cut the strings that fastened the left side of my head, which gave me the liberty of turning it to the right, and of observing the person and gesture of him that was to speak. He appeared to be of a middle age, and taller than any of the other three who attended him, whereof one was a page that held up his train, and seemed to be somewhat longer than my middle finger; the other two stood one on each side to support him. He acted every part of an orator, and I could observe many periods of threatenings, and others of promises, pity, and kindness. I answered in a few words, but in the most submissive manner, lifting up my left hand, and both my eyes to the sun, as calling him for a witness; and being almost famished with hunger, having not eaten a morsel for some hours before I left the ship, I found the demands of nature so strong upon me, that I could not forbear showing my impatience (perhaps against the strict rules of decency) by putting my finger frequently to my mouth, to signify that I wanted food. The hurgo (for so they call a great lord, as I afterwards learnt) understood me very well. He descended from the stage, and commanded that several ladders should be applied to my sides, on which above a hundred of the inhabitants mounted and walked towards my mouth, laden with baskets full of meat, which had been provided and sent thither by the king's orders, upon the first intelligence he received of me. I observed there was the flesh of several animals, but could not distinguish them by the taste. There were shoulders, legs, and loins, shaped like those of mutton, and very well dressed, but smaller than the wings of a lark. I ate them by two or three at a mouthful, and took three loaves at a time, about the bigness of musket bullets. They supplied me as fast as they could, showing a thousand marks of wonder and astonishment at my bulk and appetite. I then made another sign, that I wanted drink. They found by my eating that a small quantity would not suffice me; and being a most ingenious people, they slung up, with great dexterity, one of their largest hogsheads, then rolled it towards my hand, and beat out the top; I drank it off at a draught, which I might well do, for it did not hold half a pint, and tasted like a small wine of Burgundy, but much more delicious. They brought me a second hogshead, which I drank in the same manner, and made signs for more; but they had none to give me. When I had performed these wonders, they shouted for joy, and danced upon my breast, repeating several times as they did at first, Hekinah degul. They made me a sign that I should throw down the two hogsheads, but first warning the people below to stand out of the way, crying aloud, Borach mevolah; and when they saw the vessels in the air, there was a universal shout of Hekinah degul. I confess I was often tempted, while they were passing backwards and forwards on my body, to seize forty or fifty of the first that came in my reach, and dash them against the ground. But the remembrance of what I had felt, which probably might not be the worst they could do, and the promise of honour I made them—for so I interpreted my submissive behaviour— soon drove out these imaginations. Besides, I now considered myself as bound by the laws of hospitality, to a people who had treated me with so much expense and magnificence. However, in my thoughts I could not sufficiently wonder at the intrepidity of these diminutive mortals, who durst venture to mount and walk upon my body, while one of my hands was at liberty, without trembling at the very sight of so prodigious a creature as I must appear to them. After some time, when they observed that I made no more demands for meat, there appeared before me a person of high rank from his imperial majesty. His excellency, having mounted on the small of my right leg, advanced forwards up to my face, with about a dozen of his retinue; and producing his credentials under the signet royal, which he applied close to my eyes, spoke about ten minutes without any signs of anger, but with a kind of determinate resolution, often pointing forwards, which, as I afterwards found, was towards the capital city, about half a mile distant; whither it was agreed by his majesty in council that I must be conveyed. I answered in few words, but to no purpose, and made a sign with my hand that was loose, putting it to the other (but over his excellency's head for fear of hurting him or his train) and then to my own head and body, to signify that I desired my liberty. It appeared that he understood me well enough, for he shook his head by way of disapprobation, and held his hand in a posture to show that I must be carried as a prisoner. However, he made other signs to let me understand that I should have meat and drink enough, and very good treatment. Whereupon I once more thought of attempting to break my bonds; but again, when I felt the smart of their arrows upon my face and hands, which were all in blisters, and many of the darts still sticking in them, and observing likewise that the number of my enemies increased, I gave tokens to let them know that they might do with me what they pleased. Upon this, the hurgo and his train withdrew, with much civility and cheerful countenances. Soon after I heard a general shout, with frequent repetitions of the words Peplom selan; and I felt great numbers of people on my left side relaxing the cords to such a degree, that I was able to turn upon my right, and to ease myself with making water; which I very plentifully did, to the great astonishment of the people; who, conjecturing by my motion what I was going to do, immediately opened to the right and left on that side, to avoid the torrent, which fell with such noise and violence from me. But before this, they had daubed my face and both my hands with a sort of ointment, very pleasant to the smell, which, in a few minutes, removed all the smart of their arrows. These circumstances, added to the refreshment I had received by their victuals and drink, which were very nourishing, disposed me to sleep. I slept about eight hours, as I was afterwards assured; and it was no wonder, for the physicians, by the emperor's order, had mingled a sleepy potion in the hogsheads of wine.

It seems, that upon the first moment I was discovered sleeping on the ground, after my landing, the emperor had early notice of it by an express; and determined in council, that I should be tied in the manner I have related, (which was done in the night while I slept;) that plenty of meat and drink should be sent to me, and a machine prepared to carry me to the capital city.

This resolution perhaps may appear very bold and dangerous, and I am confident would not be imitated by any prince in Europe on the like occasion. However, in my opinion, it was extremely prudent, as well as generous: for, supposing these people had endeavoured to kill me with their spears and arrows, while I was asleep, I should certainly have awaked with the first sense of smart, which might so far have roused my rage and strength, as to have enabled me to break the strings wherewith I was tied; after which, as they were not able to make resistance, so they could expect no mercy.

These people are most excellent mathematicians, and arrived to a great perfection in mechanics, by the countenance and encouragement of the emperor, who is a renowned patron of learning. This prince has several machines fixed on wheels, for the carriage of trees and other great weights. He often builds his largest men of war, whereof some are nine feet long, in the woods where the timber grows, and has them carried on these engines three or four hundred yards to the sea. Five hundred carpenters and engineers were immediately set at work to prepare the greatest engine they had. It was a frame of wood raised three inches from the ground, about seven feet long, and four wide, moving upon twenty-two wheels. The shout I heard was upon the arrival of this engine, which, it seems, set out in four hours after my landing. It was brought parallel to me, as I lay. But the principal difficulty was to raise and place me in this vehicle. Eighty poles, each of one foot high, were erected for this purpose, and very strong cords, of the bigness of packthread, were fastened by hooks to many bandages, which the workmen had girt round my neck, my hands, my body, and my legs. Nine hundred of the strongest men were employed to draw up these cords, by many pulleys fastened on the poles; and thus, in less than three hours, I was raised and slung into the engine, and there tied fast. All this I was told; for, while the operation was performing, I lay in a profound sleep, by the force of that soporiferous medicine infused into my liquor. Fifteen hundred of the emperor's largest horses, each about four inches and a half high, were employed to draw me towards the metropolis, which, as I said, was half a mile distant.

About four hours after we began our journey, I awaked by a very ridiculous accident; for the carriage being stopped a while, to adjust something that was out of order, two or three of the young natives had the curiosity to see how I looked when I was asleep; they climbed up into the engine, and advancing very softly to my face, one of them, an officer in the guards, put the sharp end of his half-pike a good way up into my left nostril, which tickled my nose like a straw, and made me sneeze violently; whereupon they stole off unperceived, and it was three weeks before I knew the cause of my waking so suddenly. We made a long march the remaining part of the day, and, rested at night with five hundred guards on each side of me, half with torches, and half with bows and arrows, ready to shoot me if I should offer to stir. The next morning at sun-rise we continued our march, and arrived within two hundred yards of the city gates about noon. The emperor, and all his court, came out to meet us; but his great officers would by no means suffer his majesty to endanger his person by mounting on my body.

At the place where the carriage stopped there stood an ancient temple, esteemed to be the largest in the whole kingdom; which, having been polluted some years before by an unnatural murder, was, according to the zeal of those people, looked upon as profane, and therefore had been applied to common use, and all the ornaments and furniture carried away. In this edifice it was determined I should lodge. The great gate fronting to the north was about four feet high, and almost two feet wide, through which I could easily creep. On each side of the gate was a small window, not above six inches from the ground: into that on the left side, the king's smith conveyed fourscore and eleven chains, like those that hang to a lady's watch in Europe, and almost as large, which were locked to my left leg with six-and-thirty padlocks. Over against this temple, on the other side of the great highway, at twenty feet distance, there was a turret at least five feet high. Here the emperor ascended, with many principal lords of his court, to have an opportunity of viewing me, as I was told, for I could not see them. It was reckoned that above a hundred thousand inhabitants came out of the town upon the same errand; and, in spite of my guards, I believe there could not be fewer than ten thousand at several times, who mounted my body by the help of ladders. But a proclamation was soon issued, to forbid it upon pain of death. When the workmen found it was impossible for me to break loose, they cut all the strings that bound me; whereupon I rose up, with as melancholy a disposition as ever I had in my life. But the noise and astonishment of the people, at seeing me rise and walk, are not to be expressed. The chains that held my left leg were about two yards long, and gave me not only the liberty of walking backwards and forwards in a semicircle, but, being fixed within four inches of the gate, allowed me to creep in, and lie at my full length in the temple.

CHAPTER II.

[The emperor of Lilliput, attended by several of the nobility, comes to see the author in his confinement. The emperor's person and habit described. Learned men appointed to teach the author their language. He gains favour by his mild disposition. His pockets are searched, and his sword and pistols taken from him.]

When I found myself on my feet, I looked about me, and must confess I never beheld a more entertaining prospect. The country around appeared like a continued garden, and the enclosed fields, which were generally forty feet square, resembled so many beds of flowers. These fields were intermingled with woods of half a stang, {1} and the tallest trees, as I could judge, appeared to be seven feet high. I viewed the town on my left hand, which looked like the painted scene of a city in a theatre.

I had been for some hours extremely pressed by the necessities of nature; which was no wonder, it being almost two days since I had last disburdened myself. I was under great difficulties between urgency and shame. The best expedient I could think of, was to creep into my house, which I accordingly did; and shutting the gate after me, I went as far as the length of my chain would suffer, and discharged my body of that uneasy load. But this was the only time I was ever guilty of so uncleanly an action; for which I cannot but hope the candid reader will give some allowance, after he has maturely and impartially considered my case, and the distress I was in. From this time my constant practice was, as soon as I rose, to perform that business in open air, at the full extent of my chain; and due care was taken every morning before company came, that the offensive matter should be carried off in wheel-barrows, by two servants appointed for that purpose. I would not have dwelt so long upon a circumstance that, perhaps, at first sight, may appear not very momentous, if I had not thought it necessary to justify my character, in point of cleanliness, to the world; which, I am told, some of my maligners have been pleased, upon this and other occasions, to call in question.

When this adventure was at an end, I came back out of my house, having occasion for fresh air. The emperor was already descended from the tower, and advancing on horseback towards me, which had like to have cost him dear; for the beast, though very well trained, yet wholly unused to such a sight, which appeared as if a mountain moved before him, reared up on its hinder feet: but that prince, who is an excellent horseman, kept his seat, till his attendants ran in, and held the bridle, while his majesty had time to dismount. When he alighted, he surveyed me round with great admiration; but kept beyond the length of my chain. He ordered his cooks and butlers, who were already prepared, to give me victuals and drink, which they pushed forward in a sort of vehicles upon wheels, till I could reach them. I took these vehicles and soon emptied them all; twenty of them were filled with meat, and ten with liquor; each of the former afforded me two or three good mouthfuls; and I emptied the liquor of ten vessels, which

15

was contained in earthen vials, into one vehicle, drinking it off at a draught; and so I did with the rest. The empress, and young princes of the blood of both sexes, attended by many ladies, sat at some distance in their chairs; but upon the accident that happened to the emperor's horse, they alighted, and came near his person, which I am now going to describe. He is taller by almost the breadth of my nail, than any of his court; which alone is enough to strike an awe into the beholders. His features are strong and masculine, with an Austrian lip and arched nose, his complexion olive, his countenance erect, his body and limbs well proportioned, all his motions graceful, and his deportment majestic. He was then past his prime, being twenty-eight years and three quarters old, of which he had reigned about seven in great felicity, and generally victorious. For the better convenience of beholding him, I lay on my side, so that my face was parallel to his, and he stood but three yards off: however, I have had him since many times in my hand, and therefore cannot be deceived in the description. His dress was very plain and simple, and the fashion of it between the Asiatic and the European; but he had on his head a light helmet of gold, adorned with jewels, and a plume on the crest. He held his sword drawn in his hand to defend himself, if I should happen to break loose; it was almost three inches long; the hilt and scabbard were gold enriched with diamonds. His voice was shrill, but very clear and articulate; and I could distinctly hear it when I stood up. The ladies and courtiers were all most magnificently clad; so that the spot they stood upon seemed to resemble a petticoat spread upon the ground, embroidered with figures of gold and silver. His imperial majesty spoke often to me, and I returned answers: but neither of us could understand a syllable. There were several of his priests and lawyers present (as I conjectured by their habits), who were commanded to address themselves to me; and I spoke to them in as many languages as I had the least smattering of, which were High and Low Dutch, Latin, French, Spanish, Italian, and Lingua Franca, but all to no purpose. After about two hours the court retired, and I was left with a strong guard, to prevent the impertinence, and probably the malice of the rabble, who were very impatient to crowd about me as near as they durst; and some of them had the impudence to shoot their arrows at me, as I sat on the ground by the door of my house, whereof one very narrowly missed my left eye. But the colonel ordered six of the ringleaders to be seized, and thought no punishment so proper as to deliver them bound into my hands; which some of his soldiers accordingly did, pushing them forward with the butt-ends of their pikes into my reach. I took them all in my right hand, put five of them into my coat-pocket; and as to the sixth, I made a countenance as if I would eat him alive. The poor man squalled terribly, and the colonel and his officers were in much pain, especially when they saw me take out my penknife: but I soon put them out of fear; for, looking mildly, and immediately cutting the strings he was bound with, I set him gently on the ground, and away he ran. I treated the rest in the same manner, taking them one by one out of my pocket; and I observed both the soldiers and people were highly delighted at this mark of my clemency, which was represented very much to my advantage at court.

Towards night I got with some difficulty into my house, where I lay on the ground, and continued to do so about a fortnight; during which time, the emperor gave orders to have a bed prepared for me. Six hundred beds of the common measure were brought in carriages, and worked up in my house; a hundred and fifty of their beds, sewn together, made up the breadth and length; and these were four double: which, however, kept me but very indifferently from the hardness of the floor, that was of smooth stone. By the same computation, they provided me with sheets, blankets, and coverlets, tolerable enough for one who had been so long inured to hardships.

As the news of my arrival spread through the kingdom, it brought prodigious numbers of rich, idle, and curious people to see me; so that the villages were almost emptied; and great neglect of tillage and household affairs must have ensued, if his imperial majesty had not provided, by several proclamations and orders of state, against this inconveniency. He directed that those who had already beheld me should return home, and not presume to come within fifty yards of my house, without license from the court; whereby the secretaries of state got considerable fees.

In the mean time the emperor held frequent councils, to debate what course should be taken with me; and I was afterwards assured by a particular friend, a person of great quality, who was as much in the secret as any, that the court was under many difficulties concerning me. They apprehended my breaking loose; that my diet would be very expensive, and might cause a famine. Sometimes they determined to starve me; or at least to shoot me in the face and hands with poisoned arrows, which would soon despatch me; but again they considered, that the stench of so large a carcass might produce a plague in the metropolis, and probably spread through the whole kingdom. In the midst of these consultations, several officers of the army went to the door of the great council-chamber, and two of them being admitted, gave an account of my behaviour to the six criminals above-mentioned; which made so favourable an impression in the breast of his majesty and the whole board, in my behalf, that an imperial commission was issued out, obliging all the villages, nine hundred yards round the city, to deliver in every morning six beeves, forty sheep, and other victuals for my sustenance; together with a proportionable quantity of bread, and wine, and other liquors; for the due payment of which, his majesty gave assignments upon his treasury:- for this prince lives chiefly upon his own demesnes; seldom, except upon great occasions, raising any subsidies upon his subjects, who are bound to attend him in his wars at their own expense. An establishment was also made of six hundred persons to be my domestics, who had board-wages allowed for their maintenance, and tents built for them very conveniently on each side of my door. It was likewise ordered, that three hundred tailors should make me a suit of clothes, after the fashion of the country; that six of his majesty's greatest scholars should be employed to instruct me in their language; and lastly, that the emperor's horses, and those of the nobility and troops of guards, should be frequently exercised in my sight, to accustom themselves to me. All these orders were duly put in execution; and in about three weeks I made a great progress in learning their language; during which time the emperor frequently honoured me with his visits, and was pleased to assist my masters in teaching me. We began already to converse together in some sort; and the first words I learnt, were to express my desire "that he would please give me my liberty;" which I every day repeated on my knees. His answer, as I could comprehend it, was, "that this must be a work of time, not to be thought on without the advice of his council, and that first I must lumos kelmin pesso desmar lon emposo;" that is, swear a peace with him and his kingdom. However, that I should be used with all kindness. And he advised me to "acquire, by my patience and discreet behaviour, the good opinion of himself and his subjects." He desired "I would not take it ill, if he gave orders to certain proper officers to search me; for probably I might carry about me several weapons, which must needs be dangerous things, if they answered the bulk of so prodigious a person." I said, "His majesty should be satisfied; for I was ready to strip myself, and turn up my pockets before him." This I delivered part in words, and part in signs. He replied, "that, by the laws of the kingdom, I must be searched by two of his officers; that he knew this could not be done without my consent and assistance; and he had so good an opinion of my generosity and justice, as to trust their persons in my hands; that whatever they took from me, should be returned when I left the country, or paid for at the rate which I would set upon them." I took up the two officers in my hands, put them first into my coat-pockets, and then into every other pocket about me, except my two fobs, and another secret pocket, which I had no mind should be searched, wherein I had some little necessaries that were of no consequence to any but myself. In one of my fobs there was a silver watch, and in the other a small quantity of gold in a purse. These gentlemen, having pen, ink, and paper, about them, made an exact inventory of every thing they saw; and when they had done, desired I would set them down, that they might deliver it to the emperor. This inventory I afterwards translated into English, and is, word for word, as follows:

"Imprimis: In the right coat-pocket of the great man-mountain" (for so I interpret the words quinbus flestrin,) "after the strictest search, we found only one great piece of coarse-cloth, large enough to be a foot-cloth for your majesty's chief room of state. In the left pocket we saw a huge silver chest, with a cover of the same metal, which we, the searchers, were not able to lift. We desired it should be opened, and one of us stepping into it, found himself up to the mid leg in a sort of dust, some part whereof flying up to our faces set us both a sneezing for several times together. In his right waistcoat-pocket we found a prodigious bundle of white thin substances, folded one over another, about the bigness of three men, tied with a strong cable, and marked with black figures; which we humbly conceive to be writings, every letter almost half as large as the palm of our hands. In the left there was a sort of engine, from the

18

back of which were extended twenty long poles, resembling the pallisados before your majesty's court: wherewith we conjecture the man- mountain combs his head; for we did not always trouble him with questions, because we found it a great difficulty to make him understand us. In the large pocket, on the right side of his middle cover" (so I translate the word ranfulo, by which they meant my breeches,) "we saw a hollow pillar of iron, about the length of a man, fastened to a strong piece of timber larger than the pillar; and upon one side of the pillar, were huge pieces of iron sticking out, cut into strange figures, which we know not what to make of. In the left pocket, another engine of the same kind. In the smaller pocket on the right side, were several round flat pieces of white and red metal, of different bulk; some of the white, which seemed to be silver, were so large and heavy, that my comrade and I could hardly lift them. In the left pocket were two black pillars irregularly shaped: we could not, without difficulty, reach the top of them, as we stood at the bottom of his pocket. One of them was covered, and seemed all of a piece: but at the upper end of the other there appeared a white round substance, about twice the bigness of our heads. Within each of these was enclosed a prodigious plate of steel; which, by our orders, we obliged him to show us, because we apprehended they might be dangerous engines. He took them out of their cases, and told us, that in his own country his practice was to shave his beard with one of these, and cut his meat with the other. There were two pockets which we could not enter: these he called his fobs; they were two large slits cut into the top of his middle cover, but squeezed close by the pressure of his belly. Out of the right fob hung a great silver chain, with a wonderful kind of engine at the bottom. We directed him to draw out whatever was at the end of that chain; which appeared to be a globe, half silver, and half of some transparent metal; for, on the transparent side, we saw certain strange figures circularly drawn, and thought we could touch them, till we found our fingers stopped by the lucid substance. He put this engine into our ears, which made an incessant noise, like that of a water- mill: and we conjecture it is either some unknown animal, or the god that he worships; but we are more inclined to the latter opinion, because he assured us, (if we understood him right, for he expressed himself very imperfectly) that he seldom did any thing without consulting it. He called it his oracle, and said, it pointed out the time for every action of his life. From the left fob he took out a net almost large enough for a fisherman, but contrived to open and shut like a purse, and served him for the same use: we found therein several massy pieces of yellow metal, which, if they be real gold, must be of immense value.

"Having thus, in obedience to your majesty's commands, diligently searched all his pockets, we observed a girdle about his waist made of the hide of some prodigious animal, from which, on the left side, hung a sword of the length of five men; and on the right, a bag or pouch divided into two cells, each cell capable of holding three of your majesty's subjects. In one of these cells were several globes, or balls, of a most ponderous metal, about the bigness of our heads, and requiring a strong hand to lift them: the other cell contained a heap of certain black grains, but of no great bulk or weight, for we could hold above fifty of them in the palms of our hands.

"This is an exact inventory of what we found about the body of the man-mountain, who used us with great civility, and due respect to your majesty's commission. Signed and sealed on the fourth day of the eighty-ninth moon of your majesty's auspicious reign.

CLEFRIN FRELOCK, MARSI FRELOCK."

When this inventory was read over to the emperor, he directed me, although in very gentle terms, to deliver up the several particulars. He first called for my scimitar, which I took out, scabbard and all. In the mean time he ordered three thousand of his choicest troops (who then attended him) to surround me at a distance, with their bows and arrows just ready to discharge; but I did not observe it, for mine eyes were wholly fixed upon his majesty. He then desired me to draw my scimitar, which, although it had got some rust by the sea water, was, in most parts, exceeding bright. I did so, and immediately all the troops gave a shout between terror and surprise; for the sun shone clear, and the reflection dazzled their eyes, as I waved the scimitar to and fro in my hand. His majesty, who is a most magnanimous prince, was less daunted than I could expect: he ordered me to return it into the scabbard, and cast it on the ground as gently as I could, about six feet from the end of my chain. The next thing he demanded was one of the hollow iron pillars; by which he meant my pocket pistols. I drew it out, and at his desire, as well as I could, expressed to him the use of it; and charging it only with powder, which, by the closeness of my pouch, happened to escape wetting in the sea (an inconvenience against which all prudent mariners take special care to provide,) I first cautioned the emperor not to be afraid, and then I let it off in the air. The astonishment here was much greater than at the sight of my scimitar. Hundreds fell down as if they had been struck dead; and even the emperor, although he stood his ground, could not recover himself for some time. I delivered up both my pistols in the same manner as I had done my scimitar, and then my pouch of powder and bullets; begging him that the former might be kept from fire, for it would kindle with the smallest spark, and blow up his imperial palace into the air. I likewise delivered up my watch, which the emperor was very curious to see, and commanded two of his tallest yeomen of the guards to bear it on a pole upon their shoulders, as draymen in England do a barrel of ale. He was amazed at the continual noise it made, and the motion of the minute-hand, which he could easily discern; for their sight is much more acute than ours: he asked the opinions of his learned men about it, which were various and remote, as the reader may well imagine without my repeating; although indeed I could not very perfectly understand them. I then gave up my silver and copper money, my purse, with nine large pieces of gold, and some smaller ones; my knife and razor, my comb and silver snuff-box, my handkerchief and journal-book. My scimitar, pistols, and pouch, were conveyed in carriages to his majesty's stores; but the rest of my goods were returned me.

I had as I before observed, one private pocket, which escaped their search, wherein there was a pair of spectacles (which I sometimes use for the weakness of mine eyes,) a pocket perspective, and some other little conveniences; which, being of no consequence to the emperor, I did not think myself bound in honour to discover, and I apprehended they might be lost or spoiled if I ventured them out of my possession.

CHAPTER III.

[The author diverts the emperor, and his nobility of both sexes, in a very uncommon manner. The diversions of the court of Lilliput described. The author has his liberty granted him upon certain conditions.]

My gentleness and good behaviour had gained so far on the emperor and his court, and indeed upon the army and people in general, that I began to conceive hopes of getting my liberty in a short time. I took all possible methods to cultivate this favourable disposition. The natives came, by degrees, to be less apprehensive of any danger from me. I would sometimes lie down, and let five or six of them dance on my hand; and at last the boys and girls would venture to come and play at hide-and-seek in my hair. I had now made a good progress in understanding and speaking the language. The emperor had a mind one day to entertain me with several of the country shows, wherein they exceed all nations I have known, both for dexterity and magnificence. I was diverted with none so much as that of the rope-dancers, performed upon a slender white thread, extended about two feet, and twelve inches from the ground. Upon which I shall desire liberty, with the reader's patience, to enlarge a little.

This diversion is only practised by those persons who are candidates for great employments, and high favour at court. They are trained in this art from their youth, and are not always of noble birth, or liberal education. When a great office is vacant, either by death or disgrace (which often happens,) five or six of those candidates petition the emperor to entertain his majesty and the court with a dance on the rope; and whoever jumps the highest, without falling, succeeds in the office. Very often the chief ministers themselves are commanded to show their skill, and to convince the emperor that they have not lost their faculty. Flimnap, the treasurer, is allowed to cut a caper on the straight rope, at least an inch higher than any other lord in the whole empire. I have seen him do the summerset several times together, upon a trencher fixed on a rope which is no thicker than a common packthread in England. My friend Reldresal, principal secretary for private affairs, is, in my opinion, if I am not partial, the second after the treasurer; the rest of the great officers are much upon a par.

These diversions are often attended with fatal accidents, whereof great numbers are on record. I myself have seen two or three candidates break a limb. But the danger is much greater, when the ministers themselves are commanded to show their dexterity; for, by contending to excel themselves and their fellows, they strain so far that there is hardly one of them who has not received a fall, and some of them two or three. I was assured that, a year or two before my arrival, Flimnap would infallibly have broke his neck, if one of the king's cushions, that accidentally lay on the ground, had not weakened the force of his fall.

There is likewise another diversion, which is only shown before the emperor and empress, and first minister, upon particular occasions. The emperor lays on the table three fine silken threads of six inches long; one is blue, the other red, and the third green. These threads are proposed as prizes for those persons whom the emperor has a mind to distinguish by a peculiar mark of his favour. The ceremony is performed in his majesty's great chamber of state, where the candidates are to undergo a trial of dexterity very different from the former, and such as I have not observed the least resemblance of in any other country of the new or old world. The emperor holds a stick in his hands, both ends parallel to the horizon, while the candidates advancing, one by one, sometimes leap over the stick, sometimes creep under it, backward and forward, several times, according as the stick is advanced or depressed. Sometimes the emperor holds one end of the stick, and his first minister the other; sometimes the minister has it entirely to himself. Whoever performs his part with most agility, and holds out the longest in leaping and creeping, is rewarded with the blue- coloured silk; the red is given to the next, and the green to the third, which they all wear girt twice round about the middle; and you see few great persons about this court who are not adorned with one of these girdles.

The horses of the army, and those of the royal stables, having been daily led before me, were no longer shy, but would come up to my very feet without starting. The riders would leap them over my hand, as I held it on the ground; and one of the emperor's huntsmen, upon a large courser, took my foot, shoe and all; which was indeed a prodigious leap. I had the good fortune to divert the emperor one day after a very extraordinary manner. I desired he would order several sticks of two feet high, and the thickness of an ordinary cane, to be brought me; whereupon his majesty commanded the master of his woods to give directions accordingly; and the next morning six woodmen arrived with as many carriages, drawn by eight horses to each. I took nine of these sticks, and fixing them firmly in the ground in a quadrangular figure, two feet and a half square, I took four other sticks, and tied them parallel at each corner, about two feet from the ground; then I fastened my handkerchief to the nine sticks that stood erect; and extended it on all sides, till it was tight as the top of a drum; and the four parallel sticks, rising about five inches higher than the handkerchief, served as ledges on each side. When I had finished my work, I desired the emperor to let a troop of his best horses twenty-four in number, come and exercise upon this plain. His majesty approved of the proposal, and I took them up, one by one, in my hands, ready mounted and armed, with the proper officers to exercise them. As soon as they got into order they divided into two parties, performed mock skirmishes, discharged blunt arrows, drew their swords, fled and pursued, attacked and retired, and in short discovered the best military discipline I ever beheld. The parallel sticks secured them and their horses from falling over the stage; and the emperor was so much delighted, that he ordered this entertainment to be repeated several days, and once was pleased to be lifted up and give the word of command; and with great difficulty persuaded even the empress herself to let me hold her in her close chair within two yards of the stage, when she was able to take a full view of the whole performance. It was my good fortune, that no ill accident happened in these entertainments; only once a fiery horse, that belonged to one of the captains, pawing with his hoof, struck a hole in my handkerchief, and his foot slipping, he overthrew his rider and himself; but I immediately relieved them both, and covering the hole with one hand, I set down the troop with the other, in the same manner as I took them up. The horse that fell was strained in the left shoulder, but the rider got no hurt; and I repaired my handkerchief as well as I could: however, I would not trust to the strength of it any more, in such dangerous enterprises.

About two or three days before I was set at liberty, as I was entertaining the court with this kind of feat, there arrived an express to inform his majesty, that some of his subjects, riding near the place where I was first taken up, had seen a great black substance lying on the around, very oddly shaped, extending its edges round, as wide as his majesty's bedchamber, and rising up in the middle as high as a man; that it was no living creature, as they at first apprehended, for it lay on the grass without motion; and some of them had walked round it several times; that, by mounting upon each other's shoulders, they had got to the top, which was flat and even, and, stamping upon it, they found that it was hollow within; that they humbly conceived it might be something belonging to the man-mountain; and if his majesty pleased, they would undertake to bring it with only five horses. I presently knew what they meant, and was glad at heart to receive this intelligence. It seems, upon my first reaching the shore after our shipwreck, I was in such confusion, that before I came to the place where I went to sleep, my hat, which I had fastened with a string to my head while I was rowing, and had stuck on all the time I was swimming, fell off after I came to land; the string, as I conjecture, breaking by some accident, which I never observed, but thought my hat had been lost at sea. I entreated his imperial majesty to give orders it might be brought to me as soon as possible, describing to him the use and the nature of it: and the next day the waggoners arrived with it, but not in a very good condition; they had bored two holes in the brim, within an inch and half of the edge, and fastened two hooks in the holes; these hooks were tied by a long cord to the harness, and thus my hat was dragged along for above half an English mile; but, the ground in that country being extremely smooth and level, it received less damage than I expected.

Two days after this adventure, the emperor, having ordered that part of his army which quarters in and about his metropolis, to be in readiness, took a fancy of diverting himself in a very singular manner. He desired I would stand like a Colossus, with my legs as far asunder as I conveniently could. He then commanded his general (who was an old experienced leader, and a great patron of mine) to draw up the troops in close order, and march them under me; the foot by twenty-four abreast, and the horse by sixteen, with drums beating, colours flying, and pikes advanced. This body consisted of three thousand foot, and a thousand horse. His majesty gave orders, upon pain of death, that every soldier in his march should observe the strictest decency with regard to my person; which however could not prevent some of the younger officers from turning up their eyes as they passed under me: and, to confess the truth, my breeches were at that time in so ill a condition, that they afforded some opportunities for laughter and admiration.

I had sent so many memorials and petitions for my liberty, that his majesty at length mentioned the matter, first in the cabinet, and then in a full council; where it was opposed by ɔ ne, except Skyresh Bolgolam, who was pleased, without any provocation, to be my mortal enemy. But it was carried against him by the whole board, and confirmed by the emperor. That minister was galbet, or admiral of the realm, very much in his master's confidence, and a person well versed in affairs, but of a morose and sour complexion. However, he was at length persuaded to comply; but prevailed that the articles and conditions upon which I should be set free, and to which I must swear, should be drawn up by himself. These articles were brought to me by Skyresh Bolgolam in person attended by two under-secretaries, and several persons of distinction. After they were read, I was demanded to swear to the performance of them; first in the manner of my own country, and afterwards in the method prescribed by their laws; which was, to hold my right foot in my left hand, and to place the middle finger of my right hand on the crown of my head, and my thumb on the tip of my right ear. But because the reader may be curious to have some idea of the style and manner of expression peculiar to that people, as well as to know the article upon which I recovered my liberty, I have made a translation of the whole instrument, word for word, as near as I was able, which I here offer to the public.

"Golbasto Momarem Evlame Gurdilo Shefin Mully Ully Gue, most mighty Emperor of Lilliput, delight and terror of the universe, whose dominions extend five thousand blustrugs (about twelve miles in circumference) to the extremities of the globe; monarch of all monarchs, taller than the sons of men; whose feet press down to the centre, and whose head strikes against the sun; at whose nod the princes of the earth shake their knees; pleasant as the spring, comfortable as the summer, fruitful as autumn, dreadful as winter: his most sublime majesty proposes to the man-mountain, lately arrived at our celestial dominions, the following articles, which, by a solemn oath, he shall be obliged to perform:-

"1st, The man-mountain shall not depart from our dominions, without our license under our great seal.

"2d, He shall not presume to come into our metropolis, without our express order; at which time, the inhabitants shall have two hours warning to keep within doors.

"3d, The said man-mountain shall confine his walks to our principal high roads, and not offer to walk, or lie down, in a meadow or field of corn.

"4th, As he walks the said roads, he shall take the utmost care not to trample upon the bodies of any of our loving subjects, their horses, or carriages, nor take any of our subjects into his hands without their own consent.

"5th, If an express requires extraordinary despatch, the man- mountain shall be obliged to carry, in his pocket, the messenger and horse a six days journey, once in every moon, and return the said messenger back (if so required) safe to our imperial presence.

"6th, He shall be our ally against our enemies in the island of Blefuscu, and do his utmost to destroy their fleet, which is now preparing to invade us.

"7th, That the said man-mountain shall, at his times of leisure, be aiding and assisting to our workmen, in helping to raise certain great stones, towards covering the wall of the principal park, and other our royal buildings.

"8th, That the said man-mountain shall, in two moons' time, deliver in an exact survey of the circumference of our dominions, by a computation of his own paces round the coast.

"Lastly, That, upon his solemn oath to observe all the above articles, the said man-mountain shall have a daily allowance of meat and drink sufficient for the support of 1724 of our subjects, with free access to our royal person, and other marks of our favour. Given at our palace at Belfaborac, the twelfth day of the ninety-first moon of our reign."

I swore and subscribed to these articles with great cheerfulness and content, although some of them were not so honourable as I could have wished; which proceeded wholly from the malice of Skyresh Bolgolam, the high-admiral: whereupon my chains were immediately unlocked, and I was at full liberty. The emperor himself, in person, did me the honour to be by at the whole ceremony. I made my acknowledgements by prostrating myself at his majesty's feet: but he commanded me to rise; and after many gracious expressions, which, to avoid the censure of vanity, I shall not repeat, he added, "that he hoped I should prove a useful servant, and well deserve all the favours he had already conferred upon me, or might do for the future."

The reader may please to observe, that, in the last article of the recovery of my liberty, the emperor stipulates to allow me a quantity of meat and drink sufficient for the support of 1724 Lilliputians. Some time after, asking a friend at court how they came to fix on that determinate number, he told me that his majesty's mathematicians, having taken the height of my body by the help of a quadrant, and finding it to exceed theirs in the proportion of twelve to one, they concluded from the similarity of their bodies, that mine must contain at least 1724 of theirs, and consequently would require as much food as was necessary to support that number of Lilliputians. By which the reader may conceive an idea of the ingenuity of that people, as well as the prudent and exact economy of so great a prince.

CHAPTER IV.

[Mildendo, the metropolis of Lilliput, described, together with the emperor's palace. A conversation between the author and a principal secretary, concerning the affairs of that empire. The author's offers to serve the emperor in his wars.]

The first request I made, after I had obtained my liberty, was, that I might have license to see Mildendo, the metropolis; which the emperor easily granted me, but with a special charge to do no hurt either to the inhabitants or their houses. The people had notice, by proclamation, of my design to visit the town. The wall which encompassed it is two feet and a half high, and at least eleven inches broad, so that a coach and horses may be driven very safely round it; and it is flanked with strong towers at ten feet distance. I stepped over the great western gate, and passed very gently, and sidling, through the two principal streets, only in my short waistcoat, for fear of damaging the roofs and eaves of the houses with the skirts of my coat. I walked with the utmost circumspection, to avoid treading on any stragglers who might remain in the streets, although the orders were very strict, that all people should keep in their houses, at their own peril. The garret windows and tops of houses were so crowded with spectators, that I thought in all my travels I had not seen a more populous place. The city is an exact square, each side of the wall being five hundred feet long. The two great streets, which run across and divide it into four quarters, are five feet wide. The lanes and alleys, which I could not enter, but only view them as I passed, are from twelve to eighteen inches. The town is capable of holding five hundred thousand souls: the houses are from three to five stories: the shops and markets well provided.

The emperor's palace is in the centre of the city where the two great streets meet. It is enclosed by a wall of two feet high, and twenty feet distance from the buildings. I had his majesty's permission to step over this wall; and, the space being so wide between that and the palace, I could easily view it on every side. The outward court is a square of forty feet, and includes two other courts: in the inmost are the royal apartments, which I was very desirous to see, but found it extremely difficult; for the great gates, from one square into another, were but eighteen inches high, and seven inches wide. Now the buildings of the outer court were at least five feet high, and it was impossible for me to stride over them without infinite damage to the pile, though the walls were strongly built of hewn stone, and four inches thick. At the same time the emperor had a great desire that I should see the magnificence of his palace; but this I was not able to do till three days after, which I spent in cutting down with my knife some of the largest trees in the royal park, about a hundred yards distant from the city. Of these trees I made two stools, each about three feet high, and strong enough to bear my weight. The people having received notice a second time, I went again through the city to the palace with my two stools in my hands. When I came to the side of the outer court, I stood upon one stool, and took the other in my hand; this I lifted over the roof, and gently set it down on the space between the first and second court, which was eight feet wide. I then stept over the building very conveniently from one stool to the other, and drew up the first after me with a hooked stick. By this contrivance I got into the inmost court; and, lying down upon my side, I applied my face to the windows of the middle stories, which were left open on purpose, and discovered the most splendid apartments that can be imagined. There I saw the empress and the young princes, in their several lodgings, with their chief attendants about them. Her imperial majesty was pleased to smile very graciously upon me, and gave me out of the window her hand to kiss.

But I shall not anticipate the reader with further descriptions of this kind, because I reserve them for a greater work, which is now almost ready for the press; containing a general description of this empire, from its first erection, through along series of princes; with a particular account of their wars and politics, laws, learning, and religion; their plants and animals; their peculiar manners and customs, with other matters very curious and useful; my chief design at present being only to relate such events and transactions as happened to the public or to myself during a residence of about nine months in that empire.

One morning, about a fortnight after I had obtained my liberty, Reldresal, principal secretary (as they style him) for private affairs, came to my house attended only by one servant. He ordered his coach to wait at a distance, and desired I would give him an hours audience; which I readily consented to, on account of his quality and personal merits, as well as of the many good offices he had done me during my solicitations at court. I offered to lie down that he might the more conveniently reach my ear, but he chose rather to let me hold him in my hand during our conversation. He began with compliments on my liberty; said "he might pretend to some merit in it;" but, however, added, "that if it had not been for the present situation of things at court, perhaps I might not have obtained it so soon. For," said he, "as flourishing a condition as we may appear to be in to foreigners, we labour under two mighty evils: a violent faction at home, and the danger of an invasion, by a most potent enemy, from abroad. As to the first, you are to understand, that for about seventy moons past there have been two struggling parties in this empire, under the names of Tramecksan and Slamecksan, from the high and low heels of their shoes, by which they distinguish themselves. It is alleged, indeed, that the high heels are most agreeable to our ancient constitution; but, however this be, his majesty has determined to make use only of low heels in the administration of the government, and all offices in the gift of the crown, as you cannot but observe; and particularly that his majesty's imperial heels are lower at least by a drurr than any of his court (drurr is a measure about the fourteenth part of an inch). The animosities between these two parties run so high, that they will neither eat, nor drink, nor talk with each other. We compute the Tramecksan, or high heels, to exceed us in number; but the power is wholly on our side. We apprehend his imperial highness, the heir to the crown, to have some tendency towards the high heels; at least we can plainly discover that one of his heels is higher than the other, which gives him a hobble in his gait. Now, in the midst of these intestine disquiets, we are threatened with an invasion from the island of Blefuscu, which is the other great empire of the universe, almost as large and powerful as this of his majesty. For as to what we have heard you affirm, that there are other kingdoms and states in the world inhabited by human creatures as large as yourself, our philosophers are in much doubt, and would rather conjecture that you dropped from the moon, or one of the stars; because it is certain, that a hundred mortals of your bulk would in a short time destroy all the fruits and cattle of his majesty's dominions: besides, our histories of six thousand moons make no mention of any other regions than the two great empires of Lilliput and Blefuscu. Which two mighty powers have, as I was going to tell you, been engaged in a most obstinate war for six-and-thirty moons past. It began upon the following occasion. It is allowed on all hands, that the primitive way of breaking eggs, before we eat them, was upon the larger end; but his present majesty's grandfather, while he was a boy, going to eat an egg, and breaking it according to the ancient practice, happened to cut one of his fingers. Whereupon the emperor his father published an edict, commanding all his subjects, upon great penalties, to break the smaller end of their eggs. The people so highly resented this law, that our histories tell us, there have been six rebellions raised on that account; wherein one emperor lost his life, and another his crown. These civil commotions were constantly fomented by the monarchs of Blefuscu; and when they were quelled, the exiles always fled for refuge to that empire. It is computed that eleven thousand persons have at several times suffered death, rather than submit to break their eggs at the smaller end. Many hundred large volumes have been published upon this controversy: but the books of the Big- endians have been long forbidden, and the whole party rendered incapable by law of holding employments. During the course of these troubles, the emperors of Blefusca did frequently expostulate by their ambassadors, accusing us of making a schism in religion, by offending against a fundamental doctrine of our great prophet Lustrog, in the fifty-fourth chapter of the Blundecral (which is their Alcoran). This, however, is thought to be a mere strain upon the text; for the words are these: 'that all true believers break their eggs at the convenient end.' And which is the convenient end, seems, in my humble opinion to be left to every man's conscience, or at least in the power of the chief magistrate to determine. Now, the Big-endian exiles have found so much credit in the emperor of Blefuscu's court, and so much private assistance and encouragement from their party here at home, that a bloody war has been carried on between the two empires for six-and-thirty moons, with various success; during which time we have lost forty capital ships, and a much a greater number of smaller vessels, together with thirty thousand of our best seamen and soldiers; and the damage received by the enemy is reckoned to be somewhat greater than ours. However, they have now equipped a numerous fleet, and are just preparing to make a descent upon us; and his imperial majesty, placing great confidence in your valour and strength, has commanded me to lay this account of his affairs before you."

I desired the secretary to present my humble duty to the emperor; and to let him know, "that I thought it would not become me, who was a foreigner, to interfere with parties; but I was ready, with the hazard of my life, to defend his person and state against all invaders."

CHAPTER V.

[The author, by an extraordinary stratagem, prevents an invasion. A high title of honour is conferred upon him. Ambassadors arrive from the emperor of Blefuscu, and sue for peace. The empress's apartment on fire by an accident; the author instrumental in saving the rest of the palace.]

The empire of Blefuscu is an island situated to the north-east of Lilliput, from which it is parted only by a channel of eight hundred yards wide. I had not yet seen it, and upon this notice of an intended invasion, I avoided appearing on that side of the coast, for fear of being discovered, by some of the enemy's ships, who had received no intelligence of me; all intercourse between the two empires having been strictly forbidden during the war, upon pain of death, and an embargo laid by our emperor upon all vessels whatsoever. I communicated to his majesty a project I had formed of seizing the enemy's whole fleet; which, as our scouts assured us, lay at anchor in the harbour, ready to sail with the first fair wind. I consulted the most experienced seamen upon the depth of the channel, which they had often plumbed; who told me, that in the middle, at high-water, it was seventy glumgluffs deep, which is about six feet of European measure; and the rest of it fifty glumgluffs at most. I walked towards the north-east coast, over against Blefuscu, where, lying down behind a hillock, I took out my small perspective glass, and viewed the enemy's fleet at anchor, consisting of about fifty men of war, and a great number of transports: I then came back to my house, and gave orders (for which I had a warrant) for a great quantity of the strongest cable and bars of iron. The cable was about as thick as packthread and the bars of the length and size of a knitting-needle. I trebled the cable to make it stronger, and for the same reason I twisted three of the iron bars together, bending the extremities into a hook. Having thus fixed fifty hooks to as many cables, I went back to the north-east coast, and putting off my coat, shoes, and stockings, walked into the sea, in my leathern jerkin, about half an hour before high water. I waded with what haste I could, and swam in the middle about thirty yards, till I felt ground. I arrived at the fleet in less than half an hour. The enemy was so frightened when they saw me, that they leaped out of their ships, and swam to shore, where there could not be fewer than thirty thousand souls. I then took my tackling, and, fastening a hook to the hole at the prow of each, I tied all the cords together at the end. While I was thus employed, the enemy discharged several thousand arrows, many of which stuck in my hands and face, and, beside the excessive smart, gave me much disturbance in my work. My greatest apprehension was for mine eyes, which I should have infallibly lost, if I had not suddenly thought of an expedient. I kept, among other little necessaries, a pair of spectacles in a private pocket, which, as I observed before, had escaped the emperor's searchers. These I took out and fastened as strongly as I could upon my nose, and thus armed, went on boldly with my work, in spite of the enemy's arrows, many of which struck against the glasses of my spectacles, but without any other effect, further than a little to discompose them. I had now fastened all the hooks, and, taking the knot in my hand, began to pull; but not a ship would stir, for they were all too fast held by their anchors, so that the boldest part of my enterprise remained. I therefore let go the cord, and leaving the looks fixed to the ships, I resolutely cut with my knife the cables that fastened the anchors, receiving about two hundred shots in my face and hands; then I took up the knotted end of the cables, to which my hooks were tied, and with great ease drew fifty of the enemy's largest men of war after me.

The Blefuscudians, who had not the least imagination of what I intended, were at first confounded with astonishment. They had seen me cut the cables, and thought my design was only to let the ships run adrift or fall foul on each other: but when they perceived the whole fleet moving in order, and saw me pulling at the end, they set up such a scream of grief and despair as it is almost impossible to describe or conceive. When I had got out of danger, I stopped awhile to pick out the arrows that stuck in my hands and face; and rubbed on some of the same ointment that was given me at my first arrival, as I have formerly mentioned. I then took off my spectacles, and waiting about an hour, till the tide was a little fallen, I waded through the middle with my cargo, and arrived safe at the royal port of Lilliput.

The emperor and his whole court stood on the shore, expecting the issue of this great adventure. They saw the ships move forward in a large half-moon, but could not discern me, who was up to my breast in water. When I advanced to the middle of the channel, they were yet more in pain, because I was under water to my neck. The emperor concluded me to be drowned, and that the enemy's fleet was approaching in a hostile manner: but he was soon eased of his fears; for the channel growing shallower every step I made, I came in a short time within hearing, and holding up the end of the cable, by which the fleet was fastened, I cried in a loud voice, "Long live the most puissant king of Lilliput!" This great prince received me at my landing with all possible encomiums, and created me a nardac upon the spot, which is the highest title of honour among them.

His majesty desired I would take some other opportunity of bringing all the rest of his enemy's ships into his ports. And so unmeasureable is the ambition of princes, that he seemed to think of nothing less than reducing the whole empire of Blefuscu into a province, and governing it, by a viceroy; of destroying the Big-endian exiles, and compelling that people to break the smaller end of their eggs, by which he would remain the sole monarch of the whole world. But I endeavoured to divert him from this design, by many arguments drawn from the topics of policy as well as justice; and I plainly protested, "that I would never be an instrument of bringing a free and brave people into slavery." And, when the matter was debated in council, the wisest part of the ministry were of my opinion.

This open bold declaration of mine was so opposite to the schemes and politics of his imperial majesty, that he could never forgive me. He mentioned it in a very artful manner at council, where I was told that some of the wisest appeared, at least by their silence, to be of my opinion; but others, who were my secret enemies, could not forbear some expressions which, by a side-wind, reflected on me. And from this time began an intrigue between his majesty and a junto of ministers, maliciously bent against me, which broke out in less than two months, and had like to have ended in my utter destruction. Of so little weight are the greatest services to princes, when put into the balance with a refusal to gratify their passions.

About three weeks after this exploit, there arrived a solemn embassy from Blefuscu, with humble offers of a peace, which was soon concluded, upon conditions very advantageous to our emperor, wherewith I shall not trouble the reader. There were six ambassadors, with a train of about five hundred persons, and their entry was very magnificent, suitable to the grandeur of their master, and the importance of their business. When their treaty was finished, wherein I did them several good offices by the credit I now had, or at least appeared to have, at court, their excellencies, who were privately told how much I had been their friend, made me a visit in form. They began with many compliments upon my valour and generosity, invited me to that kingdom in the emperor their master's name, and desired me to show them some proofs of my prodigious strength, of which they had heard so many wonders; wherein I readily obliged them, but shall not trouble the reader with the particulars.

When I had for some time entertained their excellencies, to their infinite satisfaction and surprise, I desired they would do me the honour to present my most humble respects to the emperor their master, the renown of whose virtues had so justly filled the whole world with admiration, and whose royal person I resolved to attend, before I returned to my own country. Accordingly, the next time I had the honour to see our emperor, I desired his general license to wait on the Blefuscudian monarch, which he was pleased to grant me, as I could perceive, in a very cold manner; but could not guess the reason, till I had a whisper from a certain person, "that Flimnap and Bolgolam had represented my intercourse with those ambassadors as a mark of disaffection;" from which I am sure my heart was wholly free. And this was the first time I began to conceive some imperfect idea of courts and ministers.

It is to be observed, that these ambassadors spoke to me, by an interpreter, the languages of both empires differing as much from each other as any two in Europe, and each nation priding itself upon the antiquity, beauty, and energy of their own tongue, with an avowed contempt for that of their neighbour; yet our emperor, standing upon the advantage he had got by the seizure of their fleet, obliged them to deliver their credentials, and make their speech, in the Lilliputian tongue. And it must be confessed, that from the great intercourse of trade and commerce between both realms, from the continual reception of exiles which is mutual among them, and from the custom, in each empire, to send their young nobility and richer gentry to the other, in order to polish themselves by seeing the world, and understanding men and manners; there are few persons of distinction, or merchants, or seamen, who dwell in the maritime parts, but what can hold conversation in both tongues; as I found some weeks after, when I went to pay my respects to the emperor of Blefuscu, which, in the midst of great misfortunes, through the malice of my enemies, proved a very happy adventure to me, as I shall relate in its proper place.

The reader may remember, that when I signed those articles upon which I recovered my liberty, there were some which I disliked, upon account of their being too servile; neither could anything but an extreme necessity have forced me to submit. But being now a nardac of the highest rank in that empire, such offices were looked upon as below my dignity, and the emperor (to do him justice), never once mentioned them to me. However, it was not long before I had an opportunity of doing his majesty, at least as I then thought, a most signal service. I was alarmed at midnight with the cries of many hundred people at my door; by which, being suddenly awaked, I was in some kind of terror. I heard the word Burglum repeated incessantly: several of the emperor's court, making their way through the crowd, entreated me to come immediately to the palace, where her imperial majesty's apartment was on fire, by the carelessness of a maid of honour, who fell asleep while she was reading a romance. I got up in an instant; and orders being given to clear the way before me, and it being likewise a moonshine night, I made a shift to get to the palace without trampling on any of the people. I found they had already applied ladders to the walls of the apartment, and were well provided with buckets, but the water was at some distance. These buckets were about the size of large thimbles, and the poor people supplied me with them as fast as they could: but the flame was so violent that they did little good. I might easily have stifled it with my coat, which I unfortunately left behind me for haste, and came away only in my leathern jerkin. The case seemed wholly desperate and deplorable; and this magnificent palace would have infallibly been burnt down to the ground, if, by a presence of mind unusual to me, I had not suddenly thought of an expedient. I had, the evening before, drunk plentifully of a most delicious wine called glimigrim, (the Blefuscudians call it flunec, but ours is esteemed the better sort,) which is very diuretic. By the luckiest chance in the world, I had not discharged myself of any part of it. The heat I had contracted by coming very near the flames, and by labouring to quench them, made the wine begin to operate by urine; which I voided in such a quantity, and applied so well to the proper places, that in three minutes the fire was wholly extinguished, and the rest of that noble pile, which had cost so many ages in erecting, preserved from destruction.

It was now day-light, and I returned to my house without waiting to congratulate with the emperor: because, although I had done a very eminent piece of service, yet I could not tell how his majesty might resent the manner by which I had performed it: for, by the fundamental laws of the realm, it is capital in any person, of what quality soever, to make water within the precincts of the palace. But I was a little comforted by a message from his majesty, "that he would give orders to the grand justiciary for passing my pardon in form:" which, however, I could not obtain; and I was privately assured, "that the empress, conceiving the greatest abhorrence of what I had done, removed to the most distant side of the court, firmly resolved that those buildings should never be repaired for her use: and, in the presence of her chief confidents could not forbear vowing revenge."

CHAPTER VI.

[Of the inhabitants of Lilliput; their learning, laws, and customs; the manner of educating their children. The author's way of living in that country. His vindication of a great lady.]

Although I intend to leave the description of this empire to a particular treatise, yet, in the mean time, I am content to gratify the curious reader with some general ideas. As the common size of the natives is somewhat under six inches high, so there is an exact proportion in all other animals, as well as plants and trees: for instance, the tallest horses and oxen are between four and five inches in height, the sheep an inch and half, more or less: their geese about the bigness of a sparrow, and so the several gradations downwards till you come to the smallest, which to my sight, were almost invisible; but nature has adapted the eyes of the Lilliputians to all objects proper for their view: they see with great exactness, but at no great distance. And, to show the sharpness of their sight towards objects that are near, I have been much pleased with observing a cook pulling a lark, which was not so large as a common fly; and a young girl threading an invisible needle with invisible silk. Their tallest trees are about seven feet high: I mean some of those in the great royal park, the tops whereof I could but just reach with my fist clenched. The other vegetables are in the same proportion; but this I leave to the reader's imagination.

I shall say but little at present of their learning, which, for many ages, has flourished in all its branches among them: but their manner of writing is very peculiar, being neither from the left to the right, like the Europeans, nor from the right to the left, like the Arabians, nor from up to down, like the Chinese, but aslant, from one corner of the paper to the other, like ladies in England.

They bury their dead with their heads directly downward, because they hold an opinion, that in eleven thousand moons they are all to rise again; in which period the earth (which they conceive to be flat) will turn upside down, and by this means they shall, at their resurrection, be found ready standing on their feet. The learned among them confess the absurdity of this doctrine; but the practice still continues, in compliance to the vulgar.

There are some laws and customs in this empire very peculiar; and if they were not so directly contrary to those of my own dear country, I should be tempted to say a little in their justification. It is only to be wished they were as well executed. The first I shall mention, relates to informers. All crimes against the state, are punished here with the utmost severity; but, if the person accused makes his innocence plainly to appear upon his trial, the accuser is immediately put to an ignominious death; and out of his goods or lands the innocent person is quadruply recompensed for the loss of his time, for the danger he underwent, for the hardship of his imprisonment, and for all the charges he has been at in making his defence; or, if that fund be deficient, it is largely supplied by the crown. The emperor also confers on him some public mark of his favour, and proclamation is made of his innocence through the whole city.

They look upon fraud as a greater crime than theft, and therefore seldom fail to punish it with death; for they allege, that care and vigilance, with a very common understanding, may preserve a man's goods from thieves, but honesty has no defence against superior cunning; and, since it is necessary that there should be a perpetual intercourse of buying and selling, and dealing upon credit, where fraud is permitted and connived at, or has no law to punish it, the honest dealer is always undone, and the knave gets the advantage. I remember, when I was once interceding with the emperor for a criminal who had wronged his master of a great sum of money, which he had received by order and ran away with; and happening to tell his majesty, by way of extenuation, that it was only a breach of trust, the emperor thought it monstrous in me to offer as a defence the greatest aggravation of the crime; and truly I had little to say in return, farther than the common answer, that different nations had different customs; for, I confess, I was heartily ashamed. {2}

Although we usually call reward and punishment the two hinges upon which all government turns, yet I could never observe this maxim to be put in practice by any nation except that of Lilliput. Whoever can there bring sufficient proof, that he has strictly observed the laws of his country for seventy-three moons, has a claim to certain privileges, according to his quality or condition of life, with a proportionable sum of money out of a fund appropriated for that use: he likewise acquires the title of snilpall, or legal, which is added to his name, but does not descend to his posterity. And these people thought it a prodigious defect of policy among us, when I told them that our laws were enforced only by penalties, without any mention of reward. It is upon this account that the image of Justice, in their courts of judicature, is formed with six eyes, two before, as many behind, and on each side one, to signify circumspection; with a bag of gold open in her right hand, and a sword sheathed in her left, to show she is more disposed to reward than to punish.

In choosing persons for all employments, they have more regard to good morals than to great abilities; for, since government is necessary to mankind, they believe, that the common size of human understanding is fitted to some station or other; and that Providence never intended to make the management of public affairs a mystery to be comprehended only by a few persons of sublime genius, of which there seldom are three born in an age: but they suppose truth, justice, temperance, and the like, to be in every man's power; the practice of which virtues, assisted by experience and a good intention, would qualify any man for the service of his country, except where a course of study is required. But they thought the want of moral virtues was so far from being supplied by superior endowments of the mind, that employments could never be put into such dangerous hands as those of persons so qualified; and, at least, that the mistakes committed by ignorance, in a virtuous disposition, would never be of such fatal consequence to the public weal, as the practices of a man, whose inclinations led him to be corrupt, and who had great abilities to manage, to multiply, and defend his corruptions.

In like manner, the disbelief of a Divine Providence renders a man incapable of holding any public station; for, since kings avow themselves to be the deputies of Providence, the Lilliputians think nothing can be more absurd than for a prince to employ such men as disown the authority under which he acts.

In relating these and the following laws, I would only be understood to mean the original institutions, and not the most scandalous corruptions, into which these people are fallen by the degenerate nature of man. For, as to that infamous practice of acquiring great employments by dancing on the ropes, or badges of favour and distinction by leaping over sticks and creeping under them, the reader is to observe, that they were first introduced by the grandfather of the emperor now reigning, and grew to the present height by the gradual increase of party and faction.

Ingratitude is among them a capital crime, as we read it to have been in some other countries: for they reason thus; that whoever makes ill returns to his benefactor, must needs be a common enemy to the rest of mankind, from whom he has received no obligation, and therefore such a man is not fit to live.

Their notions relating to the duties of parents and children differ extremely from ours. For, since the conjunction of male and female is founded upon the great law of nature, in order to propagate and continue the species, the Lilliputians will needs have it, that men and women are joined together, like other animals, by the motives of concupiscence; and that their tenderness towards their young proceeds from the like natural principle: for which reason they will never allow that a child is under any obligation to his father for begetting him, or to his mother for bringing him into the world; which, considering the miseries of human life, was neither a benefit in itself, nor intended so by his parents, whose thoughts, in their love encounters, were otherwise employed. Upon these, and the like reasonings, their opinion is, that parents are the last of all others to be trusted with the education of their own children; and therefore they have in every town public nurseries, where all parents, except cottagers and labourers, are obliged to send their infants of both sexes to be reared and educated, when they come to the age of twenty moons, at which time they are supposed to have some rudiments of docility. These schools are of several kinds, suited to different qualities, and both sexes. They have certain professors well skilled in preparing children for such a condition of life as befits the rank of their parents, and their own capacities, as well as inclinations. I shall first say something of the male nurseries, and then of the female.

The nurseries for males of noble or eminent birth, are provided with grave and learned professors, and their several deputies. The clothes and food of the children are plain and simple. They are bred up in the principles of honour, justice, courage, modesty, clemency, religion, and love of their country; they are always employed in some business, except in the times of eating and sleeping, which are very short, and two hours for diversions consisting of bodily exercises. They are dressed by men till four years of age, and then are obliged to dress themselves, although their quality be ever so great; and the women attendant, who are aged proportionably to ours at fifty, perform only the most menial offices. They are never suffered to converse with servants, but go together in smaller or greater numbers to take their diversions, and always in the presence of a professor, or one of his deputies; whereby they avoid those early bad impressions of folly and vice, to which our children are subject. Their parents are suffered to see them only twice a year; the visit is to last but an hour; they are allowed to kiss the child at meeting and parting; but a professor, who always stands by on those occasions, will not suffer them to whisper, or use any fondling expressions, or bring any presents of toys, sweetmeats, and the like.

The pension from each family for the education and entertainment of a child, upon failure of due payment, is levied by the emperor's officers.

The nurseries for children of ordinary gentlemen, merchants, traders, and handicrafts, are managed proportionably after the same manner; only those designed for trades are put out apprentices at eleven years old, whereas those of persons of quality continue in their exercises till fifteen, which answers to twenty-one with us: but the confinement is gradually lessened for the last three years.

In the female nurseries, the young girls of quality are educated much like the males, only they are dressed by orderly servants of their own sex; but always in the presence of a professor or deputy, till they come to dress themselves, which is at five years old. And if it be found that these nurses ever presume to entertain the girls with frightful or foolish stories, or the common follies practised by chambermaids among us, they are publicly whipped thrice about the city, imprisoned for a year, and banished for life to the most desolate part of the country. Thus the young ladies are as much ashamed of being cowards and fools as the men, and despise all personal ornaments, beyond decency and cleanliness: neither did I perceive any difference in their education made by their difference of sex, only that the exercises of the females were not altogether so robust; and that some rules were given them relating to domestic life, and a smaller compass of learning was enjoined them: for their maxim is, that among peoples of quality, a wife should be always a reasonable and agreeable companion, because she cannot always be young. When the girls are twelve years old, which among them is the marriageable age, their parents or guardians take them home, with great expressions of gratitude to the professors, and seldom without tears of the young lady and her companions.

In the nurseries of females of the meaner sort, the children are instructed in all kinds of works proper for their sex, and their several degrees: those intended for apprentices are dismissed at seven years old, the rest are kept to eleven.

The meaner families who have children at these nurseries, are obliged, besides their annual pension, which is as low as possible, to return to the steward of the nursery a small monthly share of their gettings, to be a portion for the child; and therefore all parents are limited in their expenses by the law. For the Lilliputians think nothing can be more unjust, than for people, in subservience to their own appetites, to bring children into the world, and leave the burthen of supporting them on the public. As to persons of quality, they give security to appropriate a certain sum for each child, suitable to their condition; and these funds are always managed with good husbandry and the most exact justice.

The cottagers and labourers keep their children at home, their business being only to till and cultivate the earth, and therefore their education is of little consequence to the public: but the old and diseased among them, are supported by hospitals; for begging is a trade unknown in this empire.

And here it may, perhaps, divert the curious reader, to give some account of my domestics, and my manner of living in this country, during a residence of nine months, and thirteen days. Having a head mechanically turned, and being likewise forced by necessity, I had made for myself a table and chair convenient enough, out of the largest trees in the royal park. Two hundred sempstresses were employed to make me shirts, and linen for my bed and table, all of the strongest and coarsest kind they could get; which, however, they were forced to quilt together in several folds, for the thickest was some degrees finer than lawn. Their linen is usually three inches wide, and three feet make a piece. The sempstresses took my measure as I lay on the ground, one standing at my neck, and another at my mid-leg, with a strong cord extended, that each held by the end, while a third measured the length of the cord with a rule of an inch long. Then they measured my right thumb, and desired no more; for by a mathematical computation, that twice round the thumb is once round the wrist, and so on to the neck and the waist, and by the help of my old shirt, which I displayed on the ground before them for a pattern, they fitted me exactly. Three hundred tailors were employed in the same manner to make me clothes; but they had another contrivance for taking my measure. I kneeled down, and they raised a ladder from the ground to my neck; upon this ladder one of them mounted, and let fall a plumb-line from my collar to the floor, which just answered the length of my coat: but my waist and arms I measured myself. When my clothes were finished, which was done in my house (for the largest of theirs would not have been able to hold them), they looked like the patch-work made by the ladies in England, only that mine were all of a colour.

I had three hundred cooks to dress my victuals, in little convenient huts built about my house, where they and their families lived, and prepared me two dishes a-piece. I took up twenty waiters in my hand, and placed them on the table: a hundred more attended below on the ground, some with dishes of meat, and some with barrels of wine and other liquors slung on their shoulders; all which the waiters above drew up, as I wanted, in a very ingenious manner, by certain cords, as we draw the bucket up a well in Europe. A dish of their meat was a good mouthful, and a barrel of their liquor a reasonable draught. Their mutton yields to ours, but their beef is excellent. I have had a sirloin so large, that I have been forced to make three bites of it; but this is rare. My servants were astonished to see me eat it, bones and all, as in our country we do the leg of a lark. Their geese and turkeys I usually ate at a mouthful, and I confess they far exceed ours. Of their smaller fowl I could take up twenty or thirty at the end of my knife.

One day his imperial majesty, being informed of my way of living, desired "that himself and his royal consort, with the young princes of the blood of both sexes, might have the happiness," as he was pleased to call it, "of dining with me." They came accordingly, and I placed them in chairs of state, upon my table, just over against me, with their guards about them. Flimnap, the lord high treasurer, attended there likewise with his white staff; and I observed he often looked on me with a sour countenance, which I would not seem to regard, but ate more than usual, in honour to my dear country, as well as to fill the court with admiration. I have some private reasons to believe, that this visit from his majesty gave Flimnap an opportunity of doing me ill offices to his master. That minister had always been my secret enemy, though he outwardly caressed me more than was usual to the moroseness of his nature. He represented to the emperor "the low condition of his treasury; that he was forced to take up money at a great discount; that exchequer bills would not circulate under nine per cent. below par; that I had cost his majesty above a million and a half of sprugs" (their greatest gold coin, about the bigness of a spangle) "and, upon the whole, that it would be advisable in the emperor to take the first fair occasion of dismissing me."

I am here obliged to vindicate the reputation of an excellent lady, who was an innocent sufferer upon my account. The treasurer took a fancy to be jealous of his wife, from the malice of some evil tongues, who informed him that her grace had taken a violent affection for my person; and the court scandal ran for some time, that she once came privately to my lodging. This I solemnly declare to be a most infamous falsehood, without any grounds, further than that her grace was pleased to treat me with all innocent marks of freedom and friendship. I own she came often to my house, but always publicly, nor ever without three more in the coach, who were usually her sister and young daughter, and some particular acquaintance; but this was common to many other ladies of the court. And I still appeal to my servants round, whether they at any time saw a coach at my door, without knowing what persons were in it. On those occasions, when a servant had given me notice, my custom was to go immediately to the door, and, after paying my respects, to take up the coach and two horses very carefully in my hands (for, if there were six horses, the postillion always unharnessed four,) and place them on a table, where I had fixed a movable rim quite round, of five inches high, to prevent accidents. And I have often had four coaches and horses at once on my table, full of company, while I sat in my chair, leaning my face towards them; and when I was engaged with one set, the coachmen would gently drive the others round my table. I have passed many an afternoon very agreeably in these conversations. But I defy the treasurer, or his two informers (I will name them, and let them make the best of it) Clustril and Drunlo, to prove that any person ever came to me incognito, except the secretary Reldresal, who was sent by express command of his imperial majesty, as I have before related. I should not have dwelt so long upon this particular, if it had not been a point wherein the reputation of a great lady is so nearly concerned, to say nothing of my own; though I then had the honour to be a nardac, which the treasurer himself is not; for all the world knows, that he is only a glumglum, a title inferior by one degree, as that of a marquis is to a duke in England; yet I allow he preceded me in right of his post. These false informations, which I afterwards came to the knowledge of by an accident not proper to mention, made the treasurer show his lady for some time an ill countenance, and me a worse; and although he was at last undeceived and reconciled to her, yet I lost all credit with him, and found my interest decline very fast with the emperor himself, who was, indeed, too much governed by that favourite.

CHAPTER VII.

[The author, being informed of a design to accuse him of high- treason, makes his escape to Blefuscu. His reception there.]

Before I proceed to give an account of my leaving this kingdom, it may be proper to inform the reader of a private intrigue which had been for two months forming against me.

I had been hitherto, all my life, a stranger to courts, for which I was unqualified by the meanness of my condition. I had indeed heard and read enough of the dispositions of great princes and ministers, but never expected to have found such terrible effects of them, in so remote a country, governed, as I thought, by very different maxims from those in Europe.

When I was just preparing to pay my attendance on the emperor of Blefuscu, a considerable person at court (to whom I had been very serviceable, at a time when he lay under the highest displeasure of his imperial majesty) came to my house very privately at night, in a close chair, and, without sending his name, desired admittance. The chairmen were dismissed; I put the chair, with his lordship in it, into my coat-pocket: and, giving orders to a trusty servant, to say I was indisposed and gone to sleep, I fastened the door of my house, placed the chair on the table, according to my usual custom, and sat down by it. After the common salutations were over, observing his lordship's countenance full of concern, and inquiring into the reason, he desired "I would hear him with patience, in a matter that highly concerned my honour and my life." His speech was to the following effect, for I took notes of it as soon as he left me:-

"You are to know," said he, "that several committees of council have been lately called, in the most private manner, on your account; and it is but two days since his majesty came to a full resolution.

"You are very sensible that Skyresh Bolgolam" (galbet, or high- admiral) "has been your mortal enemy, almost ever since your arrival. His original reasons I know not; but his hatred is increased since your great success against Blefuscu, by which his glory as admiral is much obscured. This lord, in conjunction with Flimnap the high-treasurer, whose enmity against you is notorious on account of his lady, Limtoc the general, Lalcon the chamberlain, and Balmuff the grand justiciary, have prepared articles of impeachment against you, for treason and other capital crimes."

This preface made me so impatient, being conscious of my own merits and innocence, that I was going to interrupt him; when he entreated me to be silent, and thus proceeded:-

"Out of gratitude for the favours you have done me, I procured information of the whole proceedings, and a copy of the articles; wherein I venture my head for your service.

"'Articles of Impeachment against QUINBUS FLESTRIN, (the Man-Mountain.)

ARTICLE I.

43

"'Whereas, by a statute made in the reign of his imperial majesty Calin Deffar Plune, it is enacted, that, whoever shall make water within the precincts of the royal palace, shall be liable to the pains and penalties of high-treason; notwithstanding, the said Quinbus Flestrin, in open breach of the said law, under colour of extinguishing the fire kindled in the apartment of his majesty's most dear imperial consort, did maliciously, traitorously, and devilishly, by discharge of his urine, put out the said fire kindled in the said apartment, lying and being within the precincts of the said royal palace, against the statute in that case provided, etc. against the duty, etc.

ARTICLE II.

"'That the said Quinbus Flestrin, having brought the imperial fleet of Blefuscu into the royal port, and being afterwards commanded by his imperial majesty to seize all the other ships of the said empire of Blefuscu, and reduce that empire to a province, to be governed by a viceroy from hence, and to destroy and put to death, not only all the Big-endian exiles, but likewise all the people of that empire who would not immediately forsake the Big-endian heresy, he, the said Flestrin, like a false traitor against his most auspicious, serene, imperial majesty, did petition to be excused from the said service, upon pretence of unwillingness to force the consciences, or destroy the liberties and lives of an innocent people.

ARTICLE III.

"'That, whereas certain ambassadors arrived from the Court of Blefuscu, to sue for peace in his majesty's court, he, the said Flestrin, did, like a false traitor, aid, abet, comfort, and divert, the said ambassadors, although he knew them to be servants to a prince who was lately an open enemy to his imperial majesty, and in an open war against his said majesty.

ARTICLE IV.

"'That the said Quinbus Flestrin, contrary to the duty of a faithful subject, is now preparing to make a voyage to the court and empire of Blefuscu, for which he has received only verbal license from his imperial majesty; and, under colour of the said license, does falsely and traitorously intend to take the said voyage, and thereby to aid, comfort, and abet the emperor of Blefuscu, so lately an enemy, and in open war with his imperial majesty aforesaid.'

"There are some other articles; but these are the most important, of which I have read you an abstract.

"In the several debates upon this impeachment, it must be confessed that his majesty gave many marks of his great lenity; often urging the services you had done him, and endeavouring to extenuate your crimes. The treasurer and admiral insisted that you should be put to the most painful and ignominious death, by setting fire to your house at night, and the general was to attend with twenty thousand men, armed with poisoned arrows, to shoot you on the face and hands. Some of your servants were to have private orders to strew a poisonous juice on your shirts and sheets, which would soon make you tear your own flesh, and die in the utmost torture. The general came into the same opinion; so that for a long time there was a majority against you; but his majesty resolving, if possible, to spare your life, at last brought off the chamberlain.

"Upon this incident, Reldresal, principal secretary for private affairs, who always approved himself your true friend, was commanded by the emperor to deliver his opinion, which he accordingly did; and therein justified the good thoughts you have of him. He allowed your crimes to be great, but that still there was room for mercy, the most commendable virtue in a prince, and for which his majesty was so justly celebrated. He said, the friendship between you and him was so well known to the world, that perhaps the most honourable board might think him partial; however, in obedience to the command he had received, he would freely offer his sentiments. That if his majesty, in consideration of your services, and pursuant to his own merciful disposition, would please to spare your life, and only give orders to put out both your eyes, he humbly conceived, that by this expedient justice might in some measure be satisfied, and all the world would applaud the lenity of the emperor, as well as the fair and generous proceedings of those who have the honour to be his counsellors. That the loss of your eyes would be no impediment to your bodily strength, by which you might still be useful to his majesty; that blindness is an addition to courage, by concealing dangers from us; that the fear you had for your eyes, was the greatest difficulty in bringing over the enemy's fleet, and it would be sufficient for you to see by the eyes of the ministers, since the greatest princes do no more.

"This proposal was received with the utmost disapprobation by the whole board. Bolgolam, the admiral, could not preserve his temper, but, rising up in fury, said, he wondered how the secretary durst presume to give his opinion for preserving the life of a traitor; that the services you had performed were, by all true reasons of state, the great aggravation of your crimes; that you, who were able to extinguish the fire by discharge of urine in her majesty's apartment (which he mentioned with horror), might, at another time, raise an inundation by the same means, to drown the whole palace; and the same strength which enabled you to bring over the enemy's fleet, might serve, upon the first discontent, to carry it back; that he had good reasons to think you were a Big-endian in your heart; and, as treason begins in the heart, before it appears in overt-acts, so he accused you as a traitor on that account, and therefore insisted you should be put to death.

"The treasurer was of the same opinion: he showed to what straits his majesty's revenue was reduced, by the charge of maintaining you, which would soon grow insupportable; that the secretary's expedient of putting out your eyes, was so far from being a remedy against this evil, that it would probably increase it, as is manifest from the common practice of blinding some kind of fowls, after which they fed the faster, and grew sooner fat; that his sacred majesty and the council, who are your judges, were, in their own consciences, fully convinced of your guilt, which was a sufficient argument to condemn you to death, without the formal proofs required by the strict letter of the law.

"But his imperial majesty, fully determined against capital punishment, was graciously pleased to say, that since the council thought the loss of your eyes too easy a censure, some other way may be inflicted hereafter. And your friend the secretary, humbly desiring to be heard again, in answer to what the treasurer had objected, concerning the great charge his majesty was at in maintaining you, said, that his excellency, who had the sole disposal of the emperor's revenue, might easily provide against that evil, by gradually lessening your establishment; by which, for want of sufficient for you would grow weak and faint, and lose your appetite, and consequently, decay, and consume in a few months; neither would the stench of your carcass be then so dangerous, when it should become more than half diminished; and immediately upon your death five or six thousand of his majesty's subjects might, in two or three days, cut your flesh from your bones, take it away by cart-loads, and bury it in distant parts, to prevent infection, leaving the skeleton as a monument of admiration to posterity.

"Thus, by the great friendship of the secretary, the whole affair was compromised. It was strictly enjoined, that the project of starving you by degrees should be kept a secret; but the sentence of putting out your eyes was entered on the books; none dissenting, except Bolgolam the admiral, who, being a creature of the empress, was perpetually instigated by her majesty to insist upon your death, she having borne perpetual malice against you, on account of that infamous and illegal method you took to extinguish the fire in her apartment.

"In three days your friend the secretary will be directed to come to your house, and read before you the articles of impeachment; and then to signify the great lenity and favour of his majesty and council, whereby you are only condemned to the loss of your eyes, which his majesty does not question you will gratefully and humbly submit to; and twenty of his majesty's surgeons will attend, in order to see the operation well performed, by discharging very sharp-pointed arrows into the balls of your eyes, as you lie on the ground.

"I leave to your prudence what measures you will take; and to avoid suspicion, I must immediately return in as private a manner as I came."

His lordship did so; and I remained alone, under many doubts and perplexities of mind.

It was a custom introduced by this prince and his ministry (very different, as I have been assured, from the practice of former times,) that after the court had decreed any cruel execution, either to gratify the monarch's resentment, or the malice of a favourite, the emperor always made a speech to his whole council, expressing his great lenity and tenderness, as qualities known and confessed by all the world. This speech was immediately published throughout the kingdom; nor did any thing terrify the people so much as those encomiums on his majesty's mercy; because it was observed, that the more these praises were enlarged and insisted on, the more inhuman was the punishment, and the sufferer more innocent. Yet, as to myself, I must confess, having never been designed for a courtier, either by my birth or education, I was so ill a judge of things, that I could not discover the lenity and favour of this sentence, but conceived it (perhaps erroneously) rather to be rigorous than gentle. I sometimes thought of standing my trial, for, although I could not deny the facts alleged in the several articles, yet I hoped they would admit of some extenuation. But having in my life perused many state-trials, which I ever observed to terminate as the judges thought fit to direct, I durst not rely on so dangerous a decision, in so critical a juncture, and against such powerful enemies. Once I was strongly bent upon resistance, for, while I had liberty the whole strength of that empire could hardly subdue me, and I might easily with stones pelt the metropolis to pieces; but I soon rejected that project with horror, by remembering the oath I had made to the emperor, the favours I received from him, and the high title of nardac he conferred upon me. Neither had I so soon learned the gratitude of courtiers, to persuade myself, that his majesty's present seventies acquitted me of all past obligations.

At last, I fixed upon a resolution, for which it is probable I may incur some censure, and not unjustly; for I confess I owe the preserving of mine eyes, and consequently my liberty, to my own great rashness and want of experience; because, if I had then known the nature of princes and ministers, which I have since observed in many other courts, and their methods of treating criminals less obnoxious than myself, I should, with great alacrity and readiness, have submitted to so easy a punishment. But hurried on by the precipitancy of youth, and having his imperial majesty's license to pay my attendance upon the emperor of Blefuscu, I took this opportunity, before the three days were elapsed, to send a letter to my friend the secretary, signifying my resolution of setting out that morning for Blefuscu, pursuant to the leave I had got; and, without waiting for an answer, I went to that side of the island where our fleet lay. I seized a large man of war, tied a cable to the prow, and, lifting up the anchors, I stripped myself, put my clothes (together with my coverlet, which I carried under my arm) into the vessel, and, drawing it after me, between wading and swimming arrived at the royal port of Blefuscu, where the people had long expected me: they lent me two guides to direct me to the capital city, which is of the same name. I held them in my hands, till I came within two hundred yards of the gate, and desired them "to signify my arrival to one of the secretaries, and let him know, I there waited his majesty's command." I had an answer in about an hour, "that his majesty, attended by the royal family, and great officers of the court, was coming out to receive me." I advanced a hundred yards. The emperor and his train alighted from their horses, the empress and ladies from their coaches, and I did not perceive they were in any fright or concern. I lay on the ground to kiss his majesty's and the empress's hands. I told his majesty, "that I was come according to my promise, and with the license of the emperor my master, to have the honour of seeing so mighty a monarch, and to offer him any service in my power, consistent with my duty to my own prince;" not mentioning a word of my disgrace, because I had hitherto no regular information of it, and might suppose myself wholly ignorant of any such design; neither could I reasonably conceive that the emperor would discover the secret, while I was out of his power; wherein, however, it soon appeared I was deceived.

I shall not trouble the reader with the particular account of my reception at this court, which was suitable to the generosity of so great a prince; nor of the difficulties I was in for want of a house and bed, being forced to lie on the ground, wrapped up in my coverlet.

CHAPTER VIII.

[The author, by a lucky accident, finds means to leave Blefuscu; and, after some difficulties, returns safe to his native country.]

Three days after my arrival, walking out of curiosity to the north- east coast of the island, I observed, about half a league off in the sea, somewhat that looked like a boat overturned. I pulled off my shoes and stockings, and, wailing two or three hundred yards, I found the object to approach nearer by force of the tide; and then plainly saw it to be a real boat, which I supposed might by some tempest have been driven from a ship. Whereupon, I returned immediately towards the city, and desired his imperial majesty to lend me twenty of the tallest vessels he had left, after the loss of his fleet, and three thousand seamen, under the command of his vice-admiral. This fleet sailed round, while I went back the shortest way to the coast, where I first discovered the boat. I found the tide had driven it still nearer. The seamen were all provided with cordage, which I had beforehand twisted to a sufficient strength. When the ships came up, I stripped myself, and waded till I came within a hundred yards off the boat, after which I was forced to swim till I got up to it. The seamen threw me the end of the cord, which I fastened to a hole in the fore-part of the boat, and the other end to a man of war; but I found all my labour to little purpose; for, being out of my depth, I was not able to work. In this necessity I was forced to swim behind, and push the boat forward, as often as I could, with one of my hands; and the tide favouring me, I advanced so far that I could just hold up my chin and feel the ground. I rested two or three minutes, and then gave the boat another shove, and so on, till the sea was no higher than my arm-pits; and now, the most laborious part being over, I took out my other cables, which were stowed in one of the ships, and fastened them first to the boat, and then to nine of the vessels which attended me; the wind being favourable, the seamen towed, and I shoved, until we arrived within forty yards of the shore; and, waiting till the tide was out, I got dry to the boat, and by the assistance of two thousand men, with ropes and engines, I made a shift to turn it on its bottom, and found it was but little damaged.

I shall not trouble the reader with the difficulties I was under, by the help of certain paddles, which cost me ten days making, to get my boat to the royal port of Blefuscu, where a mighty concourse of people appeared upon my arrival, full of wonder at the sight of so prodigious a vessel. I told the emperor "that my good fortune had thrown this boat in my way, to carry me to some place whence I might return into my native country; and begged his majesty's orders for getting materials to fit it up, together with his license to depart;" which, after some kind expostulations, he was pleased to grant.

I did very much wonder, in all this time, not to have heard of any express relating to me from our emperor to the court of Blefuscu. But I was afterward given privately to understand, that his imperial majesty, never imagining I had the least notice of his designs, believed I was only gone to Blefuscu in performance of my promise, according to the license he had given me, which was well known at our court, and would return in a few days, when the ceremony was ended. But he was at last in pain at my long absence; and after consulting with the treasurer and the rest of that cabal, a person of quality was dispatched with the copy of the articles against me. This envoy had instructions to represent to the monarch of Blefuscu, "the great lenity of his master, who was content to punish me no farther than with the loss of mine eyes; that I had fled from justice; and if I did not return in two hours, I should be deprived of my title of nardac, and declared a traitor." The envoy further added, "that in order to maintain the peace and amity between both empires, his master expected that his brother of Blefuscu would give orders to have me sent back to Lilliput, bound hand and foot, to be punished as a traitor."

The emperor of Blefuscu, having taken three days to consult, returned an answer consisting of many civilities and excuses. He said, "that as for sending me bound, his brother knew it was impossible; that, although I had deprived him of his fleet, yet he owed great obligations to me for many good offices I had done him in making the peace. That, however, both their majesties would soon be made easy; for I had found a prodigious vessel on the shore, able to carry me on the sea, which he had given orders to fit up, with my own assistance and direction; and he hoped, in a few weeks, both empires would be freed from so insupportable an encumbrance."

With this answer the envoy returned to Lilliput; and the monarch of Blefuscu related to me all that had passed; offering me at the same time (but under the strictest confidence) his gracious protection, if I would continue in his service; wherein, although I believed him sincere, yet I resolved never more to put any confidence in princes or ministers, where I could possibly avoid it; and therefore, with all due acknowledgments for his favourable intentions, I humbly begged to be excused. I told him, "that since fortune, whether good or evil, had thrown a vessel in my way, I was resolved to venture myself on the ocean, rather than be an occasion of difference between two such mighty monarchs." Neither did I find the emperor at all displeased; and I discovered, by a certain accident, that he was very glad of my resolution, and so were most of his ministers.

These considerations moved me to hasten my departure somewhat sooner than I intended; to which the court, impatient to have me gone, very readily contributed. Five hundred workmen were employed to make two sails to my boat, according to my directions, by quilting thirteen folds of their strongest linen together. I was at the pains of making ropes and cables, by twisting ten, twenty, or thirty of the thickest and strongest of theirs. A great stone that I happened to find, after a long search, by the sea-shore, served me for an anchor. I had the tallow of three hundred cows, for greasing my boat, and other uses. I was at incredible pains in cutting down some of the largest timber-trees, for oars and masts, wherein I was, however, much assisted by his majesty's ship-carpenters, who helped me in smoothing them, after I had done the rough work.

In about a month, when all was prepared, I sent to receive his majesty's commands, and to take my leave. The emperor and royal family came out of the palace; I lay down on my face to kiss his hand, which he very graciously gave me: so did the empress and young princes of the blood. His majesty presented me with fifty purses of two hundred sprugs a-piece, together with his picture at full length, which I put immediately into one of my gloves, to keep it from being hurt. The ceremonies at my departure were too many to trouble the reader with at this time.

I stored the boat with the carcases of a hundred oxen, and three hundred sheep, with bread and drink proportionable, and as much meat ready dressed as four hundred cooks could provide. I took with me six cows and two bulls alive, with as many ewes and rams, intending to carry them into my own country, and propagate the breed. And to feed them on board, I had a good bundle of hay, and a bag of corn. I would gladly have taken a dozen of the natives, but this was a thing the emperor would by no means permit; and, besides a diligent search into my pockets, his majesty engaged my honour "not to carry away any of his subjects, although with their own consent and desire."

Having thus prepared all things as well as I was able, I set sail on the twenty-fourth day of September 1701, at six in the morning; and when I had gone about four-leagues to the northward, the wind being at south-east, at six in the evening I descried a small island, about half a league to the north-west. I advanced forward, and cast anchor on the lee-side of the island, which seemed to be uninhabited. I then took some refreshment, and went to my rest. I slept well, and as I conjectured at least six hours, for I found the day broke in two hours after I awaked. It was a clear night. I ate my breakfast before the sun was up; and heaving anchor, the wind being favourable, I steered the same course that I had done the day before, wherein I was directed by my pocket compass. My intention was to reach, if possible, one of those islands. which I had reason to believe lay to the north-east of Van Diemen's Land. I discovered nothing all that day; but upon the next, about three in the afternoon, when I had by my computation made twenty-four leagues from Blefuscu, I descried a sail steering to the south- east; my course was due east. I hailed her, but could get no answer; yet I found I gained upon her, for the wind slackened. I made all the sail I could, and in half an hour she spied me, then hung out her ancient, and discharged a gun. It is not easy to express the joy I was in, upon the unexpected hope of once more seeing my beloved country, and the dear pledges I left in it. The ship slackened her sails, and I came up with her between five and six in the evening, September 26th; but my heart leaped within me to see her English colours. I put my cows and sheep into my coat- pockets, and got on board with all my little cargo of provisions. The vessel was an English merchantman, returning from Japan by the North and South seas; the captain, Mr. John Biddel, of Deptford, a very civil man, and an excellent sailor.

We were now in the latitude of 30 degrees south; there were about fifty men in the ship; and here I met an old comrade of mine, one Peter Williams, who gave me a good character to the captain. This gentleman treated me with kindness, and desired I would let him know what place I came from last, and whither I was bound; which I did in a few words, but he thought I was raving, and that the dangers I underwent had disturbed my head; whereupon I took my black cattle and sheep out of my pocket, which, after great astonishment, clearly convinced him of my veracity. I then showed him the gold given me by the emperor of Blefuscu, together with his majesty's picture at full length, and some other rarities of that country. I gave him two purses of two hundreds sprugs each, and promised, when we arrived in England, to make him a present of a cow and a sheep big with young.

I shall not trouble the reader with a particular account of this voyage, which was very prosperous for the most part. We arrived in the Downs on the 13th of April, 1702. I had only one misfortune, that the rats on board carried away one of my sheep; I found her bones in a hole, picked clean from the flesh. The rest of my cattle I got safe ashore, and set them a-grazing in a bowling-green at Greenwich, where the fineness of the grass made them feed very heartily, though I had always feared the contrary: neither could I possibly have preserved them in so long a voyage, if the captain had not allowed me some of his best biscuit, which, rubbed to powder, and mingled with water, was their constant food. The short time I continued in England, I made a considerable profit by showing my cattle to many persons of quality and others: and before I began my second voyage, I sold them for six hundred pounds. Since my last return I find the breed is considerably increased, especially the sheep, which I hope will prove much to the advantage of the woollen manufacture, by the fineness of the fleeces.

I stayed but two months with my wife and family, for my insatiable desire of seeing foreign countries, would suffer me to continue no longer. I left fifteen hundred pounds with my wife, and fixed her in a good house at Redriff. My remaining stock I carried with me, part in money and part in goods, in hopes to improve my fortunes. My eldest uncle John had left me an estate in land, near Epping, of about thirty pounds a-year; and I had a long lease of the Black Bull in Fetter-Lane, which yielded me as much more; so that I was not in any danger of leaving my family upon the parish. My son Johnny, named so after his uncle, was at the grammar-school, and a towardly child. My daughter Betty (who is now well married, and has children) was then at her needle-work. I took leave of my wife, and boy and girl, with tears on both sides, and went on board the Adventure, a merchant ship of three hundred tons, bound for Surat, captain John Nicholas, of Liverpool, commander. But my account of this voyage must be referred to the Second Part of my Travels.

PART II. A VOYAGE TO BROBDINGNAG.

CHAPTER I.

[A great storm described; the long boat sent to fetch water; the author goes with it to discover the country. He is left on shore, is seized by one of the natives, and carried to a farmer's house. His reception, with several accidents that happened there. A description of the inhabitants.]

Having been condemned, by nature and fortune, to active and restless life, in two months after my return, I again left my native country, and took shipping in the Downs, on the 20th day of June, 1702, in the Adventure, Captain John Nicholas, a Cornish man, commander, bound for Surat. We had a very prosperous gale, till we arrived at the Cape of Good Hope, where we landed for fresh water; but discovering a leak, we unshipped our goods and wintered there; for the captain falling sick of an ague, we could not leave the Cape till the end of March. We then set sail, and had a good voyage till we passed the Straits of Madagascar; but having got northward of that island, and to about five degrees south latitude, the winds, which in those seas are observed to blow a constant equal gale between the north and west, from the beginning of December to the beginning of May, on the 19th of April began to blow with much greater violence, and more westerly than usual, continuing so for twenty days together: during which time, we were driven a little to the east of the Molucca Islands, and about three degrees northward of the line, as our captain found by an observation he took the 2nd of May, at which time the wind ceased, and it was a perfect calm, whereat I was not a little rejoiced. But he, being a man well experienced in the navigation of those seas, bid us all prepare against a storm, which accordingly happened the day following: for the southern wind, called the southern monsoon, began to set in.

Finding it was likely to overblow, we took in our sprit-sail, and stood by to hand the fore-sail; but making foul weather, we looked the guns were all fast, and handed the mizen. The ship lay very broad off, so we thought it better spooning before the sea, than trying or hulling. We reefed the fore-sail and set him, and hauled aft the fore-sheet; the helm was hard a-weather. The ship wore bravely. We belayed the fore down-haul; but the sail was split, and we hauled down the yard, and got the sail into the ship, and unbound all the things clear of it. It was a very fierce storm; the sea broke strange and dangerous. We hauled off upon the laniard of the whip-staff, and helped the man at the helm. We would not get down our topmast, but let all stand, because she scudded before the sea very well, and we knew that the top-mast being aloft, the ship was the wholesomer, and made better way through the sea, seeing we had sea-room. When the storm was over, we set fore-sail and main-sail, and brought the ship to. Then we set the mizen, main-top-sail, and the fore-top-sail. Our course was east-north-east, the wind was at south-west. We got the starboard tacks aboard, we cast off our weather-braces and lifts; we set in the lee-braces, and hauled forward by the weather- bowlings, and hauled them tight, and belayed them, and hauled over the mizen tack to windward, and kept her full and by as near as she would lie.

During this storm, which was followed by a strong wind west-south- west, we were carried, by my computation, about five hundred leagues to the east, so that the oldest sailor on board could not tell in what part of the world we were. Our provisions held out well, our ship was staunch, and our crew all in good health; but we lay in the utmost distress for water. We thought it best to hold on the same course, rather than turn more northerly, which might have brought us to the north-west part of Great Tartary, and into the Frozen Sea.

On the 16th day of June, 1703, a boy on the top-mast discovered land. On the 17th, we came in full view of a great island, or continent (for we knew not whether;) on the south side whereof was a small neck of land jutting out into the sea, and a creek too shallow to hold a ship of above one hundred tons. We cast anchor within a league of this creek, and our captain sent a dozen of his men well armed in the long-boat, with vessels for water, if any could be found. I desired his leave to go with them, that I might see the country, and make what discoveries I could. When we came to land we saw no river or spring, nor any sign of inhabitants. Our men therefore wandered on the shore to find out some fresh water near the sea, and I walked alone about a mile on the other side, where I observed the country all barren and rocky. I now began to be weary, and seeing nothing to entertain my curiosity, I returned gently down towards the creek; and the sea being full in my view, I saw our men already got into the boat, and rowing for life to the ship. I was going to holla after them, although it had been to little purpose, when I observed a huge creature walking after them in the sea, as fast as he could: he waded not much deeper than his knees, and took prodigious strides: but our men had the start of him half a league, and, the sea thereabouts being full of sharp-pointed rocks, the monster was not able to overtake the boat. This I was afterwards told, for I durst not stay to see the issue of the adventure; but ran as fast as I could the way I first went, and then climbed up a steep hill, which gave me some prospect of the country. I found it fully cultivated; but that which first surprised me was the length of the grass, which, in those grounds that seemed to be kept for hay, was about twenty feet high.

I fell into a high road, for so I took it to be, though it served to the inhabitants only as a foot-path through a field of barley. Here I walked on for some time, but could see little on either side, it being now near harvest, and the corn rising at least forty feet. I was an hour walking to the end of this field, which was fenced in with a hedge of at least one hundred and twenty feet high, and the trees so lofty that I could make no computation of their altitude. There was a stile to pass from this field into the next. It had four steps, and a stone to cross over when you came to the uppermost. It was impossible for me to climb this stile, because every step was six-feet high, and the upper stone about twenty. I was endeavouring to find some gap in the hedge, when I discovered one of the inhabitants in the next field, advancing towards the stile, of the same size with him whom I saw in the sea pursuing our boat. He appeared as tall as an ordinary spire steeple, and took about ten yards at every stride, as near as I could guess. I was struck with the utmost fear and astonishment, and ran to hide myself in the corn, whence I saw him at the top of the stile looking back into the next field on the right hand, and heard him call in a voice many degrees louder than a speaking- trumpet: but the noise was so high in the air, that at first I certainly thought it was thunder. Whereupon seven monsters, like himself, came towards him with reaping-hooks in their hands, each hook about the largeness of six scythes. These people were not so well clad as the first, whose servants or labourers they seemed to be; for, upon some words he spoke, they went to reap the corn in the field where I lay. I kept from them at as great a distance as I could, but was forced to move with extreme difficulty, for the stalks of the corn were sometimes not above a foot distant, so that I could hardly squeeze my body betwixt them. However, I made a shift to go forward, till I came to a part of the field where the corn had been laid by the rain and wind. Here it was impossible for me to advance a step; for the stalks were so interwoven, that I could not creep through, and the beards of the fallen ears so strong and pointed, that they pierced through my clothes into my flesh. At the same time I heard the reapers not a hundred yards behind me. Being quite dispirited with toil, and wholly overcome by grief and dispair, I lay down between two ridges, and heartily wished I might there end my days. I bemoaned my desolate widow and fatherless children. I lamented my own folly and wilfulness, in attempting a second voyage, against the advice of all my friends and relations. In this terrible agitation of mind, I could not forbear thinking of Lilliput, whose inhabitants looked upon me as the greatest prodigy that ever appeared in the world; where I was able to draw an imperial fleet in my hand, and perform those other actions, which will be recorded for ever in the chronicles of that empire, while posterity shall hardly believe them, although attested by millions. I reflected what a mortification it must prove to me, to appear as inconsiderable in this nation, as one single Lilliputian would be among us. But this I conceived was to be the least of my misfortunes; for, as human creatures are observed to be more savage and cruel in proportion to their bulk, what could I expect but to be a morsel in the mouth of the first among these enormous barbarians that should happen to seize me? Undoubtedly philosophers are in the right, when they tell us that nothing is great or little otherwise than by comparison. It might have pleased fortune, to have let the Lilliputians find some nation, where the people were as diminutive with respect to them, as they were to me. And who knows but that even this prodigious race of mortals might be equally overmatched in some distant part of the world, whereof we have yet no discovery.

Scared and confounded as I was, I could not forbear going on with these reflections, when one of the reapers, approaching within ten yards of the ridge where I lay, made me apprehend that with the next step I should be squashed to death under his foot, or cut in two with his reaping-hook. And therefore, when he was again about to move, I screamed as loud as fear could make me:

whereupon the huge creature trod short, and, looking round about under him for some time, at last espied me as I lay on the ground. He considered awhile, with the caution of one who endeavours to lay hold on a small dangerous animal in such a manner that it shall not be able either to scratch or bite him, as I myself have sometimes done with a weasel in England. At length he ventured to take me behind, by the middle, between his fore-finger and thumb, and brought me within three yards of his eyes, that he might behold my shape more perfectly. I guessed his meaning, and my good fortune gave me so much presence of mind, that I resolved not to struggle in the least as he held me in the air above sixty feet from the ground, although he grievously pinched my sides, for fear I should slip through his fingers. All I ventured was to raise mine eyes towards the sun, and place my hands together in a supplicating posture, and to speak some words in a humble melancholy tone, suitable to the condition I then was in: for I apprehended every moment that he would dash me against the ground, as we usually do any little hateful animal, which we have a mind to destroy. But my good star would have it, that he appeared pleased with my voice and gestures, and began to look upon me as a curiosity, much wondering to hear me pronounce articulate words, although he could not understand them. In the mean time I was not able to forbear groaning and shedding tears, and turning my head towards my sides; letting him know, as well as I could, how cruelly I was hurt by the pressure of his thumb and finger. He seemed to apprehend my meaning; for, lifting up the lappet of his coat, he put me gently into it, and immediately ran along with me to his master, who was a substantial farmer, and the same person I had first seen in the field.

The farmer having (as I suppose by their talk) received such an account of me as his servant could give him, took a piece of a small straw, about the size of a walking-staff, and therewith lifted up the lappets of my coat; which it seems he thought to be some kind of covering that nature had given me. He blew my hairs aside to take a better view of my face. He called his hinds about him, and asked them, as I afterwards learned, whether they had ever seen in the fields any little creature that resembled me. He then placed me softly on the ground upon all fours, but I got immediately up, and walked slowly backward and forward, to let those people see I had no intent to run away. They all sat down in a circle about me, the better to observe my motions. I pulled off my hat, and made a low bow towards the farmer. I fell on my knees, and lifted up my hands and eyes, and spoke several words as loud as I could: I took a purse of gold out of my pocket, and humbly presented it to him. He received it on the palm of his hand, then applied it close to his eye to see what it was, and afterwards turned it several times with the point of a pin (which he took out of his sleeve,) but could make nothing of it. Whereupon I made a sign that he should place his hand on the ground. I then took the purse, and, opening it, poured all the gold into his palm. There were six Spanish pieces of four pistoles each, beside twenty or thirty smaller coins. I saw him wet the tip of his little finger upon his tongue, and take up one of my largest pieces, and then another; but he seemed to be wholly ignorant what they were. He made me a sign to put them again into my purse, and the purse again into my pocket, which, after offering it to him several times, I thought it best to do.

The farmer, by this time, was convinced I must be a rational creature. He spoke often to me; but the sound of his voice pierced my ears like that of a water-mill, yet his words were articulate enough. I answered as loud as I could in several languages, and he often laid his ear within two yards of me: but all in vain, for we were wholly unintelligible to each other. He then sent his servants to their work, and taking his handkerchief out of his pocket, he doubled and spread it on his left hand, which he placed flat on the ground with the palm upward, making me a sign to step into it, as I could easily do, for it was not above a foot in thickness. I thought it my part to obey, and, for fear of falling, laid myself at full length upon the handkerchief, with the remainder of which he lapped me up to the head for further security, and in this manner carried me home to his house. There he called his wife, and showed me to her; but she screamed and ran back, as women in England do at the sight of a toad or a spider. However, when she had a while seen my behaviour, and how well I observed the signs her husband made, she was soon reconciled, and by degrees grew extremely tender of me.

It was about twelve at noon, and a servant brought in dinner. It was only one substantial dish of meat (fit for the plain condition of a husbandman,) in a dish of about four-and-twenty feet diameter. The company were, the farmer and his wife, three children, and an old grandmother. When they were sat down, the farmer placed me at some distance from him on the table, which was thirty feet high from the floor. I was in a terrible fright, and kept as far as I could from the edge, for fear of falling. The wife minced a bit of meat, then crumbled some bread on a trencher, and placed it before me. I made her a low bow, took out my knife and fork, and fell to eat, which gave them exceeding delight. The mistress sent her maid for a small dram cup, which held about two gallons, and filled it with drink; I took up the vessel with much difficulty in both hands, and in a most respectful manner drank to her ladyship's health, expressing the words as loud as I could in English, which made the company laugh so heartily, that I was almost deafened with the noise. This liquor tasted like a small cider, and was not unpleasant. Then the master made me a sign to come to his trencher side; but as I walked on the table, being in great surprise all the time, as the indulgent reader will easily conceive and excuse, I happened to stumble against a crust, and fell flat on my face, but received no hurt. I got up immediately, and observing the good people to be in much concern, I took my hat (which I held under my arm out of good manners,) and waving it over my head, made three huzzas, to show I had got no mischief by my fall. But advancing forward towards my master (as I shall henceforth call him,) his youngest son, who sat next to him, an arch boy of about ten years old, took me up by the legs, and held me so high in the air, that I trembled every limb: but his father snatched me from him, and at the same time gave him such a box on the left ear, as would have felled an

European troop of horse to the earth, ordering him to be taken from the table. But being afraid the boy might owe me a spite, and well remembering how mischievous all children among us naturally are to sparrows, rabbits, young kittens, and puppy dogs, I fell on my knees, and pointing to the boy, made my master to understand, as well as I could, that I desired his son might be pardoned. The father complied, and the lad took his seat again, whereupon I went to him, and kissed his hand, which my master took, and made him stroke me gently with it.

In the midst of dinner, my mistress's favourite cat leaped into her lap. I heard a noise behind me like that of a dozen stocking- weavers at work; and turning my head, I found it proceeded from the purring of that animal, who seemed to be three times larger than an ox, as I computed by the view of her head, and one of her paws, while her mistress was feeding and stroking her. The fierceness of this creature's countenance altogether discomposed me; though I stood at the farther end of the table, above fifty feet off; and although my mistress held her fast, for fear she might give a spring, and seize me in her talons. But it happened there was no danger, for the cat took not the least notice of me when my master placed me within three yards of her. And as I have been always told, and found true by experience in my travels, that flying or discovering fear before a fierce animal, is a certain way to make it pursue or attack you, so I resolved, in this dangerous juncture, to show no manner of concern. I walked with intrepidity five or six times before the very head of the cat, and came within half a yard of her; whereupon she drew herself back, as if she were more afraid of me: I had less apprehension concerning the dogs, whereof three or four came into the room, as it is usual in farmers' houses; one of which was a mastiff, equal in bulk to four elephants, and another a greyhound, somewhat taller than the mastiff, but not so large.

When dinner was almost done, the nurse came in with a child of a year old in her arms, who immediately spied me, and began a squall that you might have heard from London-Bridge to Chelsea, after the usual oratory of infants, to get me for a plaything. The mother, out of pure indulgence, took me up, and put me towards the child, who presently seized me by the middle, and got my head into his mouth, where I roared so loud that the urchin was frighted, and let me drop, and I should infallibly have broke my neck, if the mother had not held her apron under me. The nurse, to quiet her babe, made use of a rattle which was a kind of hollow vessel filled with great stones, and fastened by a cable to the child's waist: but all in vain; so that she was forced to apply the last remedy by giving it suck. I must confess no object ever disgusted me so much as the sight of her monstrous breast, which I cannot tell what to compare with, so as to give the curious reader an idea of its bulk, shape, and colour. It stood prominent six feet, and could not be less than sixteen in circumference. The nipple was about half the bigness of my head, and the hue both of that and the dug, so varied with spots, pimples, and freckles, that nothing could appear more nauseous: for I had a near sight of her, she sitting down, the more conveniently to give suck, and I standing on the table. This made me reflect upon the fair skins of our English ladies, who appear so beautiful to us, only because they are of our own size, and their defects not to be seen but through a magnifying glass; where we find by experiment that the smoothest and whitest skins look rough, and coarse, and ill-coloured.

I remember when I was at Lilliput, the complexion of those diminutive people appeared to me the fairest in the world; and talking upon this subject with a person of learning there, who was an intimate friend of mine, he said that my face appeared much fairer and smoother when he looked on me from the ground, than it did upon a nearer view, when I took him up in my hand, and brought him close, which he confessed was at first a very shocking sight. He said, "he could discover great holes in my skin; that the stumps of my beard were ten times stronger than the bristles of a boar, and my complexion made up of several colours altogether disagreeable:" although I must beg leave to say for myself, that I am as fair as most of my sex and country, and very little sunburnt by all my travels. On the other side, discoursing of the ladies in that emperor's court, he used to tell me, "one had freckles; another too wide a mouth; a third too large a nose:" nothing of which I was able to distinguish. I confess this reflection was obvious enough; which, however, I could not forbear, lest the reader might think those vast creatures were actually deformed: for I must do them the justice to say, they are a comely race of people, and particularly the features of my master's countenance, although he was but a farmer, when I beheld him from the height of sixty feet, appeared very well proportioned.

When dinner was done, my master went out to his labourers, and, as I could discover by his voice and gesture, gave his wife strict charge to take care of me. I was very much tired, and disposed to sleep, which my mistress perceiving, she put me on her own bed, and covered me with a clean white handkerchief, but larger and coarser than the mainsail of a man-of-war.

I slept about two hours, and dreamt I was at home with my wife and children, which aggravated my sorrows when I awaked, and found myself alone in a vast room, between two and three hundred feet wide, and above two hundred high, lying in a bed twenty yards wide. My mistress was gone about her household affairs, and had locked me in. The bed was eight yards from the floor. Some natural necessities required me to get down; I durst not presume to call; and if I had, it would have been in vain, with such a voice as mine, at so great a distance from the room where I lay to the kitchen where the family kept. While I was under these circumstances, two rats crept up the curtains, and ran smelling backwards and forwards on the bed. One of them came up almost to my face, whereupon I rose in a fright, and drew out my hanger to defend myself. These horrible animals had the boldness to attack me on both sides, and one of them held his fore-feet at my collar; but I had the good fortune to rip up his belly before he could do me any mischief. He fell down at my feet; and the other, seeing the fate of his comrade, made his escape, but not without one good wound on the back, which I gave him as he fled, and made the blood run trickling from him. After this exploit, I walked gently to and fro on the bed, to recover my breath and loss of spirits. These creatures were of the size of a large mastiff, but infinitely more nimble and fierce; so that if I had taken off my belt before I went to sleep, I must have infallibly been torn to pieces and devoured. I measured the tail of the dead rat, and found it to be two yards long, wanting an inch; but it went against my stomach to drag the carcass off the bed, where it lay still bleeding; I observed it had yet some life, but with a strong slash across the neck, I thoroughly despatched it.

Soon after my mistress came into the room, who seeing me all bloody, ran and took me up in her hand. I pointed to the dead rat, smiling, and making other signs to show I was not hurt; whereat she was extremely rejoiced, calling the maid to take up the dead rat with a pair of tongs, and throw it out of the window. Then she set me on a table, where I showed her my hanger all bloody, and wiping it on the lappet of my coat, returned it to the scabbard. I was pressed to do more than one thing which another could not do for me, and therefore endeavoured to make my mistress understand, that I desired to be set down on the floor; which after she had done, my bashfulness would not suffer me to express myself farther, than by pointing to the door, and bowing several times. The good woman, with much difficulty, at last perceived what I would be at, and taking me up again in her hand, walked into the garden, where she set me down. I went on one side about two hundred yards, and beckoning to her not to look or to follow me, I hid myself between two leaves of sorrel, and there discharged the necessities of nature.

I hope the gentle reader will excuse me for dwelling on these and the like particulars, which, however insignificant they may appear to groveling vulgar minds, yet will certainly help a philosopher to enlarge his thoughts and imagination, and apply them to the benefit of public as well as private life, which was my sole design in presenting this and other accounts of my travels to the world; wherein I have been chiefly studious of truth, without affecting any ornaments of learning or of style. But the whole scene of this voyage made so strong an impression on my mind, and is so deeply fixed in my memory, that, in committing it to paper I did not omit one material circumstance: however, upon a strict review, I blotted out several passages. Of less moment which were in my first copy, for fear of being censured as tedious and trifling, whereof travellers are often, perhaps not without justice, accused.

CHAPTER II.

[A description of the farmer's daughter. The author carried to a market-town, and then to the metropolis. The particulars of his journey.]

My mistress had a daughter of nine years old, a child of towardly parts for her age, very dexterous at her needle, and skilful in dressing her baby. Her mother and she contrived to fit up the baby's cradle for me against night: the cradle was put into a small drawer of a cabinet, and the drawer placed upon a hanging shelf for fear of the rats. This was my bed all the time I staid with those people, though made more convenient by degrees, as I began to learn their language and make my wants known. This young girl was so handy, that after I had once or twice pulled off my clothes before her, she was able to dress and undress me, though I never gave her that trouble when she would let me do either myself. She made me seven shirts, and some other linen, of as fine cloth as could be got, which indeed was coarser than sackcloth; and these she constantly washed for me with her own hands. She was likewise my school-mistress, to teach me the language: when I pointed to any thing, she told me the name of it in her own tongue, so that in a few days I was able to call for whatever I had a mind to. She was very good-natured, and not above forty feet high, being little for her age. She gave me the name of Grildrig, which the family took up, and afterwards the whole kingdom. The word imports what the Latins call nanunculus, the Italians homunceletino, and the English mannikin. To her I chiefly owe my preservation in that country: we never parted while I was there; I called her my Glumdalclitch, or little nurse; and should be guilty of great ingratitude, if I omitted this honourable mention of her care and affection towards me, which I heartily wish it lay in my power to requite as she deserves, instead of being the innocent, but unhappy instrument of her disgrace, as I have too much reason to fear.

It now began to be known and talked of in the neighbourhood, that my master had found a strange animal in the field, about the bigness of a splacnuck, but exactly shaped in every part like a human creature; which it likewise imitated in all its actions; seemed to speak in a little language of its own, had already learned several words of theirs, went erect upon two legs, was tame and gentle, would come when it was called, do whatever it was bid, had the finest limbs in the world, and a complexion fairer than a nobleman's daughter of three years old. Another farmer, who lived hard by, and was a particular friend of my master, came on a visit on purpose to inquire into the truth of this story. I was immediately produced, and placed upon a table, where I walked as I was commanded, drew my hanger, put it up again, made my reverence to my master's guest, asked him in his own language how he did, and told him HE WAS WELCOME, just as my little nurse had instructed me. This man, who was old and dim-sighted, put on his spectacles to behold me better; at which I could not forbear laughing very heartily, for his eyes appeared like the full moon shining into a chamber at two windows. Our people, who discovered the cause of my mirth, bore me company in laughing, at which the old fellow was fool enough to be angry and out of countenance. He had the character of a great miser; and, to my misfortune, he well deserved it, by the cursed advice he gave my master, to show me as a sight upon a market-day in the next town, which was half an hour's riding, about two-and-twenty miles from our house. I guessed there was some mischief when I observed my master and his friend whispering together, sometimes pointing at me; and my fears made me fancy that I overheard and understood some of their words. But the next morning Glumdalclitch, my little nurse, told me the whole matter, which she had cunningly picked out from her mother. The poor girl laid me on her bosom, and fell a weeping with shame and grief. She apprehended some mischief would happen to me from rude vulgar folks, who might squeeze me to death, or break one of my limbs by taking me in their hands. She had also observed how modest I was in my nature, how nicely I regarded my honour, and what an indignity I should conceive it, to be exposed for money as a public spectacle, to the meanest of the people. She said, her papa and mamma had promised that Grildrig should be hers; but now she found they meant to serve her as they did last year, when they pretended to give her a lamb, and yet, as soon as it was fat, sold it to a butcher. For my own part, I may truly affirm, that I was less concerned than my nurse. I had a strong hope, which never left me, that I should one day recover my liberty: and as to the ignominy of being carried about for a monster, I considered myself to be a perfect stranger in the country, and that such a misfortune could never be charged upon me as a reproach, if ever I should return to England, since the king of Great Britain himself, in my condition, must have undergone the same distress.

My master, pursuant to the advice of his friend, carried me in a box the next market-day to the neighbouring town, and took along with him his little daughter, my nurse, upon a pillion behind him. The box was close on every side, with a little door for me to go in and out, and a few gimlet holes to let in air. The girl had been so careful as to put the quilt of her baby's bed into it, for me to lie down on. However, I was terribly shaken and discomposed in this journey, though it was but of half an hour: for the horse went about forty feet at every step and trotted so high, that the agitation was equal to the rising and falling of a ship in a great storm, but much more frequent. Our journey was somewhat farther than from London to St. Alban's. My master alighted at an inn which he used to frequent; and after consulting awhile with the inn-keeper, and making some necessary preparations, he hired the grultrud, or crier, to give notice through the town of a strange creature to be seen at the sign of the Green Eagle, not so big as a splacnuck (an animal in that country very finely shaped, about six feet long,) and in every part of the body resembling a human creature, could speak several words, and perform a hundred diverting tricks.

I was placed upon a table in the largest room of the inn, which might be near three hundred feet square. My little nurse stood on a low stool close to the table, to take care of me, and direct what I should do. My master, to avoid a crowd, would suffer only thirty people at a time to see me. I walked about on the table as the girl commanded; she asked me questions, as far as she knew my understanding of the language reached, and I answered them as loud as I could. I turned about several times to the company, paid my humble respects, said THEY WERE WELCOME, and used some other speeches I had been taught. I took up a thimble filled with liquor, which Glumdalclitch had given me for a cup, and drank their health, I drew out my hanger, and flourished with it after the manner of fencers in England. My nurse gave me a part of a straw, which I exercised as a pike, having learnt the art in my youth. I was that day shown to twelve sets of company, and as often forced to act over again the same fopperies, till I was half dead with weariness and vexation; for those who had seen me made such wonderful reports, that the people were ready to break down the doors to come in. My master, for his own interest, would not suffer any one to touch me except my nurse; and to prevent danger, benches were set round the table at such a distance as to put me out of every body's reach. However, an unlucky school-boy aimed a hazel nut directly at my head, which very narrowly missed me; otherwise it came with so much violence, that it would have infallibly knocked out my brains, for it was almost as large as a small pumpkin, but I had the satisfaction to see the young rogue well beaten, and turned out of the room.

My master gave public notice that he would show me again the next market-day; and in the meantime he prepared a convenient vehicle for me, which he had reason enough to do; for I was so tired with my first journey, and with entertaining company for eight hours together, that I could hardly stand upon my legs, or speak a word. It was at least three days before I recovered my strength; and that I might have no rest at home, all the neighbouring gentlemen from a hundred miles round, hearing of my fame, came to see me at my master's own house. There could not be fewer than thirty persons with their wives and children (for the country is very populous;) and my master demanded the rate of a full room whenever he showed me at home, although it were only to a single family; so that for some time I had but little ease every day of the week (except Wednesday, which is their Sabbath,) although I were not carried to the town.

My master, finding how profitable I was likely to be, resolved to carry me to the most considerable cities of the kingdom. Having therefore provided himself with all things necessary for a long journey, and settled his affairs at home, he took leave of his wife, and upon the 17th of August, 1703, about two months after my arrival, we set out for the metropolis, situate near the middle of that empire, and about three thousand miles distance from our house. My master made his daughter Glumdalclitch ride behind him. She carried me on her lap, in a box tied about her waist. The girl had lined it on all sides with the softest cloth she could get, well quilted underneath, furnished it with her baby's bed, provided me with linen and other necessaries, and made everything as convenient as she could. We had no other company but a boy of the house, who rode after us with the luggage.

My master's design was to show me in all the towns by the way, and to step out of the road for fifty or a hundred miles, to any village, or person of quality's house, where he might expect custom. We made easy journeys, of not above seven or eight score miles a-day; for Glumdalclitch, on purpose to spare me, complained she was tired with the trotting of the horse. She often took me out of my box, at my own desire, to give me air, and show me the country, but always held me fast by a leading-string. We passed over five or six rivers, many degrees broader and deeper than the Nile or the Ganges: and there was hardly a rivulet so small as the Thames at London-bridge. We were ten weeks in our journey, and I was shown in eighteen large towns, besides many villages, and private families.

On the 26th day of October we arrived at the metropolis, called in their language Lorbrulgrud, or Pride of the Universe. My master took a lodging in the principal street of the city, not far from the royal palace, and put out bills in the usual form, containing an exact description of my person and parts. He hired a large room between three and four hundred feet wide. He provided a table sixty feet in diameter, upon which I was to act my part, and pallisadoed it round three feet from the edge, and as many high, to prevent my falling over. I was shown ten times a-day, to the wonder and satisfaction of all people. I could now speak the language tolerably well, and perfectly understood every word, that was spoken to me. Besides, I had learnt their alphabet, and could make a shift to explain a sentence here and there; for Glumdalclitch had been my instructor while we were at home, and at leisure hours during our journey. She carried a little book in her pocket, not much larger than a Sanson's Atlas; it was a common treatise for the use of young girls, giving a short account of their religion: out of this she taught me my letters, and interpreted the words.

CHAPTER III.

[The author sent for to court. The queen buys him of his master the farmer, and presents him to the king. He disputes with his majesty's great scholars. An apartment at court provided for the author. He is in high favour with the queen. He stands up for the honour of his own country. His quarrels with the queen's dwarf.]

The frequent labours I underwent every day, made, in a few weeks, a very considerable change in my health: the more my master got by me, the more insatiable he grew. I had qu__e lost my stomach, and was almost reduced to a skeleton. The farmer observed it, and concluding I must soon die, resolved to make as good a hand of me as he could. While he was thus reasoning and resolving with himself, a sardral, or gentleman-usher, came from court, commanding my master to carry me immediately thither for the diversion of the queen and her ladies. Some of the latter had already been to see me, and reported strange things of my beauty, behaviour, and good sense. Her majesty, and those who attended her, were beyond measure delighted with my demeanour. I fell on my knees, and begged the honour of kissing her imperial foot; but this gracious princess held out her little finger towards me, after I was set on the table, which I embraced in both my arms, and put the tip of it with the utmost respect to my lip. She made me some general questions about my country and my travels, which I answered as distinctly, and in as few words as I could. She asked, "whether I could be content to live at court?" I bowed down to the board of the table, and humbly answered "that I was my master's slave: but, if I were at my own disposal, I should be proud to devote my life to her majesty's service." She then asked my master, "whether he was willing to sell me at a good price?" He, who apprehended I could not live a month, was ready enough to part with me, and demanded a thousand pieces of gold, which were ordered him on the spot, each piece being about the bigness of eight hundred moidores; but allowing for the proportion of all things between that country and Europe, and the high price of gold among them, was hardly so great a sum as a thousand guineas would be in England. I then said to the queen, "since I was now her majesty's most humble creature and vassal, I must beg the favour, that Glumdalclitch, who had always tended me with so much care and kindness, and understood to do it so well, might be admitted into her service, and continue to be my nurse and instructor."

Her majesty agreed to my petition, and easily got the farmer's consent, who was glad enough to have his daughter preferred at court, and the poor girl herself was not able to hide her joy. My late master withdrew, bidding me farewell, and saying he had left me in a good service; to which I replied not a word, only making him a slight bow.

The queen observed my coldness; and, when the farmer was gone out of the apartment, asked me the reason. I made bold to tell her majesty, "that I owed no other obligation to my late master, than his not dashing out the brains of a poor harmless creature, found by chance in his fields: which obligation was amply recompensed, by the gain he had made in showing me through half the kingdom, and the price he had now sold me for. That the life I had since led was laborious enough to kill an animal of ten times my strength. That my health was much impaired, by the continual drudgery of entertaining the rabble every hour of the day; and that, if my master had not thought my life in danger, her majesty would not have got so cheap a bargain. But as I was out of all fear of being ill-treated under the protection of so great and good an empress, the ornament of nature, the darling of the world, the delight of her subjects, the phoenix of the creation, so I hoped my late master's apprehensions would appear to be groundless; for I already found my spirits revive, by the influence of her most august presence."

This was the sum of my speech, delivered with great improprieties and hesitation. The latter part was altogether framed in the style peculiar to that people, whereof I learned some phrases from Glumdalclitch, while she was carrying me to court.

The queen, giving great allowance for my defectiveness in speaking, was, however, surprised at so much wit and good sense in so diminutive an animal. She took me in her own hand, and carried me to the king, who was then retired to his cabinet. His majesty, a prince of much gravity and austere countenance, not well observing my shape at first view, asked the queen after a cold manner "how long it was since she grew fond of a splacnuck?" for such it seems he took me to be, as I lay upon my breast in her majesty's right hand. But this princess, who has an infinite deal of wit and humour, set me gently on my feet upon the scrutoire, and commanded me to give his majesty an account of myself, which I did in a very few words: and Glumdalclitch who attended at the cabinet door, and could not endure I should be out of her sight, being admitted, confirmed all that had passed from my arrival at her father's house.

The king, although he be as learned a person as any in his dominions, had been educated in the study of philosophy, and particularly mathematics; yet when he observed my shape exactly, and saw me walk erect, before I began to speak, conceived I might be a piece of clock-work (which is in that country arrived to a very great perfection) contrived by some ingenious artist. But when he heard my voice, and found what I delivered to be regular and rational, he could not conceal his astonishment. He was by no means satisfied with the relation I gave him of the manner I came into his kingdom, but thought it a story concerted between Glumdalclitch and her father, who had taught me a set of words to make me sell at a better price. Upon this imagination, he put several other questions to me, and still received rational answers: no otherwise defective than by a foreign accent, and an imperfect knowledge in the language, with some rustic phrases which I had learned at the farmer's house, and did not suit the polite style of a court.

His majesty sent for three great scholars, who were then in their weekly waiting, according to the custom in that country. These gentlemen, after they had a while examined my shape with much nicety, were of different opinions concerning me. They all agreed that I could not be produced according to the regular laws of nature, because I was not framed with a capacity of preserving my life, either by swiftness, or climbing of trees, or digging holes in the earth. They observed by my teeth, which they viewed with great exactness, that I was a carnivorous animal; yet most quadrupeds being an overmatch for me, and field mice, with some others, too nimble, they could not imagine how I should be able to support myself, unless I fed upon snails and other insects, which they offered, by many learned arguments, to evince that I could not possibly do. One of these virtuosi seemed to think that I might be an embryo, or abortive birth. But this opinion was rejected by the other two, who observed my limbs to be perfect and finished; and that I had lived several years, as it was manifest from my beard, the stumps whereof they plainly discovered through a magnifying glass. They would not allow me to be a dwarf, because my littleness was beyond all degrees of comparison; for the queen's favourite dwarf, the smallest ever known in that kingdom, was near thirty feet high. After much debate, they concluded unanimously, that I was only relplum scalcath, which is interpreted literally lusus naturae; a determination exactly agreeable to the modern philosophy of Europe, whose professors, disdaining the old evasion of occult causes, whereby the followers of Aristotle endeavoured in vain to disguise their ignorance, have invented this wonderful solution of all difficulties, to the unspeakable advancement of human knowledge.

After this decisive conclusion, I entreated to be heard a word or two. I applied myself to the king, and assured his majesty, "that I came from a country which abounded with several millions of both sexes, and of my own stature; where the animals, trees, and houses, were all in proportion, and where, by consequence, I might be as able to defend myself, and to find sustenance, as any of his majesty's subjects could do here; which I took for a full answer to those gentlemen's arguments." To this they only replied with a smile of contempt, saying, "that the farmer had instructed me very well in my lesson." The king, who had a much better understanding, dismissing his learned men, sent for the farmer, who by good fortune was not yet gone out of town. Having therefore first examined him privately, and then confronted him with me and the young girl, his majesty began to think that what we told him might possibly be true. He desired the queen to order that a particular care should be taken of me; and was of opinion that Glumdalclitch should still continue in her office of tending me, because he observed we had a great affection for each other. A convenient apartment was provided for her at court: she had a sort of governess appointed to take care of her education, a maid to dress her, and two other servants for menial offices; but the care of me was wholly appropriated to herself. The queen commanded her own cabinet-maker to contrive a box, that might serve me for a bedchamber, after the model that Glumdalclitch and I should agree upon. This man was a most ingenious artist, and according to my direction, in three weeks finished for me a wooden chamber of sixteen feet square, and twelve high, with sash-windows, a door, and two closets, like a London bed-chamber. The board, that made the ceiling, was to be lifted up and down by two hinges, to put in a bed ready furnished by her majesty's upholsterer, which Glumdalclitch took out every day to air, made it with her own hands, and letting it down at night, locked up the roof over me. A nice workman, who was famous for little curiosities, undertook to make me two chairs, with backs and frames, of a substance not unlike ivory, and two tables, with a cabinet to put my things in. The room was quilted on all sides, as well as the floor and the ceiling, to prevent any accident from the carelessness of those who carried me, and to break the force of a jolt, when I went in a coach. I desired a lock for my door, to prevent rats and mice from coming in. The smith, after several attempts, made the smallest that ever was seen among them, for I have known a larger at the gate of a gentleman's house in England. I made a shift to keep the key in a pocket of my own, fearing Glumdalclitch might lose it. The queen likewise ordered the thinnest silks that could be gotten, to make me clothes, not much thicker than an English blanket, very cumbersome till I was accustomed to them. They were after the fashion of the kingdom, partly resembling the Persian, and partly the Chinese, and are a very grave and decent habit.

The queen became so fond of my company, that she could not dine without me. I had a table placed upon the same at which her majesty ate, just at her left elbow, and a chair to sit on. Glumdalclitch stood on a stool on the floor near my table, to assist and take care of me. I had an entire set of silver dishes and plates, and other necessaries, which, in proportion to those of the queen, were not much bigger than what I have seen in a London toy-shop for the furniture of a baby-house: these my little nurse kept in her pocket in a silver box, and gave me at meals as I wanted them, always cleaning them herself. No person dined with the queen but the two princesses royal, the eldest sixteen years old, and the younger at that time thirteen and a month. Her majesty used to put a bit of meat upon one of my dishes, out of which I carved for myself, and her diversion was to see me eat in miniature: for the queen (who had indeed but a weak stomach) took up, at one mouthful, as much as a dozen English farmers could eat at a meal, which to me was for some time a very nauseous sight. She would craunch the wing of a lark, bones and all, between her teeth, although it were nine times as large as that of a full-grown turkey; and put a bit of bread into her mouth as big as two twelve- penny loaves. She drank out of a golden cup, above a hogshead at a draught. Her knives were twice as long as a scythe, set straight upon the handle. The spoons, forks, and other instruments, were all in the same proportion. I remember when Glumdalclitch carried me, out of curiosity, to see some of the tables at court, where ten or a dozen of those enormous knives and forks were lifted up together, I thought I had never till then beheld so terrible a sight.

It is the custom, that every Wednesday (which, as I have observed, is their Sabbath) the king and queen, with the royal issue of both sexes, dine together in the apartment of his majesty, to whom I was now become a great favourite; and at these times, my little chair and table were placed at his left hand, before one of the salt- cellars. This prince took a pleasure in conversing with me, inquiring into the manners, religion, laws, government, and learning of Europe; wherein I gave him the best account I was able. His apprehension was so clear, and his judgment so exact, that he made very wise reflections and observations upon all I said. But I confess, that, after I had been a little too copious in talking of my own beloved country, of our trade and wars by sea and land, of our schisms in religion, and parties in the state; the prejudices of his education prevailed so far, that he could not forbear taking me up in his right hand, and stroking me gently with the other, after a hearty fit of laughing, asked me, "whether I was a whig or tory?" Then turning to his first minister, who waited behind him with a white staff, near as tall as the mainmast of the Royal Sovereign, he observed "how contemptible a thing was human grandeur, which could be mimicked by such diminutive insects as I: and yet," says he, "I dare engage these creatures have their titles and distinctions of honour; they contrive little nests and burrows, that they call houses and cities; they make a figure in dress and equipage; they love, they fight, they dispute, they cheat, they betray!" And thus he continued on, while my colour came and went several times, with indignation, to hear our noble country, the mistress of arts and arms, the scourge of France, the arbitress of Europe, the seat of virtue, piety, honour, and truth, the pride and envy of the world, so contemptuously treated.

But as I was not in a condition to resent injuries, so upon mature thoughts I began to doubt whether I was injured or no. For, after having been accustomed several months to the sight and converse of this people, and observed every object upon which I cast mine eyes to be of proportionable magnitude, the horror I had at first conceived from their bulk and aspect was so far worn off, that if I had then beheld a company of English lords and ladies in their finery and birth-day clothes, acting their several parts in the most courtly manner of strutting, and bowing, and prating, to say the truth, I should have been strongly tempted to laugh as much at them as the king and his grandees did at me. Neither, indeed, could I forbear smiling at myself, when the queen used to place me upon her hand towards a looking-glass, by which both our persons appeared before me in full view together; and there could be nothing more ridiculous than the comparison; so that I really began to imagine myself dwindled many degrees below my usual size.

Nothing angered and mortified me so much as the queen's dwarf; who being of the lowest stature that was ever in that country (for I verily think he was not full thirty feet high), became so insolent at seeing a creature so much beneath him, that he would always affect to swagger and look big as he passed by me in the queen's antechamber, while I was standing on some table talking with the lords or ladies of the court, and he seldom failed of a smart word or two upon my littleness; against which I could only revenge myself by calling him brother, challenging him to wrestle, and such repartees as are usually in the mouths of court pages. One day, at dinner, this malicious little cub was so nettled with something I had said to him, that, raising himself upon the frame of her majesty's chair, he took me up by the middle, as I was sitting down, not thinking any harm, and let me drop into a large silver bowl of cream, and then ran away as fast as he could. I fell over head and ears, and, if I had not been a good swimmer, it might have gone very hard with me; for Glumdalclitch in that instant happened to be at the other end of the room, and the queen was in such a fright, that she wanted presence of mind to assist me. But my little nurse ran to my relief, and took me out, after I had swallowed above a quart of cream. I was put to bed: however, I received no other damage than the loss of a suit of clothes, which was utterly spoiled. The dwarf was soundly whipt, and as a farther punishment, forced to drink up the bowl of cream into which he had thrown me: neither was he ever restored to favour; for soon after the queen bestowed him on a lady of high quality, so that I saw him no more, to my very great satisfaction; for I could not tell to what extremities such a malicious urchin might have carried his resentment.

He had before served me a scurvy trick, which set the queen a- laughing, although at the same time she was heartily vexed, and would have immediately cashiered him, if I had not been so generous as to intercede. Her majesty had taken a marrow-bone upon her plate, and, after knocking out the marrow, placed the bone again in the dish erect, as it stood before; the dwarf, watching his opportunity, while Glumdalclitch was gone to the side-board, mounted the stool that she stood on to take care of me at meals, took me up in both hands, and squeezing my legs together, wedged them into the marrow bone above my waist, where I stuck for some time, and made a very ridiculous figure. I believe it was near a minute before any one knew what was become of me; for I thought it below me to cry out. But, as princes seldom get their meat hot, my legs were not scalded, only my stockings and breeches in a sad condition. The dwarf, at my entreaty, had no other punishment than a sound whipping.

I was frequently rallied by the queen upon account of my fearfulness; and she used to ask me whether the people of my country were as great cowards as myself? The occasion was this: the kingdom is much pestered with flies in summer; and these odious insects, each of them as big as a Dunstable lark, hardly gave me any rest while I sat at dinner, with their continual humming and buzzing about mine ears. They would sometimes alight upon my victuals, and leave their loathsome excrement, or spawn behind, which to me was very visible, though not to the natives of that country, whose large optics were not so acute as mine, in viewing smaller objects. Sometimes they would fix upon my nose, or forehead, where they stung me to the quick, smelling very offensively; and I could easily trace that viscous matter, which, our naturalists tell us, enables those creatures to walk with their feet upwards upon a ceiling. I had much ado to defend myself against these detestable animals, and could not forbear starting when they came on my face. It was the common practice of the dwarf, to catch a number of these insects in his hand, as schoolboys do among us, and let them out suddenly under my nose, on purpose to frighten me, and divert the queen.

My remedy was to cut them in pieces with my knife, as they flew in the air, wherein my dexterity was much admired.

I remember, one morning, when Glumdalclitch had set me in a box upon a window, as she usually did in fair days to give me air (for I durst not venture to let the box be hung on a nail out of the window, as we do with cages in England), after I had lifted up one of my sashes, and sat down at my table to eat a piece of sweet cake for my breakfast, above twenty wasps, allured by the smell, came flying into the room, humming louder than the drones of as many bagpipes. Some of them seized my cake, and carried it piecemeal away; others flew about my head and face, confounding me with the noise, and putting me in the utmost terror of their stings. However, I had the courage to rise and draw my hanger, and attack them in the air. I dispatched four of them, but the rest got away, and I presently shut my window. These insects were as large as partridges: I took out their stings, found them an inch and a half long, and as sharp as needles. I carefully preserved them all; and having since shown them, with some other curiosities, in several parts of Europe, upon my return to England I gave three of them to Gresham College, and kept the fourth for myself.

CHAPTER IV.

[The country described. A proposal for correcting modern maps. The king's palace; and some account of the metropolis. The author's way of travelling. The chief temple described.]

I now intend to give the reader a short description of this country, as far as I travelled in it, which was not above two thousand miles round Lorbrulgrud, the metropolis. For the queen, whom I always attended, never went farther when she accompanied the king in his progresses, and there staid till his majesty returned from viewing his frontiers. The whole extent of this prince's dominions reaches about six thousand miles in length, and from three to five in breadth: whence I cannot but conclude, that our geographers of Europe are in a great error, by supposing nothing but sea between Japan and California; for it was ever my opinion, that there must be a balance of earth to counterpoise the great continent of Tartary; and therefore they ought to correct their maps and charts, by joining this vast tract of land to the north- west parts of America, wherein I shall be ready to lend them my assistance.

The kingdom is a peninsula, terminated to the north-east by a ridge of mountains thirty miles high, which are altogether impassable, by reason of the volcanoes upon the tops: neither do the most learned know what sort of mortals inhabit beyond those mountains, or whether they be inhabited at all. On the three other sides, it is bounded by the ocean. There is not one seaport in the whole kingdom: and those parts of the coasts into which the rivers issue, are so full of pointed rocks, and the sea generally so rough, that there is no venturing with the smallest of their boats; so that these people are wholly excluded from any commerce with the rest of the world. But the large rivers are full of vessels, and abound with excellent fish; for they seldom get any from the sea, because the sea fish are of the same size with those in Europe, and consequently not worth catching; whereby it is manifest, that nature, in the production of plants and animals of so extraordinary a bulk, is wholly confined to this continent, of which I leave the reasons to be determined by philosophers. However, now and then they take a whale that happens to be dashed against the rocks, which the common people feed on heartily. These whales I have known so large, that a man could hardly carry one upon his shoulders; and sometimes, for curiosity, they are brought in hampers to Lorbrulgrud; I saw one of them in a dish at the king's table, which passed for a rarity, but I did not observe he was fond of it; for I think, indeed, the bigness disgusted him, although I have seen one somewhat larger in Greenland.

The country is well inhabited, for it contains fifty-one cities, near a hundred walled towns, and a great number of villages. To satisfy my curious reader, it may be sufficient to describe Lorbrulgrud. This city stands upon almost two equal parts, on each side the river that passes through. It contains above eighty thousand houses, and about six hundred thousand inhabitants. It is in length three glomglungs (which make about fifty-four English miles,) and two and a half in breadth; as I measured it myself in the royal map made by the king's order, which was laid on the ground on purpose for me, and extended a hundred feet: I paced the diameter and circumference several times barefoot, and, computing by the scale, measured it pretty exactly.

The king's palace is no regular edifice, but a heap of buildings, about seven miles round: the chief rooms are generally two hundred and forty feet high, and broad and long in proportion. A coach was allowed to Glumdalclitch and me, wherein her governess frequently took her out to see the town, or go among the shops; and I was always of the party, carried in my box; although the girl, at my own desire, would often take me out, and hold me in her hand, that I might more conveniently view the houses and the people, as we passed along the streets. I reckoned our coach to be about a square of Westminster-hall, but not altogether so high: however, I cannot be very exact. One day the governess ordered our coachman to stop at several shops, where the beggars, watching their opportunity, crowded to the sides of the coach, and gave me the most horrible spectacle that ever a European eye beheld. There was a woman with a cancer in her breast, swelled to a monstrous size, full of holes, in two or three of which I could have easily crept, and covered my whole body. There was a fellow with a wen in his neck, larger than five wool-packs; and another, with a couple of wooden legs, each about twenty feet high. But the most hateful sight of all, was the lice crawling on their clothes. I could see distinctly the limbs of these vermin with my naked eye, much better than those of a European louse through a microscope, and their snouts with which they rooted like swine. They were the first I had ever beheld, and I should have been curious enough to dissect one of them, if I had had proper instruments, which I unluckily left behind me in the ship, although, indeed, the sight was so nauseous, that it perfectly turned my stomach.

Besides the large box in which I was usually carried, the queen ordered a smaller one to be made for me, of about twelve feet square, and ten high, for the convenience of travelling; because the other was somewhat too large for Glumdalclitch's lap, and cumbersome in the coach; it was made by the same artist, whom I directed in the whole contrivance. This travelling-closet was an exact square, with a window in the middle of three of the squares, and each window was latticed with iron wire on the outside, to prevent accidents in long journeys. On the fourth side, which had no window, two strong staples were fixed, through which the person that carried me, when I had a mind to be on horseback, put a leathern belt, and buckled it about his waist. This was always the office of some grave trusty servant, in whom I could confide, whether I attended the king and queen in their progresses, or were disposed to see the gardens, or pay a visit to some great lady or minister of state in the court, when Glumdalclitch happened to be out of order; for I soon began to be known and esteemed among the greatest officers, I suppose more upon account of their majesties' favour, than any merit of my own. In journeys, when I was weary of the coach, a servant on horseback would buckle on my box, and place it upon a cushion before him; and there I had a full prospect of the country on three sides, from my three windows. I had, in this closet, a field-bed and a hammock, hung from the ceiling, two chairs and a table, neatly screwed to the floor, to prevent being tossed about by the agitation of the horse or the coach. And having been long used to sea-voyages, those motions, although sometimes very violent, did not much discompose me.

Whenever I had a mind to see the town, it was always in my travelling-closet; which Glumdalclitch held in her lap in a kind of open sedan, after the fashion of the country, borne by four men, and attended by two others in the queen's livery. The people, who had often heard of me, were very curious to crowd about the sedan, and the girl was complaisant enough to make the bearers stop, and to take me in her hand, that I might be more conveniently seen.

I was very desirous to see the chief temple, and particularly the tower belonging to it, which is reckoned the highest in the kingdom. Accordingly one day my nurse carried me thither, but I may truly say I came back disappointed; for the height is not above three thousand feet, reckoning from the ground to the highest pinnacle top; which, allowing for the difference between the size of those people and us in Europe, is no great matter for admiration, nor at all equal in proportion (if I rightly remember) to Salisbury steeple. But, not to detract from a nation, to which, during my life, I shall acknowledge myself extremely obliged, it must be allowed, that whatever this famous tower wants in height, is amply made up in beauty and strength: for the walls are near a hundred feet thick, built of hewn stone, whereof each is about forty feet square, and adorned on all sides with statues of gods and emperors, cut in marble, larger than the life, placed in their several niches. I measured a little finger which had fallen down from one of these statues, and lay unperceived among some rubbish, and found it exactly four feet and an inch in length. Glumdalclitch wrapped it up in her handkerchief, and carried it home in her pocket, to keep among other trinkets, of which the girl was very fond, as children at her age usually are.

The king's kitchen is indeed a noble building, vaulted at top, and about six hundred feet high. The great oven is not so wide, by ten paces, as the cupola at St. Paul's: for I measured the latter on purpose, after my return. But if I should describe the kitchen grate, the prodigious pots and kettles, the joints of meat turning on the spits, with many other particulars, perhaps I should be hardly believed; at least a severe critic would be apt to think I enlarged a little, as travellers are often suspected to do. To avoid which censure I fear I have run too much into the other extreme; and that if this treatise should happen to be translated into the language of Brobdingnag (which is the general name of that kingdom,) and transmitted thither, the king and his people would have reason to complain that I had done them an injury, by a false and diminutive representation.

His majesty seldom keeps above six hundred horses in his stables: they are generally from fifty-four to sixty feet high. But, when he goes abroad on solemn days, he is attended, for state, by a military guard of five hundred horse, which, indeed, I thought was the most splendid sight that could be ever beheld, till I saw part of his army in battalia, whereof I shall find another occasion to speak.

CHAPTER V.

[Several adventurers that happened to the author. The execution of a criminal. The author shows his skill in navigation.]

I should have lived happy enough in that country, if my littleness had not exposed me to several ridiculous and troublesome accidents; some of which I shall venture to relate. Glumdalclitch often carried me into the gardens of the court in my smaller box, and would sometimes take me out of it, and hold me in her hand, or set me down to walk. I remember, before the dwarf left the queen, he followed us one day into those gardens, and my nurse having set me down, he and I being close together, near some dwarf apple trees, I must needs show my wit, by a silly allusion between him and the trees, which happens to hold in their language as it does in ours. Whereupon, the malicious rogue, watching his opportunity, when I was walking under one of them, shook it directly over my head, by which a dozen apples, each of them near as large as a Bristol barrel, came tumbling about my ears; one of them hit me on the back as I chanced to stoop, and knocked me down flat on my face; but I received no other hurt, and the dwarf was pardoned at my desire, because I had given the provocation.

Another day, Glumdalclitch left me on a smooth grass-plot to divert myself, while she walked at some distance with her governess. In the meantime, there suddenly fell such a violent shower of hail, that I was immediately by the force of it, struck to the ground: and when I was down, the hailstones gave me such cruel bangs all over the body, as if I had been pelted with tennis-balls; however, I made a shift to creep on all fours, and shelter myself, by lying flat on my face, on the lee-side of a border of lemon-thyme, but so bruised from head to foot, that I could not go abroad in ten days. Neither is this at all to be wondered at, because nature, in that country, observing the same proportion through all her operations, a hailstone is near eighteen hundred times as large as one in Europe; which I can assert upon experience, having been so curious as to weigh and measure them.

But a more dangerous accident happened to me in the same garden, when my little nurse, believing she had put me in a secure place (which I often entreated her to do, that I might enjoy my own thoughts,) and having left my box at home, to avoid the trouble of carrying it, went to another part of the garden with her governess and some ladies of her acquaintance. While she was absent, and out of hearing, a small white spaniel that belonged to one of the chief gardeners, having got by accident into the garden, happened to range near the place where I lay: the dog, following the scent, came directly up, and taking me in his mouth, ran straight to his master wagging his tail, and set me gently on the ground. By good fortune he had been so well taught, that I was carried between his teeth without the least hurt, or even tearing my clothes. But the poor gardener, who knew me well, and had a great kindness for me, was in a terrible fright: he gently took me up in both his hands, and asked me how I did? but I was so amazed and out of breath, that I could not speak a word. In a few minutes I came to myself, and he carried me safe to my little nurse, who, by this time, had returned to the place where she left me, and was in cruel agonies when I did not appear, nor answer when she called. She severely reprimanded the gardener on account of his dog. But the thing was hushed up, and never known at court, for the girl was afraid of the queen's anger; and truly, as to myself, I thought it would not be for my reputation, that such a story should go about.

This accident absolutely determined Glumdalclitch never to trust me abroad for the future out of her sight. I had been long afraid of this resolution, and therefore concealed from her some little unlucky adventures, that happened in those times when I was left by myself. Once a kite, hovering over the garden, made a stoop at me, and if I had not resolutely drawn my hanger, and run under a thick espalier, he would have certainly carried me away in his talons. Another time, walking to the top of a fresh mole-hill, I fell to my neck in the hole, through which that animal had cast up the earth, and coined some lie, not worth remembering, to excuse myself for spoiling my clothes. I likewise broke my right shin against the shell of a snail, which I happened to stumble over, as I was walking alone and thinking on poor England.

I cannot tell whether I were more pleased or mortified to observe, in those solitary walks, that the smaller birds did not appear to be at all afraid of me, but would hop about within a yard's distance, looking for worms and other food, with as much indifference and security as if no creature at all were near them. I remember, a thrush had the confidence to snatch out of my hand, with his bill, a of cake that Glumdalclitch had just given me for my breakfast. When I attempted to catch any of these birds, they would boldly turn against me, endeavouring to peck my fingers, which I durst not venture within their reach; and then they would hop back unconcerned, to hunt for worms or snails, as they did before. But one day, I took a thick cudgel, and threw it with all my strength so luckily, at a linnet, that I knocked him down, and seizing him by the neck with both my hands, ran with him in triumph to my nurse. However, the bird, who had only been stunned, recovering himself gave me so many boxes with his wings, on both sides of my head and body, though I held him at arm's-length, and was out of the reach of his claws, that I was twenty times thinking to let him go. But I was soon relieved by one of our servants, who wrung off the bird's neck, and I had him next day for dinner, by the queen's command. This linnet, as near as I can remember, seemed to be somewhat larger than an English swan.

The maids of honour often invited Glumdalclitch to their apartments, and desired she would bring me along with her, on purpose to have the pleasure of seeing and touching me. They would often strip me naked from top to toe, and lay me at full length in their bosoms; wherewith I was much disgusted because, to say the truth, a very offensive smell came from their skins; which I do not mention, or intend, to the disadvantage of those excellent ladies, for whom I have all manner of respect; but I conceive that my sense was more acute in proportion to my littleness, and that those illustrious persons were no more disagreeable to their lovers, or to each other, than people of the same quality are with us in England. And, after all, I found their natural smell was much more supportable, than when they used perfumes, under which I immediately swooned away. I cannot forget, that an intimate friend of mine in Lilliput, took the freedom in a warm day, when I had used a good deal of exercise, to complain of a strong smell about me, although I am as little faulty that way, as most of my sex: but I suppose his faculty of smelling was as nice with regard to me, as mine was to that of this people. Upon this point, I cannot forbear doing justice to the queen my mistress, and Glumdalclitch my nurse, whose persons were as sweet as those of any lady in England.

That which gave me most uneasiness among these maids of honour (when my nurse carried me to visit then) was, to see them use me without any manner of ceremony, like a creature who had no sort of consequence: for they would strip themselves to the skin, and put on their smocks in my presence, while I was placed on their toilet, directly before their naked bodies, which I am sure to me was very far from being a tempting sight, or from giving me any other emotions than those of horror and disgust: their skins appeared so coarse and uneven, so variously coloured, when I saw them near, with a mole here and there as broad as a trencher, and hairs hanging from it thicker than packthreads, to say nothing farther concerning the rest of their persons. Neither did they at all scruple, while I was by, to discharge what they had drank, to the quantity of at least two hogsheads, in a vessel that held above three tuns. The handsomest among these maids of honour, a pleasant, frolicsome girl of sixteen, would sometimes set me astride upon one of her nipples, with many other tricks, wherein the reader will excuse me for not being over particular. But I was so much displeased, that I entreated Glumdalclitch to contrive some excuse for not seeing that young lady any more.

One day, a young gentleman, who was nephew to my nurse's governess, came and pressed them both to see an execution. It was of a man, who had murdered one of that gentleman's intimate acquaintance. Glumdalclitch was prevailed on to be of the company, very much against her inclination, for she was naturally tender-hearted: and, as for myself, although I abhorred such kind of spectacles, yet my curiosity tempted me to see something that I thought must be extraordinary. The malefactor was fixed in a chair upon a scaffold erected for that purpose, and his head cut off at one blow, with a sword of about forty feet long. The veins and arteries spouted up such a prodigious quantity of blood, and so high in the air, that the great jet d'eau at Versailles was not equal to it for the time it lasted: and the head, when it fell on the scaffold floor, gave such a bounce as made me start, although I was at least half an English mile distant.

The queen, who often used to hear me talk of my sea-voyages, and took all occasions to divert me when I was melancholy, asked me whether I understood how to handle a sail or an oar, and whether a little exercise of rowing might not be convenient for my health? I answered, that I understood both very well: for although my proper employment had been to be surgeon or doctor to the ship, yet often, upon a pinch, I was forced to work like a common mariner. But I could not see how this could be done in their country, where the smallest wherry was equal to a first-rate man of war among us; and such a boat as I could manage would never live in any of their rivers. Her majesty said, if I would contrive a boat, her own joiner should make it, and she would provide a place for me to sail in. The fellow was an ingenious workman, and by my instructions, in ten days, finished a pleasure-boat with all its tackling, able conveniently to hold eight Europeans. When it was finished, the queen was so delighted, that she ran with it in her lap to the king, who ordered it to be put into a cistern full of water, with me in it, by way of trial, where I could not manage my two sculls, or little oars, for want of room. But the queen had before contrived another project. She ordered the joiner to make a wooden trough of three hundred feet long, fifty broad, and eight deep; which, being well pitched, to prevent leaking, was placed on the floor, along the wall, in an outer room of the palace. It had a cock near the bottom to let out the water, when it began to grow stale; and two servants could easily fill it in half an hour. Here I often used to row for my own diversion, as well as that of the queen and her ladies, who thought themselves well entertained with my skill and agility. Sometimes I would put up my sail, and then my business was only to steer, while the ladies gave me a gale with their fans; and, when they were weary, some of their pages would blow my sail forward with their breath, while I showed my art by steering starboard or larboard as I pleased. When I had done, Glumdalclitch always carried back my boat into her closet, and hung it on a nail to dry.

In this exercise I once met an accident, which had like to have cost me my life; for, one of the pages having put my boat into the trough, the governess who attended Glumdalclitch very officiously lifted me up, to place me in the boat: but I happened to slip through her fingers, and should infallibly have fallen down forty feet upon the floor, if, by the luckiest chance in the world, I had not been stopped by a corking-pin that stuck in the good gentlewoman's stomacher; the head of the pin passing between my shirt and the waistband of my breeches, and thus I was held by the middle in the air, till Glumdalclitch ran to my relief.

Another time, one of the servants, whose office it was to fill my trough every third day with fresh water, was so careless as to let a huge frog (not perceiving it) slip out of his pail. The frog lay concealed till I was put into my boat, but then, seeing a resting- place, climbed up, and made it lean so much on one side, that I was forced to balance it with all my weight on the other, to prevent overturning. When the frog was got in, it hopped at once half the length of the boat, and then over my head, backward and forward, daubing my face and clothes with its odious slime. The largeness of its features made it appear the most deformed animal that can be conceived. However, I desired Glumdalclitch to let me deal with it alone. I banged it a good while with one of my sculls, and at last forced it to leap out of the boat.

But the greatest danger I ever underwent in that kingdom, was from a monkey, who belonged to one of the clerks of the kitchen. Glumdalclitch had locked me up in her closet, while she went somewhere upon business, or a visit.

The weather being very warm, the closet-window was left open, as well as the windows and the door of my bigger box, in which I usually lived, because of its largeness and conveniency. As I sat quietly meditating at my table, I heard something bounce in at the closet-window, and skip about from one side to the other: whereat, although I was much alarmed, yet I ventured to look out, but not stirring from my seat; and then I saw this frolicsome animal frisking and leaping up and down, till at last he came to my box, which he seemed to view with great pleasure and curiosity, peeping in at the door and every window. I retreated to the farther corner of my room; or box; but the monkey looking in at every side, put me in such a fright, that I wanted presence of mind to conceal myself under the bed, as I might easily have done. After some time spent in peeping, grinning, and chattering, he at last espied me; and reaching one of his paws in at the door, as a cat does when she plays with a mouse, although I often shifted place to avoid him, he at length seized the lappet of my coat (which being made of that country silk, was very thick and strong), and dragged me out. He took me up in his right fore-foot and held me as a nurse does a child she is going to suckle, just as I have seen the same sort of creature do with a kitten in Europe; and when I offered to struggle he squeezed me so hard, that I thought it more prudent to submit. I have good reason to believe, that he took me for a young one of his own species, by his often stroking my face very gently with his other paw. In these diversions he was interrupted by a noise at the closet door, as if somebody were opening it: whereupon he suddenly leaped up to the window at which he had come in, and thence upon the leads and gutters, walking upon three legs, and holding me in the fourth, till he clambered up to a roof that was next to ours. I heard Glumdalclitch give a shriek at the moment he was carrying me out. The poor girl was almost distracted: that quarter of the palace was all in an uproar; the servants ran for ladders; the monkey was seen by hundreds in the court, sitting upon the ridge of a building, holding me like a baby in one of his forepaws, and feeding me with the other, by cramming into my mouth some victuals he had squeezed out of the bag on one side of his chaps, and patting me when I would not eat; whereat many of the rabble below could not forbear laughing; neither do I think they justly ought to be blamed, for, without question, the sight was ridiculous enough to every body but myself. Some of the people threw up stones, hoping to drive the monkey down; but this was strictly forbidden, or else, very probably, my brains had been dashed out.

The ladders were now applied, and mounted by several men; which the monkey observing, and finding himself almost encompassed, not being able to make speed enough with his three legs, let me drop on a ridge tile, and made his escape. Here I sat for some time, five hundred yards from the ground, expecting every moment to be blown down by the wind, or to fall by my own giddiness, and come tumbling over and over from the ridge to the eaves; but an honest lad, one of my nurse's footmen, climbed up, and putting me into his breeches pocket, brought me down safe.

I was almost choked with the filthy stuff the monkey had crammed down my throat: but my dear little nurse picked it out of my mouth with a small needle, and then I fell a-vomiting, which gave me great relief. Yet I was so weak and bruised in the sides with the squeezes given me by this odious animal, that I was forced to keep my bed a fortnight. The king, queen, and all the court, sent every day to inquire after my health; and her majesty made me several visits during my sickness. The monkey was killed, and an order made, that no such animal should be kept about the palace.

When I attended the king after my recovery, to return him thanks for his favours, he was pleased to rally me a good deal upon this adventure. He asked me, "what my thoughts and speculations were, while I lay in the monkey's paw; how I liked the victuals he gave me; his manner of feeding; and whether the fresh air on the roof had sharpened my stomach." He desired to know, "what I would have done upon such an occasion in my own country." I told his majesty, "that in Europe we had no monkeys, except such as were brought for curiosity from other places, and so small, that I could deal with a dozen of them together, if they presumed to attack me. And as for that monstrous animal with whom I was so lately engaged (it was indeed as large as an elephant), if my fears had suffered me to think so far as to make use of my hanger," (looking fiercely, and clapping my hand on the hilt, as I spoke) "when he poked his paw into my chamber, perhaps I should have given him such a wound, as would have made him glad to withdraw it with more haste than he put it in." This I delivered in a firm tone, like a person who was jealous lest his courage should be called in question. However, my speech produced nothing else beside a laud laughter, which all the respect due to his majesty from those about him could not make them contain. This made me reflect, how vain an attempt it is for a man to endeavour to do himself honour among those who are out of all degree of equality or comparison with him. And yet I have seen the moral of my own behaviour very frequent in England since my return; where a little contemptible varlet, without the least title to birth, person, wit, or common sense, shall presume to look with importance, and put himself upon a foot with the greatest persons of the kingdom.

I was every day furnishing the court with some ridiculous story: and Glumdalclitch, although she loved me to excess, yet was arch enough to inform the queen, whenever I committed any folly that she thought would be diverting to her majesty. The girl, who had been out of order, was carried by her governess to take the air about an hour's distance, or thirty miles from town. They alighted out of the coach near a small foot-path in a field, and Glumdalclitch setting down my travelling box, I went out of it to walk. There was a cow-dung in the path, and I must need try my activity by attempting to leap over it. I took a run, but unfortunately jumped short, and found myself just in the middle up to my knees. I waded through with some difficulty, and one of the footmen wiped me as clean as he could with his handkerchief, for I was filthily bemired; and my nurse confined me to my box, till we returned home;

where the queen was soon informed of what had passed, and the footmen spread it about the court: so that all the mirth for some days was at my expense.

CHAPTER VI.

[Several contrivances of the author to please the king and queen. He shows his skill in music. The king inquires into the state of England, which the author relates to him. The king's observations thereon.]

I used to attend the king's levee once or twice a week, and had often seen him under the barber's hand, which indeed was at first very terrible to behold; for the razor was almost twice as long as an ordinary scythe. His majesty, according to the custom of the country, was only shaved twice a-week. I once prevailed on the barber to give me some of the suds or lather, out of which I picked forty or fifty of the strongest stumps of hair. I then took a piece of fine wood, and cut it like the back of a comb, making several holes in it at equal distances with as small a needle as I could get from Glumdalclitch. I fixed in the stumps so artificially, scraping and sloping them with my knife toward the points, that I made a very tolerable comb; which was a seasonable supply, my own being so much broken in the teeth, that it was almost useless: neither did I know any artist in that country so nice and exact, as would undertake to make me another.

And this puts me in mind of an amusement, wherein I spent many of my leisure hours. I desired the queen's woman to save for me the combings of her majesty's hair, whereof in time I got a good quantity; and consulting with my friend the cabinet-maker, who had received general orders to do little jobs for me, I directed him to make two chair-frames, no larger than those I had in my box, and to bore little holes with a fine awl, round those parts where I designed the backs and seats; through these holes I wove the strongest hairs I could pick out, just after the manner of cane chairs in England. When they were finished, I made a present of them to her majesty; who kept them in her cabinet, and used to show them for curiosities, as indeed they were the wonder of every one that beheld them. The queen would have me sit upon one of these chairs, but I absolutely refused to obey her, protesting I would rather die than place a dishonourable part of my body on those precious hairs, that once adorned her majesty's head. Of these hairs (as I had always a mechanical genius) I likewise made a neat little purse, about five feet long, with her majesty's name deciphered in gold letters, which I gave to Glumdalclitch, by the queen's consent. To say the truth, it was more for show than use, being not of strength to bear the weight of the larger coins, and therefore she kept nothing in it but some little toys that girls are fond of.

The king, who delighted in music, had frequent concerts at court, to which I was sometimes carried, and set in my box on a table to hear them: but the noise was so great that I could hardly distinguish the tunes. I am confident that all the drums and trumpets of a royal army, beating and sounding together just at your ears, could not equal it. My practice was to have my box removed from the place where the performers sat, as far as I could, then to shut the doors and windows of it, and draw the window curtains; after which I found their music not disagreeable.

I had learned in my youth to play a little upon the spinet. Glumdalclitch kept one in her chamber, and a master attended twice a-week to teach her: I called it a spinet, because it somewhat resembled that instrument, and was played upon in the same manner. A fancy came into my head, that I would entertain the king and queen with an English tune upon this instrument. But this appeared extremely difficult: for the spinet was near sixty feet long, each key being almost a foot wide, so that with my arms extended I could not reach to above five keys, and to press them down required a good smart stroke with my fist, which would be too great a labour, and to no purpose. The method I contrived was this: I prepared two round sticks, about the bigness of common cudgels; they were thicker at one end than the other, and I covered the thicker ends with pieces of a mouse's skin, that by rapping on them I might neither damage the tops of the keys nor interrupt the sound. Before the spinet a bench was placed, about four feet below the keys, and I was put upon the bench. I ran sideling upon it, that way and this, as fast as I could, banging the proper keys with my two sticks, and made a shift to play a jig, to the great satisfaction of both their majesties; but it was the most violent exercise I ever underwent; and yet I could not strike above sixteen keys, nor consequently play the bass and treble together, as other artists do; which was a great disadvantage to my performance.

The king, who, as I before observed, was a prince of excellent understanding, would frequently order that I should be brought in my box, and set upon the table in his closet: he would then command me to bring one of my chairs out of the box, and sit down within three yards distance upon the top of the cabinet, which brought me almost to a level with his face. In this manner I had several conversations with him. I one day took the freedom to tell his majesty, "that the contempt he discovered towards Europe, and the rest of the world, did not seem answerable to those excellent qualities of mind that he was master of; that reason did not extend itself with the bulk of the body; on the contrary, we observed in our country, that the tallest persons were usually the least provided with it; that among other animals, bees and ants had the reputation of more industry, art, and sagacity, than many of the larger kinds; and that, as inconsiderable as he took me to be, I hoped I might live to do his majesty some signal service." The king heard me with attention, and began to conceive a much better opinion of me than he had ever before. He desired "I would give him as exact an account of the government of England as I possibly could; because, as fond as princes commonly are of their own customs (for so he conjectured of other monarchs, by my former discourses), he should be glad to hear of any thing that might deserve imitation."

Imagine with thyself, courteous reader, how often I then wished for the tongue of Demosthenes or Cicero, that might have enabled me to celebrate the praise of my own dear native country in a style equal to its merits and felicity.

I began my discourse by informing his majesty, that our dominions consisted of two islands, which composed three mighty kingdoms, under one sovereign, beside our plantations in America. I dwelt long upon the fertility of our soil, and the temperature of our climate. I then spoke at large upon the constitution of an English parliament; partly made up of an illustrious body called the House of Peers; persons of the noblest blood, and of the most ancient and ample patrimonies. I described that extraordinary care always taken of their education in arts and arms, to qualify them for being counsellors both to the king and kingdom; to have a share in the legislature; to be members of the highest court of judicature, whence there can be no appeal; and to be champions always ready for the defence of their prince and country, by their valour, conduct, and fidelity. That these were the ornament and bulwark of the kingdom, worthy followers of their most renowned ancestors, whose honour had been the reward of their virtue, from which their posterity were never once known to degenerate. To these were joined several holy persons, as part of that assembly, under the title of bishops, whose peculiar business is to take care of religion, and of those who instruct the people therein. These were searched and sought out through the whole nation, by the prince and his wisest counsellors, among such of the priesthood as were most deservedly distinguished by the sanctity of their lives, and the depth of their erudition; who were indeed the spiritual fathers of the clergy and the people.

That the other part of the parliament consisted of an assembly called the House of Commons, who were all principal gentlemen, freely picked and culled out by the people themselves, for their great abilities and love of their country, to represent the wisdom of the whole nation. And that these two bodies made up the most august assembly in Europe; to whom, in conjunction with the prince, the whole legislature is committed.

I then descended to the courts of justice; over which the judges, those venerable sages and interpreters of the law, presided, for determining the disputed rights and properties of men, as well as for the punishment of vice and protection of innocence. I mentioned the prudent management of our treasury; the valour and achievements of our forces, by sea and land. I computed the number of our people, by reckoning how many millions there might be of each religious sect, or political party among us. I did not omit even our sports and pastimes, or any other particular which I thought might redound to the honour of my country. And I finished all with a brief historical account of affairs and events in England for about a hundred years past.

This conversation was not ended under five audiences, each of several hours; and the king heard the whole with great attention, frequently taking notes of what I spoke, as well as memorandums of what questions he intended to ask me.

When I had put an end to these long discources, his majesty, in a sixth audience, consulting his notes, proposed many doubts, queries, and objections, upon every article. He asked, "What methods were used to cultivate the minds and bodies of our young nobility, and in what kind of business they commonly spent the first and teachable parts of their lives? What course was taken to supply that assembly, when any noble family became extinct? What qualifications were necessary in those who are to be created new lords: whether the humour of the prince, a sum of money to a court lady, or a design of strengthening a party opposite to the public interest, ever happened to be the motive in those advancements? What share of knowledge these lords had in the laws of their country, and how they came by it, so as to enable them to decide the properties of their fellow-subjects in the last resort? Whether they were always so free from avarice, partialities, or want, that a bribe, or some other sinister view, could have no place among them? Whether those holy lords I spoke of were always promoted to that rank upon account of their knowledge in religious matters, and the sanctity of their lives; had never been compliers with the times, while they were common priests; or slavish prostitute chaplains to some nobleman, whose opinions they continued servilely to follow, after they were admitted into that assembly?"

He then desired to know, "What arts were practised in electing those whom I called commoners: whether a stranger, with a strong purse, might not influence the vulgar voters to choose him before their own landlord, or the most considerable gentleman in the neighbourhood? How it came to pass, that people were so violently bent upon getting into this assembly, which I allowed to be a great trouble and expense, often to the ruin of their families, without any salary or pension? because this appeared such an exalted strain of virtue and public spirit, that his majesty seemed to doubt it might possibly not be always sincere." And he desired to know, "Whether such zealous gentlemen could have any views of refunding themselves for the charges and trouble they were at by sacrificing the public good to the designs of a weak and vicious prince, in conjunction with a corrupted ministry?" He multiplied his questions, and sifted me thoroughly upon every part of this head, proposing numberless inquiries and objections, which I think it not prudent or convenient to repeat.

Upon what I said in relation to our courts of justice, his majesty desired to be satisfied in several points: and this I was the better able to do, having been formerly almost ruined by a long suit in chancery, which was decreed for me with costs. He asked, "What time was usually spent in determining between right and wrong, and what degree of expense? Whether advocates and orators had liberty to plead in causes manifestly known to be unjust, vexatious, or oppressive? Whether party, in religion or politics, were observed to be of any weight in the scale of justice? Whether those pleading orators were persons educated in the general knowledge of equity, or only in provincial, national, and other local customs? Whether they or their judges had any part in penning those laws, which they assumed the liberty of interpreting, and glossing upon at their pleasure? Whether they had ever, at different times, pleaded for and against the same cause, and cited precedents to prove contrary opinions? Whether they were a rich or a poor corporation? Whether they received any pecuniary reward for pleading, or delivering their opinions? And particularly, whether they were ever admitted as members in the lower senate?"

He fell next upon the management of our treasury; and said, "he thought my memory had failed me, because I computed our taxes at about five or six millions a-year, and when I came to mention the issues, he found they sometimes amounted to more than double; for the notes he had taken were very particular in this point, because he hoped, as he told me, that the knowledge of our conduct might be useful to him, and he could not be deceived in his calculations. But, if what I told him were true, he was still at a loss how a kingdom could run out of its estate, like a private person." He asked me, "who were our creditors; and where we found money to pay them?" He wondered to hear me talk of such chargeable and expensive wars; "that certainly we must be a quarrelsome people, or live among very bad neighbours, and that our generals must needs be richer than our kings." He asked, what business we had out of our own islands, unless upon the score of trade, or treaty, or to defend the coasts with our fleet?" Above all, he was amazed to hear me talk of a mercenary standing army, in the midst of peace, and among a free people. He said, "if we were governed by our own consent, in the persons of our representatives, he could not imagine of whom we were afraid, or against whom we were to fight; and would hear my opinion, whether a private man's house might not be better defended by himself, his children, and family, than by half-a-dozen rascals, picked up at a venture in the streets for small wages, who might get a hundred times more by cutting their throats?"

He laughed at my "odd kind of arithmetic," as he was pleased to call it, "in reckoning the numbers of our people, by a computation drawn from the several sects among us, in religion and politics." He said, "he knew no reason why those, who entertain opinions prejudicial to the public, should be obliged to change, or should not be obliged to conceal them. And as it was tyranny in any government to require the first, so it was weakness not to enforce the second: for a man may be allowed to keep poisons in his closet, but not to vend them about for cordials."

He observed, "that among the diversions of our nobility and gentry, I had mentioned gaming: he desired to know at what age this entertainment was usually taken up, and when it was laid down; how much of their time it employed; whether it ever went so high as to affect their fortunes; whether mean, vicious people, by their dexterity in that art, might not arrive at great riches, and sometimes keep our very nobles in dependence, as well as habituate them to vile companions, wholly take them from the improvement of their minds, and force them, by the losses they received, to learn and practise that infamous dexterity upon others?"

He was perfectly astonished with the historical account gave him of our affairs during the last century; protesting "it was only a heap of conspiracies, rebellions, murders, massacres, revolutions, banishments, the very worst effects that avarice, faction, hypocrisy, perfidiousness, cruelty, rage, madness, hatred, envy, lust, malice, and ambition, could produce."

His majesty, in another audience, was at the pains to recapitulate the sum of all I had spoken; compared the questions he made with the answers I had given; then taking me into his hands, and stroking me gently, delivered himself in these words, which I shall never forget, nor the manner he spoke them in: "My little friend Grildrig, you have made a most admirable panegyric upon your country; you have clearly proved, that ignorance, idleness, and vice, are the proper ingredients for qualifying a legislator; that laws are best explained, interpreted, and applied, by those whose interest and abilities lie in perverting, confounding, and eluding them. I observe among you some lines of an institution, which, in its original, might have been tolerable, but these half erased, and the rest wholly blurred and blotted by corruptions. It does not appear, from all you have said, how any one perfection is required toward the procurement of any one station among you; much less, that men are ennobled on account of their virtue; that priests are advanced for their piety or learning; soldiers, for their conduct or valour; judges, for their integrity; senators, for the love of their country; or counsellors for their wisdom. As for yourself," continued the king, "who have spent the greatest part of your life in travelling, I am well disposed to hope you may hitherto have escaped many vices of your country. But by what I have gathered from your own relation, and the answers I have with much pains wrung and extorted from you, I cannot but conclude the bulk of your natives to be the most pernicious race of little odious vermin that nature ever suffered to crawl upon the surface of the earth."

CHAPTER VII.

[The author's love of his country. He makes a proposal of much advantage to the king, which is rejected. The king's great ignorance in politics. The learning of that country very imperfect and confined. The laws, and military affairs, and parties in the state.]

Nothing but an extreme love of truth could have hindered me from concealing this part of my story. It was in vain to discover my resentments, which were always turned into ridicule; and I was forced to rest with patience, while my noble and beloved country was so injuriously treated. I am as heartily sorry as any of my readers can possibly be, that such an occasion was given: but this prince happened to be so curious and inquisitive upon every particular, that it could not consist either with gratitude or good manners, to refuse giving him what satisfaction I was able. Yet thus much I may be allowed to say in my own vindication, that I artfully eluded many of his questions, and gave to every point a more favourable turn, by many degrees, than the strictness of truth would allow. For I have always borne that laudable partiality to my own country, which Dionysius Halicarnassensis, with so much justice, recommends to an historian: I would hide the frailties and deformities of my political mother, and place her virtues and beauties in the most advantageous light. This was my sincere endeavour in those many discourses I had with that monarch, although it unfortunately failed of success.

But great allowances should be given to a king, who lives wholly secluded from the rest of the world, and must therefore be altogether unacquainted with the manners and customs that most prevail in other nations: the want of which knowledge will ever produce many prejudices, and a certain narrowness of thinking, from which we, and the politer countries of Europe, are wholly exempted. And it would be hard indeed, if so remote a prince's notions of virtue and vice were to be offered as a standard for all mankind.

To confirm what I have now said, and further to show the miserable effects of a confined education, I shall here insert a passage, which will hardly obtain belief. In hopes to ingratiate myself further into his majesty's favour, I told him of "an invention, discovered between three and four hundred years ago, to make a certain powder, into a heap of which, the smallest spark of fire falling, would kindle the whole in a moment, although it were as big as a mountain, and make it all fly up in the air together, with a noise and agitation greater than thunder. That a proper quantity of this powder rammed into a hollow tube of brass or iron, according to its bigness, would drive a ball of iron or lead, with such violence and speed, as nothing was able to sustain its force. That the largest balls thus discharged, would not only destroy whole ranks of an army at once, but batter the strongest walls to the ground, sink down ships, with a thousand men in each, to the bottom of the sea, and when linked together by a chain, would cut through masts and rigging, divide hundreds of bodies in the middle, and lay all waste before them. That we often put this powder into large hollow balls of iron, and discharged them by an engine into some city we were besieging, which would rip up the pavements, tear the houses to pieces, burst and throw splinters on every side, dashing out the brains of all who came near. That I knew the ingredients very well, which were cheap and common; I understood the manner of compounding them, and could direct his workmen how to make those tubes, of a size proportionable to all other things in his majesty's kingdom, and the largest need not be above a hundred feet long; twenty or thirty of which tubes, charged with the proper quantity of powder and balls, would batter down the walls of the strongest town in his dominions in a few hours, or destroy the whole metropolis, if ever it should pretend to dispute his absolute commands." This I humbly offered to his majesty, as a small tribute of acknowledgment, in turn for so many marks that I had received, of his royal favour and protection.

The king was struck with horror at the description I had given of those terrible engines, and the proposal I had made. "He was amazed, how so impotent and grovelling an insect as I" (these were his expressions) "could entertain such inhuman ideas, and in so familiar a manner, as to appear wholly unmoved at all the scenes of blood and desolation which I had painted as the common effects of those destructive machines; whereof," he said, "some evil genius, enemy to mankind, must have been the first contriver. As for himself, he protested, that although few things delighted him so much as new discoveries in art or in nature, yet he would rather lose half his kingdom, than be privy to such a secret; which he commanded me, as I valued any life, never to mention any more."

A strange effect of narrow principles and views! that a prince possessed of every quality which procures veneration, love, and esteem; of strong parts, great wisdom, and profound learning, endowed with admirable talents, and almost adored by his subjects, should, from a nice, unnecessary scruple, whereof in Europe we can have no conception, let slip an opportunity put into his hands that would have made him absolute master of the lives, the liberties, and the fortunes of his people! Neither do I say this, with the least intention to detract from the many virtues of that excellent king, whose character, I am sensible, will, on this account, be very much lessened in the opinion of an English reader: but I take this defect among them to have risen from their ignorance, by not having hitherto reduced politics into a science, as the more acute wits of Europe have done. For, I remember very well, in a discourse one day with the king, when I happened to say, "there were several thousand books among us written upon the art of government," it gave him (directly contrary to my intention) a very mean opinion of our understandings. He professed both to abominate and despise all mystery, refinement, and intrigue, either in a prince or a minister. He could not tell what I meant by secrets of state, where an enemy, or some rival nation, were not in the case. He confined the knowledge of governing within very narrow bounds, to common sense and reason, to justice and lenity, to the speedy determination of civil and criminal causes; with some other obvious topics, which are not worth considering. And he gave it for his opinion, "that whoever could make two ears of corn, or two blades of grass, to grow upon a spot of ground where only one grew before, would deserve better of mankind, and do more essential service to his country, than the whole race of politicians put together."

The learning of this people is very defective, consisting only in morality, history, poetry, and mathematics, wherein they must be allowed to excel. But the last of these is wholly applied to what may be useful in life, to the improvement of agriculture, and all mechanical arts; so that among us, it would be little esteemed. And as to ideas, entities, abstractions, and transcendentals, I could never drive the least conception into their heads.

No law in that country must exceed in words the number of letters in their alphabet, which consists only of two and twenty. But indeed few of them extend even to that length. They are expressed in the most plain and simple terms, wherein those people are not mercurial enough to discover above one interpretation: and to write a comment upon any law, is a capital crime. As to the decision of civil causes, or proceedings against criminals, their precedents are so few, that they have little reason to boast of any extraordinary skill in either.

They have had the art of printing, as well as the Chinese, time out of mind: but their libraries are not very large; for that of the king, which is reckoned the largest, does not amount to above a thousand volumes, placed in a gallery of twelve hundred feet long, whence I had liberty to borrow what books I pleased. The queen's joiner had contrived in one of Glumdalclitch's rooms, a kind of wooden machine five-and-twenty feet high, formed like a standing ladder; the steps were each fifty feet long. It was indeed a moveable pair of stairs, the lowest end placed at ten feet distance from the wall of the chamber. The book I had a mind to read, was put up leaning against the wall: I first mounted to the upper step of the ladder, and turning my face towards the book, began at the top of the page, and so walking to the right and left about eight or ten paces, according to the length of the lines, till I had gotten a little below the level of mine eyes, and then descending gradually till I came to the bottom: after which I mounted again, and began the other page in the same manner, and so turned over the leaf, which I could easily do with both my hands, for it was as thick and stiff as a pasteboard, and in the largest folios not above eighteen or twenty feet long.

Their style is clear, masculine, and smooth, but not florid; for they avoid nothing more than multiplying unnecessary words, or using various expressions. I have perused many of their books, especially those in history and morality. Among the rest, I was much diverted with a little old treatise, which always lay in Glumdalclitch's bed chamber, and belonged to her governess, a grave elderly gentlewoman, who dealt in writings of morality and devotion. The book treats of the weakness of human kind, and is in little esteem, except among the women and the vulgar. However, I was curious to see what an author of that country could say upon such a subject. This writer went through all the usual topics of European moralists, showing "how diminutive, contemptible, and helpless an animal was man in his own nature; how unable to defend himself from inclemencies of the air, or the fury of wild beasts: how much he was excelled by one creature in strength, by another in speed, by a third in foresight, by a fourth in industry." He added, "that nature was degenerated in these latter declining ages of the world, and could now produce only small abortive births, in comparison of those in ancient times." He said "it was very reasonable to think, not only that the species of men were originally much larger, but also that there must have been giants in former ages; which, as it is asserted by history and tradition, so it has been confirmed by huge bones and skulls, casually dug up in several parts of the kingdom, far exceeding the common dwindled race of men in our days." He argued, "that the very laws of nature absolutely required we should have been made, in the beginning of a size more large and robust; not so liable to destruction from every little accident, of a tile falling from a house, or a stone cast from the hand of a boy, or being drowned in a little brook." From this way of reasoning, the author drew several moral applications, useful in the conduct of life, but needless here to repeat. For my own part, I could not avoid reflecting how universally this talent was spread, of drawing lectures in morality, or indeed rather matter of discontent and repining, from the quarrels we raise with nature. And I believe, upon a strict inquiry, those quarrels might be shown as ill-grounded among us as they are among that people.

As to their military affairs, they boast that the king's army consists of a hundred and seventy-six thousand foot, and thirty-two thousand horse: if that may be called an army, which is made up of tradesmen in the several cities, and farmers in the country, whose commanders are only the nobility and gentry, without pay or reward. They are indeed perfect enough in their exercises, and under very good discipline, wherein I saw no great merit; for how should it be otherwise, where every farmer is under the command of his own landlord, and every citizen under that of the principal men in his own city, chosen after the manner of Venice, by ballot?

I have often seen the militia of Lorbrulgrud drawn out to exercise, in a great field near the city of twenty miles square. They were in all not above twenty-five thousand foot, and six thousand horse; but it was impossible for me to compute their number, considering the space of ground they took up. A cavalier, mounted on a large steed, might be about ninety feet high. I have seen this whole body of horse, upon a word of command, draw their swords at once, and brandish them in the air. Imagination can figure nothing so grand, so surprising, and so astonishing! it looked as if ten thousand flashes of lightning were darting at the same time from every quarter of the sky.

I was curious to know how this prince, to whose dominions there is no access from any other country, came to think of armies, or to teach his people the practice of military discipline. But I was soon informed, both by conversation and reading their histories; for, in the course of many ages, they have been troubled with the same disease to which the whole race of mankind is subject; the nobility often contending for power, the people for liberty, and the king for absolute dominion. All which, however happily tempered by the laws of that kingdom, have been sometimes violated by each of the three parties, and have more than once occasioned civil wars; the last whereof was happily put an end to by this prince's grand-father, in a general composition; and the militia, then settled with common consent, has been ever since kept in the strictest duty.

CHAPTER VIII.

[The king and queen make a progress to the frontiers. The author attends them. The manner in which he leaves the country very particularly related. He returns to England.]

I had always a strong impulse that I should some time recover my liberty, though it was impossible to conjecture by what means, or to form any project with the least hope of succeeding. The ship in which I sailed, was the first ever known to be driven within sight of that coast, and the king had given strict orders, that if at any time another appeared, it should be taken ashore, and with all its crew and passengers brought in a tumbril to Lorbrulgrud. He was strongly bent to get me a woman of my own size, by whom I might propagate the breed: but I think I should rather have died than undergone the disgrace of leaving a posterity to be kept in cages, like tame canary-birds, and perhaps, in time, sold about the kingdom, to persons of quality, for curiosities. I was indeed treated with much kindness: I was the favourite of a great king and queen, and the delight of the whole court; but it was upon such a foot as ill became the dignity of humankind. I could never forget those domestic pledges I had left behind me. I wanted to be among people, with whom I could converse upon even terms, and walk about the streets and fields without being afraid of being trod to death like a frog or a young puppy. But my deliverance came sooner than I expected, and in a manner not very common; the whole story and circumstances of which I shall faithfully relate.

I had now been two years in this country; and about the beginning of the third, Glumdalclitch and I attended the king and queen, in a progress to the south coast of the kingdom. I was carried, as usual, in my travelling-box, which as I have already described, was a very convenient closet, of twelve feet wide. And I had ordered a hammock to be fixed, by silken ropes from the four corners at the top, to break the jolts, when a servant carried me before him on horseback, as I sometimes desired; and would often sleep in my hammock, while we were upon the road. On the roof of my closet, not directly over the middle of the hammock, I ordered the joiner to cut out a hole of a foot square, to give me air in hot weather, as I slept; which hole I shut at pleasure with a board that drew backward and forward through a groove.

When we came to our journey's end, the king thought proper to pass a few days at a palace he has near Flanflasnic, a city within eighteen English miles of the seaside. Glumdalclitch and I were much fatigued: I had gotten a small cold, but the poor girl was so ill as to be confined to her chamber. I longed to see the ocean, which must be the only scene of my escape, if ever it should happen. I pretended to be worse than I really was, and desired leave to take the fresh air of the sea, with a page, whom I was very fond of, and who had sometimes been trusted with me. I shall never forget with what unwillingness Glumdalclitch consented, nor the strict charge she gave the page to be careful of me, bursting at the same time into a flood of tears, as if she had some forboding of what was to happen. The boy took me out in my box, about half an hours walk from the palace, towards the rocks on the sea-shore. I ordered him to set me down, and lifting up one of my sashes, cast many a wistful melancholy look towards the sea. I found myself not very well, and told the page that I had a mind to take a nap in my hammock, which I hoped would do me good. I got in, and the boy shut the window close down, to keep out the cold. I soon fell asleep, and all I can conjecture is, while I slept, the page, thinking no danger could happen, went among the rocks to look for birds' eggs, having before observed him from my window searching about, and picking up one or two in the clefts. Be that as it will, I found myself suddenly awaked with a violent pull upon the ring, which was fastened at the top of my box for the conveniency of carriage. I felt my box raised very high in the air, and then borne forward with prodigious speed. The first jolt had like to have shaken me out of my hammock, but afterward the motion was easy enough. I called out several times, as loud as I could raise my voice, but all to no purpose. I looked towards my windows, and could see nothing but the clouds and sky. I heard a noise just over my head, like the clapping of wings, and then began to perceive the woful condition I was in; that some eagle had got the ring of my box in his beak, with an intent to let it fall on a rock, like a tortoise in a shell, and then pick out my body, and devour it: for the sagacity and smell of this bird enables him to discover his quarry at a great distance, though better concealed than I could be within a two-inch board.

In a little time, I observed the noise and flutter of wings to increase very fast, and my box was tossed up and down, like a sign in a windy day. I heard several bangs or buffets, as I thought given to the eagle (for such I am certain it must have been that held the ring of my box in his beak), and then, all on a sudden, felt myself falling perpendicularly down, for above a minute, but with such incredible swiftness, that I almost lost my breath. My fall was stopped by a terrible squash, that sounded louder to my ears than the cataract of Niagara; after which, I was quite in the dark for another minute, and then my box began to rise so high, that I could see light from the tops of the windows. I now perceived I was fallen into the sea. My box, by the weight of my body, the goods that were in, and the broad plates of iron fixed for strength at the four corners of the top and bottom, floated about five feet deep in water. I did then, and do now suppose, that the eagle which flew away with my box was pursued by two or three others, and forced to let me drop, while he defended himself against the rest, who hoped to share in the prey. The plates of iron fastened at the bottom of the box (for those were the strongest) preserved the balance while it fell, and hindered it from being broken on the surface of the water. Every joint of it was well grooved; and the door did not move on hinges, but up and down like a sash, which kept my closet so tight that very little water came in. I got with much difficulty out of my hammock, having first ventured to draw back the slip-board on the roof already mentioned, contrived on purpose to let in air, for want of which I found myself almost stifled.

How often did I then wish myself with my dear Glumdalclitch, from whom one single hour had so far divided me! And I may say with truth, that in the midst of my own misfortunes I could not forbear lamenting my poor nurse, the grief she would suffer for my loss, the displeasure of the queen, and the ruin of her fortune. Perhaps many travellers have not been under greater difficulties and distress than I was at this juncture, expecting every moment to see my box dashed to pieces, or at least overset by the first violent blast, or rising wave. A breach in one single pane of glass would have been immediate death: nor could any thing have preserved the windows, but the strong lattice wires placed on the outside, against accidents in travelling. I saw the water ooze in at several crannies, although the leaks were not considerable, and I endeavoured to stop them as well as I could. I was not able to lift up the roof of my closet, which otherwise I certainly should have done, and sat on the top of it; where I might at least preserve myself some hours longer, than by being shut up (as I may call it) in the hold. Or if I escaped these dangers for a day or two, what could I expect but a miserable death of cold and hunger? I was four hours under these circumstances, expecting, and indeed wishing, every moment to be my last.

I have already told the reader that there were two strong staples fixed upon that side of my box which had no window, and into which the servant, who used to carry me on horseback, would put a leathern belt, and buckle it about his waist. Being in this disconsolate state, I heard, or at least thought I heard, some kind of grating noise on that side of my box where the staples were fixed; and soon after I began to fancy that the box was pulled or towed along the sea; for I now and then felt a sort of tugging, which made the waves rise near the tops of my windows, leaving me almost in the dark. This gave me some faint hopes of relief, although I was not able to imagine how it could be brought about. I ventured to unscrew one of my chairs, which were always fastened to the floor; and having made a hard shift to screw it down again, directly under the slipping-board that I had lately opened, I mounted on the chair, and putting my mouth as near as I could to the hole, I called for help in a loud voice, and in all the languages I understood. I then fastened my handkerchief to a stick I usually carried, and thrusting it up the hole, waved it several times in the air, that if any boat or ship were near, the seamen might conjecture some unhappy mortal to be shut up in the box.

I found no effect from all I could do, but plainly perceived my closet to be moved along; and in the space of an hour, or better, that side of the box where the staples were, and had no windows, struck against something that was hard. I apprehended it to be a rock, and found myself tossed more than ever. I plainly heard a noise upon the cover of my closet, like that of a cable, and the grating of it as it passed through the ring. I then found myself hoisted up, by degrees, at least three feet higher than I was before. Whereupon I again thrust up my stick and handkerchief, calling for help till I was almost hoarse. In return to which, I heard a great shout repeated three times, giving me such transports of joy as are not to be conceived but by those who feel them. I now heard a trampling over my head, and somebody calling through the hole with a loud voice, in the English tongue, "If there be any body below, let them speak." I answered, "I was an Englishman, drawn by ill fortune into the greatest calamity that ever any creature underwent, and begged, by all that was moving, to be delivered out of the dungeon I was in." The voice replied, "I was safe, for my box was fastened to their ship; and the carpenter should immediately come and saw a hole in the cover, large enough to pull me out." I answered, "that was needless, and would take up too much time; for there was no more to be done, but let one of the crew put his finger into the ring, and take the box out of the sea into the ship, and so into the captain's cabin." Some of them, upon hearing me talk so wildly, thought I was mad: others laughed; for indeed it never came into my head, that I was now got among people of my own stature and strength. The carpenter came, and in a few minutes sawed a passage about four feet square, then let down a small ladder, upon which I mounted, and thence was taken into the ship in a very weak condition.

The sailors were all in amazement, and asked me a thousand questions, which I had no inclination to answer. I was equally confounded at the sight of so many pigmies, for such I took them to be, after having so long accustomed mine eyes to the monstrous objects I had left. But the captain, Mr. Thomas Wilcocks, an honest worthy Shropshire man, observing I was ready to faint, took me into his cabin, gave me a cordial to comfort me, and made me turn in upon his own bed, advising me to take a little rest, of which I had great need. Before I went to sleep, I gave him to understand that I had some valuable furniture in my box, too good to be lost: a fine hammock, a handsome field-bed, two chairs, a table, and a cabinet; that my closet was hung on all sides, or rather quilted, with silk and cotton; that if he would let one of the crew bring my closet into his cabin, I would open it there before him, and show him my goods. The captain, hearing me utter these absurdities, concluded I was raving; however (I suppose to pacify me) he promised to give order as I desired, and going upon deck, sent some of his men down into my closet, whence (as I afterwards found) they drew up all my goods, and stripped off the quilting; but the chairs, cabinet, and bedstead, being screwed to the floor, were much damaged by the ignorance of the seamen, who tore them up by force. Then they knocked off some of the boards for the use of the ship, and when they had got all they had a mind for, let the hull drop into the sea, which by reason of many breaches made in the bottom and sides, sunk to rights. And, indeed, I was glad not to have been a spectator of the havoc they made, because I am confident it would have sensibly touched me, by bringing former passages into my mind, which I would rather have forgot.

I slept some hours, but perpetually disturbed with dreams of the place I had left, and the dangers I had escaped. However, upon waking, I found myself much recovered. It was now about eight o'clock at night, and the captain ordered supper immediately, thinking I had already fasted too long. He entertained me with great kindness, observing me not to look wildly, or talk inconsistently: and, when we were left alone, desired I would give him a relation of my travels, and by what accident I came to be set adrift, in that monstrous wooden chest. He said "that about twelve o'clock at noon, as he was looking through his glass, he spied it at a distance, and thought it was a sail, which he had a mind to make, being not much out of his course, in hopes of buying some biscuit, his own beginning to fall short. That upon coming nearer, and finding his error, he sent out his long-boat to discover what it was; that his men came back in a fright, swearing they had seen a swimming house. That he laughed at their folly, and went himself in the boat, ordering his men to take a strong cable along with them. That the weather being calm, he rowed round me several times, observed my windows and wire lattices that defended them. That he discovered two staples upon one side, which was all of boards, without any passage for light. He then commanded his men to row up to that side, and fastening a cable to one of the staples, ordered them to tow my chest, as they called it, toward the ship. When it was there, he gave directions to fasten another cable to the ring fixed in the cover, and to raise up my chest with pulleys, which all the sailors were not able to do above two or three feet." He said, "they saw my stick and handkerchief thrust out of the hole, and concluded that some unhappy man must be shut up in the cavity." I asked, "whether he or the crew had seen any prodigious birds in the air, about the time he first discovered me." To which he answered, that discoursing this matter with the sailors while I was asleep, one of them said, he had observed three eagles flying towards the north, but remarked nothing of their being larger than the usual size:" which I suppose must be imputed to the great height they were at; and he could not guess the reason of my question. I then asked the captain, "how far he reckoned we might be from land?" He said, "by the best computation he could make, we were at least a hundred leagues." I assured him, "that he must be mistaken by almost half, for I had not left the country whence I came above two hours before I dropped into the sea." Whereupon he began again to think that my brain was disturbed, of which he gave me a hint, and advised me to go to bed in a cabin he had provided. I assured him, "I was well refreshed with his good entertainment and company, and as much in my senses as ever I was in my life." He then grew serious, and desired to ask me freely, "whether I were not troubled in my mind by the consciousness of some enormous crime, for which I was punished, at the command of some prince, by exposing me in that chest; as great criminals, in other countries, have been forced to sea in a leaky vessel, without provisions: for although he should be sorry to have taken so ill a man into his ship, yet he would engage his word to set me safe ashore, in the first port where we arrived." He added, "that his suspicions were much increased by some very absurd speeches I had delivered at first to his sailors, and afterwards to himself, in relation to my closet or chest, as well as by my odd looks and behaviour while I was at supper."

I begged his patience to hear me tell my story, which I faithfully did, from the last time I left England, to the moment he first discovered me. And, as truth always forces its way into rational minds, so this honest worthy gentleman, who had some tincture of learning, and very good sense, was immediately convinced of my candour and veracity. But further to confirm all I had said, I entreated him to give order that my cabinet should be brought, of which I had the key in my pocket; for he had already informed me how the seamen disposed of my closet. I opened it in his own presence, and showed him the small collection of rarities I made in the country from which I had been so strangely delivered. There was the comb I had contrived out of the stumps of the king's beard, and another of the same materials, but fixed into a paring of her majesty's thumb-nail, which served for the back. There was a collection of needles and pins, from a foot to half a yard long; four wasp stings, like joiner's tacks; some combings of the queen's hair; a gold ring, which one day she made me a present of, in a most obliging manner, taking it from her little finger, and throwing it over my head like a collar. I desired the captain would please to accept this ring in return for his civilities; which he absolutely refused. I showed him a corn that I had cut off with my own hand, from a maid of honour's toe; it was about the bigness of Kentish pippin, and grown so hard, that when I returned England, I got it hollowed into a cup, and set in silver. Lastly, I desired him to see the breeches I had then on, which were made of a mouse's skin.

I could force nothing on him but a footman's tooth, which I observed him to examine with great curiosity, and found he had a fancy for it. He received it with abundance of thanks, more than such a trifle could deserve. It was drawn by an unskilful surgeon, in a mistake, from one of Glumdalclitch's men, who was afflicted with the tooth-ache, but it was as sound as any in his head. I got it cleaned, and put it into my cabinet. It was about a foot long, and four inches in diameter.

The captain was very well satisfied with this plain relation I had given him, and said, "he hoped, when we returned to England, I would oblige the world by putting it on paper, and making it public." My answer was, "that we were overstocked with books of travels: that nothing could now pass which was not extraordinary; wherein I doubted some authors less consulted truth, than their own vanity, or interest, or the diversion of ignorant readers; that my story could contain little beside common events, without those ornamental descriptions of strange plants, trees, birds, and other animals; or of the barbarous customs and idolatry of savage people, with which most writers abound. However, I thanked him for his good opinion, and promised to take the matter into my thoughts."

He said "he wondered at one thing very much, which was, to hear me speak so loud;" asking me "whether the king or queen of that country were thick of hearing?" I told him, "it was what I had been used to for above two years past, and that I admired as much at the voices of him and his men, who seemed to me only to whisper, and yet I could hear them well enough. But, when I spoke in that country, it was like a man talking in the streets, to another looking out from the top of a steeple, unless when I was placed on a table, or held in any person's hand." I told him, "I had likewise observed another thing, that, when I first got into the ship, and the sailors stood all about me, I thought they were the most little contemptible creatures I had ever beheld." For indeed, while I was in that prince's country, I could never endure to look in a glass, after mine eyes had been accustomed to such prodigious objects, because the comparison gave me so despicable a conceit of myself. The captain said, "that while we were at supper, he observed me to look at every thing with a sort of wonder, and that I often seemed hardly able to contain my laughter, which he knew not well how to take, but imputed it to some disorder in my brain." I answered, "it was very true; and I wondered how I could forbear, when I saw his dishes of the size of a silver three-pence, a leg of pork hardly a mouthful, a cup not so big as a nut-shell;" and so I went on, describing the rest of his household-stuff and provisions, after the same manner. For, although he queen had ordered a little equipage of all things necessary for me, while I was in her service, yet my ideas were wholly taken up with what I saw on every side of me, and I winked at my own littleness, as people do at their own faults. The captain understood my raillery very well, and merrily replied with the old English proverb, "that he doubted mine eyes were bigger than my belly, for he did not observe my stomach so good, although I had fasted all day;" and, continuing in his mirth, protested "he would have gladly given a hundred pounds, to have seen my closet in the eagle's bill, and afterwards in its fall from so great a height into the sea; which would certainly have been a most astonishing object, worthy to have the description of it transmitted to future ages:" and the comparison of Phaeton was so obvious, that he could not forbear applying it, although I did not much admire the conceit.

The captain having been at Tonquin, was, in his return to England, driven north-eastward to the latitude of 44 degrees, and longitude of 143. But meeting a trade-wind two days after I came on board him, we sailed southward a long time, and coasting New Holland, kept our course west-south-west, and then south-south-west, till we doubled the Cape of Good Hope. Our voyage was very prosperous, but I shall not trouble the reader with a journal of it. The captain called in at one or two ports, and sent in his long-boat for provisions and fresh water; but I never went out of the ship till we came into the Downs, which was on the third day of June, 1706, about nine months after my escape. I offered to leave my goods in security for payment of my freight: but the captain protested he would not receive one farthing. We took a kind leave of each other, and I made him promise he would come to see me at my house in Redriff. I hired a horse and guide for five shillings, which I borrowed of the captain.

As I was on the road, observing the littleness of the houses, the trees, the cattle, and the people, I began to think myself in Lilliput. I was afraid of trampling on every traveller I met, and often called aloud to have them stand out of the way, so that I had like to have gotten one or two broken heads for my impertinence.

When I came to my own house, for which I was forced to inquire, one of the servants opening the door, I bent down to go in, (like a goose under a gate,) for fear of striking my head. My wife run out to embrace me, but I stooped lower than her knees, thinking she could otherwise never be able to reach my mouth. My daughter kneeled to ask my blessing, but I could not see her till she arose, having been so long used to stand with my head and eyes erect to above sixty feet; and then I went to take her up with one hand by the waist. I looked down upon the servants, and one or two friends who were in the house, as if they had been pigmies and I a giant. I told my wife, "she had been too thrifty, for I found she had starved herself and her daughter to nothing." In short, I behaved myself so unaccountably, that they were all of the captain's opinion when he first saw me, and concluded I had lost my wits. This I mention as an instance of the great power of habit and prejudice.

In a little time, I and my family and friends came to a right understanding: but my wife protested "I should never go to sea any more;" although my evil destiny so ordered, that she had not power to hinder me, as the reader may know hereafter. In the mean time, I here conclude the second part of my unfortunate voyages.

PART III. A VOYAGE TO LAPUTA, BALNIBARBI, LUGGNAGG, GLUBBDUBDRIB, AND JAPAN.

CHAPTER I.

[The author sets out on his third voyage. Is taken by pirates. The malice of a Dutchman. His arrival at an island. He is received into Laputa.]

I had not been at home above ten days, when Captain William Robinson, a Cornish man, commander of the Hopewell, a stout ship of three hundred tons, came to my house. I had formerly been surgeon of another ship where he was master, and a fourth part owner, in a voyage to the Levant. He had always treated me more like a brother, than an inferior officer; and, hearing of my arrival, made me a visit, as I apprehended only out of friendship, for nothing passed more than what is usual after long absences. But repeating his visits often, expressing his joy to find I me in good health, asking, "whether I were now settled for life?" adding, "that he intended a voyage to the East Indies in two months," at last he plainly invited me, though with some apologies, to be surgeon of the ship; "that I should have another surgeon under me, beside our two mates; that my salary should be double to the usual pay; and that having experienced my knowledge in sea-affairs to be at least equal to his, he would enter into any engagement to follow my advice, as much as if I had shared in the command."

He said so many other obliging things, and I knew him to be so honest a man, that I could not reject this proposal; the thirst I had of seeing the world, notwithstanding my past misfortunes, continuing as violent as ever. The only difficulty that remained, was to persuade my wife, whose consent however I at last obtained, by the prospect of advantage she proposed to her children.

We set out the 5th day of August, 1706, and arrived at Fort St. George the 11th of April, 1707. We staid there three weeks to refresh our crew, many of whom were sick. From thence we went to Tonquin, where the captain resolved to continue some time, because many of the goods he intended to buy were not ready, nor could he expect to be dispatched in several months. Therefore, in hopes to defray some of the charges he must be at, he bought a sloop, loaded it with several sorts of goods, wherewith the Tonquinese usually trade to the neighbouring islands, and putting fourteen men on board, whereof three were of the country, he appointed me master of the sloop, and gave me power to traffic, while he transacted his affairs at Tonquin.

We had not sailed above three days, when a great storm arising, we were driven five days to the north-north-east, and then to the east: after which we had fair weather, but still with a pretty strong gale from the west. Upon the tenth day we were chased by two pirates, who soon overtook us; for my sloop was so deep laden, that she sailed very slow, neither were we in a condition to defend ourselves.

We were boarded about the same time by both the pirates, who entered furiously at the head of their men; but finding us all prostrate upon our faces (for so I gave order), they pinioned us with strong ropes, and setting guard upon us, went to search the sloop.

I observed among them a Dutchman, who seemed to be of some authority, though he was not commander of either ship. He knew us by our countenances to be Englishmen, and jabbering to us in his own language, swore we should be tied back to back and thrown into the sea. I spoken Dutch tolerably well; I told him who we were, and begged him, in consideration of our being Christians and Protestants, of neighbouring countries in strict alliance, that he would move the captains to take some pity on us. This inflamed his rage; he repeated his threatenings, and turning to his companions, spoke with great vehemence in the Japanese language, as I suppose, often using the word Christianos.

The largest of the two pirate ships was commanded by a Japanese captain, who spoke a little Dutch, but very imperfectly. He came up to me, and after several questions, which I answered in great humility, he said, "we should not die." I made the captain a very low bow, and then, turning to the Dutchman, said, "I was sorry to find more mercy in a heathen, than in a brother christian." But I had soon reason to repent those foolish words: for that malicious reprobate, having often endeavoured in vain to persuade both the captains that I might be thrown into the sea (which they would not yield to, after the promise made me that I should not die), however, prevailed so far, as to have a punishment inflicted on me, worse, in all human appearance, than death itself. My men were sent by an equal division into both the pirate ships, and my sloop new manned. As to myself, it was determined that I should be set adrift in a small canoe, with paddles and a sail, and four days' provisions; which last, the Japanese captain was so kind to double out of his own stores, and would permit no man to search me. I got down into the canoe, while the Dutchman, standing upon the deck, loaded me with all the curses and injurious terms his language could afford.

About an hour before we saw the pirates I had taken an observation, and found we were in the latitude of 46 N. and longitude of 183. When I was at some distance from the pirates, I discovered, by my pocket-glass, several islands to the south-east. I set up my sail, the wind being fair, with a design to reach the nearest of those islands, which I made a shift to do, in about three hours. It was all rocky: however I got many birds' eggs; and, striking fire, I kindled some heath and dry sea-weed, by which I roasted my eggs. I ate no other supper, being resolved to spare my provisions as much as I could. I passed the night under the shelter of a rock, strewing some heath under me, and slept pretty well.

The next day I sailed to another island, and thence to a third and fourth, sometimes using my sail, and sometimes my paddles. But, not to trouble the reader with a particular account of my distresses, let it suffice, that on the fifth day I arrived at the last island in my sight, which lay south-south-east to the former.

This island was at a greater distance than I expected, and I did not reach it in less than five hours. I encompassed it almost round, before I could find a convenient place to land in; which was a small creek, about three times the wideness of my canoe. I found the island to be all rocky, only a little intermingled with tufts of grass, and sweet-smelling herbs. I took out my small provisions and after having refreshed myself, I secured the remainder in a cave, whereof there were great numbers; I gathered plenty of eggs upon the rocks, and got a quantity of dry sea-weed, and parched grass, which I designed to kindle the next day, and roast my eggs as well as I could, for I had about me my flint, steel, match, and burning-glass. I lay all night in the cave where I had lodged my provisions. My bed was the same dry grass and sea-weed which I intended for fuel. I slept very little, for the disquiets of my mind prevailed over my weariness, and kept me awake. I considered how impossible it was to preserve my life in so desolate a place, and how miserable my end must be: yet found myself so listless and desponding, that I had not the heart to rise; and before I could get spirits enough to creep out of my cave, the day was far advanced. I walked awhile among the rocks: the sky was perfectly clear, and the sun so hot, that I was forced to turn my face from it: when all on a sudden it became obscure, as I thought, in a manner very different from what happens by the interposition of a cloud. I turned back, and perceived a vast opaque body between me and the sun moving forwards towards the island: it seemed to be about two miles high, and hid the sun six or seven minutes; but I did not observe the air to be much colder, or the sky more darkened, than if I had stood under the shade of a mountain. As it approached nearer over the place where I was, it appeared to be a firm substance, the bottom flat, smooth, and shining very bright, from the reflection of the sea below. I stood upon a height about two hundred yards from the shore, and saw this vast body descending almost to a parallel with me, at less than an English mile distance. I took out my pocket perspective, and could plainly discover numbers of people moving up and down the sides of it, which appeared to be sloping; but what those people where doing I was not able to distinguish.

The natural love of life gave me some inward motion of joy, and I was ready to entertain a hope that this adventure might, some way or other, help to deliver me from the desolate place and condition I was in. But at the same time the reader can hardly conceive my astonishment, to behold an island in the air, inhabited by men, who were able (as it should seem) to raise or sink, or put it into progressive motion, as they pleased. But not being at that time in a disposition to philosophise upon this phenomenon, I rather chose to observe what course the island would take, because it seemed for awhile to stand still. Yet soon after, it advanced nearer, and I could see the sides of it encompassed with several gradations of galleries, and stairs, at certain intervals, to descend from one to the other. In the lowest gallery, I beheld some people fishing with long angling rods, and others looking on. I waved my cap (for my hat was long since worn out) and my handkerchief toward the island; and upon its nearer approach, I called and shouted with the utmost strength of my voice; and then looking circumspectly, I beheld a crowd gather to that side which was most in my view. I found by their pointing towards me and to each other, that they plainly discovered me, although they made no return to my shouting. But I could see four or five men running in great haste, up the stairs, to the top of the island, who then disappeared. I happened rightly to conjecture, that these were sent for orders to some person in authority upon this occasion.

The number of people increased, and, in less than half all hour, the island was moved and raised in such a manner, that the lowest gallery appeared in a parallel of less then a hundred yards distance from the height where I stood. I then put myself in the most supplicating posture, and spoke in the humblest accent, but received no answer. Those who stood nearest over against me, seemed to be persons of distinction, as I supposed by their habit. They conferred earnestly with each other, looking often upon me. At length one of them called out in a clear, polite, smooth dialect, not unlike in sound to the Italian: and therefore I returned an answer in that language, hoping at least that the cadence might be more agreeable to his ears. Although neither of us understood the other, yet my meaning was easily known, for the people saw the distress I was in.

They made signs for me to come down from the rock, and go towards the shore, which I accordingly did; and the flying island being raised to a convenient height, the verge directly over me, a chain was let down from the lowest gallery, with a seat fastened to the bottom, to which I fixed myself, and was drawn up by pulleys.

CHAPTER II.

[The humours and dispositions of the Laputians described. An account of their learning. Of the king and his court. The author's reception there. The inhabitants subject to fear and disquietudes. An account of the women.]

At my alighting, I was surrounded with a crowd of people, but those who stood nearest seemed to be of better quality. They beheld me with all the marks and circumstances of wonder; neither indeed was I much in their debt, having never till then seen a race of mortals so singular in their shapes, habits, and countenances. Their heads were all reclined, either to the right, or the left; one of their eyes turned inward, and the other directly up to the zenith. Their outward garments were adorned with the figures of suns, moons, and stars; interwoven with those of fiddles, flutes, harps, trumpets, guitars, harpsichords, and many other instruments of music, unknown to us in Europe. I observed, here and there, many in the habit of servants, with a blown bladder, fastened like a flail to the end of a stick, which they carried in their hands. In each bladder was a small quantity of dried peas, or little pebbles, as I was afterwards informed. With these bladders, they now and then flapped the mouths and ears of those who stood near them, of which practice I could not then conceive the meaning. It seems the minds of these people are so taken up with intense speculations, that they neither can speak, nor attend to the discourses of others, without being roused by some external taction upon the organs of speech and hearing; for which reason, those persons who are able to afford it always keep a flapper (the original is climenole) in their family, as one of their domestics; nor ever walk abroad, or make visits, without him. And the business of this officer is, when two, three, or more persons are in company, gently to strike with his bladder the mouth of him who is to speak, and the right ear of him or them to whom the speaker addresses himself. This flapper is likewise employed diligently to attend his master in his walks, and upon occasion to give him a soft flap on his eyes; because he is always so wrapped up in cogitation, that he is in manifest danger of falling down every precipice, and bouncing his head against every post; and in the streets, of justling others, or being justled himself into the kennel.

It was necessary to give the reader this information, without which he would be at the same loss with me to understand the proceedings of these people, as they conducted me up the stairs to the top of the island, and from thence to the royal palace. While we were ascending, they forgot several times what they were about, and left me to myself, till their memories were again roused by their flappers; for they appeared altogether unmoved by the sight of my foreign habit and countenance, and by the shouts of the vulgar, whose thoughts and minds were more disengaged.

At last we entered the palace, and proceeded into the chamber of presence, where I saw the king seated on his throne, attended on each side by persons of prime quality. Before the throne, was a large table filled with globes and spheres, and mathematical instruments of all kinds. His majesty took not the least notice of us, although our entrance was not without sufficient noise, by the concourse of all persons belonging to the court. But he was then deep in a problem; and we attended at least an hour, before he could solve it. There stood by him, on each side, a young page with flaps in their hands, and when they saw he was at leisure, one of them gently struck his mouth, and the other his right ear; at which he startled like one awaked on the sudden, and looking towards me and the company I was in, recollected the occasion of our coming, whereof he had been informed before. He spoke some words, whereupon immediately a young man with a flap came up to my side, and flapped me gently on the right ear; but I made signs, as well as I could, that I had no occasion for such an instrument; which, as I afterwards found, gave his majesty, and the whole court, a very mean opinion of my understanding. The king, as far as I could conjecture, asked me several questions, and I addressed myself to him in all the languages I had. When it was found I could neither understand nor be understood, I was conducted by his order to an apartment in his palace (this prince being distinguished above all his predecessors for his hospitality to strangers), where two servants were appointed to attend me. My dinner was brought, and four persons of quality, whom I remembered to have seen very near the king's person, did me the honour to dine with me. We had two courses, of three dishes each. In the first course, there was a shoulder of mutton cut into an equilateral triangle, a piece of beef into a rhomboides, and a pudding into a cycloid. The second course was two ducks trussed up in the form of fiddles; sausages and puddings resembling flutes and hautboys, and a breast of veal in the shape of a harp. The servants cut our bread into cones, cylinders, parallelograms, and several other mathematical figures.

While we were at dinner, I made bold to ask the names of several things in their language, and those noble persons, by the assistance of their flappers, delighted to give me answers, hoping to raise my admiration of their great abilities if I could be brought o converse with them. I was soon able to call for bread and drink, or whatever else I wanted.

After dinner my company withdrew, and a person was sent to me by the king's order, attended by a flapper. He brought with him pen, ink, and paper, and three or four books, giving me to understand by signs, that he was sent to teach me the language. We sat together four hours, in which time I wrote down a great number of words in columns, with the translations over against them; I likewise made a shift to learn several short sentences; for my tutor would order one of my servants to fetch something, to turn about, to make a bow, to sit, or to stand, or walk, and the like. Then I took down the sentence in writing. He showed me also, in one of his books, the figures of the sun, moon, and stars, the zodiac, the tropics, and polar circles, together with the denominations of many plains and solids. He gave me the names and descriptions of all the musical instruments, and the general terms of art in playing on each of them. After he had left me, I placed all my words, with their interpretations, in alphabetical order. And thus, in a few days, by the help of a very faithful memory, I got some insight into their language. The word, which I interpret the flying or floating island, is in the original Laputa, whereof I could never learn the true etymology. Lap, in the old obsolete language, signifies high; and untuh, a governor; from which they say, by corruption, was derived Laputa, from Lapuntuh. But I do not approve of this derivation, which seems to be a little strained. I ventured to offer to the learned among them a conjecture of my own, that Laputa was quasi lap outed; lap, signifying properly, the dancing of the sunbeams in the sea, and outed, a wing; which, however, I shall not obtrude, but submit to the judicious reader.

Those to whom the king had entrusted me, observing how ill I was clad, ordered a tailor to come next morning, and take measure for a suit of clothes. This operator did his office after a different manner from those of his trade in Europe. He first took my altitude by a quadrant, and then, with a rule and compasses, described the dimensions and outlines of my whole body, all which he entered upon paper; and in six days brought my clothes very ill made, and quite out of shape, by happening to mistake a figure in the calculation. But my comfort was, that I observed such accidents very frequent, and little regarded.

During my confinement for want of clothes, and by an indisposition that held me some days longer, I much enlarged my dictionary; and when I went next to court, was able to understand many things the king spoke, and to return him some kind of answers. His majesty had given orders, that the island should move north-east and by east, to the vertical point over Lagado, the metropolis of the whole kingdom below, upon the firm earth. It was about ninety leagues distant, and our voyage lasted four days and a half. I was not in the least sensible of the progressive motion made in the air by the island. On the second morning, about eleven o'clock, the king himself in person, attended by his nobility, courtiers, and officers, having prepared all their musical instruments, played on them for three hours without intermission, so that I was quite stunned with the noise; neither could I possibly guess the meaning, till my tutor informed me. He said that, the people of their island had their ears adapted to hear "the music of the spheres, which always played at certain periods, and the court was now prepared to bear their part, in whatever instrument they most excelled."

In our journey towards Lagado, the capital city, his majesty ordered that the island should stop over certain towns and villages, from whence he might receive the petitions of his subjects. And to this purpose, several packthreads were let down, with small weights at the bottom. On these packthreads the people strung their petitions, which mounted up directly, like the scraps of paper fastened by school boys at the end of the string that holds their kite. Sometimes we received wine and victuals from below, which were drawn up by pulleys.

The knowledge I had in mathematics, gave me great assistance in acquiring their phraseology, which depended much upon that science, and music; and in the latter I was not unskilled. Their ideas are perpetually conversant in lines and figures. If they would, for example, praise the beauty of a woman, or any other animal, they describe it by rhombs, circles, parallelograms, ellipses, and other geometrical terms, or by words of art drawn from music, needless here to repeat. I observed in the king's kitchen all sorts of mathematical and musical instruments, after the figures of which they cut up the joints that were served to his majesty's table.

Their houses are very ill built, the walls bevil, without one right angle in any apartment; and this defect arises from the contempt they bear to practical geometry, which they despise as vulgar and mechanic; those instructions they give being too refined for the intellects of their workmen, which occasions perpetual mistakes. And although they are dexterous enough upon a piece of paper, in the management of the rule, the pencil, and the divider, yet in the common actions and behaviour of life, I have not seen a more clumsy, awkward, and unhandy people, nor so slow and perplexed in their conceptions upon all other subjects, except those of mathematics and music. They are very bad reasoners, and vehemently given to opposition, unless when they happen to be of the right opinion, which is seldom their case. Imagination, fancy, and invention, they are wholly strangers to, nor have any words in their language, by which those ideas can be expressed; the whole compass of their thoughts and mind being shut up within the two forementioned sciences.

Most of them, and especially those who deal in the astronomical part, have great faith in judicial astrology, although they are ashamed to own it publicly. But what I chiefly admired, and thought altogether unaccountable, was the strong disposition I observed in them towards news and politics, perpetually inquiring into public affairs, giving their judgments in matters of state, and passionately disputing every inch of a party opinion. I have indeed observed the same disposition among most of the mathematicians I have known in Europe, although I could never discover the least analogy between the two sciences; unless those people suppose, that because the smallest circle has as many degrees as the largest, therefore the regulation and management of the world require no more abilities than the handling and turning of a globe; but I rather take this quality to spring from a very common infirmity of human nature, inclining us to be most curious and conceited in matters where we have least concern, and for which we are least adapted by study or nature.

These people are under continual disquietudes, never enjoying a minutes peace of mind; and their disturbances proceed from causes which very little affect the rest of mortals. Their apprehensions arise from several changes they dread in the celestial bodies: for instance, that the earth, by the continual approaches of the sun towards it, must, in course of time, be absorbed, or swallowed up; that the face of the sun, will, by degrees, be encrusted with its own effluvia, and give no more light to the world; that the earth very narrowly escaped a brush from the tail of the last comet, which would have infallibly reduced it to ashes; and that the next, which they have calculated for one-and-thirty years hence, will probably destroy us. For if, in its perihelion, it should approach within a certain degree of the sun (as by their calculations they have reason to dread) it will receive a degree of heat ten thousand times more intense than that of red hot glowing iron, and in its absence from the sun, carry a blazing tail ten hundred thousand and fourteen miles long, through which, if the earth should pass at the distance of one hundred thousand miles from the nucleus, or main body of the comet, it must in its passage be set on fire, and reduced to ashes: that the sun, daily spending its rays without any nutriment to supply them, will at last be wholly consumed and annihilated; which must be attended with the destruction of this earth, and of all the planets that receive their light from it.

They are so perpetually alarmed with the apprehensions of these, and the like impending dangers, that they can neither sleep quietly in their beds, nor have any relish for the common pleasures and amusements of life. When they meet an acquaintance in the morning, the first question is about the sun's health, how he looked at his setting and rising, and what hopes they have to avoid the stroke of the approaching comet. This conversation they are apt to run into with the same temper that boys discover in delighting to hear terrible stories of spirits and hobgoblins, which they greedily listen to, and dare not go to bed for fear.

The women of the island have abundance of vivacity: they, contemn their husbands, and are exceedingly fond of strangers, whereof there is always a considerable number from the continent below, attending at court, either upon affairs of the several towns and corporations, or their own particular occasions, but are much despised, because they want the same endowments. Among these the ladies choose their gallants: but the vexation is, that they act with too much ease and security; for the husband is always so rapt in speculation, that the mistress and lover may proceed to the greatest familiarities before his face, if he be but provided with paper and implements, and without his flapper at his side.

The wives and daughters lament their confinement to the island, although I think it the most delicious spot of ground in the world; and although they live here in the greatest plenty and magnificence, and are allowed to do whatever they please, they long to see the world, and take the diversions of the metropolis, which they are not allowed to do without a particular license from the king; and this is not easy to be obtained, because the people of quality have found, by frequent experience, how hard it is to persuade their women to return from below. I was told that a great court lady, who had several children,—is married to the prime minister, the richest subject in the kingdom, a very graceful person, extremely fond of her, and lives in the finest palace of the island,—went down to Lagado on the pretence of health, there hid herself for several months, till the king sent a warrant to search for her; and she was found in an obscure eating-house all in rags, having pawned her clothes to maintain an old deformed footman, who beat her every day, and in whose company she was taken, much against her will. And although her husband received her with all possible kindness, and without the least reproach, she soon after contrived to steal down again, with all her jewels, to the same gallant, and has not been heard of since.

This may perhaps pass with the reader rather for an European or English story, than for one of a country so remote. But he may please to consider, that the caprices of womankind are not limited by any climate or nation, and that they are much more uniform, than can be easily imagined.

In about a month's time, I had made a tolerable proficiency in their language, and was able to answer most of the king's questions, when I had the honour to attend him. His majesty discovered not the least curiosity to inquire into the laws, government, history, religion, or manners of the countries where I had been; but confined his questions to the state of mathematics, and received the account I gave him with great contempt and indifference, though often roused by his flapper on each side.

CHAPTER III.

[A phenomenon solved by modern philosophy and astronomy. The Laputians' great improvements in the latter. The king's method of suppressing insurrections.]

I desired leave of this prince to see the curiosities of the island, which he was graciously pleased to grant, and ordered my tutor to attend me. I chiefly wanted to know, to what cause, in art or in nature, it owed its several motions, whereof I will now give a philosophical account to the reader.

The flying or floating island is exactly circular, its diameter 7837 yards, or about four miles and a half, and consequently contains ten thousand acres. It is three hundred yards thick. The bottom, or under surface, which appears to those who view it below, is one even regular plate of adamant, shooting up to the height of about two hundred yards. Above it lie the several minerals in their usual order, and over all is a coat of rich mould, ten or twelve feet deep. The declivity of the upper surface, from the circumference to the centre, is the natural cause why all the dews and rains, which fall upon the island, are conveyed in small rivulets toward the middle, where they are emptied into four large basins, each of about half a mile in circuit, and two hundred yards distant from the centre. From these basins the water is continually exhaled by the sun in the daytime, which effectually prevents their overflowing. Besides, as it is in the power of the monarch to raise the island above the region of clouds and vapours, he can prevent the falling of dews and rain whenever he pleases. For the highest clouds cannot rise above two miles, as naturalists agree, at least they were never known to do so in that country.

At the centre of the island there is a chasm about fifty yards in diameter, whence the astronomers descend into a large dome, which is therefore called flandona gagnole, or the astronomer's cave, situated at the depth of a hundred yards beneath the upper surface of the adamant. In this cave are twenty lamps continually burning, which, from the reflection of the adamant, cast a strong light into every part. The place is stored with great variety of sextants, quadrants, telescopes, astrolabes, and other astronomical instruments. But the greatest curiosity, upon which the fate of the island depends, is a loadstone of a prodigious size, in shape resembling a weaver's shuttle. It is in length six yards, and in the thickest part at least three yards over. This magnet is sustained by a very strong axle of adamant passing through its middle, upon which it plays, and is poised so exactly that the weakest hand can turn it. It is hooped round with a hollow cylinder of adamant, four feet yards in diameter, placed horizontally, and supported by eight adamantine feet, each six yards high. In the middle of the concave side, there is a groove twelve inches deep, in which the extremities of the axle are lodged, and turned round as there is occasion.

The stone cannot be removed from its place by any force, because the hoop and its feet are one continued piece with that body of adamant which constitutes the bottom of the island.

By means of this loadstone, the island is made to rise and fall, and move from one place to another. For, with respect to that part of the earth over which the monarch presides, the stone is endued at one of its sides with an attractive power, and at the other with a repulsive. Upon placing the magnet erect, with its attracting end towards the earth, the island descends; but when the repelling extremity points downwards, the island mounts directly upwards. When the position of the stone is oblique, the motion of the island is so too: for in this magnet, the forces always act in lines parallel to its direction.

By this oblique motion, the island is conveyed to different parts of the monarch's dominions. To explain the manner of its progress, let A B represent a line drawn across the dominions of Balnibarbi, let the line c d represent the loadstone, of which let d be ᴜᴇ repelling end, and c the attracting end, the island being over C: let the stone be placed in position c d, with its repelling end downwards; then the island will be driven upwards obliquely towards D. When it is arrived at D, let the stone be turned upon its axle, till its attracting end points towards E, and then the island will be carried obliquely towards E; where, if the stone be again turned upon its axle till it stands in the position E F, with its repelling point downwards, the island will rise obliquely towards F, where, by directing the attracting end towards G, the island may be carried to G, and from G to H, by turning the stone, so as to make its repelling extremity to point directly downward. And thus, by changing the situation of the stone, as often as there is occasion, the island is made to rise and fall by turns in an oblique direction, and by those alternate risings and fallings (the obliquity being not considerable) is conveyed from one part of the dominions to the other.

But it must be observed, that this island cannot move beyond the extent of the dominions below, nor can it rise above the height of four miles. For which the astronomers (who have written large systems concerning the stone) assign the following reason: that the magnetic virtue does not extend beyond the distance of four miles, and that the mineral, which acts upon the stone in the bowels of the earth, and in the sea about six leagues distant from the shore, is not diffused through the whole globe, but terminated with the limits of the king's dominions; and it was easy, from the great advantage of such a superior situation, for a prince to bring under his obedience whatever country lay within the attraction of that magnet.

When the stone is put parallel to the plane of the horizon, the island stands still; for in that case the extremities of it, being at equal distance from the earth, act with equal force, the one in drawing downwards, the other in pushing upwards, and consequently no motion can ensue.

This loadstone is under the care of certain astronomers, who, from time to time, give it such positions as the monarch directs. They spend the greatest part of their lives in observing the celestial bodies, which they do by the assistance of glasses, far excelling ours in goodness. For, although their largest telescopes do not exceed three feet, they magnify much more than those of a hundred with us, and show the stars with greater clearness. This advantage has enabled them to extend their discoveries much further than our astronomers in Europe; for they have made a catalogue of ten thousand fixed stars, whereas the largest of ours do not contain above one third part of that number. They have likewise discovered two lesser stars, or satellites, which revolve about Mars; whereof the innermost is distant from the centre of the primary planet exactly three of his diameters, and the outermost, five; the former revolves in the space of ten hours, and the latter in twenty-one and a half; so that the squares of their periodical times are very near in the same proportion with the cubes of their distance from the centre of Mars; which evidently shows them to be governed by the same law of gravitation that influences the other heavenly bodies.

They have observed ninety-three different comets, and settled their periods with great exactness. If this be true (and they affirm it with great confidence) it is much to be wished, that their observations were made public, whereby the theory of comets, which at present is very lame and defective, might be brought to the same perfection with other arts of astronomy.

The king would be the most absolute prince in the universe, if he could but prevail on a ministry to join with him; but these having their estates below on the continent, and considering that the office of a favourite has a very uncertain tenure, would never consent to the enslaving of their country.

If any town should engage in rebellion or mutiny, fall into violent factions, or refuse to pay the usual tribute, the king has two methods of reducing them to obedience. The first and the mildest course is, by keeping the island hovering over such a town, and the lands about it, whereby he can deprive them of the benefit of the sun and the rain, and consequently afflict the inhabitants with dearth and diseases: and if the crime deserve it, they are at the same time pelted from above with great stones, against which they have no defence but by creeping into cellars or caves, while the roofs of their houses are beaten to pieces. But if they still continue obstinate, or offer to raise insurrections, he proceeds to the last remedy, by letting the island drop directly upon their heads, which makes a universal destruction both of houses and men. However, this is an extremity to which the prince is seldom driven, neither indeed is he willing to put it in execution; nor dare his ministers advise him to an action, which, as it would render them odious to the people, so it would be a great damage to their own estates, which all lie below; for the island is the king's demesne.

But there is still indeed a more weighty reason, why the kings of this country have been always averse from executing so terrible an action, unless upon the utmost necessity. For, if the town intended to be destroyed should have in it any tall rocks, as it generally falls out in the larger cities, a situation probably chosen at first with a view to prevent such a catastrophe; or if it abound in high spires, or pillars of stone, a sudden fall might endanger the bottom or under surface of the island, which, although it consist, as I have said, of one entire adamant, two hundred yards thick, might happen to crack by too great a shock, or burst by approaching too near the fires from the houses below, as the backs, both of iron and stone, will often do in our chimneys. Of all this the people are well apprised, and understand how far to carry their obstinacy, where their liberty or property is concerned. And the king, when he is highest provoked, and most determined to press a city to rubbish, orders the island to descend with great gentleness, out of a pretence of tenderness to his people, but, indeed, for fear of breaking the adamantine bottom; in which case, it is the opinion of all their philosophers, that the loadstone could no longer hold it up, and the whole mass would fall to the ground.

By a fundamental law of this realm, neither the king, nor either of his two eldest sons, are permitted to leave the island; nor the queen, till she is past child-bearing.

CHAPTER IV.

[The author leaves Laputa; is conveyed to Balnibarbi; arrives at the metropolis. A description of the metropolis, and the country adjoining. The author hospitably received by a great lord. His conversation with that lord.]

Although I cannot say that I was ill treated in this island, yet I must confess I thought myself too much neglected, not without some degree of contempt; for neither prince nor people appeared to be curious in any part of knowledge, except mathematics and music, wherein I was far their inferior, and upon that account very little regarded.

On the other side, after having seen all the curiosities of the island, I was very desirous to leave it, being heartily weary of those people. They were indeed excellent in two sciences for which I have great esteem, and wherein I am not unversed; but, at the same time, so abstracted and involved in speculation, that I never met with such disagreeable companions. I conversed only with women, tradesmen, flappers, and court-pages, during two months of my abode there; by which, at last, I rendered myself extremely contemptible; yet these were the only people from whom I could ever receive a reasonable answer.

I had obtained, by hard study, a good degree of knowledge in their language: I was weary of being confined to an island where I received so little countenance, and resolved to leave it with the first opportunity.

There was a great lord at court, nearly related to the king, and for that reason alone used with respect. He was universally reckoned the most ignorant and stupid person among them. He had performed many eminent services for the crown, had great natural and acquired parts, adorned with integrity and honour; but so ill an ear for music, that his detractors reported, "he had been often known to beat time in the wrong place;" neither could his tutors, without extreme difficulty, teach him to demonstrate the most easy proposition in the mathematics. He was pleased to show me many marks of favour, often did me the honour of a visit, desired to be informed in the affairs of Europe, the laws and customs, the manners and learning of the several countries where I had travelled. He listened to me with great attention, and made very wise observations on all I spoke. He had two flappers attending him for state, but never made use of them, except at court and in visits of ceremony, and would always command them to withdraw, when we were alone together.

I entreated this illustrious person, to intercede in my behalf with his majesty, for leave to depart; which he accordingly did, as he was pleased to tell me, with regret: for indeed he had made me several offers very advantageous, which, however, I refused, with expressions of the highest acknowledgment.

On the 16th of February I took leave of his majesty and the court. The king made me a present to the value of about two hundred pounds English, and my protector, his kinsman, as much more, together with a letter of recommendation to a friend of his in Lagado, the metropolis. The island being then hovering over

116

a mountain about two miles from it, I was let down from the lowest gallery, in the same manner as I had been taken up.

The continent, as far as it is subject to the monarch of the flying island, passes under the general name of Balnibarbi; and the metropolis, as I said before, is called Lagado. I felt some little satisfaction in finding myself on firm ground. I walked to the city without any concern, being clad like one of the natives, and sufficiently instructed to converse with them. I soon found out the person's house to whom I was recommended, presented my letter from his friend the grandee in the island, and was received with much kindness. This great lord, whose name was Munodi, ordered me an apartment in his own house, where I continued during my stay, and was entertained in a most hospitable manner.

The next morning after my arrival, he took me in his chariot to see the town, which is about half the bigness of London; but the houses very strangely built, and most of them out of repair. The people in the streets walked fast, looked wild, their eyes fixed, and were generally in rags. We passed through one of the town gates, and went about three miles into the country, where I saw many labourers working with several sorts of tools in the ground, but was not able to conjecture what they were about: neither did observe any expectation either of corn or grass, although the soil appeared to be excellent. I could not forbear admiring at these odd appearances, both in town and country; and I made bold to desire my conductor, that he would be pleased to explain to me, what could be meant by so many busy heads, hands, and faces, both in the streets and the fields, because I did not discover any good effects they produced; but, on the contrary, I never knew a soil so unhappily cultivated, houses so ill contrived and so ruinous, or a people whose countenances and habit expressed so much misery and want.

This lord Munodi was a person of the first rank, and had been some years governor of Lagado; but, by a cabal of ministers, was discharged for insufficiency. However, the king treated him with tenderness, as a well-meaning man, but of a low contemptible understanding.

When I gave that free censure of the country and its inhabitants, he made no further answer than by telling me, "that I had not been long enough among them to form a judgment; and that the different nations of the world had different customs;" with other common topics to the same purpose. But, when we returned to his palace, he asked me "how I liked the building, what absurdities I observed, and what quarrel I had with the dress or looks of his domestics?" This he might safely do; because every thing about him was magnificent, regular, and polite. I answered, "that his excellency's prudence, quality, and fortune, had exempted him from those defects, which folly and beggary had produced in others." He said, "if I would go with him to his country-house, about twenty miles distant, where his estate lay, there would be more leisure for this kind of conversation." I told his excellency "that I was entirely at his disposal;" and accordingly we set out next morning.

During our journey he made me observe the several methods used by farmers in managing their lands, which to me were wholly unaccountable; for, except in some very few places, I could not discover one ear of corn or blade of grass. But, in three hours travelling, the scene was wholly altered; we came into a most beautiful country; farmers' houses, at small distances, neatly built; the fields enclosed, containing vineyards, corn-grounds, and meadows. Neither do I remember to have seen a more delightful prospect. His excellency observed my countenance to clear up; he told me, with a sigh, "that there his estate began, and would continue the same, till we should come to his house: that his countrymen ridiculed and despised him, for managing his affairs no better, and for setting so ill an example to the kingdom; which, however, was followed by very few, such as were old, and wilful, and weak like himself."

We came at length to the house, which was indeed a noble structure, built according to the best rules of ancient architecture. The fountains, gardens, walks, avenues, and groves, were all disposed with exact judgment and taste. I gave due praises to every thing I saw, whereof his excellency took not the least notice till after supper; when, there being no third companion, he told me with a very melancholy air "that he doubted he must throw down his houses in town and country, to rebuild them after the present mode; destroy all his plantations, and cast others into such a form as modern usage required, and give the same directions to all his tenants, unless he would submit to incur the censure of pride, singularity, affectation, ignorance, caprice, and perhaps increase his majesty's displeasure; that the admiration I appeared to be under would cease or diminish, when he had informed me of some particulars which, probably, I never heard of at court, the people there being too much taken up in their own speculations, to have regard to what passed here below."

The sum of his discourse was to this effect: "That about forty years ago, certain persons went up to Laputa, either upon business or diversion, and, after five months continuance, came back with a very little smattering in mathematics, but full of volatile spirits acquired in that airy region: that these persons, upon their return, began to dislike the management of every thing below, and fell into schemes of putting all arts, sciences, languages, and mechanics, upon a new foot. To this end, they procured a royal patent for erecting an academy of projectors in Lagado; and the humour prevailed so strongly among the people, that there is not a town of any consequence in the kingdom without such an academy. In these colleges the professors contrive new rules and methods of agriculture and building, and new instruments, and tools for all trades and manufactures; whereby, as they undertake, one man shall do the work of ten; a palace may be built in a week, of materials so durable as to last for ever without repairing. All the fruits of the earth shall come to maturity at whatever season we think fit to choose, and increase a hundred fold more than they do at present; with innumerable other happy proposals. The only inconvenience is, that none of these projects are yet brought to perfection; and in the mean time, the whole country lies miserably waste, the houses in ruins, and the people without food or clothes. By all which, instead of being discouraged, they are fifty times more violently bent upon prosecuting their schemes, driven equally on by hope and despair: that as for himself, being not of an enterprising spirit, he was content to go on in the old forms, to live in the houses his ancestors had built, and act as they did, in every part of life, without innovation: that some few other persons of quality and gentry had done the same, but were looked on with an eye of contempt and ill-will, as enemies to art, ignorant, and ill common-wealth's men, preferring their own ease and sloth before the general improvement of their country."

His lordship added, "That he would not, by any further particulars, prevent the pleasure I should certainly take in viewing the grand academy, whither he was resolved I should go." He only desired me to observe a ruined building, upon the side of a mountain about three miles distant, of which he gave me this account: "That he had a very convenient mill within half a mile of his house, turned by a current from a large river, and sufficient for his own family, as well as a great number of his tenants; that about seven years ago, a club of those projectors came to him with proposals to destroy this mill, and build another on the side of that mountain, on the long ridge whereof a long canal must be cut, for a repository of water, to be conveyed up by pipes and engines to supply the mill, because the wind and air upon a height agitated the water, and thereby made it fitter for motion, and because the water, descending down a declivity, would turn the mill with half the current of a river whose course is more upon a level." He said, "that being then not very well with the court, and pressed by many of his friends, he complied with the proposal; and after employing a hundred men for two years, the work miscarried, the projectors went off, laying the blame entirely upon him, railing at him ever since, and putting others upon the same experiment, with equal assurance of success, as well as equal disappointment."

In a few days we came back to town; and his excellency, considering the bad character he had in the academy, would not go with me himself, but recommended me to a friend of his, to bear me company thither. My lord was pleased to represent me as a great admirer of projects, and a person of much curiosity and easy belief; which, indeed, was not without truth; for I had myself been a sort of projector in my younger days.

CHAPTER V.

[The author permitted to see the grand academy of Lagado. The academy largely described. The arts wherein the professors employ themselves.]

This academy is not an entire single building, but a continuation of several houses on both sides of a street, which growing waste, was purchased and applied to that use.

I was received very kindly by the warden, and went for many days to the academy. Every room has in it one or more projectors; and I believe I could not be in fewer than five hundred rooms.

The first man I saw was of a meagre aspect, with sooty hands and face, his hair and beard long, ragged, and singed in several places. His clothes, shirt, and skin, were all of the same colour. He has been eight years upon a project for extracting sunbeams out of cucumbers, which were to be put in phials hermetically sealed, and let out to warm the air in raw inclement summers. He told me, he did not doubt, that, in eight years more, he should be able to supply the governor's gardens with sunshine, at a reasonable rate: but he complained that his stock was low, and entreated me "to give him something as an encouragement to ingenuity, especially since this had been a very dear season for cucumbers." I made him a small present, for my lord had furnished me with money on purpose, because he knew their practice of begging from all who go to see them.

I went into another chamber, but was ready to hasten back, being almost overcome with a horrible stink. My conductor pressed me forward, conjuring me in a whisper "to give no offence, which would be highly resented;" and therefore I durst not so much as stop my nose. The projector of this cell was the most ancient student of the academy; his face and beard were of a pale yellow; his hands and clothes daubed over with filth. When I was presented to him, he gave me a close embrace, a compliment I could well have excused. His employment, from his first coming into the academy, was an operation to reduce human excrement to its original food, by separating the several parts, removing the tincture which it receives from the gall, making the odour exhale, and scumming off the saliva. He had a weekly allowance, from the society, of a vessel filled with human ordure, about the bigness of a Bristol barrel.

I saw another at work to calcine ice into gunpowder; who likewise showed me a treatise he had written concerning the malleability of fire, which he intended to publish.

There was a most ingenious architect, who had contrived a new method for building houses, by beginning at the roof, and working downward to the foundation; which he justified to me, by the like practice of those two prudent insects, the bee and the spider.

There was a man born blind, who had several apprentices in his own condition: their employment was to mix colours for painters, which their master taught them to distinguish by feeling and smelling. It was indeed my misfortune to find them at that time not very perfect in their lessons, and the professor himself happened to be generally mistaken. This artist is much encouraged and esteemed by the whole fraternity.

In another apartment I was highly pleased with a projector who had found a device of ploughing the ground with hogs, to save the charges of ploughs, cattle, and labour. The method is this: in an acre of ground you bury, at six inches distance and eight deep, a quantity of acorns, dates, chestnuts, and other mast or vegetables, whereof these animals are fondest; then you drive six hundred or more of them into the field, where, in a few days, they will root up the whole ground in search of their food, and make it fit for sowing, at the same time manuring it with their dung: it is true, upon experiment, they found the charge and trouble very great, and they had little or no crop. However it is not doubted, that this invention may be capable of great improvement.

I went into another room, where the walls and ceiling were all hung round with cobwebs, except a narrow passage for the artist to go in and out. At my entrance, he called aloud to me, "not to disturb his webs." He lamented "the fatal mistake the world had been so long in, of using silkworms, while we had such plenty of domestic insects who infinitely excelled the former, because they understood how to weave, as well as spin." And he proposed further, "that by employing spiders, the charge of dyeing silks should be wholly saved;" whereof I was fully convinced, when he showed me a vast number of flies most beautifully coloured, wherewith he fed his spiders, assuring us "that the webs would take a tincture from them; and as he had them of all hues, he hoped to fit everybody's fancy, as soon as he could find proper food for the flies, of certain gums, oils, and other glutinous matter, to give a strength and consistence to the threads."

There was an astronomer, who had undertaken to place a sun-dial upon the great weathercock on the town-house, by adjusting the annual and diurnal motions of the earth and sun, so as to answer and coincide with all accidental turnings of the wind.

I was complaining of a small fit of the colic, upon which my conductor led me into a room where a great physician resided, who was famous for curing that disease, by contrary operations from the same instrument. He had a large pair of bellows, with a long slender muzzle of ivory: this he conveyed eight inches up the anus, and drawing in the wind, he affirmed he could make the guts as lank as a dried bladder. But when the disease was more stubborn and violent, he let in the muzzle while the bellows were full of wind, which he discharged into the body of the patient; then withdrew the instrument to replenish it, clapping his thumb strongly against the orifice of then fundament; and this being repeated three or four times, the adventitious wind would rush out, bringing the noxious along with it, (like water put into a pump), and the patient recovered. I saw him try both experiments upon a dog, but could not discern any effect from the former. After the latter the animal was ready to burst, and made so violent a discharge as was very offensive to me and my companion. The dog died on the spot, and we left the doctor endeavouring to recover him, by the same operation.

I visited many other apartments, but shall not trouble my reader with all the curiosities I observed, being studious of brevity.

I had hitherto seen only one side of the academy, the other being appropriated to the advancers of speculative learning, of whom I shall say something, when I have mentioned one illustrious person more, who is called among them "the universal artist." He told us "he had been thirty years employing his thoughts for the improvement of human life." He had two large rooms full of wonderful curiosities, and fifty men at work. Some were condensing air into a dry tangible substance, by extracting the nitre, and letting the aqueous or fluid particles percolate; others softening marble, for pillows and pin-cushions; others petrifying the hoofs of a living horse, to preserve them from foundering. The artist himself was at that time busy upon two great designs; the first, to sow land with chaff, wherein he affirmed the true seminal virtue to be contained, as he demonstrated by several experiments, which I was not skilful enough to comprehend. The other was, by a certain composition of gums, minerals, and vegetables, outwardly applied, to prevent the growth of wool upon two young lambs; and he hoped, in a reasonable time to propagate the breed of naked sheep, all over the kingdom.

We crossed a walk to the other part of the academy, where, as I have already said, the projectors in speculative learning resided.

The first professor I saw, was in a very large room, with forty pupils about him. After salutation, observing me to look earnestly upon a frame, which took up the greatest part of both the length and breadth of the room, he said, "Perhaps I might wonder to see him employed in a project for improving speculative knowledge, by practical and mechanical operations. But the world would soon be sensible of its usefulness; and he flattered himself, that a more noble, exalted thought never sprang in any other man's head. Every one knew how laborious the usual method is of attaining to arts and sciences; whereas, by his contrivance, the most ignorant person, at a reasonable charge, and with a little bodily labour, might write books in philosophy, poetry, politics, laws, mathematics, and theology, without the least assistance from genius or study." He then led me to the frame, about the sides, whereof all his pupils stood in ranks. It was twenty feet square, placed in the middle of the room. The superfices was composed of several bits of wood, about the bigness of a die, but some larger than others. They were all linked together by slender wires. These bits of wood were covered, on every square, with paper pasted on them; and on these papers were written all the words of their language, in their several moods, tenses, and declensions; but without any order. The professor then desired me "to observe; for he was going to set his engine at work." The pupils, at his command, took each of them hold of an iron handle, whereof there were forty fixed round the edges of the frame; and giving them a sudden turn, the whole disposition of the words was entirely changed. He then commanded six-and-thirty of the lads, to read the several lines softly, as they appeared upon the frame; and where they found three or four words together that might make part of a sentence, they dictated to the four remaining boys, who were scribes. This work was repeated three or four times, and at every turn, the engine was so contrived, that the words shifted into new places, as the square bits of wood moved upside down.

Six hours a day the young students were employed in this labour; and the professor showed me several volumes in large folio, already collected, of broken sentences, which he intended to piece together, and out of those rich materials, to give the world a complete body of all arts and sciences; which, however, might be still improved, and much expedited, if the public would raise a fund for making and employing five hundred such frames in Lagado, and oblige the managers to contribute in common their several collections.

He assured me "that this invention had employed all his thoughts from his youth; that he had emptied the whole vocabulary into his frame, and made the strictest computation of the general proportion there is in books between the numbers of particles, nouns, and verbs, and other parts of speech."

I made my humblest acknowledgment to this illustrious person, for his great communicativeness; and promised, "if ever I had the good fortune to return to my native country, that I would do him justice, as the sole inventor of this wonderful machine;" the form and contrivance of which I desired leave to delineate on paper, as in the figure here annexed. I told him, "although it were the custom of our learned in Europe to steal inventions from each other, who had thereby at least this advantage, that it became a controversy which was the right owner; yet I would take such caution, that he should have the honour entire, without a rival."

We next went to the school of languages, where three professors sat in consultation upon improving that of their own country.

The first project was, to shorten discourse, by cutting polysyllables into one, and leaving out verbs and participles, because, in reality, all things imaginable are but norms.

The other project was, a scheme for entirely abolishing all words whatsoever; and this was urged as a great advantage in point of health, as well as brevity. For it is plain, that every word we speak is, in some degree, a diminution of our lunge by corrosion, and, consequently, contributes to the shortening of our lives. An expedient was therefore offered, "that since words are only names for things, it would be more convenient for all men to carry about them such things as were necessary to express a particular business they are to discourse on." And this invention would certainly have taken place, to the great ease as well as health of the subject, if the women, in conjunction with the vulgar and illiterate, had not threatened to raise a rebellion unless they might be allowed the liberty to speak with their tongues, after the manner of their forefathers; such constant irreconcilable enemies to science are the common people. However, many of the most learned and wise adhere to the new scheme of expressing themselves by things; which has only this inconvenience attending it, that if a man's business be very great, and of various kinds, he must be obliged, in proportion, to carry a greater bundle of things upon his back, unless he can afford one or two strong servants to attend him. I have often beheld two of those sages almost sinking under the weight of their packs, like pedlars among us, who, when they met in the street, would lay down their loads, open their sacks, and hold conversation for an hour together; then put up their implements, help each other to resume their burdens, and take their leave.

But for short conversations, a man may carry implements in his pockets, and under his arms, enough to supply him; and in his house, he cannot be at a loss. Therefore the room where company meet who practise this art, is full of all things, ready at hand, requisite to furnish matter for this kind of artificial converse.

Another great advantage proposed by this invention was, that it would serve as a universal language, to be understood in all civilised nations, whose goods and utensils are generally of the same kind, or nearly resembling, so that their uses might easily be comprehended. And thus ambassadors would be qualified to treat with foreign princes, or ministers of state, to whose tongues they were utter strangers.

I was at the mathematical school, where the master taught his pupils after a method scarce imaginable to us in Europe. The proposition, and demonstration, were fairly written on a thin wafer, with ink composed of a cephalic tincture. This, the student was to swallow upon a fasting stomach, and for three days following, eat nothing but bread and water. As the wafer digested, the tincture mounted to his brain, bearing the proposition along with it. But the success has not hitherto been answerable, partly by some error in the quantum or composition, and partly by the perverseness of lads, to whom this bolus is so nauseous, that they generally steal aside, and discharge it upwards, before it can operate; neither have they been yet persuaded to use so long an abstinence, as the prescription requires.

CHAPTER VI.

[A further account of the academy. The author proposes some improvements, which are honourably received.]

In the school of political projectors, I was but ill entertained; the professors appearing, in my judgment, wholly out of their senses, which is a scene that never fails to make me melancholy. These unhappy people were proposing schemes for persuading monarchs to choose favourites upon the score of their wisdom, capacity, and virtue; of teaching ministers to consult the public good; of rewarding merit, great abilities, eminent services; of instructing princes to know their true interest, by placing it on the same foundation with that of their people; of choosing for employments persons qualified to exercise them, with many other wild, impossible chimeras, that never entered before into the heart of man to conceive; and confirmed in me the old observation, "that there is nothing so extravagant and irrational, which some philosophers have not maintained for truth."

But, however, I shall so far do justice to this part of the Academy, as to acknowledge that all of them were not so visionary. There was a most ingenious doctor, who seemed to be perfectly versed in the whole nature and system of government. This illustrious person had very usefully employed his studies, in finding out effectual remedies for all diseases and corruptions to which the several kinds of public administration are subject, by the vices or infirmities of those who govern, as well as by the licentiousness of those who are to obey. For instance: whereas all writers and reasoners have agreed, that there is a strict universal resemblance between the natural and the political body; can there be any thing more evident, than that the health of both must be preserved, and the diseases cured, by the same prescriptions? It is allowed, that senates and great councils are often troubled with redundant, ebullient, and other peccant humours; with many diseases of the head, and more of the heart; with strong convulsions, with grievous contractions of the nerves and sinews in both hands, but especially the right; with spleen, flatus, vertigos, and deliriums; with scrofulous tumours, full of fetid purulent matter; with sour frothy ructations: with canine appetites, and crudeness of digestion, besides many others, needless to mention. This doctor therefore proposed, "that upon the meeting of the senate, certain physicians should attend it the three first days of their sitting, and at the close of each day's debate feel the pulses of every senator; after which, having maturely considered and consulted upon the nature of the several maladies, and the methods of cure, they should on the fourth day return to the senate house, attended by their apothecaries stored with proper medicines; and before the members sat, administer to each of them lenitives, aperitives, abstersives, corrosives, restringents, palliatives, laxatives, cephalalgics, icterics, apophlegmatics, acoustics, as their several cases required; and, according as these medicines should operate, repeat, alter, or omit them, at the next meeting."

This project could not be of any great expense to the public; and might in my poor opinion, be of much use for the despatch of business, in those countries where senates have any share in the legislative power; beget unanimity, shorten debates, open a few mouths which are now closed, and close many more which are now open; curb the petulancy of the young, and correct the positiveness of the old; rouse the stupid, and damp the pert.

Again: because it is a general complaint, that the favourites of princes are troubled with short and weak memories; the same doctor proposed, "that whoever attended a first minister, after having told his business, with the utmost brevity and in the plainest words, should, at his departure, give the said minister a tweak by the nose, or a kick in the belly, or tread on his corns, or lug him thrice by both ears, or run a pin into his breech; or pinch his arm black and blue, to prevent forgetfulness; and at every levee day, repeat the same operation, till the business were done, or absolutely refused."

He likewise directed, "that every senator in the great council of a nation, after he had delivered his opinion, and argued in the defence of it, should be obliged to give his vote directly contrary; because if that were done, the result would infallibly terminate in the good of the public."

When parties in a state are violent, he offered a wonderful contrivance to reconcile them. The method is this: You take a hundred leaders of each party; you dispose them into couples of such whose heads are nearest of a size; then let two nice operators saw off the occiput of each couple at the same time, in such a manner that the brain may be equally divided. Let the occiputs, thus cut off, be interchanged, applying each to the head of his opposite party-man. It seems indeed to be a work that requires some exactness, but the professor assured us, "that if it were dexterously performed, the cure would be infallible." For he argued thus: "that the two half brains being left to debate the matter between themselves within the space of one skull, would soon come to a good understanding, and produce that moderation, as well as regularity of thinking, so much to be wished for in the heads of those, who imagine they come into the world only to watch and govern its motion: and as to the difference of brains, in quantity or quality, among those who are directors in faction, the doctor assured us, from his own knowledge, that "it was a perfect trifle."

I heard a very warm debate between two professors, about the most commodious and effectual ways and means of raising money, without grieving the subject. The first affirmed, "the justest method would be, to lay a certain tax upon vices and folly; and the sum fixed upon every man to be rated, after the fairest manner, by a jury of his neighbours." The second was of an opinion directly contrary; "to tax those qualities of body and mind, for which men chiefly value themselves; the rate to be more or less, according to the degrees of excelling; the decision whereof should be left entirely to their own breast." The highest tax was upon men who are the greatest favourites of the other sex, and the assessments, according to the number and nature of the favours they have received; for which, they are allowed to be their own vouchers. Wit, valour, and politeness, were likewise proposed to be largely taxed, and collected in the same manner, by every person's giving his own word for the quantum of what he possessed. But as to honour, justice, wisdom, and learning, they should not be taxed at all; because they are qualifications of so singular a kind, that no man will either allow them in his neighbour or value them in himself.

The women were proposed to be taxed according to their beauty and skill in dressing, wherein they had the same privilege with the men, to be determined by their own judgment. But constancy, chastity, good sense, and good nature, were not rated, because they would not bear the charge of collecting.

To keep senators in the interest of the crown, it was proposed that the members should raffle for employment; every man first taking an oath, and giving security, that he would vote for the court, whether he won or not; after which, the losers had, in their turn, the liberty of raffling upon the next vacancy. Thus, hope and expectation would be kept alive; none would complain of broken promises, but impute their disappointments wholly to fortune, whose shoulders are broader and stronger than those of a ministry.

Another professor showed me a large paper of instructions for discovering plots and conspiracies against the government. He advised great statesmen to examine into the diet of all suspected persons; their times of eating; upon which side they lay in bed; with which hand they wipe their posteriors; take a strict view of their excrements, and, from the colour, the odour, the taste, the consistence, the crudeness or maturity of digestion, form a judgment of their thoughts and designs; because men are never so serious, thoughtful, and intent, as when they are at stool, which he found by frequent experiment; for, in such conjunctures, when he used, merely as a trial, to consider which was the best way of murdering the king, his ordure would have a tincture of green; but quite different, when he thought only of raising an insurrection, or burning the metropolis.

The whole discourse was written with great acuteness, containing many observations, both curious and useful for politicians; but, as I conceived, not altogether complete. This I ventured to tell the author, and offered, if he pleased, to supply him with some additions. He received my proposition with more compliance than is usual among writers, especially those of the projecting species, professing "he would be glad to receive further information."

I told him, "that in the kingdom of Tribnia, {3} by the natives called Langdon, {4} where I had sojourned some time in my travels, the bulk of the people consist in a manner wholly of discoverers, witnesses, informers, accusers, prosecutors, evidences, swearers, together with their several subservient and subaltern instruments, all under the colours, the conduct, and the pay of ministers of state, and their deputies. The plots, in that kingdom, are usually the workmanship of those persons who desire to raise their own characters of profound politicians; to restore new vigour to a crazy administration; to stifle or divert general discontents; to fill their coffers with forfeitures; and raise, or sink the opinion of public credit, as either shall best answer their private advantage. It is first agreed and settled among them, what suspected persons shall be accused of a plot; then, effectual care is taken to secure all their letters and papers, and put the owners in chains. These papers are delivered to a set of artists, very dexterous in finding out the mysterious meanings of words, syllables, and letters: for instance, they can discover a close stool, to signify a privy council; a flock of geese, a senate; a lame dog, an invader; the plague, a standing army; a buzzard, a prime minister; the gout, a high priest; a gibbet, a secretary of state; a chamber pot, a committee of grandees; a sieve, a court lady; a broom, a revolution; a mouse-trap, an employment; a bottomless pit, a treasury; a sink, a court; a cap and bells, a favourite; a broken reed, a court of justice; an empty tun, a general; a running sore, the administration. {5}

"When this method fails, they have two others more effectual, which the learned among them call acrostics and anagrams. First, they can decipher all initial letters into political meanings. Thus N, shall signify a plot; B, a regiment of horse; L, a fleet at sea; or, secondly, by transposing the letters of the alphabet in any suspected paper, they can lay open the deepest designs of a discontented party. So, for example, if I should say, in a letter to a friend, 'Our brother Tom has just got the piles,' a skilful decipherer would discover, that the same letters which compose that sentence, may be analysed into the following words, 'Resist -, a plot is brought home—The tour.' And this is the anagrammatic method."

The professor made me great acknowledgments for communicating these observations, and promised to make honourable mention of me in his treatise.

I saw nothing in this country that could invite me to a longer continuance, and began to think of returning home to England.

CHAPTER VII.

[The author leaves Lagado: arrives at Maldonada. No ship ready. He takes a short voyage to Glubbdubdrib. His reception by the governor.]

The continent, of which this kingdom is apart, extends itself, as I have reason to believe, eastward, to that unknown tract of America westward of California; and north, to the Pacific Ocean, which is not above a hundred and fifty miles from Lagado; where there is a good port, and much commerce with the great island of Luggnagg, situated to the north-west about 29 degrees north latitude, and 140 longitude. This island of Luggnagg stands south-eastward of Japan, about a hundred leagues distant. There is a strict alliance between the Japanese emperor and the king of Luggnagg; which affords frequent opportunities of sailing from one island to the other. I determined therefore to direct my course this way, in order to my return to Europe. I hired two mules, with a guide, to show me the way, and carry my small baggage. I took leave of my noble protector, who had shown me so much favour, and made me a generous present at my departure.

My journey was without any accident or adventure worth relating. When I arrived at the port of Maldonada (for so it is called) there was no ship in the harbour bound for Luggnagg, nor likely to be in some time. The town is about as large as Portsmouth. I soon fell into some acquaintance, and was very hospitably received. A gentleman of distinction said to me, "that since the ships bound for Luggnagg could not be ready in less than a month, it might be no disagreeable amusement for me to take a trip to the little island of Glubbdubdrib, about five leagues off to the south-west." He offered himself and a friend to accompany me, and that I should be provided with a small convenient bark for the voyage.

Glubbdubdrib, as nearly as I can interpret the word, signifies the island of sorcerers or magicians. It is about one third as large as the Isle of Wight, and extremely fruitful: it is governed by the head of a certain tribe, who are all magicians. This tribe marries only among each other, and the eldest in succession is prince or governor. He has a noble palace, and a park of about three thousand acres, surrounded by a wall of hewn stone twenty feet high. In this park are several small enclosures for cattle, corn, and gardening.

The governor and his family are served and attended by domestics of a kind somewhat unusual. By his skill in necromancy he has a power of calling whom he pleases from the dead, and commanding their service for twenty-four hours, but no longer; nor can he call the same persons up again in less than three months, except upon very extraordinary occasions.

When we arrived at the island, which was about eleven in the morning, one of the gentlemen who accompanied me went to the governor, and desired admittance for a stranger, who came on purpose to have the honour of attending on his highness. This was immediately granted, and we all three entered the gate of the palace between two rows of guards, armed and dressed after a very antic manner, and with something in their countenances that made my flesh creep with a horror I cannot express. We passed through several apartments, between servants of the same sort, ranked on each side as before, till we came to the chamber of presence; where, after three profound obeisances, and a few general questions, we were permitted to sit on three stools, near the lowest step of his highness's throne. He understood the language of Balnibarbi, although it was different from that of this island. He desired me to give him some account of my travels; and, to let me see that I should be treated without ceremony, he dismissed all his attendants with a turn of his finger; at which, to my great astonishment, they vanished in an instant, like visions in a dream when we awake on a sudden. I could not recover myself in some time, till the governor assured me, "that I should receive no hurt:" and observing my two companions to be under no concern, who had been often entertained in the same manner, I began to take courage, and related to his highness a short history of my several adventures; yet not without some hesitation, and frequently looking behind me to the place where I had seen those domestic spectres. I had the honour to dine with the governor, where a new set of ghosts served up the meat, and waited at table. I now observed myself to be less terrified than I had been in the morning. I stayed till sunset, but humbly desired his highness to excuse me for not accepting his invitation of lodging in the palace. My two friends and I lay at a private house in the town adjoining, which is the capital of this little island; and the next morning we returned to pay our duty to the governor, as he was pleased to command us.

After this manner we continued in the island for ten days, most part of every day with the governor, and at night in our lodging. I soon grew so familiarized to the sight of spirits, that after the third or fourth time they gave me no emotion at all: or, if I had any apprehensions left, my curiosity prevailed over them. For his highness the governor ordered me "to call up whatever persons I would choose to name, and in whatever numbers, among all the dead from the beginning of the world to the present time, and command them to answer any questions I should think fit to ask; with this condition, that my questions must be confined within the compass of the times they lived in. And one thing I might depend upon, that they would certainly tell me the truth, for lying was a talent of no use in the lower world."

I made my humble acknowledgments to his highness for so great a favour. We were in a chamber, from whence there was a fair prospect into the park. And because my first inclination was to be entertained with scenes of pomp and magnificence, I desired to see Alexander the Great at the head of his army, just after the battle of Arbela: which, upon a motion of the governor's finger, immediately appeared in a large field, under the window where we stood. Alexander was called up into the room: it was with great difficulty that I understood his Greek, and had but little of my own. He assured me upon his honour "that he was not poisoned, but died of a bad fever by excessive drinking."

Next, I saw Hannibal passing the Alps, who told me "he had not a drop of vinegar in his camp."

I saw Caesar and Pompey at the head of their troops, just ready to engage. I saw the former, in his last great triumph. I desired that the senate of Rome might appear before me, in one large chamber, and an assembly of somewhat a later age in counterview, in another. The first seemed to be an assembly of heroes and demigods; the other, a knot of pedlars, pick-pockets, highwayman, and bullies.

The governor, at my request, gave the sign for Caesar and Brutus to advance towards us. I was struck with a profound veneration at the sight of Brutus, and could easily discover the most consummate virtue, the greatest intrepidity and firmness of mind, the truest love of his country, and general benevolence for mankind, in every lineament of his countenance. I observed, with much pleasure, that these two persons were in good intelligence with each other; and Caesar freely confessed to me, "that the greatest actions of his own life were not equal, by many degrees, to the glory of taking it away." I had the honour to have much conversation with Brutus; and was told, "that his ancestor Junius, Socrates, Epaminondas, Cato the younger, Sir Thomas More, and himself were perpetually together:" a sextumvirate, to which all the ages of the world cannot add a seventh.

It would be tedious to trouble the reader with relating what vast numbers of illustrious persons were called up to gratify that insatiable desire I had to see the world in every period of antiquity placed before me. I chiefly fed mine eyes with beholding the destroyers of tyrants and usurpers, and the restorers of liberty to oppressed and injured nations. But it is impossible to express the satisfaction I received in my own mind, after such a manner as to make it a suitable entertainment to the reader.

CHAPTER VIII.

[A further account of Glubbdubdrib. Ancient and modern history corrected.]

Having a desire to see those ancients who were most renowned for wit and learning, I set apart one day on purpose. I proposed that Homer and Aristotle might appear at the head of all their commentators; but these were so numerous, that some hundreds were forced to attend in the court, and outward rooms of the palace. I knew, and could distinguish those two heroes, at first sight, not only from the crowd, but from each other. Homer was the taller and comelier person of the two, walked very erect for one of his age, and his eyes were the most quick and piercing I ever beheld. Aristotle stooped much, and made use of a staff. His visage was meagre, his hair lank and thin, and his voice hollow. I soon discovered that both of them were perfect strangers to the rest of the company, and had never seen or heard of them before; and I had a whisper from a ghost who shall be nameless, "that these commentators always kept in the most distant quarters from their principals, in the lower world, through a consciousness of shame and guilt, because they had so horribly misrepresented the meaning of those authors to posterity." I introduced Didymus and Eustathius to Homer, and prevailed on him to treat them better than perhaps they deserved, for he soon found they wanted a genius to enter into the spirit of a poet. But Aristotle was out of all patience with the account I gave him of Scotus and Ramus, as I presented them to him; and he asked them, "whether the rest of the tribe were as great dunces as themselves?"

I then desired the governor to call up Descartes and Gassendi, with whom I prevailed to explain their systems to Aristotle. This great philosopher freely acknowledged his own mistakes in natural philosophy, because he proceeded in many things upon conjecture, as all men must do; and he found that Gassendi, who had made the doctrine of Epicurus as palatable as he could, and the vortices of Descartes, were equally to be exploded. He predicted the same fate to ATTRACTION, whereof the present learned are such zealous asserters. He said, "that new systems of nature were but new fashions, which would vary in every age; and even those, who pretend to demonstrate them from mathematical principles, would flourish but a short period of time, and be out of vogue when that was determined."

I spent five days in conversing with many others of the ancient learned. I saw most of the first Roman emperors. I prevailed on the governor to call up Heliogabalus's cooks to dress us a dinner, but they could not show us much of their skill, for want of materials. A helot of Agesilaus made us a dish of Spartan broth, but I was not able to get down a second spoonful.

The two gentlemen, who conducted me to the island, were pressed by their private affairs to return in three days, which I employed in seeing some of the modern dead, who had made the greatest figure, for two or three hundred years past, in our own and other countries of Europe; and having been always a great admirer of old illustrious families, I desired the governor would call up a dozen or two of kings, with their ancestors in order for eight or nine generations. But my disappointment was grievous and unexpected. For, instead of a long train with royal diadems, I saw in one family two fiddlers, three spruce courtiers, and an Italian prelate. In another, a barber, an abbot, and two cardinals. I have too great a veneration for crowned heads, to dwell any longer on so nice a subject. But as to counts, marquises, dukes, earls, and the like, I was not so scrupulous. And I confess, it was not without some pleasure, that I found myself able to trace the particular features, by which certain families are distinguished, up to their originals. I could plainly discover whence one family derives a long chin; why a second has abounded with knaves for two generations, and fools for two more; why a third happened to be crack-brained, and a fourth to be sharpers; whence it came, what Polydore Virgil says of a certain great house, Nec vir fortis, nec foemina casta; h v cruelty, falsehood, and cowardice, grew to be characteristics by which certain families are distinguished as much as by their coats of arms; who first brought the pox into a noble house, which has lineally descended scrofulous tumours to their posterity. Neither could I wonder at all this, when I saw such an interruption of lineages, by pages, lackeys, valets, coachmen, gamesters, fiddlers, players, captains, and pickpockets.

I was chiefly disgusted with modern history. For having strictly examined all the persons of greatest name in the courts of princes, for a hundred years past, I found how the world had been misled by prostitute writers, to ascribe the greatest exploits in war, to cowards; the wisest counsel, to fools; sincerity, to flatterers; Roman virtue, to betrayers of their country; piety, to atheists; chastity, to sodomites; truth, to informers: how many innocent and excellent persons had been condemned to death or banishment by the practising of great ministers upon the corruption of judges, and the malice of factions: how many villains had been exalted to the highest places of trust, power, dignity, and profit: how great a share in the motions and events of courts, councils, and senates might be challenged by bawds, whores, pimps, parasites, and buffoons. How low an opinion I had of human wisdom and integrity, when I was truly informed of the springs and motives of great enterprises and revolutions in the world, and of the contemptible accidents to which they owed their success.

Here I discovered the roguery and ignorance of those who pretend to write anecdotes, or secret history; who send so many kings to their graves with a cup of poison; will repeat the discourse between a prince and chief minister, where no witness was by; unlock the thoughts and cabinets of ambassadors and secretaries of state; and have the perpetual misfortune to be mistaken. Here I discovered the true causes of many great events that have surprised the world; how a whore can govern the back-stairs, the back-stairs a council, and the council a senate. A general confessed, in my presence, "that he got a victory purely by the force of cowardice and ill conduct;" and an admiral, "that, for want of proper intelligence, he beat the enemy, to whom he intended to betray the fleet." Three kings protested to me, "that in their whole reigns they never did once prefer any person of merit, unless by mistake, or treachery of some minister in whom they confided; neither would they do it if they were to live again:" and they showed, with great strength of reason, "that the royal throne could not be supported without corruption, because that positive, confident, restiff temper, which virtue infused into a man, was a perpetual clog to public business."

I had the curiosity to inquire in a particular manner, by what methods great numbers had procured to themselves high titles of honour, and prodigious estates; and I confined my inquiry to a very modern period: however, without grating upon present times, because I would be sure to give no offence even to foreigners (for I hope the reader need not be told, that I do not in the least intend my own country, in what I say upon this occasion,) a great number of persons concerned were called up; and, upon a very slight examination, discovered such a scene of infamy, that I cannot reflect upon it without some seriousness. Perjury, oppression, subornation, fraud, pandarism, and the like infirmities, were among the most excusable arts they had to mention; and for these I gave, as it was reasonable, great allowance. But when some confessed they owed their greatness and wealth to sodomy, or incest; others, to the prostituting of their own wives and daughters; others, to the betraying of their country or their prince; some, to poisoning; more to the perverting of justice, in order to destroy the innocent, I hope I may be pardoned, if these discoveries inclined me a little to abate of that profound veneration, which I am naturally apt to pay to persons of high rank, who ought to be treated with the utmost respect due to their sublime dignity, by us their inferiors.

I had often read of some great services done to princes and states, and desired to see the persons by whom those services were performed. Upon inquiry I was told, "that their names were to be found on no record, except a few of them, whom history has represented as the vilest of rogues and traitors." As to the rest, I had never once heard of them. They all appeared with dejected looks, and in the meanest habit; most of them telling me, "they died in poverty and disgrace, and the rest on a scaffold or a gibbet."

Among others, there was one person, whose case appeared a little singular. He had a youth about eighteen years old standing by his side. He told me, "he had for many years been commander of a ship; and in the sea fight at Actium had the good fortune to break through the enemy's great line of battle, sink three of their capital ships, and take a fourth, which was the sole cause of Antony's flight, and of the victory that ensued; that the youth standing by him, his only son, was killed in the action." He added, "that upon the confidence of some merit, the war being at an end, he went to Rome, and solicited at the court of Augustus to be preferred to a greater ship, whose commander had been killed; but, without any regard to his pretensions, it was given to a boy who had never seen the sea, the son of Libertina, who waited on one of the emperor's mistresses. Returning back to his own vessel, he was charged with neglect of duty, and the ship given to a favourite page of Publicola, the vice-admiral;

whereupon he retired to a poor farm at a great distance from Rome, and there ended his life." I was so curious to know the truth of this story, that I desired Agrippa might be called, who was admiral in that fight. He appeared, and confirmed the whole account: but with much more advantage to the captain, whose modesty had extenuated or concealed a great part of his merit.

I was surprised to find corruption grown so high and so quick in that empire, by the force of luxury so lately introduced; which made me less wonder at many parallel cases in other countries, where vices of all kinds have reigned so much longer, and where the whole praise, as well as pillage, has been engrossed by the chief commander, who perhaps had the least title to either.

As every person called up made exactly the same appearance he had done in the world, it gave me melancholy reflections to observe how much the race of human kind was degenerated among us within these hundred years past; how the pox, under all its consequences and denominations had altered every lineament of an English countenance; shortened the size of bodies, unbraced the nerves, relaxed the sinews and muscles, introduced a sallow complexion, and rendered the flesh loose and rancid.

I descended so low, as to desire some English yeoman of the old stamp might be summoned to appear; once so famous for the simplicity of their manners, diet, and dress; for justice in their dealings; for their true spirit of liberty; for their valour, and love of their country. Neither could I be wholly unmoved, after comparing the living with the dead, when I considered how all these pure native virtues were prostituted for a piece of money by their grand-children; who, in selling their votes and managing at elections, have acquired every vice and corruption that can possibly be learned in a court.

CHAPTER IX.

[The author returns to Maldonada. Sails to the kingdom of Luggnagg. The author confined. He is sent for to court. The manner of his admittance. The king's great lenity to his subjects.]

The day of our departure being come, I took leave of his highness, the Governor of Glubbdubdrib, and returned with my two companions to Maldonada, where, after a fortnight's waiting, a ship was ready to sail for Luggnagg. The two gentlemen, and some others, were so generous and kind as to furnish me with provisions, and see me on board. I was a month in this voyage. We had one violent storm, and were under a necessity of steering westward to get into the trade wind, which holds for above sixty leagues. On the 21st of April, 1708, we sailed into the river of Clumegnig, which is a seaport town, at the south-east point of Luggnagg. We cast anchor within a league of the town, and made a signal for a pilot. Two of them came on board in less than half an hour, by whom we were guided between certain shoals and rocks, which are very dangerous in the passage, to a large basin, where a fleet may ride in safety within a cable's length of the town-wall.

Some of our sailors, whether out of treachery or inadvertence, had informed the pilots "that I was a stranger, and great traveller;" whereof these gave notice to a custom-house officer, by whom I was examined very strictly upon my landing. This officer spoke to me in the language of Balnibarbi, which, by the force of much commerce, is generally understood in that town, especially by seamen and those employed in the customs. I gave him a short account of some particulars, and made my story as plausible and consistent as I could; but I thought it necessary to disguise my country, and call myself a Hollander; because my intentions were for Japan, and I knew the Dutch were the only Europeans permitted to enter into that kingdom. I therefore told the officer, "that having been shipwrecked on the coast of Balnibarbi, and cast on a rock, I was received up into Laputa, or the flying island (of which he had often heard), and was now endeavouring to get to Japan, whence I might find a convenience of returning to my own country." The officer said, "I must be confined till he could receive orders from court, for which he would write immediately, and hoped to receive an answer in a fortnight." I was carried to a convenient lodging with a sentry placed at the door; however, I had the liberty of a large garden, and was treated with humanity enough, being maintained all the time at the king's charge. I was invited by several persons, chiefly out of curiosity, because it was reported that I came from countries very remote, of which they had never heard.

I hired a young man, who came in the same ship, to be an interpreter; he was a native of Luggnagg, but had lived some years at Maldonada, and was a perfect master of both languages. By his assistance, I was able to hold a conversation with those who came to visit me; but this consisted only of their questions, and my answers.

The despatch came from court about the time we expected. It contained a warrant for conducting me and my retinue to Traldragdubh, or Trildrogdrib (for it is pronounced both ways as near as I can remember), by a party of ten horse. All my retinue was that poor lad for an interpreter, whom I persuaded into my service, and, at my humble request, we had each of us a mule to ride on. A messenger was despatched half a day's journey before us, to give the king notice of my approach, and to desire, "that his majesty would please to appoint a day and hour, when it would by his gracious pleasure that I might have the honour to lick the dust before his footstool." This is the court style, and I found it to be more than matter of form: for, upon my admittance two days after my arrival, I was commanded to crawl upon my belly, and lick the floor as I advanced; but, on account of my being a stranger, care was taken to have it made so clean, that the dust was not offensive. However, this was a peculiar grace, not allowed to any but persons of the highest rank, when they desire an admittance. Nay, sometimes the floor is strewed with dust on purpose, when the person to be admitted happens to have powerful enemies at court; and I have seen a great lord with his mouth so crammed, that when he had crept to the proper distance from the throne; he was not able to speak a word. Neither is there any remedy; because it is capital for those, who receive an audience to spit or wipe their mouths in his majesty's presence. There is indeed another custom, which I cannot altogether approve of: when the king has a mind to put any of his nobles to death in a gentle indulgent manner, he commands the floor to be strewed with a certain brown powder of a deadly composition, which being licked up, infallibly kills him in twenty-four hours. But in justice to this prince's great clemency, and the care he has of his subjects' lives (wherein it were much to be wished that the Monarchs of Europe would imitate him), it must be mentioned for his honour, that strict orders are given to have the infected parts of the floor well washed after every such execution, which, if his domestics neglect, they are in danger of incurring his royal displeasure. I myself heard him give directions, that one of his pages should be whipped, whose turn it was to give notice about washing the floor after an execution, but maliciously had omitted it; by which neglect a young lord of great hopes, coming to an audience, was unfortunately poisoned, although the king at that time had no design against his life. But this good prince was so gracious as to forgive the poor page his whipping, upon promise that he would do so no more, without special orders.

To return from this digression. When I had crept within four yards of the throne, I raised myself gently upon my knees, and then striking my forehead seven times against the ground, I pronounced the following words, as they had been taught me the night before, Inckpling gloffthrobb squut serummblhiop mlashnalt zwin tnodbalkuffh slhiophad gurdlubh asht. This is the compliment, established by the laws of the land, for all persons admitted to the king's presence. It may be rendered into English thus: "May your celestial majesty outlive the sun, eleven moons and a half!" To this the king returned some answer, which, although I could not understand, yet I replied as I had been directed: Fluft drin yalerick dwuldom prastrad mirpush, which properly signifies, "My tongue is in the mouth of my friend;" and by this expression was meant, that I desired leave to bring my interpreter; whereupon the young man already mentioned was accordingly introduced, by whose intervention I answered as many questions as his majesty could put in above an hour. I spoke in the Balnibarbian tongue, and my interpreter delivered my meaning in that of Luggnagg.

The king was much delighted with my company, and ordered his bliffmarklub, or high-chamberlain, to appoint a lodging in the court for me and my interpreter; with a daily allowance for my table, and a large purse of gold for my common expenses.

I staid three months in this country, out of perfect obedience to his majesty; who was pleased highly to favour me, and made me very honourable offers. But I thought it more consistent with prudence and justice to pass the remainder of my days with my wife and family.

CHAPTER X.

[The Luggnaggians commended. A particular description of the Struldbrugs, with many conversations between the author and some eminent persons upon that subject.]

The Luggnaggians are a polite and generous people; and although they are not without some share of that pride which is peculiar to all Eastern countries, yet they show themselves courteous to strangers, especially such who are countenanced by the court. I had many acquaintance, and among persons of the best fashion; and being always attended by my interpreter, the conversation we had was not disagreeable.

One day, in much good company, I was asked by a person of quality, "whether I had seen any of their struldbrugs, or immortals?" I said, "I had not;" and desired he would explain to me "what he meant by such an appellation, applied to a mortal creature." He told me "that sometimes, though very rarely, a child happened to be born in a family, with a red circular spot in the forehead, directly over the left eyebrow, which was an infallible mark that it should never die." The spot, as he described it, "was about the compass of a silver threepence, but in the course of time grew larger, and changed its colour; for at twelve years old it became green, so continued till five and twenty, then turned to a deep blue: at five and forty it grew coal black, and as large as an English shilling; but never admitted any further alteration." He said, "these births were so rare, that he did not believe there could be above eleven hundred struldbrugs, of both sexes, in the whole kingdom; of which he computed about fifty in the metropolis, and, among the rest, a young girl born; about three years ago: that these productions were not peculiar to any family, but a mere effect of chance; and the children of the struldbrugs themselves were equally mortal with the rest of the people."

I freely own myself to have been struck with inexpressible delight, upon hearing this account: and the person who gave it me happening to understand the Balnibarbian language, which I spoke very well, I could not forbear breaking out into expressions, perhaps a little too extravagant. I cried out, as in a rapture, "Happy nation, where every child hath at least a chance for being immortal! Happy people, who enjoy so many living examples of ancient virtue, and have masters ready to instruct them in the wisdom of all former ages! but happiest, beyond all comparison, are those excellent struldbrugs, who, being born exempt from that universal calamity of human nature, have their minds free and disengaged, without the weight and depression of spirits caused by the continual apprehensions of death!" I discovered my admiration that I had not observed any of these illustrious persons at court; the black spot on the forehead being so remarkable a distinction, that I could not have easily overlooked it: and it was impossible that his majesty, a most judicious prince, should not provide himself with a good number of such wise and able counsellors. Yet perhaps the virtue of those reverend sages was too strict for the corrupt and libertine manners of a court: and we often find by experience, that young men are too opinionated and volatile to be guided by the sober dictates of their seniors. However, since the king was pleased to allow me access to his royal person, I was resolved, upon the very first occasion, to deliver my opinion to him on this matter freely and at large, by the help of my interpreter; and whether he would please to take my advice or not, yet in one thing I was determined, that his majesty having frequently offered me an establishment in this country, I would, with great thankfulness, accept the favour, and pass my life here in the conversation of those superior beings the struldbrugs, if they would please to admit me."

The gentleman to whom I addressed my discourse, because (as I have already observed) he spoke the language of Balnibarbi, said to me, with a sort of a smile which usually arises from pity to the ignorant, "that he was glad of any occasion to keep me among them, and desired my permission to explain to the company what I had spoke." He did so, and they talked together for some time in their own language, whereof I understood not a syllable, neither could I observe by their countenances, what impression my discourse had made on them. After a short silence, the same person told me, "that his friends and mine (so he thought fit to express himself) were very much pleased with the judicious remarks I had made on the great happiness and advantages of immortal life, and they were desirous to know, in a particular manner, what scheme of living I should have formed to myself, if it had fallen to my lot to have been born a struldbrug."

I answered, "it was easy to be eloquent on so copious and delightful a subject, especially to me, who had been often apt to amuse myself with visions of what I should do, if I were a king, a general, or a great lord: and upon this very case, I had frequently run over the whole system how I should employ myself, and pass the time, if I were sure to live for ever.

"That, if it had been my good fortune to come into the world a struldbrug, as soon as I could discover my own happiness, by understanding the difference between life and death, I would first resolve, by all arts and methods, whatsoever, to procure myself riches. In the pursuit of which, by thrift and management, I might reasonably expect, in about two hundred years, to be the wealthiest man in the kingdom. In the second place, I would, from my earliest youth, apply myself to the study of arts and sciences, by which I should arrive in time to excel all others in learning. Lastly, I would carefully record every action and event of consequence, that happened in the public, impartially draw the characters of the several successions of princes and great ministers of state, with my own observations on every point. I would exactly set down the several changes in customs, language, fashions of dress, diet, and diversions. By all which acquirements, I should be a living treasure of knowledge and wisdom, and certainly become the oracle of the nation.

"I would never marry after threescore, but live in a hospitable manner, yet still on the saving side. I would entertain myself in forming and directing the minds of hopeful young men, by convincing them, from my own remembrance, experience, and observation, fortified by numerous examples, of the usefulness of virtue in public and private life. But my choice and constant companions should be a set of my own immortal brotherhood; among whom, I would elect a dozen from the most ancient, down to my own contemporaries. Where any of these wanted fortunes, I would provide them with convenient lodges round my own estate, and have some of them always at my table; only mingling a few of the most valuable among you mortals, whom length of time would harden me to lose with little or no reluctance, and treat your posterity after the same manner; just as a man diverts himself with the annual succession of pinks and tulips in his garden, without regretting the loss of those which withered the preceding year.

"These struldbrugs and I would mutually communicate our observations and memorials, through the course of time; remark the several gradations by which corruption steals into the world, and oppose it in every step, by giving perpetual warning and instruction to mankind; which, added to the strong influence of our own example, would probably prevent that continual degeneracy of human nature so justly complained of in all ages.

"Add to this, the pleasure of seeing the various revolutions of states and empires; the changes in the lower and upper world; ancient cities in ruins, and obscure villages become the seats of kings; famous rivers lessening into shallow brooks; the ocean leaving one coast dry, and overwhelming another; the discovery of many countries yet unknown; barbarity overrunning the politest nations, and the most barbarous become civilized. I should then see the discovery of the longitude, the perpetual motion, the universal medicine, and many other great inventions, brought to the utmost perfection.

"What wonderful discoveries should we make in astronomy, by outliving and confirming our own predictions; by observing the progress and return of comets, with the changes of motion in the sun, moon, and stars!"

I enlarged upon many other topics, which the natural desire of endless life, and sublunary happiness, could easily furnish me with. When I had ended, and the sum of my discourse had been interpreted, as before, to the rest of the company, there was a good deal of talk among them in the language of the country, not without some laughter at my expense. At last, the same gentleman who had been my interpreter, said, "he was desired by the rest to set me right in a few mistakes, which I had fallen into through the common imbecility of human nature, and upon that allowance was less answerable for them. That this breed of struldbrugs was peculiar to their country, for there were no such people either in Balnibarbi or Japan, where he had the honour to be ambassador from his majesty, and found the natives in both those kingdoms very hard to believe that the fact was possible: and it appeared from my astonishment when he first mentioned the matter to me, that I received it as a thing wholly new, and scarcely to be credited. That in the two kingdoms above mentioned, where, during his residence, he had conversed very much, he observed long life to be the universal desire and wish of mankind. That whoever had one foot in the grave was sure to hold back the other as strongly as he could. That the oldest had still hopes of living one day longer, and looked on death as the greatest evil, from which nature always prompted him to retreat. Only in this island of Luggnagg the appetite for living was not so eager, from the continual example of the struldbrugs before their eyes.

"That the system of living contrived by me, was unreasonable and unjust; because it supposed a perpetuity of youth, health, and vigour, which no man could be so foolish to hope, however extravagant he may be in his wishes. That the question therefore was not, whether a man would choose to be always in the prime of youth, attended with prosperity and health; but how he would pass a perpetual life under all the usual disadvantages which old age brings along with it. For although few men will avow their desires of being immortal, upon such hard conditions, yet in the two kingdoms before mentioned, of Balnibarbi and Japan, he observed that every man desired to put off death some time longer, let it approach ever so late: and he rarely heard of any man who died willingly, except he were incited by the extremity of grief or torture. And he appealed to me, whether in those countries I had travelled, as well as my own, I had not observed the same general disposition."

After this preface, he gave me a particular account of the struldbrugs among them. He said, "they commonly acted like mortals till about thirty years old; after which, by degrees, they grew melancholy and dejected, increasing in both till they came to fourscore. This he learned from their own confession: for otherwise, there not being above two or three of that species born in an age, they were too few to form a general observation by. When they came to fourscore years, which is reckoned the extremity of living in this country, they had not only all the follies and infirmities of other old men, but many more which arose from the dreadful prospect of never dying. They were not only opinionative, peevish, covetous, morose, vain, talkative, but incapable of friendship, and dead to all natural affection, which never descended below their grandchildren. Envy and impotent desires are their prevailing passions. But those objects against which their envy seems principally directed, are the vices of the younger sort and the deaths of the old. By reflecting on the former, they find themselves cut off from all possibility of pleasure; and whenever they see a funeral, they lament and repine that others have gone to a harbour of rest to which they themselves never can hope to arrive. They have no remembrance of anything but what they learned and observed in their youth and middle-age, and even that is very imperfect; and for the truth or particulars of any fact, it is safer to depend on common tradition, than upon their best recollections. The least miserable among them appear to be those who turn to dotage, and entirely lose their memories; these meet with more pity and assistance, because they want many bad qualities which abound in others.

"If a struldbrug happen to marry one of his own kind, the marriage is dissolved of course, by the courtesy of the kingdom, as soon as the younger of the two comes to be fourscore; for the law thinks it a reasonable indulgence, that those who are condemned, without any fault of their own, to a perpetual continuance in the world, should not have their misery doubled by the load of a wife.

"As soon as they have completed the term of eighty years, they are looked on as dead in law; their heirs immediately succeed to their estates; only a small pittance is reserved for their support; and the poor ones are maintained at the public charge. After that period, they are held incapable of any employment of trust or profit; they cannot purchase lands, or take leases; neither are they allowed to be witnesses in any cause, either civil or criminal, not even for the decision of meers and bounds.

"At ninety, they lose their teeth and hair; they have at that age no distinction of taste, but eat and drink whatever they can get, without relish or appetite. The diseases they were subject to still continue, without increasing or diminishing. In talking, they forget the common appellation of things, and the names of persons, even of those who are their nearest friends and relations. For the same reason, they never can amuse themselves with reading, because their memory will not serve to carry them from the beginning of a sentence to the end; and by this defect, they are deprived of the only entertainment whereof they might otherwise be capable.

The language of this country being always upon the flux, the struldbrugs of one age do not understand those of another; neither are they able, after two hundred years, to hold any conversation (farther than by a few general words) with their neighbours the mortals; and thus they lie under the disadvantage of living like foreigners in their own country."

This was the account given me of the struldbrugs, as near as I can remember. I afterwards saw five or six of different ages, the youngest not above two hundred years old, who were brought to me at several times by some of my friends; but although they were told, "that I was a great traveller, and had seen all the world," they had not the least curiosity to ask me a question; only desired "I would give them slumskudask," or a token of remembrance; which is a modest way of begging, to avoid the law, that strictly forbids it, because they are provided for by the public, although indeed with a very scanty allowance.

They are despised and hated by all sorts of people. When one of them is born, it is reckoned ominous, and their birth is recorded very particularly so that you may know their age by consulting the register, which, however, has not been kept above a thousand years past, or at least has been destroyed by time or public disturbances. But the usual way of computing how old they are, is by asking them what kings or great persons they can remember, and then consulting history; for infallibly the last prince in their mind did not begin his reign after they were fourscore years old.

They were the most mortifying sight I ever beheld; and the women more horrible than the men. Besides the usual deformities in extreme old age, they acquired an additional ghastliness, in proportion to their number of years, which is not to be described; and among half a dozen, I soon distinguished which was the eldest, although there was not above a century or two between them.

The reader will easily believe, that from what I had hear and seen, my keen appetite for perpetuity of life was much abated. I grew heartily ashamed of the pleasing visions I had formed; and thought no tyrant could invent a death into which I would not run with pleasure, from such a life. The king heard of all that had passed between me and my friends upon this occasion, and rallied me very pleasantly; wishing I could send a couple of struldbrugs to my own country, to arm our people against the fear of death; but this, it seems, is forbidden by the fundamental laws of the kingdom, or else I should have been well content with the trouble and expense of transporting them.

I could not but agree, that the laws of this kingdom relative to the struldbrugs were founded upon the strongest reasons, and such as any other country would be under the necessity of enacting, in the like circumstances. Otherwise, as avarice is the necessary consequence of old age, those immortals would in time become proprietors of the whole nation, and engross the civil power, which, for want of abilities to manage, must end in the ruin of the public.

CHAPTER XI.

[The author leaves Luggnagg, and sails to Japan. From thence he returns in a Dutch ship to Amsterdam, and from Amsterdam to England.]

I thought this account of the struldbrugs might be some entertainment to the reader, because it seems to be a little out of the common way; at least I do not remember to have met the like in any book of travels that has come to my hands: and if I am deceived, my excuse must be, that it is necessary for travellers who describe the same country, very often to agree in dwelling on the same particulars, without deserving the censure of having borrowed or transcribed from those who wrote before them.

There is indeed a perpetual commerce between this kingdom and the great empire of Japan; and it is very probable, that the Japanese authors may have given some account of the struldbrugs; but my stay in Japan was so short, and I was so entirely a stranger to the language, that I was not qualified to make any inquiries. But I hope the Dutch, upon this notice, will be curious and able enough to supply my defects.

His majesty having often pressed me to accept some employment in his court, and finding me absolutely determined to return to my native country, was pleased to give me his license to depart; and honoured me with a letter of recommendation, under his own hand, to the Emperor of Japan. He likewise presented me with four hundred and forty-four large pieces of gold (this nation delighting in even numbers), and a red diamond, which I sold in England for eleven hundred pounds.

On the 6th of May, 1709, I took a solemn leave of his majesty, and all my friends. This prince was so gracious as to order a guard to conduct me to Glanguenstald, which is a royal port to the south- west part of the island. In six days I found a vessel ready to carry me to Japan, and spent fifteen days in the voyage. We landed at a small port-town called Xamoschi, situated on the south-east part of Japan; the town lies on the western point, where there is a narrow strait leading northward into along arm of the sea, upon the north-west part of which, Yedo, the metropolis, stands. At landing, I showed the custom-house officers my letter from the king of Luggnagg to his imperial majesty. They knew the seal perfectly well; it was as broad as the palm of my hand. The impression was, A KING LIFTING UP A LAME BEGGAR FROM THE EARTH. The magistrates of the town, hearing of my letter, received me as a public minister. They provided me with carriages and servants, and bore my charges to Yedo; where I was admitted to an audience, and delivered my letter, which was opened with great ceremony, and explained to the Emperor by an interpreter, who then gave me notice, by his majesty's order, "that I should signify my request, and, whatever it were, it should be granted, for the sake of his royal brother of Luggnagg." This interpreter was a person employed to transact affairs with the Hollanders. He soon conjectured, by my countenance, that I was a European, and therefore repeated his majesty's commands in Low Dutch, which he spoke perfectly well. I answered, as I had before determined, "that I was a Dutch merchant, shipwrecked in a very remote country, whence I had travelled by sea and land to Luggnagg, and then took shipping for Japan; where I knew my countrymen often traded, and with some of these I hoped to get an opportunity of returning into Europe: I therefore most humbly entreated his royal favour, to give order that I should be conducted in safety to Nangasac." To this I added another petition, "that for the sake of my patron the king of Luggnagg, his majesty would condescend to excuse my performing the ceremony imposed on my countrymen, of trampling upon the crucifix: because I had been thrown into his kingdom by my misfortunes, without any intention of trading." When this latter petition was interpreted to the Emperor, he seemed a little surprised; and said, "he believed I was the first of my countrymen who ever made any scruple in this point; and that he began to doubt, whether I was a real Hollander, or not; but rather suspected I must be a Christian. However, for the reasons I had offered, but chiefly to gratify the king of Luggnagg by an uncommon mark of his favour, he would comply with the singularity of my humour; but the affair must be managed with dexterity, and his officers should be commanded to let me pass, as it were by forgetfulness. For he assured me, that if the secret should be discovered by my countrymen the Dutch, they would cut my throat in the voyage." I returned my thanks, by the interpreter, for so unusual a favour; and some troops being at that time on their march to Nangasac, the commanding officer had orders to convey me safe thither, with particular instructions about the business of the crucifix.

On the 9th day of June, 1709, I arrived at Nangasac, after a very long and troublesome journey. I soon fell into the company of some Dutch sailors belonging to the Amboyna, of Amsterdam, a stout ship of 450 tons. I had lived long in Holland, pursuing my studies at Leyden, and I spoke Dutch well. The seamen soon knew whence I came last: they were curious to inquire into my voyages and course of life. I made up a story as short and probable as I could, but concealed the greatest part. I knew many persons in Holland. I was able to invent names for my parents, whom I pretended to be obscure people in the province of Gelderland. I would have given the captain (one Theodorus Vangrult) what he pleased to ask for my voyage to Holland; but understanding I was a surgeon, he was contented to take half the usual rate, on condition that I would serve him in the way of my calling. Before we took shipping, I was often asked by some of the crew, whether I had performed the ceremony above mentioned? I evaded the question by general answers; "that I had satisfied the Emperor and court in all particulars." However, a malicious rogue of a skipper went to an officer, and pointing to me, told him, "I had not yet trampled on the crucifix;" but the other, who had received instructions to let me pass, gave the rascal twenty strokes on the shoulders with a bamboo; after which I was no more troubled with such questions.

Nothing happened worth mentioning in this voyage. We sailed with a fair wind to the Cape of Good Hope, where we staid only to take in fresh water. On the 10th of April, 1710, we arrived safe at Amsterdam, having lost only three men by sickness in the voyage, and a fourth, who fell from the foremast into the sea, not far from the coast of Guinea. From Amsterdam I soon after set sail for England, in a small vessel belonging to that city.

On the 16th of April we put in at the Downs. I landed next morning, and saw once more my native country, after an absence of five years and six months complete. I went straight to Redriff, where I arrived the same day at two in the afternoon, and found my wife and family in good health.

PART IV—A VOYAGE TO THE COUNTRY OF THE HOUYHNHNMS.

CHAPTER I.

[The author sets out as captain of a ship. His men conspire against him, confine him a long time to his cabin, and set him on shore in an unknown land. He travels up into the country. The Yahoos, a strange sort of animal, described. The author meets two Houyhnhnms.]

I continued at home with my wife and children about five months, in a very happy condition, if I could have learned the lesson of knowing when I was well. I left my poor wife big with child, and accepted an advantageous offer made me to be captain of the Adventurer, a stout merchantman of 350 tons: for I understood navigation well, and being grown weary of a surgeon's employment at sea, which, however, I could exercise upon occasion, I took a skilful young man of that calling, one Robert Purefoy, into my ship. We set sail from Portsmouth upon the 7th day of September, 1710; on the 14th we met with Captain Pocock, of Bristol, at Teneriffe, who was going to the bay of Campechy to cut logwood. On the 16th, he was parted from us by a storm; I heard since my return, that his ship foundered, and none escaped but one cabin boy. He was an honest man, and a good sailor, but a little too positive in his own opinions, which was the cause of his destruction, as it has been with several others; for if he had followed my advice, he might have been safe at home with his family at this time, as well as myself.

I had several men who died in my ship of calentures, so that I was forced to get recruits out of Barbadoes and the Leeward Islands, where I touched, by the direction of the merchants who employed me; which I had soon too much cause to repent: for I found afterwards, that most of them had been buccaneers. I had fifty hands onboard; and my orders were, that I should trade with the Indians in the South-Sea, and make what discoveries I could. These rogues, whom I had picked up, debauched my other men, and they all formed a conspiracy to seize the ship, and secure me; which they did one morning, rushing into my cabin, and binding me hand and foot, threatening to throw me overboard, if I offered to stir. I told them, "I was their prisoner, and would submit." This they made me swear to do, and then they unbound me, only fastening one of my legs with a chain, near my bed, and placed a sentry at my door with his piece charged, who was commanded to shoot me dead if I attempted my liberty. They sent me own victuals and drink, and took the government of the ship to themselves. Their design was to turn pirates and, plunder the Spaniards, which they could not do till they got more men. But first they resolved to sell the goods the ship, and then go to Madagascar for recruits, several among them having died since my confinement. They sailed many weeks, and traded with the Indians; but I knew not what course they took, being kept a close prisoner in my cabin, and expecting nothing less than to be murdered, as they often threatened me.

Upon the 9th day of May, 1711, one James Welch came down to my cabin, and said, "he had orders from the captain to set me ashore." I expostulated with him, but in vain; neither would he so much as tell me who their new captain was. They forced me into the long- boat, letting me put on my best suit of clothes, which were as good as new, and take a small bundle of linen, but no arms, except my hanger; and they were so civil as not to search my pockets, into which I conveyed what money I had, with some other little necessaries. They rowed about a league, and then set me down on a strand. I desired them to tell me what country it was. They all swore, "they knew no more than myself;" but said, "that the captain" (as they called him) "was resolved, after they had sold the lading, to get rid of me in the first place where they could discover land." They pushed off immediately, advising me to make haste for fear of being overtaken by the tide, and so bade me farewell.

In this desolate condition I advanced forward, and soon got upon firm ground, where I sat down on a bank to rest myself, and consider what I had best do. When I was a little refreshed, I went up into the country, resolving to deliver myself to the first savages I should meet, and purchase my life from them by some bracelets, glass rings, and other toys, which sailors usually provide themselves with in those voyages, and whereof I had some about me. The land was divided by long rows of trees, not regularly planted, but naturally growing; there was great plenty of grass, and several fields of oats. I walked very circumspectly, for fear of being surprised, or suddenly shot with an arrow from behind, or on either side. I fell into a beaten road, where I saw many tracts of human feet, and some of cows, but most of horses. At last I beheld several animals in a field, and one or two of the same kind sitting in trees. Their shape was very singular and deformed, which a little discomposed me, so that I lay down behind a thicket to observe them better. Some of them coming forward near the place where I lay, gave me an opportunity of distinctly marking their form. Their heads and breasts were covered with a thick hair, some frizzled, and others lank; they had beards like goats, and a long ridge of hair down their backs, and the fore parts of their legs and feet; but the rest of their bodies was bare, so that I might see their skins, which were of a brown buff colour. They had no tails, nor any hair at all on their buttocks, except about the anus, which, I presume, nature had placed there to defend them as they sat on the ground, for this posture they used, as well as lying down, and often stood on their hind feet. They climbed high trees as nimbly as a squirrel, for they had strong extended claws before and behind, terminating in sharp points, and hooked. They would often spring, and bound, and leap, with prodigious agility. The females were not so large as the males; they had long lank hair on their heads, but none on their faces, nor any thing more than a sort of down on the rest of their bodies, except about the anus and pudenda. The dugs hung between their fore feet, and often reached almost to the ground as they walked. The hair of both sexes was of several colours, brown, red, black, and yellow. Upon the whole, I never beheld, in all my travels, so disagreeable an animal, or one against which I naturally conceived so strong an antipathy. So that, thinking I had seen enough, full of contempt and aversion, I got up, and pursued the beaten road, hoping it might direct me to the cabin of some Indian. I had not got far, when I met one of these creatures full in my way, and coming up directly to me. The ugly monster, when he saw me, distorted several ways, every feature of his visage, and stared, as at an object he had never seen before; then approaching nearer, lifted up his fore-paw, whether out of curiosity or mischief I could not tell; but I drew my hanger, and gave him a good blow with the flat side of it, for I durst not strike with the edge, fearing the inhabitants might be provoked against me, if they should come to know that I had killed or maimed any of their cattle. When the beast felt the smart, he drew back, and roared so loud, that a herd of at least forty came flocking about me from the next field, howling and making odious faces; but I ran to the body of a tree, and leaning my back against it, kept them off by waving my hanger. Several of this cursed brood, getting hold of the branches behind, leaped up into the tree, whence they began to discharge their excrements on my head; however, I escaped pretty well by sticking close to the stem of the tree, but was almost stifled with the filth, which fell about me on every side.

In the midst of this distress, I observed them all to run away on a sudden as fast as they could; at which I ventured to leave the tree and pursue the road, wondering what it was that could put them into this fright. But looking on my left hand, I saw a horse walking softly in the field; which my persecutors having sooner discovered, was the cause of their flight. The horse started a little, when he came near me, but soon recovering himself, looked full in my face with manifest tokens of wonder; he viewed my hands and feet, walking round me several times. I would have pursued my journey, but he placed himself directly in the way, yet looking with a very mild aspect, never offering the least violence. We stood gazing at each other for some time; at last I took the boldness to reach my hand towards his neck with a design to stroke it, using the common style and whistle of jockeys, when they are going to handle a strange horse. But this animal seemed to receive my civilities with disdain, shook his head, and bent his brows, softly raising up his right fore-foot to remove my hand. Then he neighed three or four times, but in so different a cadence, that I almost began to think he was speaking to himself, in some language of his own.

While he and I were thus employed, another horse came up; who applying himself to the first in a very formal manner, they gently struck each other's right hoof before, neighing several times by turns, and varying the sound, which seemed to be almost articulate. They went some paces off, as if it were to confer together, walking side by side, backward and forward, like persons deliberating upon some affair of weight, but often turning their eyes towards me, as it were to watch that I might not escape. I was amazed to see such actions and behaviour in brute beasts; and concluded with myself, that if the inhabitants of this country were endued with a proportionable degree of reason, they must needs be the wisest people upon earth. This thought gave me so much comfort, that I resolved to go forward, until I could discover some house or village, or meet with any of the natives, leaving the two horses to discourse together as they pleased. But the first, who was a dapple gray, observing me to steal off, neighed after me in so expressive a tone, that I fancied myself to understand what he meant; whereupon I turned back, and came near to him to expect his farther commands: but concealing my fear as much as I could, for I began to be in some pain how this adventure might terminate; and the reader will easily believe I did not much like my present situation.

The two horses came up close to me, looking with great earnestness upon my face and hands. The gray steed rubbed my hat all round with his right forehoof, and discomposed it so much that I was forced to adjust it better by taking it off and settling it again; whereat, both he and his companion (who was a brown bay) appeared to be much surprised: the latter felt the lappet of my coat, and finding it to hang loose about me, they both looked with new signs of wonder. He stroked my right hand, seeming to admire the softness and colour; but he squeezed it so hard between his hoof and his pastern, that I was forced to roar; after which they both touched me with all possible tenderness. They were under great perplexity about my shoes and stockings, which they felt very often, neighing to each other, and using various gestures, not unlike those of a philosopher, when he would attempt to solve some new and difficult phenomenon.

Upon the whole, the behaviour of these animals was so orderly and rational, so acute and judicious, that I at last concluded they must needs be magicians, who had thus metamorphosed themselves upon some design, and seeing a stranger in the way, resolved to divert themselves with him; or, perhaps, were really amazed at the sight of a man so very different in habit, feature, and complexion, from those who might probably live in so remote a climate. Upon the strength of this reasoning, I ventured to address them in the following manner: "Gentlemen, if you be conjurers, as I have good cause to believe, you can understand my language; therefore I make bold to let your worships know that I am a poor distressed Englishman, driven by his misfortunes upon your coast; and I entreat one of you to let me ride upon his back, as if he were a real horse, to some house or village where I can be relieved. In return of which favour, I will make you a present of this knife and bracelet," taking them out of my pocket. The two creatures stood silent while I spoke, seeming to listen with great attention, and when I had ended, they neighed frequently towards each other, as if they were engaged in serious conversation. I plainly observed that their language expressed the passions very well, and the words might, with little pains, be resolved into an alphabet more easily than the Chinese.

I could frequently distinguish the word Yahoo, which was repeated by each of them several times: and although it was impossible for me to conjecture what it meant, yet while the two horses were busy in conversation, I endeavoured to practise this word upon my tongue; and as soon as they were silent, I boldly pronounced Yahoo in a loud voice, imitating at the same time, as near as I could, the neighing of a horse; at which they were both visibly surprised; and the gray repeated the same word twice, as if he meant to teach me the right accent; wherein I spoke after him as well as I could, and found myself perceivably to improve every time, though very far from any degree of perfection. Then the bay tried me with a second word, much harder to be pronounced; but reducing it to the English orthography, may be spelt thus, Houyhnhnm. I did not succeed in this so well as in the former; but after two or three farther trials, I had better fortune; and they both appeared amazed at my capacity.

After some further discourse, which I then conjectured might relate to me, the two friends took their leaves, with the same compliment of striking each other's hoof; and the gray made me signs that I should walk before him; wherein I thought it prudent to comply, till I could find a better director. When I offered to slacken my pace, he would cry hhuun hhuun: I guessed his meaning, and gave him to understand, as well as I could, "that I was weary, and not able to walk faster;" upon which he would stand awhile to let me rest.

CHAPTER II.

[The author conducted by a Houyhnhnm to his house. The house described. The author's reception. The food of the Houyhnhnms. The author in distress for want of meat. Is at last relieved. His manner of feeding in this country.]

Having travelled about three miles, we came to a long kind of building, made of timber stuck in the ground, and wattled across; the roof was low and covered with straw. I now began to be a little comforted; and took out some toys, which travellers usually carry for presents to the savage Indians of America, and other parts, in hopes the people of the house would be thereby encouraged to receive me kindly. The horse made me a sign to go in first; it was a large room with a smooth clay floor, and a rack and manger, extending the whole length on one side. There were three nags and two mares, not eating, but some of them sitting down upon their hams, which I very much wondered at; but wondered more to see the rest employed in domestic business; these seemed but ordinary cattle. However, this confirmed my first opinion, that a people who could so far civilise brute animals, must needs excel in wisdom all the nations of the world. The gray came in just after, and thereby prevented any ill treatment which the others might have given me. He neighed to them several times in a style of authority, and received answers.

Beyond this room there were three others, reaching the length of the house, to which you passed through three doors, opposite to each other, in the manner of a vista. We went through the second room towards the third. Here the gray walked in first, beckoning me to attend: I waited in the second room, and got ready my presents for the master and mistress of the house; they were two knives, three bracelets of false pearls, a small looking-glass, and a bead necklace. The horse neighed three or four times, and I waited to hear some answers in a human voice, but I heard no other returns than in the same dialect, only one or two a little shriller than his. I began to think that this house must belong to some person of great note among them, because there appeared so much ceremony before I could gain admittance. But, that a man of quality should be served all by horses, was beyond my comprehension. I feared my brain was disturbed by my sufferings and misfortunes. I roused myself, and looked about me in the room where I was left alone: this was furnished like the first, only after a more elegant manner. I rubbed my eyes often, but the same objects still occurred. I pinched my arms and sides to awake myself, hoping I might be in a dream. I then absolutely concluded, that all these appearances could be nothing else but necromancy and magic. But I had no time to pursue these reflections; for the gray horse came to the door, and made me a sign to follow him into the third room where I saw a very comely mare, together with a colt and foal, sitting on their haunches upon mats of straw, not unartfully made, and perfectly neat and clean.

The mare soon after my entrance rose from her mat, and coming up close, after having nicely observed my hands and face, gave me a most contemptuous look; and turning to the horse, I heard the word Yahoo often repeated betwixt them; the meaning of which word I could not then comprehend, although it was the first I had learned to pronounce. But I was soon better informed, to my everlasting mortification; for the horse, beckoning to me with his head, and repeating the hhuun, hhuun, as he did upon the road, which I understood was to attend him, led me out into a kind of court, where was another building, at some distance from the house. Here we entered, and I saw three of those detestable creatures, which I first met after my landing, feeding upon roots, and the flesh of some animals, which I afterwards found to be that of asses and dogs, and now and then a cow, dead by accident or disease. They were all tied by the neck with strong withes fastened to a beam; they held their food between the claws of their fore feet, and tore it with their teeth.

The master horse ordered a sorrel nag, one of his servants, to untie the largest of these animals, and take him into the yard. The beast and I were brought close together, and by our countenances diligently compared both by master and servant, who thereupon repeated several times the word Yahoo. My horror and astonishment are not to be described, when I observed in this abominable animal, a perfect human figure: the face of it indeed was flat and broad, the nose depressed, the lips large, and the mouth wide; but these differences are common to all savage nations, where the lineaments of the countenance are distorted, by the natives suffering their infants to lie grovelling on the earth, or by carrying them on their backs, nuzzling with their face against the mothers' shoulders. The fore-feet of the Yahoo differed from my hands in nothing else but the length of the nails, the coarseness and brownness of the palms, and the hairiness on the backs. There was the same resemblance between our feet, with the same differences; which I knew very well, though the horses did not, because of my shoes and stockings; the same in every part of our bodies except as to hairiness and colour, which I have already described.

The great difficulty that seemed to stick with the two horses, was to see the rest of my body so very different from that of a Yahoo, for which I was obliged to my clothes, whereof they had no conception. The sorrel nag offered me a root, which he held (after their manner, as we shall describe in its proper place) between his hoof and pastern; I took it in my hand, and, having smelt it, returned it to him again as civilly as I could. He brought out of the Yahoos' kennel a piece of ass's flesh; but it smelt so offensively that I turned from it with loathing: he then threw it to the Yahoo, by whom it was greedily devoured. He afterwards showed me a wisp of hay, and a fetlock full of oats; but I shook my head, to signify that neither of these were food for me. And indeed I now apprehended that I must absolutely starve, if I did not get to some of my own species; for as to those filthy Yahoos, although there were few greater lovers of mankind at that time than myself, yet I confess I never saw any sensitive being so detestable on all accounts; and the more I came near them the more hateful they grew, while I stayed in that country. This the master horse observed by my behaviour, and therefore sent the Yahoo back to his kennel. He then put his fore-hoof to his mouth, at which I was much surprised, although he did it with ease, and with a motion that appeared perfectly natural, and made other signs, to know what I would eat; but I could not return him such an answer as he was able to apprehend; and if he had understood me, I did not see how it was possible to contrive any way for finding myself nourishment. While we were thus engaged, I observed a cow passing by, whereupon I pointed to her, and expressed a desire to go and milk her. This had its effect; for he led me back into the house, and ordered a mare-servant to open a room, where a good store of milk lay in earthen and wooden vessels, after a very orderly and cleanly manner. She gave me a large bowlful, of which I drank very heartily, and found myself well refreshed.

About noon, I saw coming towards the house a kind of vehicle drawn like a sledge by four Yahoos. There was in it an old steed, who seemed to be of quality; he alighted with his hind-feet forward, having by accident got a hurt in his left fore-foot. He came to dine with our horse, who received him with great civility. They dined in the best room, and had oats boiled in milk for the second course, which the old horse ate warm, but the rest cold. Their mangers were placed circular in the middle of the room, and divided into several partitions, round which they sat on their haunches, upon bosses of straw. In the middle was a large rack, with angles answering to every partition of the manger; so that each horse and mare ate their own hay, and their own mash of oats and milk, with much decency and regularity. The behaviour of the young colt and foal appeared very modest, and that of the master and mistress extremely cheerful and complaisant to their guest. The gray ordered me to stand by him; and much discourse passed between him and his friend concerning me, as I found by the stranger's often looking on me, and the frequent repetition of the word Yahoo.

I happened to wear my gloves, which the master gray observing, seemed perplexed, discovering signs of wonder what I had done to my fore-feet. He put his hoof three or four times to them, as if he would signify, that I should reduce them to their former shape, which I presently did, pulling off both my gloves, and putting them into my pocket. This occasioned farther talk; and I saw the company was pleased with my behaviour, whereof I soon found the good effects. I was ordered to speak the few words I understood; and while they were at dinner, the master taught me the names for oats, milk, fire, water, and some others, which I could readily pronounce after him, having from my youth a great facility in learning languages.

When dinner was done, the master horse took me aside, and by signs and words made me understand the concern he was in that I had nothing to eat. Oats in their tongue are called hlunnh. This word I pronounced two or three times; for although I had refused them at first, yet, upon second thoughts, I considered that I could contrive to make of them a kind of bread, which might be sufficient, with milk, to keep me alive, till I could make my escape to some other country, and to creatures of my own species. The horse immediately ordered a white mare servant of his family to bring me a good quantity of oats in a sort of wooden tray. These I heated before the fire, as well as I could, and rubbed them till the husks came off, which I made a shift to winnow from the grain. I ground and beat them between two stones; then took water, and made them into a paste or cake, which I toasted at the fire and eat warm with milk. It was at first a very insipid diet, though common enough in many parts of Europe, but grew tolerable by time; and having been often reduced to hard fare in my life, this was not the first experiment I had made how easily nature is satisfied. And I cannot but observe, that I never had one hours sickness while I stayed in this island. It is true, I sometimes made a shift to catch a rabbit, or bird, by springs made of Yahoo's hairs; and I often gathered wholesome herbs, which I boiled, and ate as salads with my bread; and now and then, for a rarity, I made a little butter, and drank the whey. I was at first at a great loss for salt, but custom soon reconciled me to the want of it; and I am confident that the frequent use of salt among us is an effect of luxury, and was first introduced only as a provocative to drink, except where it is necessary for preserving flesh in long voyages, or in places remote from great markets; for we observe no animal to be fond of it but man, and as to myself, when I left this country, it was a great while before I could endure the taste of it in anything that I ate.

This is enough to say upon the subject of my diet, wherewith other travellers fill their books, as if the readers were personally concerned whether we fare well or ill. However, it was necessary to mention this matter, lest the world should think it impossible that I could find sustenance for three years in such a country, and among such inhabitants.

When it grew towards evening, the master horse ordered a place for me to lodge in; it was but six yards from the house and separated from the stable of the Yahoos. Here I got some straw, and covering myself with my own clothes, slept very sound. But I was in a short time better accommodated, as the reader shall know hereafter, when I come to treat more particularly about my way of living.

CHAPTER III.

[The author studies to learn the language. The Houyhnhnm, his master, assists in teaching him. The language described. Several Houyhnhnms of quality come out of curiosity to see the author. He gives his master a short account of his voyage.]

My principal endeavour was to learn the language, which my master (for so I shall henceforth call him), and his children, and every servant of his house, were desirous to teach me; for they looked upon it as a prodigy, that a brute animal should discover such marks of a rational creature. I pointed to every thing, and inquired the name of it, which I wrote down in my journal-book when I was alone, and corrected my bad accent by desiring those of the family to pronounce it often. In this employment, a sorrel nag, one of the under-servants, was very ready to assist me.

In speaking, they pronounced through the nose and throat, and their language approaches nearest to the High-Dutch, or German, of any I know in Europe; but is much more graceful and significant. The emperor Charles V. made almost the same observation, when he said "that if he were to speak to his horse, it should be in High- Dutch."

The curiosity and impatience of my master were so great, that he spent many hours of his leisure to instruct me. He was convinced (as he afterwards told me) that I must be a Yahoo; but my teachableness, civility, and cleanliness, astonished him; which were qualities altogether opposite to those animals. He was most perplexed about my clothes, reasoning sometimes with himself, whether they were a part of my body: for I never pulled them off till the family were asleep, and got them on before they waked in the morning. My master was eager to learn "whence I came; how I acquired those appearances of reason, which I discovered in all my actions; and to know my story from my own mouth, which he hoped he should soon do by the great proficiency I made in learning and pronouncing their words and sentences." To help my memory, I formed all I learned into the English alphabet, and writ the words down, with the translations. This last, after some time, I ventured to do in my master's presence. It cost me much trouble to explain to him what I was doing; for the inhabitants have not the least idea of books or literature.

In about ten weeks time, I was able to understand most of his questions; and in three months, could give him some tolerable answers. He was extremely curious to know "from what part of the country I came, and how I was taught to imitate a rational creature; because the Yahoos (whom he saw I exactly resembled in my head, hands, and face, that were only visible), with some appearance of cunning, and the strongest disposition to mischief, were observed to be the most unteachable of all brutes." I answered, "that I came over the sea, from a far place, with many others of my own kind, in a great hollow vessel made of the bodies of trees: that my companions forced me to land on this coast, and then left me to shift for myself." It was with some difficulty, and by the help of many signs, that I brought him to understand me. He replied, "that I must needs be mistaken, or that I said the thing which was not;" for they have no word in their language to express lying or falsehood. "He knew it was impossible that there could be a country beyond the sea, or that a parcel of brutes could move a wooden vessel whither they pleased upon water. He was sure no Houyhnhnm alive could make such a vessel, nor would trust Yahoos to manage it."

The word Houyhnhnm, in their tongue, signifies a HORSE, and, in its etymology, the PERFECTION OF NATURE. I told my master, "that I was at a loss for expression, but would improve as fast as I could; and hoped, in a short time, I should be able to tell him wonders." He was pleased to direct his own mare, his colt, and foal, and the servants of the family, to take all opportunities of instructing me; and every day, for two or three hours, he was at the same pains himself. Several horses and mares of quality in the neighbourhood came often to our house, upon the report spread of "a wonderful Yahoo, that could speak like a Houyhnhnm, and seemed, in his words and actions, to discover some glimmerings of reason." These delighted to converse with me: they put many questions, and received such answers as I was able to return. By all these advantages I made so great a progress, that, in five months from my arrival I understood whatever was spoken, and could express myself tolerably well.

The Houyhnhnms, who came to visit my master out of a design of seeing and talking with me, could hardly believe me to be a right Yahoo, because my body had a different covering from others of my kind. They were astonished to observe me without the usual hair or skin, except on my head, face, and hands; but I discovered that secret to my master upon an accident which happened about a fortnight before.

I have already told the reader, that every night, when the family were gone to bed, it was my custom to strip, and cover myself with my clothes. It happened, one morning early, that my master sent for me by the sorrel nag, who was his valet. When he came I was fast asleep, my clothes fallen off on one side, and my shirt above my waist. I awaked at the noise he made, and observed him to deliver his message in some disorder; after which he went to my master, and in a great fright gave him a very confused account of what he had seen. This I presently discovered, for, going as soon as I was dressed to pay my attendance upon his honour, he asked me "the meaning of what his servant had reported, that I was not the same thing when I slept, as I appeared to be at other times; that his vale assured him, some part of me was white, some yellow, at least not so white, and some brown."

I had hitherto concealed the secret of my dress, in order to distinguish myself, as much as possible, from that cursed race of Yahoos; but now I found it in vain to do so any longer. Besides, I considered that my clothes and shoes would soon wear out, which already were in a declining condition, and must be supplied by some contrivance from the hides of Yahoos, or other brutes; whereby the whole secret would be known. I therefore told my master, "that in the country whence I came, those of my kind always covered their bodies with the hairs of certain animals prepared by art, as well for decency as to avoid the inclemencies of air, both hot and cold; of which, as to my own person, I would give him immediate conviction, if he pleased to command me: only desiring his excuse, if I did not expose those parts that nature taught us to conceal." He said, "my discourse was all very strange, but especially the last part; for he could not understand, why nature should teach us to conceal what nature had given; that neither himself nor family were ashamed of any parts of their bodies; but, however, I might do as I pleased." Whereupon I first unbuttoned my coat, and pulled it off. I did the same with my waistcoat. I drew off my shoes, stockings, and breeches. I let my shirt down to my waist, and drew up the bottom; fastening it like a girdle about my middle, to hide my nakedness.

My master observed the whole performance with great signs of curiosity and admiration. He took up all my clothes in his pastern, one piece after another, and examined them diligently; he then stroked my body very gently, and looked round me several times; after which, he said, it was plain I must be a perfect Yahoo; but that I differed very much from the rest of my species in the softness, whiteness, and smoothness of my skin; my want of hair in several parts of my body; the shape and shortness of my claws behind and before; and my affectation of walking continually on my two hinder feet. He desired to see no more; and gave me leave to put on my clothes again, for I was shuddering with cold.

I expressed my uneasiness at his giving me so often the appellation of Yahoo, an odious animal, for which I had so utter a hatred and contempt: I begged he would forbear applying that word to me, and make the same order in his family and among his friends whom he suffered to see me. I requested likewise, "that the secret of my having a false covering to my body, might be known to none but himself, at least as long as my present clothing should last; for as to what the sorrel nag, his valet, had observed, his honour might command him to conceal it."

All this my master very graciously consented to; and thus the secret was kept till my clothes began to wear out, which I was forced to supply by several contrivances that shall hereafter be mentioned. In the meantime, he desired "I would go on with my utmost diligence to learn their language, because he was more astonished at my capacity for speech and reason, than at the figure of my body, whether it were covered or not;" adding, "that he waited with some impatience to hear the wonders which I promised to tell him."

Thenceforward he doubled the pains he had been at to instruct me: he brought me into all company, and made them treat me with civility; "because," as he told them, privately, "this would put me into good humour, and make me more diverting."

Every day, when I waited on him, beside the trouble he was at in teaching, he would ask me several questions concerning myself, which I answered as well as I could, and by these means he had already received some general ideas, though very imperfect. It would be tedious to relate the several steps by which I advanced to a more regular conversation; but the first account I gave of myself in any order and length was to this purpose:

"That I came from a very far country, as I already had attempted to tell him, with about fifty more of my own species; that we travelled upon the seas in a great hollow vessel made of wood, and larger than his honour's house. I described the ship to him in the best terms I could, and explained, by the help of my handkerchief displayed, how it was driven forward by the wind. That upon a quarrel among us, I was set on shore on this coast, where I walked forward, without knowing whither, till he delivered me from the persecution of those execrable Yahoos." He asked me, "who made the ship, and how it was possible that the Houyhnhnms of my country would leave it to the management of brutes?" My answer was, "that I durst proceed no further in my relation, unless he would give me his word and honour that he would not be offended, and then I would tell him the wonders I had so often promised." He agreed; and I went on by assuring him, that the ship was made by creatures like myself; who, in all the countries I had travelled, as well as in my own, were the only governing rational animals; and that upon my arrival hither, I was as much astonished to see the Houyhnhnms act like rational beings, as he, or his friends, could be, in finding some marks of reason in a creature he was pleased to call a Yahoo; to which I owned my resemblance in every part, but could not account for their degenerate and brutal nature. I said farther, "that if good fortune ever restored me to my native country, to relate my travels hither, as I resolved to do, everybody would believe, that I said the thing that was not, that I invented the story out of my own head; and (with all possible respect to himself, his family, and friends, and under his promise of not being offended) our countrymen would hardly think it probable that a Houyhnhnm should be the presiding creature of a nation, and a Yahoo the brute."

CHAPTER IV.

[The Houyhnhnm's notion of truth and falsehood. The author's discourse disapproved by his master. The author gives a more particular account of himself, and the accidents of his voyage.]

My master heard me with great appearances of uneasiness in his countenance; because doubting, or not believing, are so little known in this country, that the inhabitants cannot tell how to behave themselves under such circumstances. And I remember, in frequent discourses with my master concerning the nature of manhood in other parts of the world, having occasion to talk of lying and false representation, it was with much difficulty that he comprehended what I meant, although he had otherwise a most acute judgment. For he argued thus: "that the use of speech was to make us understand one another, and to receive information of facts; now, if any one said the thing which was not, these ends were defeated, because I cannot properly be said to understand him; and I am so far from receiving information, that he leaves me worse than in ignorance; for I am led to believe a thing black, when it is white, and short, when it is long." And these were all the notions he had concerning that faculty of lying, so perfectly well understood, and so universally practised, among human creatures.

To return from this digression. When I asserted that the Yahoos were the only governing animals in my country, which my master said was altogether past his conception, he desired to know, "whether we had Houyhnhnms among us, and what was their employment?" I told him, "we had great numbers; that in summer they grazed in the fields, and in winter were kept in houses with hay and oats, where Yahoo servants were employed to rub their skins smooth, comb their manes, pick their feet, serve them with food, and make their beds." "I understand you well," said my master: "it is now very plain, from all you have spoken, that whatever share of reason the Yahoos pretend to, the Houyhnhnms are your masters; I heartily wish our Yahoos would be so tractable." I begged "his honour would please to excuse me from proceeding any further, because I was very certain that the account he expected from me would be highly displeasing." But he insisted in commanding me to let him know the best and the worst. I told him "he should be obeyed." I owned "that the Houyhnhnms among us, whom we called horses, were the most generous and comely animals we had; that they excelled in strength and swiftness; and when they belonged to persons of quality, were employed in travelling, racing, or drawing chariots; they were treated with much kindness and care, till they fell into diseases, or became foundered in the feet; but then they were sold, and used to all kind of drudgery till they died; after which their skins were stripped, and sold for what they were worth, and their bodies left to be devoured by dogs and birds of prey. But the common race of horses had not so good fortune, being kept by farmers and carriers, and other mean people, who put them to greater labour, and fed them worse." I described, as well as I could, our way of riding; the shape and use of a bridle, a saddle, a spur, and a whip; of harness and wheels. I added, "that we fastened plates of a certain hard substance, called iron, at the bottom of their feet, to preserve their hoofs from being broken by the stony ways, on which we often travelled."

My master, after some expressions of great indignation, wondered "how we dared to venture upon a Houyhnhnm's back; for he was sure, that the weakest servant in his house would be able to shake off the strongest Yahoo; or by lying down and rolling on his back, squeeze the brute to death." I answered "that our horses were trained up, from three or four years old, to the several uses we intended them for; that if any of them proved intolerably vicious, they were employed for carriages; that they were severely beaten, while they were young, for any mischievous tricks; that the males, designed for the common use of riding or draught, were generally castrated about two years after their birth, to take down their spirits, and make them more tame and gentle; that they were indeed sensible of rewards and punishments; but his honour would please to consider, that they had not the least tincture of reason, any more than the Yahoos in this country."

It put me to the pains of many circumlocutions, to give my master a right idea of what I spoke; for their language does not abound in variety of words, because their wants and passions are fewer than among us. But it is impossible to express his noble resentment at our savage treatment of the Houyhnhnm race; particularly after I had explained the manner and use of castrating horses among us, to hinder them from propagating their kind, and to render them more servile. He said, "if it were possible there could be any country where Yahoos alone were endued with reason, they certainly must be the governing animal; because reason in time will always prevail against brutal strength. But, considering the frame of our bodies, and especially of mine, he thought no creature of equal bulk was so ill-contrived for employing that reason in the common offices of life;" whereupon he desired to know whether those among whom I lived resembled me, or the Yahoos of his country?" I assured him, "that I was as well shaped as most of my age; but the younger, and the females, were much more soft and tender, and the skins of the latter generally as white as milk." He said, "I differed indeed from other Yahoos, being much more cleanly, and not altogether so deformed; but, in point of real advantage, he thought I differed for the worse: that my nails were of no use either to my fore or hinder feet; as to my fore feet, he could not properly call them by that name, for he never observed me to walk upon them; that they were too soft to bear the ground; that I generally went with them uncovered; neither was the covering I sometimes wore on them of the same shape, or so strong as that on my feet behind: that I could not walk with any security, for if either of my hinder feet slipped, I must inevitably fail." He then began to find fault with other parts of my body: "the flatness of my face, the prominence of my nose, mine eyes placed directly in front, so that I could not look on either side without turning my head: that I was not able to feed myself, without lifting one of my fore-feet to my mouth: and therefore nature had placed those joints to answer that necessity. He knew not what could be the use of those several clefts and divisions in my feet behind; that these were too soft to bear the hardness and sharpness of stones, without a covering made from the skin of some other brute; that my whole body wanted a fence against heat and cold, which I was forced to put on and off every day, with tediousness and trouble: and lastly, that he observed every animal in this country naturally to abhor the Yahoos, whom the weaker avoided, and the stronger drove from them. So that, supposing us to have the gift of reason, he could not see how it were possible to cure that natural antipathy, which every creature discovered against us; nor consequently how we could tame and render them serviceable. However, he would," as he said, "debate the matter no farther, because he was more desirous to know my own story, the country where I was born, and the several actions and events of my life, before I came hither."

I assured him, "how extremely desirous I was that he should be satisfied on every point; but I doubted much, whether it would be possible for me to explain myself on several subjects, whereof his honour could have no conception; because I saw nothing in his country to which I could resemble them; that, however, I would do my best, and strive to express myself by similitudes, humbly desiring his assistance when I wanted proper words;" which he was pleased to promise me.

I said, "my birth was of honest parents, in an island called England; which was remote from his country, as many days' journey as the strongest of his honour's servants could travel in the annual course of the sun; that I was bred a surgeon, whose trade it is to cure wounds and hurts in the body, gotten by accident or violence; that my country was governed by a female man, whom we called queen; that I left it to get riches, whereby I might maintain myself and family, when I should return; that, in my last voyage, I was commander of the ship, and had about fifty Yahoos under me, many of which died at sea, and I was forced to supply them by others picked out from several nations; that our ship was twice in danger of being sunk, the first time by a great storm, and the second by striking against a rock." Here my master interposed, by asking me, "how I could persuade strangers, out of different countries, to venture with me, after the losses I had sustained, and the hazards I had run?" I said, "they were fellows of desperate fortunes, forced to fly from the places of their birth on account of their poverty or their crimes. Some were undone by lawsuits; others spent all they had in drinking, whoring, and gaming; others fled for treason; many for murder, theft, poisoning, robbery, perjury, forgery, coining false money, for committing rapes, or sodomy; for flying from their colours, or deserting to the enemy; and most of them had broken prison; none of these durst return to their native countries, for fear of being hanged, or of starving in a jail; and therefore they were under the necessity of seeking a livelihood in other places."

During this discourse, my master was pleased to interrupt me several times. I had made use of many circumlocutions in describing to him the nature of the several crimes for which most of our crew had been forced to fly their country. This labour took up several days' conversation, before he was able to comprehend me. He was wholly at a loss to know what could be the use or necessity of practising those vices. To clear up which, I endeavoured to give some ideas of the desire of power and riches; of the terrible effects of lust, intemperance, malice, and envy. All this I was forced to define and describe by putting cases and making suppositions. After which, like one whose imagination was struck with something never seen or heard of before, he would lift up his eyes with amazement and indignation. Power, government, war, law, punishment, and a thousand other things, had no terms wherein that language could express them, which made the difficulty almost insuperable, to give my master any conception of what I meant. But being of an excellent understanding, much improved by contemplation and converse, he at last arrived at a competent knowledge of what human nature, in our parts of the world, is capable to perform, and desired I would give him some particular account of that land which we call Europe, but especially of my own country.

CHAPTER V.

[The author at his master's command, informs him of the state of England. The causes of war among the princes of Europe. The author begins to explain the English constitution.]

The reader may please to observe, that the following extract of many conversations I had with my master, contains a summary of the most material points which were discoursed at several times for above two years; his honour often desiring fuller satisfaction, as I farther improved in the Houyhnhnm tongue. I laid before him, as well as I could, the whole state of Europe; I discoursed of trade and manufactures, of arts and sciences; and the answers I gave to all the questions he made, as they arose upon several subjects, were a fund of conversation not to be exhausted. But I shall here only set down the substance of what passed between us concerning my own country, reducing it in order as well as I can, without any regard to time or other circumstances, while I strictly adhere to truth. My only concern is, that I shall hardly be able to do justice to my master's arguments and expressions, which must needs suffer by my want of capacity, as well as by a translation into our barbarous English.

In obedience, therefore, to his honour's commands, I related to him the Revolution under the Prince of Orange; the long war with France, entered into by the said prince, and renewed by his successor, the present queen, wherein the greatest powers of Christendom were engaged, and which still continued: I computed, at his request, "that about a million of Yahoos might have been killed in the whole progress of it; and perhaps a hundred or more cities taken, and five times as many ships burnt or sunk."

He asked me, "what were the usual causes or motives that made one country go to war with another?" I answered "they were innumerable; but I should only mention a few of the chief. Sometimes the ambition of princes, who never think they have land or people enough to govern; sometimes the corruption of ministers, who engage their master in a war, in order to stifle or divert the clamour of the subjects against their evil administration. Difference in opinions has cost many millions of lives: for instance, whether flesh be bread, or bread be flesh; whether the juice of a certain berry be blood or wine; whether whistling be a vice or a virtue; whether it be better to kiss a post, or throw it into the fire; what is the best colour for a coat, whether black, white, red, or gray; and whether it should be long or short, narrow or wide, dirty or clean; with many more. Neither are any wars so furious and bloody, or of so long a continuance, as those occasioned by difference in opinion, especially if it be in things indifferent.

"Sometimes the quarrel between two princes is to decide which of them shall dispossess a third of his dominions, where neither of them pretend to any right. Sometimes one prince quarrels with another for fear the other should quarrel with him. Sometimes a war is entered upon, because the enemy is too strong; and sometimes, because he is too weak. Sometimes our neighbours want the things which we have, or have the things which we want, and we both fight, till they take ours, or give us theirs. It is a very justifiable cause of a war, to invade a country after the people have been wasted by famine, destroyed by pestilence, or embroiled by factions among themselves. It is justifiable to enter into war against our nearest ally, when one of his towns lies convenient for us, or a territory of land, that would render our dominions round and complete. If a prince sends forces into a nation, where the people are poor and ignorant, he may lawfully put half of them to death, and make slaves of the rest, in order to civilize and reduce them from their barbarous way of living. It is a very kingly, honourable, and frequent practice, when one prince desires the assistance of another, to secure him against an invasion, that the assistant, when he has driven out the invader, should seize on the dominions himself, and kill, imprison, or banish, the prince he came to relieve. Alliance by blood, or marriage, is a frequent cause of war between princes; and the nearer the kindred is, the greater their disposition to quarrel; poor nations are hungry, and rich nations are proud; and pride and hunger will ever be at variance. For these reasons, the trade of a soldier is held the most honourable of all others; because a soldier is a Yahoo hired to kill, in cold blood, as many of his own species, who have never offended him, as possibly he can.

"There is likewise a kind of beggarly princes in Europe, not able to make war by themselves, who hire out their troops to richer nations, for so much a day to each man; of which they keep three- fourths to themselves, and it is the best part of their maintenance: such are those in many northern parts of Europe."

"What you have told me," said my master, "upon the subject of war, does indeed discover most admirably the effects of that reason you pretend to: however, it is happy that the shame is greater than the danger; and that nature has left you utterly incapable of doing much mischief. For, your mouths lying flat with your faces, you can hardly bite each other to any purpose, unless by consent. Then as to the claws upon your feet before and behind, they are so short and tender, that one of our Yahoos would drive a dozen of yours before him. And therefore, in recounting the numbers of those who have been killed in battle, I cannot but think you have said the thing which is not."

I could not forbear shaking my head, and smiling a little at his ignorance. And being no stranger to the art of war, I gave him a description of cannons, culverins, muskets, carabines, pistols, bullets, powder, swords, bayonets, battles, sieges, retreats, attacks, undermines, countermines, bombardments, sea fights, ships sunk with a thousand men, twenty thousand killed on each side, dying groans, limbs flying in the air, smoke, noise, confusion, trampling to death under horses' feet, flight, pursuit, victory; fields strewed with carcases, left for food to dogs and wolves and birds of prey; plundering, stripping, ravishing, burning, and destroying. And to set forth the valour of my own dear countrymen, I assured him, "that I had seen them blow up a hundred enemies at once in a siege, and as many in a ship, and beheld the dead bodies drop down in pieces from the clouds, to the great diversion of the spectators."

I was going on to more particulars, when my master commanded me silence. He said, "whoever understood the nature of Yahoos, might easily believe it possible for so vile an animal to be capable of every action I had named, if their strength and cunning equalled their malice. But as my discourse had increased his abhorrence of the whole species, so he found it gave him a disturbance in his mind to which he was wholly a stranger before. He thought his ears, being used to such abominable words, might, by degrees, admit them with less detestation: that although he hated the Yahoos of this country, yet he no more blamed them for their odious qualities, than he did a gnnayh (a bird of prey) for its cruelty, or a sharp stone for cutting his hoof. But when a creature pretending to reason could be capable of such enormities, he dreaded lest the corruption of that faculty might be worse than brutality itself. He seemed therefore confident, that, instead of reason we were only possessed of some quality fitted to increase our natural vices; as the reflection from a troubled stream returns the image of an ill shapen body, not only larger but more distorted."

He added, "that he had heard too much upon the subject of war, both in this and some former discourses. There was another point, which a little perplexed him at present. I had informed him, that some of our crew left their country on account of being ruined by law; that I had already explained the meaning of the word; but he was at a loss how it should come to pass, that the law, which was intended for every man's preservation, should be any man's ruin. Therefore he desired to be further satisfied what I meant by law, and the dispensers thereof, according to the present practice in my own country; because he thought nature and reason were sufficient guides for a reasonable animal, as we pretended to be, in showing us what he ought to do, and what to avoid."

I assured his honour, "that the law was a science in which I had not much conversed, further than by employing advocates, in vain, upon some injustices that had been done me: however, I would give him all the satisfaction I was able."

I said, "there was a society of men among us, bred up from their youth in the art of proving, by words multiplied for the purpose, that white is black, and black is white, according as they are paid. To this society all the rest of the people are slaves. For example, if my neighbour has a mind to my cow, he has a lawyer to prove that he ought to have my cow from me. I must then hire another to defend my right, it being against all rules of law that any man should be allowed to speak for himself. Now, in this case, I, who am the right owner, lie under two great disadvantages: first, my lawyer, being practised almost from his cradle in defending falsehood, is quite out of his element when he would be an advocate for justice, which is an unnatural office he always attempts with great awkwardness, if not with ill-will. The second disadvantage is, that my lawyer must proceed with great caution, or else he will be reprimanded by the judges, and abhorred by his brethren, as one that would lessen the practice of the law.

And therefore I have but two methods to preserve my cow. The first is, to gain over my adversary's lawyer with a double fee, who will then betray his client by insinuating that he hath justice on his side. The second way is for my lawyer to make my cause appear as unjust as he can, by allowing the cow to belong to my adversary: and this, if it be skilfully done, will certainly bespeak the favour of the bench. Now your honour is to know, that these judges are persons appointed to decide all controversies of property, as well as for the trial of criminals, and picked out from the most dexterous lawyers, who are grown old or lazy; and having been biassed all their lives against truth and equity, lie under such a fatal necessity of favouring fraud, perjury, and oppression, that I have known some of them refuse a large bribe from the side where justice lay, rather than injure the faculty, by doing any thing unbecoming their nature or their office.

"It is a maxim among these lawyers that whatever has been done before, may legally be done again: and therefore they take special care to record all the decisions formerly made against common justice, and the general reason of mankind. These, under the name of precedents, they produce as authorities to justify the most iniquitous opinions; and the judges never fail of directing accordingly.

"In pleading, they studiously avoid entering into the merits of the cause; but are loud, violent, and tedious, in dwelling upon all circumstances which are not to the purpose. For instance, in the case already mentioned; they never desire to know what claim or title my adversary has to my cow; but whether the said cow were red or black; her horns long or short; whether the field I graze her in be round or square; whether she was milked at home or abroad; what diseases she is subject to, and the like; after which they consult precedents, adjourn the cause from time to time, and in ten, twenty, or thirty years, come to an issue.

"It is likewise to be observed, that this society has a peculiar cant and jargon of their own, that no other mortal can understand, and wherein all their laws are written, which they take special care to multiply; whereby they have wholly confounded the very essence of truth and falsehood, of right and wrong; so that it will take thirty years to decide, whether the field left me by my ancestors for six generations belongs to me, or to a stranger three hundred miles off.

"In the trial of persons accused for crimes against the state, the method is much more short and commendable: the judge first sends to sound the disposition of those in power, after which he can easily hang or save a criminal, strictly preserving all due forms of law."

Here my master interposing, said, "it was a pity, that creatures endowed with such prodigious abilities of mind, as these lawyers, by the description I gave of them, must certainly be, were not rather encouraged to be instructors of others in wisdom and knowledge." In answer to which I assured his honour, "that in all points out of their own trade, they were usually the most ignorant and stupid generation among us, the most despicable in common conversation, avowed enemies to all knowledge and learning, and equally disposed to pervert the general reason of mankind in every other subject of discourse as in that of their own profession."

CHAPTER VI.

[A continuation of the state of England under Queen Anne. The character of a first minister of state in European courts.]

My master was yet wholly at a loss to understand what motives could incite this race of lawyers to perplex, disquiet, and weary themselves, and engage in a confederacy of injustice, merely for the sake of injuring their fellow-animals; neither could he comprehend what I meant in saying, they did it for hire. Whereupon I was at much pains to describe to him the use of money, the materials it was made of, and the value of the metals; "that when a Yahoo had got a great store of this precious substance, he was able to purchase whatever he had a mind to; the finest clothing, the noblest houses, great tracts of land, the most costly meats and drinks, and have his choice of the most beautiful females. Therefore since money alone was able to perform all these feats, our Yahoos thought they could never have enough of it to spend, or to save, as they found themselves inclined, from their natural bent either to profusion or avarice; that the rich man enjoyed the fruit of the poor man's labour, and the latter were a thousand to one in proportion to the former; that the bulk of our people were forced to live miserably, by labouring every day for small wages, to make a few live plentifully."

I enlarged myself much on these, and many other particulars to the same purpose; but his honour was still to seek; for he went upon a supposition, that all animals had a title to their share in the productions of the earth, and especially those who presided over the rest. Therefore he desired I would let him know, "what these costly meats were, and how any of us happened to want them?" Whereupon I enumerated as many sorts as came into my head, with the various methods of dressing them, which could not be done without sending vessels by sea to every part of the world, as well for liquors to drink as for sauces and innumerable other conveniences. I assured him "that this whole globe of earth must be at least three times gone round before one of our better female Yahoos could get her breakfast, or a cup to put it in." He said "that must needs be a miserable country which cannot furnish food for its own inhabitants. But what he chiefly wondered at was, how such vast tracts of ground as I described should be wholly without fresh water, and the people put to the necessity of sending over the sea for drink." I replied "that England (the dear place of my nativity) was computed to produce three times the quantity of food more than its inhabitants are able to consume, as well as liquors extracted from grain, or pressed out of the fruit of certain trees, which made excellent drink, and the same proportion in every other convenience of life. But, in order to feed the luxury and intemperance of the males, and the vanity of the females, we sent away the greatest part of our necessary things to other countries, whence, in return, we brought the materials of diseases, folly, and vice, to spend among ourselves. Hence it follows of necessity, that vast numbers of our people are compelled to seek their livelihood by begging, robbing, stealing, cheating, pimping, flattering, suborning, forswearing, forging, gaming, lying, fawning, hectoring, voting, scribbling, star-gazing, poisoning, whoring, canting, libelling, freethinking, and the like occupations:" every one of which terms I was at much pains to make him understand.

"That wine was not imported among us from foreign countries to supply the want of water or other drinks, but because it was a sort of liquid which made us merry by putting us out of our senses, diverted all melancholy thoughts, begat wild extravagant imaginations in the brain, raised our hopes and banished our fears, suspended every office of reason for a time, and deprived us of the use of our limbs, till we fell into a profound sleep; although it must be confessed, that we always awaked sick and dispirited; and that the use of this liquor filled us with diseases which made our lives uncomfortable and short.

"But beside all this, the bulk of our people supported themselves by furnishing the necessities or conveniences of life to the rich and to each other. For instance, when I am at home, and dressed as I ought to be, I carry on my body the workmanship of a hundred tradesmen; the building and furniture of my house employ as many more, and five times the number to adorn my wife."

I was going on to tell him of another sort of people, who get their livelihood by attending the sick, having, upon some occasions, informed his honour that many of my crew had died of diseases. But here it was with the utmost difficulty that I brought him to apprehend what I meant. "He could easily conceive, that a Houyhnhnm, grew weak and heavy a few days before his death, or by some accident might hurt a limb; but that nature, who works all things to perfection, should suffer any pains to breed in our bodies, he thought impossible, and desired to know the reason of so unaccountable an evil."

I told him "we fed on a thousand things which operated contrary to each other; that we ate when we were not hungry, and drank without the provocation of thirst; that we sat whole nights drinking strong liquors, without eating a bit, which disposed us to sloth, inflamed our bodies, and precipitated or prevented digestion; that prostitute female Yahoos acquired a certain malady, which bred rottenness in the bones of those who fell into their embraces; that this, and many other diseases, were propagated from father to son; so that great numbers came into the world with complicated maladies upon them; that it would be endless to give him a catalogue of all diseases incident to human bodies, for they would not be fewer than five or six hundred, spread over every limb and joint— in short, every part, external and intestine, having diseases appropriated to itself. To remedy which, there was a sort of people bred up among us in the profession, or pretence, of curing the sick. And because I had some skill in the faculty, I would, in gratitude to his honour, let him know the whole mystery and method by which they proceed.

"Their fundamental is, that all diseases arise from repletion; whence they conclude, that a great evacuation of the body is necessary, either through the natural passage or upwards at the mouth. Their next business is from herbs, minerals, gums, oils, shells, salts, juices, sea-weed, excrements, barks of trees, serpents, toads, frogs, spiders, dead men's flesh and bones, birds, beasts, and fishes, to form a composition, for smell and taste, the most abominable, nauseous, and detestable, they can possibly contrive, which the stomach immediately rejects with loathing, and this they call a vomit; or else, from the same store-house, with some other poisonous additions, they command us to take in at the orifice above or below (just as the physician then happens to be disposed) a medicine equally annoying and disgustful to the bowels; which, relaxing the belly, drives down all before it; and this they call a purge, or a clyster. For nature (as the physicians allege) having intended the superior anterior orifice only for the intromission of solids and liquids, and the inferior posterior for ejection, these artists ingeniously considering that in all diseases nature is forced out of her seat, therefore, to replace her in it, the body must be treated in a manner directly contrary, by interchanging the use of each orifice; forcing solids and liquids in at the anus, and making evacuations at the mouth.

"But, besides real diseases, we are subject to many that are only imaginary, for which the physicians have invented imaginary cures; these have their several names, and so have the drugs that are proper for them; and with these our female Yahoos are always infested.

"One great excellency in this tribe, is their skill at prognostics, wherein they seldom fail; their predictions in real diseases, when they rise to any degree of malignity, generally portending death, which is always in their power, when recovery is not: and therefore, upon any unexpected signs of amendment, after they have pronounced their sentence, rather than be accused as false prophets, they know how to approve their sagacity to the world, by a seasonable dose.

"They are likewise of special use to husbands and wives who are grown weary of their mates; to eldest sons, to great ministers of state, and often to princes."

I had formerly, upon occasion, discoursed with my master upon the nature of government in general, and particularly of our own excellent constitution, deservedly the wonder and envy of the whole world. But having here accidentally mentioned a minister of state, he commanded me, some time after, to inform him, "what species of Yahoo I particularly meant by that appellation."

I told him, "that a first or chief minister of state, who was the person I intended to describe, was the creature wholly exempt from joy and grief, love and hatred, pity and anger; at least, makes use of no other passions, but a violent desire of wealth, power, and titles; that he applies his words to all uses, except to the indication of his mind; that he never tells a truth but with an intent that you should take it for a lie; nor a lie, but with a design that you should take it for a truth; that those he speaks worst of behind their backs are in the surest way of preferment; and whenever he begins to praise you to others, or to yourself, you are from that day forlorn. The worst mark you can receive is a promise, especially when it is confirmed with an oath; after which, every wise man retires, and gives over all hopes.

"There are three methods, by which a man may rise to be chief minister. The first is, by knowing how, with prudence, to dispose of a wife, a daughter, or a sister; the second, by betraying or undermining his predecessor; and the third is, by a furious zeal, in public assemblies, against the corruption's of the court. But a wise prince would rather choose to employ those who practise the last of these methods; because such zealots prove always the most obsequious and subservient to the will and passions of their master. That these ministers, having all employments at their disposal, preserve themselves in power, by bribing the majority of a senate or great council; and at last, by an expedient, called an act of indemnity" (whereof I described the nature to him), "they secure themselves from after-reckonings, and retire from the public laden with the spoils of the nation.

"The palace of a chief minister is a seminary to breed up others in his own trade: the pages, lackeys, and porters, by imitating their master, become ministers of state in their several districts, and learn to excel in the three principal ingredients, of insolence, lying, and bribery. Accordingly, they have a subaltern court paid to them by persons of the best rank; and sometimes by the force of dexterity and impudence, arrive, through several gradations, to be successors to their lord.

"He is usually governed by a decayed wench, or favourite footman, who are the tunnels through which all graces are conveyed, and may properly be called, in the last resort, the governors of the kingdom."

One day, in discourse, my master, having heard me mention the nobility of my country, was pleased to make me a compliment which I could not pretend to deserve: "that he was sure I must have been born of some noble family, because I far exceeded in shape, colour, and cleanliness, all the Yahoos of his nation, although I seemed to fail in strength and agility, which must be imputed to my different way of living from those other brutes; and besides I was not only endowed with the faculty of speech, but likewise with some rudiments of reason, to a degree that, with all his acquaintance, I passed for a prodigy."

He made me observe, "that among the Houyhnhnms, the white, the sorrel, and the iron-gray, were not so exactly shaped as the bay, the dapple-gray, and the black; nor born with equal talents of mind, or a capacity to improve them; and therefore continued always in the condition of servants, without ever aspiring to match out of their own race, which in that country would be reckoned monstrous and unnatural."

I made his honour my most humble acknowledgments for the good opinion he was pleased to conceive of me, but assured him at the same time, "that my birth was of the lower sort, having been born of plain honest parents, who were just able to give me a tolerable education; that nobility, among us, was altogether a different thing from the idea he had of it; that our young noblemen are bred from their childhood in idleness and luxury; that, as soon as years will permit, they consume their vigour, and contract odious diseases among lewd females; and when their fortunes are almost ruined, they marry some woman of mean birth, disagreeable person, and unsound constitution (merely for the sake of money), whom they hate and despise. That the productions of such marriages are generally scrofulous, rickety, or deformed children; by which means the family seldom continues above three generations, unless the wife takes care to provide a healthy father, among her neighbours or domestics, in order to improve and continue the breed. That a weak diseased body, a meagre countenance, and sallow complexion, are the true marks of noble blood; and a healthy robust appearance is so disgraceful in a man of quality, that the world concludes his real father to have been a groom or a coachman. The imperfections of his mind run parallel with those of his body, being a composition of spleen, dullness, ignorance, caprice, sensuality, and pride.

"Without the consent of this illustrious body, no law can be enacted, repealed, or altered: and these nobles have likewise the decision of all our possessions, without appeal." {6}

CHAPTER VII.

[The author's great love of his native country. His master's observations upon the constitution and administration of England, as described by the author, with parallel cases and comparisons. His master's observations upon human nature.]

The reader may be disposed to wonder how I could prevail on myself to give so free a representation of my own species, among a race of mortals who are already too apt to conceive the vilest opinion of humankind, from that entire congruity between me and their Yahoos. But I must freely confess, that the many virtues of those excellent quadrupeds, placed in opposite view to human corruptions, had so far opened my eyes and enlarged my understanding, that I began to view the actions and passions of man in a very different light, and to think the honour of my own kind not worth managing; which, besides, it was impossible for me to do, before a person of so acute a judgment as my master, who daily convinced me of a thousand faults in myself, whereof I had not the least perception before, and which, with us, would never be numbered even among human infirmities. I had likewise learned, from his example, an utter detestation of all falsehood or disguise; and truth appeared so amiable to me, that I determined upon sacrificing every thing to it.

Let me deal so candidly with the reader as to confess that there was yet a much stronger motive for the freedom I took in my representation of things. I had not yet been a year in this country before I contracted such a love and veneration for the inhabitants, that I entered on a firm resolution never to return to humankind, but to pass the rest of my life among these admirable Houyhnhnms, in the contemplation and practice of every virtue, where I could have no example or incitement to vice. But it was decreed by fortune, my perpetual enemy, that so great a felicity should not fall to my share. However, it is now some comfort to reflect, that in what I said of my countrymen, I extenuated their faults as much as I durst before so strict an examiner; and upon every article gave as favourable a turn as the matter would bear. For, indeed, who is there alive that will not be swayed by his bias and partiality to the place of his birth?

I have related the substance of several conversations I had with my master during the greatest part of the time I had the honour to be in his service; but have, indeed, for brevity sake, omitted much more than is here set down.

When I had answered all his questions, and his curiosity seemed to be fully satisfied, he sent for me one morning early, and commanded me to sit down at some distance (an honour which he had never before conferred upon me). He said, "he had been very seriously considering my whole story, as far as it related both to myself and my country; that he looked upon us as a sort of animals, to whose share, by what accident he could not conjecture, some small pittance of reason had fallen, whereof we made no other use, than by its assistance, to aggravate our natural corruptions, and to acquire new ones, which nature had not given us; that we disarmed ourselves of the few abilities she had bestowed; had been very successful in multiplying our original wants, and seemed to spend our whole lives in vain endeavours to supply them by our own inventions; that, as to myself, it was manifest I had neither the strength nor agility of a common Yahoo; that I walked infirmly on my hinder feet; had found out a contrivance to make my claws of no use or defence, and to remove the hair from my chin, which was intended as a shelter from the sun and the weather: lastly, that I could neither run with speed, nor climb trees like my brethren," as he called them, "the Yahoos in his country.

"That our institutions of government and law were plainly owing to our gross defects in reason, and by consequence in virtue; because reason alone is sufficient to govern a rational creature; which was, therefore, a character we had no pretence to challenge, even from the account I had given of my own people; although he manifestly perceived, that, in order to favour them, I had concealed many particulars, and often said the thing which was not.

"He was the more confirmed in this opinion, because, he observed, that as I agreed in every feature of my body with other Yahoos, except where it was to my real disadvantage in point of strength, speed, and activity, the shortness of my claws, and some other particulars where nature had no part; so from the representation I had given him of our lives, our manners, and our actions, he found as near a resemblance in the disposition of our minds." He said, "the Yahoos were known to hate one another, more than they did any different species of animals; and the reason usually assigned was, the odiousness of their own shapes, which all could see in the rest, but not in themselves. He had therefore begun to think it not unwise in us to cover our bodies, and by that invention conceal many of our deformities from each other, which would else be hardly supportable. But he now found he had been mistaken, and that the dissensions of those brutes in his country were owing to the same cause with ours, as I had described them. For if," said he, "you throw among five Yahoos as much food as would be sufficient for fifty, they will, instead of eating peaceably, fall together by the ears, each single one impatient to have all to itself; and therefore a servant was usually employed to stand by while they were feeding abroad, and those kept at home were tied at a distance from each other: that if a cow died of age or accident, before a Houyhnhnm could secure it for his own Yahoos, those in the neighbourhood would come in herds to seize it, and then would ensue such a battle as I had described, with terrible wounds made by their claws on both sides, although they seldom were able to kill one another, for want of such convenient instruments of death as we had invented. At other times, the like battles have been fought between the Yahoos of several neighbourhoods, without any visible cause; those of one district watching all opportunities to surprise the next, before they are prepared. But if they find their project has miscarried, they return home, and, for want of enemies, engage in what I call a civil war among themselves.

"That in some fields of his country there are certain shining stones of several colours, whereof the Yahoos are violently fond: and when part of these stones is fixed in the earth, as it sometimes happens, they will dig with their claws for whole days to get them out; then carry them away, and hide them by heaps in their kennels; but still looking round with great caution, for fear their comrades should find out their treasure." My master said, "he could never discover the reason of this unnatural appetite, or how these stones could be of any use to a Yahoo; but now he believed it might proceed from the same principle of avarice which I had ascribed to mankind. That he had once, by way of experiment, privately removed a heap of these stones from the place where one of his Yahoos had buried it; whereupon the sordid animal, missing his treasure, by his loud lamenting brought the whole herd to the place, there miserably howled, then fell to biting and tearing the rest, began to pine away, would neither eat, nor sleep, nor work, till he ordered a servant privately to convey the stones into the same hole, and hide them as before; which, when his Yahoo had found, he presently recovered his spirits and good humour, but took good care to remove them to a better hiding place, and has ever since been a very serviceable brute."

My master further assured me, which I also observed myself, "that in the fields where the shining stones abound, the fiercest and most frequent battles are fought, occasioned by perpetual inroads of the neighbouring Yahoos."

He said, "it was common, when two Yahoos discovered such a stone in a field, and were contending which of them should be the proprietor, a third would take the advantage, and carry it away from them both;" which my master would needs contend to have some kind of resemblance with our suits at law; wherein I thought it for our credit not to undeceive him; since the decision he mentioned was much more equitable than many decrees among us; because the plaintiff and defendant there lost nothing beside the stone they contended for: whereas our courts of equity would never have dismissed the cause, while either of them had any thing left.

My master, continuing his discourse, said, "there was nothing that rendered the Yahoos more odious, than their undistinguishing appetite to devour every thing that came in their way, whether herbs, roots, berries, the corrupted flesh of animals, or all mingled together: and it was peculiar in their temper, that they were fonder of what they could get by rapine or stealth, at a greater distance, than much better food provided for them at home. If their prey held out, they would eat till they were ready to burst; after which, nature had pointed out to them a certain root that gave them a general evacuation.

"There was also another kind of root, very juicy, but somewhat rare and difficult to be found, which the Yahoos sought for with much eagerness, and would suck it with great delight; it produced in them the same effects that wine has upon us. It would make them sometimes hug, and sometimes tear one another; they would howl, and grin, and chatter, and reel, and tumble, and then fall asleep in the mud."

I did indeed observe that the Yahoos were the only animals in this country subject to any diseases; which, however, were much fewer than horses have among us, and contracted, not by any ill-treatment they meet with, but by the nastiness and greediness of that sordid brute. Neither has their language any more than a general appellation for those maladies, which is borrowed from the name of the beast, and called hnea-yahoo, or Yahoo's evil; and the cure prescribed is a mixture of their own dung and urine, forcibly put down the Yahoo's throat. This I have since often known to have been taken with success, and do here freely recommend it to my countrymen for the public good, as an admirable specific against all diseases produced by repletion.

"As to learning, government, arts, manufactures, and the like," my master confessed, "he could find little or no resemblance between the Yahoos of that country and those in ours; for he only meant to observe what parity there was in our natures. He had heard, indeed, some curious Houyhnhnms observe, that in most herds there was a sort of ruling Yahoo (as among us there is generally some leading or principal stag in a park), who was always more deformed in body, and mischievous in disposition, than any of the rest; that this leader had usually a favourite as like himself as he could get, whose employment was to lick his master's feet and posteriors, and drive the female Yahoos to his kennel; for which he was now and then rewarded with a piece of ass's flesh. This favourite is hated by the whole herd, and therefore, to protect himself, keeps always near the person of his leader. He usually continues in office till a worse can be found; but the very moment he is discarded, his successor, at the head of all the Yahoos in that district, young and old, male and female, come in a body, and discharge their excrements upon him from head to foot. But how far this might be applicable to our courts, and favourites, and ministers of state, my master said I could best determine."

I durst make no return to this malicious insinuation, which debased human understanding below the sagacity of a common hound, who has judgment enough to distinguish and follow the cry of the ablest dog in the pack, without being ever mistaken.

My master told me, "there were some qualities remarkable in the Yahoos, which he had not observed me to mention, or at least very slightly, in the accounts I had given of humankind." He said, "those animals, like other brutes, had their females in common; but in this they differed, that the she Yahoo would admit the males while she was pregnant; and that the hes would quarrel and fight with the females, as fiercely as with each other; both which practices were such degrees of infamous brutality, as no other sensitive creature ever arrived at.

"Another thing he wondered at in the Yahoos, was their strange disposition to nastiness and dirt; whereas there appears to be a natural love of cleanliness in all other animals." As to the two former accusations, I was glad to let them pass without any reply, because I had not a word to offer upon them in defence of my species, which otherwise I certainly had done from my own inclinations. But

I could have easily vindicated humankind from the imputation of singularity upon the last article, if there had been any swine in that country (as unluckily for me there were not), which, although it may be a sweeter quadruped than a Yahoo, cannot, I humbly conceive, in justice, pretend to more cleanliness; and so his honour himself must have owned, if he had seen their filthy way of feeding, and their custom of wallowing and sleeping in the mud.

My master likewise mentioned another quality which his servants had discovered in several Yahoos, and to him was wholly unaccountable. He said, "a fancy would sometimes take a Yahoo to retire into a corner, to lie down, and howl, and groan, and spurn away all that came near him, although he were young and fat, wanted neither food nor water, nor did the servant imagine what could possibly ail him. And the only remedy they found was, to set him to hard work, after which he would infallibly come to himself." To this I was silent out of partiality to my own kind; yet here I could plainly discover the true seeds of spleen, which only seizes on the lazy, the luxurious, and the rich; who, if they were forced to undergo the same regimen, I would undertake for the cure.

His honour had further observed, "that a female Yahoo would often stand behind a bank or a bush, to gaze on the young males passing by, and then appear, and hide, using many antic gestures and grimaces, at which time it was observed that she had a most offensive smell; and when any of the males advanced, would slowly retire, looking often back, and with a counterfeit show of fear, run off into some convenient place, where she knew the male would follow her.

"At other times, if a female stranger came among them, three or four of her own sex would get about her, and stare, and chatter, and grin, and smell her all over; and then turn off with gestures, that seemed to express contempt and disdain."

Perhaps my master might refine a little in these speculations, which he had drawn from what he observed himself, or had been told him by others; however, I could not reflect without some amazement, and much sorrow, that the rudiments of lewdness, coquetry, censure, and scandal, should have place by instinct in womankind.

I expected every moment that my master would accuse the Yahoos of those unnatural appetites in both sexes, so common among us. But nature, it seems, has not been so expert a school-mistress; and these politer pleasures are entirely the productions of art and reason on our side of the globe.

CHAPTER VIII.

[The author relates several particulars of the Yahoos. The great virtues of the Houyhnhnms. The education and exercise of their youth. Their general assembly.]

As I ought to have understood human nature much better than I supposed it possible for my master to do, so it was easy to apply the character he gave of the Yahoos to myself and my countrymen; and I believed I could yet make further discoveries, from my own observation. I therefore often begged his honour to let me go among the herds of Yahoos in the neighbourhood; to which he always very graciously consented, being perfectly convinced that the hatred I bore these brutes would never suffer me to be corrupted by them; and his honour ordered one of his servants, a strong sorrel nag, very honest and good-natured, to be my guard; without whose protection I durst not undertake such adventures. For I have already told the reader how much I was pestered by these odious animals, upon my first arrival; and I afterwards failed very narrowly, three or four times, of falling into their clutches, when I happened to stray at any distance without my hanger. And I have reason to believe they had some imagination that I was of their own species, which I often assisted myself by stripping up my sleeves, and showing my naked arms and breasts in their sight, when my protector was with me. At which times they would approach as near as they durst, and imitate my actions after the manner of monkeys, but ever with great signs of hatred; as a tame jackdaw with cap and stockings is always persecuted by the wild ones, when he happens to be got among them.

They are prodigiously nimble from their infancy. However, I once caught a young male of three years old, and endeavoured, by all marks of tenderness, to make it quiet; but the little imp fell a squalling, and scratching, and biting with such violence, that I was forced to let it go; and it was high time, for a whole troop of old ones came about us at the noise, but finding the cub was safe (for away it ran), and my sorrel nag being by, they durst not venture near us. I observed the young animal's flesh to smell very rank, and the stink was somewhat between a weasel and a fox, but much more disagreeable. I forgot another circumstance (and perhaps I might have the reader's pardon if it were wholly omitted), that while I held the odious vermin in my hands, it voided its filthy excrements of a yellow liquid substance all over my clothes; but by good fortune there was a small brook hard by, where I washed myself as clean as I could; although I durst not come into my master's presence until I were sufficiently aired.

By what I could discover, the Yahoos appear to be the most unteachable of all animals: their capacity never reaching higher than to draw or carry burdens. Yet I am of opinion, this defect arises chiefly from a perverse, restive disposition; for they are cunning, malicious, treacherous, and revengeful. They are strong and hardy, but of a cowardly spirit, and, by consequence, insolent, abject, and cruel. It is observed, that the red haired of both sexes are more libidinous and mischievous than the rest, whom yet they much exceed in strength and activity.

The Houyhnhnms keep the Yahoos for present use in huts not far from the house; but the rest are sent abroad to certain fields, where they dig up roots, eat several kinds of herbs, and search about for carrion, or sometimes catch weasels and luhimuhs (a sort of wild rat), which they greedily devour. Nature has taught them to dig deep holes with their nails on the side of a rising ground, wherein they lie by themselves; only the kennels of the females are larger, sufficient to hold two or three cubs.

They swim from their infancy like frogs, and are able to continue long under water, where they often take fish, which the females carry home to their young. And, upon this occasion, I hope the reader will pardon my relating an odd adventure.

Being one day abroad with my protector the sorrel nag, and the weather exceeding hot, I entreated him to let me bathe in a river that was near. He consented, and I immediately stripped myself stark naked, and went down softly into the stream. It happened that a young female Yahoo, standing behind a bank, saw the whole proceeding, and inflamed by desire, as the nag and I conjectured, came running with all speed, and leaped into the water, within five yards of the place where I bathed. I was never in my life so terribly frightened. The nag was grazing at some distance, not suspecting any harm. She embraced me after a most fulsome manner. I roared as loud as I could, and the nag came galloping towards me, whereupon she quitted her grasp, with the utmost reluctancy, and leaped upon the opposite bank, where she stood gazing and howling all the time I was putting on my clothes.

This was a matter of diversion to my master and his family, as well as of mortification to myself. For now I could no longer deny that I was a real Yahoo in every limb and feature, since the females had a natural propensity to me, as one of their own species. Neither was the hair of this brute of a red colour (which might have been some excuse for an appetite a little irregular), but black as a sloe, and her countenance did not make an appearance altogether so hideous as the rest of her kind; for I think she could not be above eleven years old.

Having lived three years in this country, the reader, I suppose, will expect that I should, like other travellers, give him some account of the manners and customs of its inhabitants, which it was indeed my principal study to learn.

As these noble Houyhnhnms are endowed by nature with a general disposition to all virtues, and have no conceptions or ideas of what is evil in a rational creature, so their grand maxim is, to cultivate reason, and to be wholly governed by it. Neither is reason among them a point problematical, as with us, where men can argue with plausibility on both sides of the question, but strikes you with immediate conviction; as it must needs do, where it is not mingled, obscured, or discoloured, by passion and interest. I remember it was with extreme difficulty that I could bring my master to understand the meaning of the word opinion, or how a point could be disputable; because reason taught us to affirm or deny only where we are certain; and beyond our knowledge we cannot do either. So that controversies, wranglings, disputes, and positiveness, in false or dubious propositions, are evils unknown among the Houyhnhnms. In the like manner, when I used to explain to him our several systems of natural philosophy, he would laugh, "that a creature pretending to reason, should value itself upon the knowledge of other people's conjectures, and in things where that knowledge, if it were certain, could be of no use." Wherein he agreed entirely with the sentiments of Socrates, as Plato delivers them; which I mention as the highest honour I can do that prince of philosophers. I have often since reflected, what destruction such doctrine would make in the libraries of Europe; and how many paths of fame would be then shut up in the learned world.

Friendship and benevolence are the two principal virtues among the Houyhnhnms; and these not confined to particular objects, but universal to the whole race; for a stranger from the remotest part is equally treated with the nearest neighbour, and wherever he goes, looks upon himself as at home. They preserve decency and civility in the highest degrees, but are altogether ignorant of ceremony. They have no fondness for their colts or foals, but the care they take in educating them proceeds entirely from the dictates of reason. And I observed my master to show the same affection to his neighbour's issue, that he had for his own. They will have it that nature teaches them to love the whole species, and it is reason only that makes a distinction of persons, where there is a superior degree of virtue.

When the matron Houyhnhnms have produced one of each sex, they no longer accompany with their consorts, except they lose one of their issue by some casualty, which very seldom happens; but in such a case they meet again; or when the like accident befalls a person whose wife is past bearing, some other couple bestow on him one of their own colts, and then go together again until the mother is pregnant. This caution is necessary, to prevent the country from being overburdened with numbers. But the race of inferior Houyhnhnms, bred up to be servants, is not so strictly limited upon this article: these are allowed to produce three of each sex, to be domestics in the noble families.

In their marriages, they are exactly careful to choose such colours as will not make any disagreeable mixture in the breed. Strength is chiefly valued in the male, and comeliness in the female; not upon the account of love, but to preserve the race from degenerating; for where a female happens to excel in strength, a consort is chosen, with regard to comeliness.

Courtship, love, presents, jointures, settlements have no place in their thoughts, or terms whereby to express them in their language. The young couple meet, and are joined, merely because it is the determination of their parents and friends; it is what they see done every day, and they look upon it as one of the necessary actions of a reasonable being. But the violation of marriage, or any other unchastity, was never heard of; and the married pair pass their lives with the same friendship and mutual benevolence, that they bear to all others of the same species who come in their way, without jealousy, fondness, quarrelling, or discontent.

In educating the youth of both sexes, their method is admirable, and highly deserves our imitation. These are not suffered to taste a grain of oats, except upon certain days, till eighteen years old; nor milk, but very rarely; and in summer they graze two hours in the morning, and as many in the evening, which their parents likewise observe; but the servants are not allowed above half that time, and a great part of their grass is brought home, which they eat at the most convenient hours, when they can be best spared from work.

Temperance, industry, exercise, and cleanliness, are the lessons equally enjoined to the young ones of both sexes: and my master thought it monstrous in us, to give the females a different kind of education from the males, except in some articles of domestic management; whereby, as he truly observed, one half of our natives were good for nothing but bringing children into the world; and to trust the care of our children to such useless animals, he said, was yet a greater instance of brutality.

But the Houyhnhnms train up their youth to strength, speed, and hardiness, by exercising them in running races up and down steep hills, and over hard stony grounds; and when they are all in a sweat, they are ordered to leap over head and ears into a pond or river. Four times a year the youth of a certain district meet to show their proficiency in running and leaping, and other feats of strength and agility; where the victor is rewarded with a song in his or her praise. On this festival, the servants drive a herd of Yahoos into the field, laden with hay, and oats, and milk, for a repast to the Houyhnhnms; after which, these brutes are immediately driven back again, for fear of being noisome to the assembly.

Every fourth year, at the vernal equinox, there is a representative council of the whole nation, which meets in a plain about twenty miles from our house, and continues about five or six days. Here they inquire into the state and condition of the several districts; whether they abound or be deficient in hay or oats, or cows, or Yahoos; and wherever there is any want (which is but seldom) it is immediately supplied by unanimous consent and contribution. Here likewise the regulation of children is settled: as for instance, if a Houyhnhnm has two males, he changes one of them with another that has two females; and when a child has been lost by any casualty, where the mother is past breeding, it is determined what family in the district shall breed another to supply the loss.

CHAPTER IX.

[A grand debate at the general assembly of the Houyhnhnms, and how it was determined. The learning of the Houyhnhnms. Their buildings. Their manner of burials. The defectiveness of their language.]

One of these grand assemblies was held in my time, about three months before my departure, whither my master went as the representative of our district. In this council was resumed their old debate, and indeed the only debate that ever happened in their country; whereof my master, after his return, give me a very particular account.

The question to be debated was, "whether the Yahoos should be exterminated from the face of the earth?" One of the members for the affirmative offered several arguments of great strength and weight, alleging, "that as the Yahoos were the most filthy, noisome, and deformed animals which nature ever produced, so they were the most restive and indocible, mischievous and malicious; they would privately suck the teats of the Houyhnhnms' cows, kill and devour their cats, trample down their oats and grass, if they were not continually watched, and commit a thousand other extravagancies." He took notice of a general tradition, "that Yahoos had not been always in their country; but that many ages ago, two of these brutes appeared together upon a mountain; whether produced by the heat of the sun upon corrupted mud and slime, or from the ooze and froth of the sea, was never known; that these Yahoos engendered, and their brood, in a short time, grew so numerous as to overrun and infest the whole nation; that the Houyhnhnms, to get rid of this evil, made a general hunting, and at last enclosed the whole herd; and destroying the elder, every Houyhnhnm kept two young ones in a kennel, and brought them to such a degree of tameness, as an animal, so savage by nature, can be capable of acquiring, using them for draught and carriage; that there seemed to be much truth in this tradition, and that those creatures could not be yinhniamshy (or aborigines of the land), because of the violent hatred the Houyhnhnms, as well as all other animals, bore them, which, although their evil disposition sufficiently deserved, could never have arrived at so high a degree if they had been aborigines, or else they would have long since been rooted out; that the inhabitants, taking a fancy to use the service of the Yahoos, had, very imprudently, neglected to cultivate the breed of asses, which are a comely animal, easily kept, more tame and orderly, without any offensive smell, strong enough for labour, although they yield to the other in agility of body, and if their braying be no agreeable sound, it is far preferable to the horrible howlings of the Yahoos."

Several others declared their sentiments to the same purpose, when my master proposed an expedient to the assembly, whereof he had indeed borrowed the hint from me. "He approved of the tradition mentioned by the honourable member who spoke before, and affirmed, that the two Yahoos said to be seen first among them, had been driven thither over the sea; that coming to land, and being forsaken by their companions, they retired to the mountains, and degenerating by degrees, became in process of time much more savage than those of their own species in the country whence these two originals came. The reason of this assertion was, that he had now in his possession a certain wonderful Yahoo (meaning myself) which most of them had heard of, and many of them had seen. He then related to them how he first found me; that my body was all covered with an artificial composure of the skins and hairs of other animals; that I spoke in a language of my own, and had thoroughly learned theirs; that I had related to him the accidents which brought me thither; that when he saw me without my covering, I was an exact Yahoo in every part, only of a whiter colour, less hairy, and with shorter claws. He added, how I had endeavoured to persuade him, that in my own and other countries, the Yahoos acted as the governing, rational animal, and held the Houyhnhnms in servitude; that he observed in me all the qualities of a Yahoo, only a little more civilized by some tincture of reason, which, however, was in a degree as far inferior to the Houyhnhnm race, as the Yahoos of their country were to me; that, among other things, I mentioned a custom we had of castrating Houyhnhnms when they were young, in order to render them tame; that the operation was easy and safe; that it was no shame to learn wisdom from brutes, as industry is taught by the ant, and building by the swallow (for so I translate the word lyhannh, although it be a much larger fowl); that this invention might be practised upon the younger Yahoos here, which besides rendering them tractable and fitter for use, would in an age put an end to the whole species, without destroying life; that in the mean time the Houyhnhnms should be exhorted to cultivate the breed of asses, which, as they are in all respects more valuable brutes, so they have this advantage, to be fit for service at five years old, which the others are not till twelve."

This was all my master thought fit to tell me, at that time, of what passed in the grand council. But he was pleased to conceal one particular, which related personally to myself, whereof I soon felt the unhappy effect, as the reader will know in its proper place, and whence I date all the succeeding misfortunes of my life.

The Houyhnhnms have no letters, and consequently their knowledge is all traditional. But there happening few events of any moment among a people so well united, naturally disposed to every virtue, wholly governed by reason, and cut off from all commerce with other nations, the historical part is easily preserved without burdening their memories. I have already observed that they are subject to no diseases, and therefore can have no need of physicians. However, they have excellent medicines, composed of herbs, to cure accidental bruises and cuts in the pastern or frog of the foot, by sharp stones, as well as other maims and hurts in the several parts of the body.

They calculate the year by the revolution of the sun and moon, but use no subdivisions into weeks. They are well enough acquainted with the motions of those two luminaries, and understand the nature of eclipses; and this is the utmost progress of their astronomy.

In poetry, they must be allowed to excel all other mortals; wherein the justness of their similes, and the minuteness as well as exactness of their descriptions, are indeed inimitable. Their verses abound very much in both of these, and usually contain either some exalted notions of friendship and benevolence or the praises of those who were victors in races and other bodily exercises. Their buildings, although very rude and simple, are not inconvenient, but well contrived to defend them from all injuries of and heat. They have a kind of tree, which at forty years old loosens in the root, and falls with the first storm: it grows very straight, and being pointed like stakes with a sharp stone (for the Houyhnhnms know not the use of iron), they stick them erect in the ground, about ten inches asunder, and then weave in oat straw, or sometimes wattles, between them. The roof is made after the same manner, and so are the doors.

The Houyhnhnms use the hollow part, between the pastern and the hoof of their fore-foot, as we do our hands, and this with greater dexterity than I could at first imagine. I have seen a white mare of our family thread a needle (which I lent her on purpose) with that joint. They milk their cows, reap their oats, and do all the work which requires hands, in the same manner. They have a kind of hard flints, which, by grinding against other stones, they form into instruments, that serve instead of wedges, axes, and hammers. With tools made of these flints, they likewise cut their hay, and reap their oats, which there grow naturally in several fields; the Yahoos draw home the sheaves in carriages, and the servants tread them in certain covered huts to get out the grain, which is kept in stores. They make a rude kind of earthen and wooden vessels, and bake the former in the sun.

If they can avoid casualties, they die only of old age, and are buried in the obscurest places that can be found, their friends and relations expressing neither joy nor grief at their departure; nor does the dying person discover the least regret that he is leaving the world, any more than if he were upon returning home from a visit to one of his neighbours. I remember my master having once made an appointment with a friend and his family to come to his house, upon some affair of importance: on the day fixed, the mistress and her two children came very late; she made two excuses, first for her husband, who, as she said, happened that very morning to shnuwnh. The word is strongly expressive in their language, but not easily rendered into English; it signifies, "to retire to his first mother." Her excuse for not coming sooner, was, that her husband dying late in the morning, she was a good while consulting her servants about a convenient place where his body should be laid; and I observed, she behaved herself at our house as cheerfully as the rest. She died about three months after.

They live generally to seventy, or seventy-five years, very seldom to fourscore. Some weeks before their death, they feel a gradual decay; but without pain. During this time they are much visited by their friends, because they cannot go abroad with their usual ease and satisfaction. However, about ten days before their death, which they seldom fail in computing, they return the visits that have been made them by those who are nearest in the neighbourhood, being carried in a convenient sledge drawn by Yahoos; which vehicle they use, not only upon this occasion, but when they grow old, upon long journeys, or when they are lamed by any accident: and therefore when the dying Houyhnhnms return those visits, they take a solemn leave of their friends, as if they were going to some remote part of the country, where they designed to pass the rest of their lives.

I know not whether it may be worth observing, that the Houyhnhnms have no word in their language to express any thing that is evil, except what they borrow from the deformities or ill qualities of the Yahoos. Thus they denote the folly of a servant, an omission of a child, a stone that cuts their feet, a continuance of foul or unseasonable weather, and the like, by adding to each the epithet of Yahoo. For instance, hhnm Yahoo; whnaholm Yahoo, ynlhmndwihlma Yahoo, and an ill-contrived house ynholmhnmrohlnw Yahoo.

I could, with great pleasure, enlarge further upon the manners and virtues of this excellent people; but intending in a short time to publish a volume by itself, expressly upon that subject, I refer the reader thither; and, in the mean time, proceed to relate my own sad catastrophe.

CHAPTER X.

[The author's economy, and happy life, among the Houyhnhnms. His great improvement in virtue by conversing with them. Their conversations. The author has notice given him by his master, that he must depart from the country. He falls into a swoon for grief; but submits. He contrives and finishes a canoe by the help of a fellow-servant, and puts to sea at a venture.]

I had settled my little economy to my own heart's content. My master had ordered a room to be made for me, after their manner, about six yards from the house: the sides and floors of which I plastered with clay, and covered with rush-mats of my own contriving. I had beaten hemp, which there grows wild, and made of it a sort of ticking; this I filled with the feathers of several birds I had taken with springes made of Yahoos' hairs, and were excellent food. I had worked two chairs with my knife, the sorrel nag helping me in the grosser and more laborious part. When my clothes were worn to rags, I made myself others with the skins of rabbits, and of a certain beautiful animal, about the same size, called nnuhnoh, the skin of which is covered with a fine down. Of these I also made very tolerable stockings. I soled my shoes with wood, which I cut from a tree, and fitted to the upper-leather; and when this was worn out, I supplied it with the skins of Yahoos dried in the sun. I often got honey out of hollow trees, which I mingled with water, or ate with my bread. No man could more verify the truth of these two maxims, "That nature is very easily satisfied;" and, "That necessity is the mother of invention." I enjoyed perfect health of body, and tranquillity of mind; I did not feel the treachery or inconstancy of a friend, nor the injuries of a secret or open enemy. I had no occasion of bribing, flattering, or pimping, to procure the favour of any great man, or of his minion; I wanted no fence against fraud or oppression: here was neither physician to destroy my body, nor lawyer to ruin my fortune; no informer to watch my words and actions, or forge accusations against me for hire: here were no gibers, censurers, backbiters, pickpockets, highwaymen, housebreakers, attorneys, bawds, buffoons, gamesters, politicians, wits, splenetics, tedious talkers, controvertists, ravishers, murderers, robbers, virtuosos; no leaders, or followers, of party and faction; no encouragers to vice, by seducement or examples; no dungeon, axes, gibbets, whipping-posts, or pillories; no cheating shopkeepers or mechanics; no pride, vanity, or affectation; no fops, bullies, drunkards, strolling whores, or poxes; no ranting, lewd, expensive wives; no stupid, proud pedants; no importunate, overbearing, quarrelsome, noisy, roaring, empty, conceited, swearing companions; no scoundrels raised from the dust upon the merit of their vices, or nobility thrown into it on account of their virtues; no lords, fiddlers, judges, or dancing-masters.

I had the favour of being admitted to several Houyhnhnms, who came to visit or dine with my master; where his honour graciously suffered me to wait in the room, and listen to their discourse. Both he and his company would often descend to ask me questions, and receive my answers. I had also sometimes the honour of attending my master in his visits to others. I never presumed to speak, except in answer to a question; and then I did it with inward regret, because it was a loss of so much time for improving myself; but I was infinitely delighted with the station of an humble auditor in such conversations, where nothing passed but what was useful, expressed in the fewest and most significant words; where, as I have already said, the greatest decency was observed, without the least degree of ceremony; where no person spoke without being pleased himself, and pleasing his companions; where there was no interruption, tediousness, heat, or difference of sentiments. They have a notion, that when people are met together, a short silence does much improve conversation: this I found to be true; for during those little intermissions of talk, new ideas would arise in their minds, which very much enlivened the discourse. Their subjects are, generally on friendship and benevolence, on order and economy; sometimes upon the visible operations of nature, or ancient traditions; upon the bounds and limits of virtue; upon the unerring rules of reason, or upon some determinations to be taken at the next great assembly: and often upon the various excellences of poetry. I may add, without vanity, that my presence often gave them sufficient matter for discourse, because it afforded my master an occasion of letting his friends into the history of me and my country, upon which they were all pleased to descant, in a manner not very advantageous to humankind: and for that reason I shall not repeat what they said; only I may be allowed to observe, that his honour, to my great admiration, appeared to understand the nature of Yahoos much better than myself. He went through all our vices and follies, and discovered many, which I had never mentioned to him, by only supposing what qualities a Yahoo of their country, with a small proportion of reason, might be capable of exerting; and concluded, with too much probability, "how vile, as well as miserable, such a creature must be."

I freely confess, that all the little knowledge I have of any value, was acquired by the lectures I received from my master, and from hearing the discourses of him and his friends; to which I should be prouder to listen, than to dictate to the greatest and wisest assembly in Europe. I admired the strength, comeliness, and speed of the inhabitants; and such a constellation of virtues, in such amiable persons, produced in me the highest veneration. At first, indeed, I did not feel that natural awe, which the Yahoos and all other animals bear toward them; but it grew upon me by decrees, much sooner than I imagined, and was mingled with a respectful love and gratitude, that they would condescend to distinguish me from the rest of my species.

When I thought of my family, my friends, my countrymen, or the human race in general, I considered them, as they really were, Yahoos in shape and disposition, perhaps a little more civilized, and qualified with the gift of speech; but making no other use of reason, than to improve and multiply those vices whereof their brethren in this country had only the share that nature allotted them. When I happened to behold the reflection of my own form in a lake or fountain, I turned away my face in horror and detestation of myself, and could better endure the sight of a common Yahoo than of my own person. By conversing with the Houyhnhnms, and looking upon them with delight, I fell to imitate their gait and gesture, which is now grown into a habit; and my friends often tell me, in a blunt way, "that I trot like a horse;" which, however, I take for a great compliment. Neither shall I disown, that in speaking I am apt to fall into the voice and manner of the Houyhnhnms, and hear myself ridiculed on that account, without the least mortification.

In the midst of all this happiness, and when I looked upon myself to be fully settled for life, my master sent for me one morning a little earlier than his usual hour. I observed by his countenance that he was in some perplexity, and at a loss how to begin what he had to speak. After a short silence, he told me, "he did not know how I would take what he was going to say: that in the last general assembly, when the affair of the Yahoos was entered upon, the representatives had taken offence at his keeping a Yahoo (meaning myself) in his family, more like a Houyhnhnm than a brute animal; that he was known frequently to converse with me, as if he could receive some advantage or pleasure in my company; that such a practice was not agreeable to reason or nature, or a thing ever heard of before among them; the assembly did therefore exhort him either to employ me like the rest of my species, or command me to swim back to the place whence I came: that the first of these expedients was utterly rejected by all the Houyhnhnms who had ever seen me at his house or their own; for they alleged, that because I had some rudiments of reason, added to the natural pravity of those animals, it was to be feared I might be able to seduce them into the woody and mountainous parts of the country, and bring them in troops by night to destroy the Houyhnhnms' cattle, as being naturally of the ravenous kind, and averse from labour."

My master added, "that he was daily pressed by the Houyhnhnms of the neighbourhood to have the assembly's exhortation executed, which he could not put off much longer. He doubted it would be impossible for me to swim to another country; and therefore wished I would contrive some sort of vehicle, resembling those I had described to him, that might carry me on the sea; in which work I should have the assistance of his own servants, as well as those of his neighbours." He concluded, "that for his own part, he could have been content to keep me in his service as long as I lived; because he found I had cured myself of some bad habits and dispositions, by endeavouring, as far as my inferior nature was capable, to imitate the Houyhnhnms."

I should here observe to the reader, that a decree of the general assembly in this country is expressed by the word hnhloayn, which signifies an exhortation, as near as I can render it; for they have no conception how a rational creature can be compelled, but only advised, or exhorted; because no person can disobey reason, without giving up his claim to be a rational creature.

I was struck with the utmost grief and despair at my master's discourse; and being unable to support the agonies I was under, I fell into a swoon at his feet. When I came to myself, he told me "that he concluded I had been dead;" for these people are subject to no such imbecilities of nature. I answered in a faint voice, "that death would have been too great a happiness; that although I could not blame the assembly's exhortation, or the urgency of his friends; yet, in my weak and corrupt judgment, I thought it might consist with reason to have been less rigorous; that I could not swim a league, and probably the nearest land to theirs might be distant above a hundred: that many materials, necessary for making a small vessel to carry me off, were wholly wanting in this country; which, however, I would attempt, in obedience and gratitude to his honour, although I concluded the thing to be impossible, and therefore looked on myself as already devoted to destruction; that the certain prospect of an unnatural death was the least of my evils; for, supposing I should escape with life by some strange adventure, how could I think with temper of passing my days among Yahoos, and relapsing into my old corruptions, for want of examples to lead and keep me within the paths of virtue? that I knew too well upon what solid reasons all the determinations of the wise Houyhnhnms were founded, not to be shaken by arguments of mine, a miserable Yahoo; and therefore, after presenting him with my humble thanks for the offer of his servants' assistance in making a vessel, and desiring a reasonable time for so difficult a work, I told him I would endeavour to preserve a wretched being; and if ever I returned to England, was not without hopes of being useful to my own species, by celebrating the praises of the renowned Houyhnhnms, and proposing their virtues to the imitation of mankind."

My master, in a few words, made me a very gracious reply; allowed me the space of two months to finish my boat; and ordered the sorrel nag, my fellow-servant (for so, at this distance, I may presume to call him), to follow my instruction; because I told my master, "that his help would be sufficient, and I knew he had a tenderness for me."

In his company, my first business was to go to that part of the coast where my rebellious crew had ordered me to be set on shore. I got upon a height, and looking on every side into the sea; fancied I saw a small island toward the north-east. I took out my pocket glass, and could then clearly distinguish it above five leagues off, as I computed; but it appeared to the sorrel nag to be only a blue cloud: for as he had no conception of any country beside his own, so he could not be as expert in distinguishing remote objects at sea, as we who so much converse in that element.

After I had discovered this island, I considered no further; but resolved it should if possible, be the first place of my banishment, leaving the consequence to fortune.

I returned home, and consulting with the sorrel nag, we went into a copse at some distance, where I with my knife, and he with a sharp flint, fastened very artificially after their manner, to a wooden handle, cut down several oak wattles, about the thickness of a walking-staff, and some larger pieces. But I shall not trouble the reader with a particular description of my own mechanics; let it suffice to say, that in six weeks time with the help of the sorrel nag, who performed the parts that required most labour, I finished a sort of Indian canoe, but much larger, covering it with the skins of Yahoos, well stitched together with hempen threads of my own making. My sail was likewise composed of the skins of the same animal; but I made use of the youngest I could get, the older being too tough and thick; and I likewise provided myself with four paddles. I laid in a stock of boiled flesh, of rabbits and fowls, and took with me two vessels, one filled with milk and the other with water.

I tried my canoe in a large pond, near my master's house, and then corrected in it what was amiss; stopping all the chinks with Yahoos' tallow, till I found it staunch, and able to bear me and my freight; and, when it was as complete as I could possibly make it, I had it drawn on a carriage very gently by Yahoos to the sea-side, under the conduct of the sorrel nag and another servant.

When all was ready, and the day came for my departure, I took leave of my master and lady and the whole family, my eyes flowing with tears, and my heart quite sunk with grief. But his honour, out of curiosity, and, perhaps, (if I may speak without vanity,) partly out of kindness, was determined to see me in my canoe, and got several of his neighbouring friends to accompany him. I was forced to wait above an hour for the tide; and then observing the wind very fortunately bearing toward the island to which I intended to steer my course, I took a second leave of my master: but as I was going to prostrate myself to kiss his hoof, he did me the honour to raise it gently to my mouth. I am not ignorant how much I have been censured for mentioning this last particular. Detractors are pleased to think it improbable, that so illustrious a person should descend to give so great a mark of distinction to a creature so inferior as I. Neither have I forgotten how apt some travellers are to boast of extraordinary favours they have received. But, if these censurers were better acquainted with the noble and courteous disposition of the Houyhnhnms, they would soon change their opinion.

I paid my respects to the rest of the Houyhnhnms in his honour's company; then getting into my canoe, I pushed off from shore.

CHAPTER XI.

[The author's dangerous voyage. He arrives at New Holland, hoping to settle there. Is wounded with an arrow by one of the natives. Is seized and carried by force into a Portuguese ship. The great civilities of the captain. The author arrives at England.]

I began this desperate voyage on February 15, 1714-15, at nine o'clock in the morning. The wind was very favourable; however, I made use at first only of my paddles; but considering I should soon be weary, and that the wind might chop about, I ventured to set up my little sail; and thus, with the help of the tide, I went at the rate of a league and a half an hour, as near as I could guess. My master and his friends continued on the shore till I was almost out of sight; and I often heard the sorrel nag (who always loved me) crying out, "Hnuy illa nyha, majah Yahoo;" "Take care of thyself, gentle Yahoo."

My design was, if possible, to discover some small island uninhabited, yet sufficient, by my labour, to furnish me with the necessaries of life, which I would have thought a greater happiness, than to be first minister in the politest court of Europe; so horrible was the idea I conceived of returning to live in the society, and under the government of Yahoos. For in such a solitude as I desired, I could at least enjoy my own thoughts, and reflect with delight on the virtues of those inimitable Houyhnhnms, without an opportunity of degenerating into the vices and corruptions of my own species.

The reader may remember what I related, when my crew conspired against me, and confined me to my cabin; how I continued there several weeks without knowing what course we took; and when I was put ashore in the long-boat, how the sailors told me, with oaths, whether true or false, "that they knew not in what part of the world we were." However, I did then believe us to be about 10 degrees southward of the Cape of Good Hope, or about 45 degrees southern latitude, as I gathered from some general words I overheard among them, being I supposed to the south-east in their intended voyage to Madagascar. And although this were little better than conjecture, yet I resolved to steer my course eastward, hoping to reach the south-west coast of New Holland, and perhaps some such island as I desired lying westward of it. The wind was full west, and by six in the evening I computed I had gone eastward at least eighteen leagues; when I spied a very small island about half a league off, which I soon reached. It was nothing but a rock, with one creek naturally arched by the force of tempests. Here I put in my canoe, and climbing a part of the rock, I could plainly discover land to the east, extending from south to north. I lay all night in my canoe; and repeating my voyage early in the morning, I arrived in seven hours to the south-east point of New Holland. This confirmed me in the opinion I have long entertained, that the maps and charts place this country at least three degrees more to the east than it really is; which thought I communicated many years ago to my worthy friend, Mr. Herman Moll, and gave him my reasons for it, although he has rather chosen to follow other authors.

I saw no inhabitants in the place where I landed, and being unarmed, I was afraid of venturing far into the country. I found some shellfish on the shore, and ate them raw, not daring to kindle a fire, for fear of being discovered by the natives. I continued three days feeding on oysters and limpets, to save my own provisions; and I fortunately found a brook of excellent water, which gave me great relief.

On the fourth day, venturing out early a little too far, I saw twenty or thirty natives upon a height not above five hundred yards from me. They were stark naked, men, women, and children, round a fire, as I could discover by the smoke. One of them spied me, and gave notice to the rest; five of them advanced toward me, leaving the women and children at the fire. I made what haste I could to the shore, and, getting into my canoe, shoved off: the savages, observing me retreat, ran after me: and before I could get far enough into the sea, discharged an arrow which wounded me deeply on the inside of my left knee: I shall carry the mark to my grave. I apprehended the arrow might be poisoned, and paddling out of the reach of their darts (being a calm day), I made a shift to suck the wound, and dress it as well as I could.

I was at a loss what to do, for I durst not return to the same landing-place, but stood to the north, and was forced to paddle, for the wind, though very gentle, was against me, blowing north- west. As I was looking about for a secure landing-place, I saw a sail to the north-north-east, which appearing every minute more visible, I was in some doubt whether I should wait for them or not; but at last my detestation of the Yahoo race prevailed: and turning my canoe, I sailed and paddled together to the south, and got into the same creek whence I set out in the morning, choosing rather to trust myself among these barbarians, than live with European Yahoos. I drew up my canoe as close as I could to the shore, and hid myself behind a stone by the little brook, which, as I have already said, was excellent water.

The ship came within half a league of this creek, and sent her long boat with vessels to take in fresh water (for the place, it seems, was very well known); but I did not observe it, till the boat was almost on shore; and it was too late to seek another hiding-place. The seamen at their landing observed my canoe, and rummaging it all over, easily conjectured that the owner could not be far off. Four of them, well armed, searched every cranny and lurking-hole, till at last they found me flat on my face behind the stone. They gazed awhile in admiration at my strange uncouth dress; my coat made of skins, my wooden-soled shoes, and my furred stockings; whence, however, they concluded, I was not a native of the place, who all go naked. One of the seamen, in Portuguese, bid me rise, and asked who I was. I understood that language very well, and getting upon my feet, said, "I was a poor Yahoo banished from the Houyhnhnms, and desired they would please to let me depart." They admired to hear me answer them in their own tongue, and saw by my complexion I must be a European; but were at a loss to know what I meant by Yahoos and Houyhnhnms; and at the same time fell a-laughing at my strange tone in speaking, which resembled the neighing of a horse. I trembled all the while betwixt fear and hatred. I again desired leave to depart, and was gently moving to my canoe; but they laid hold of me, desiring to know, "what country I was of? whence I came?" with many other questions. I told them "I was born in England, whence I came about five years ago, and then their country and ours were at peace. I therefore hoped they would not treat me as an enemy, since I meant them no harm, but was a poor Yahoo seeking some desolate place where to pass the remainder of his unfortunate life."

When they began to talk, I thought I never heard or saw any thing more unnatural; for it appeared to me as monstrous as if a dog or a cow should speak in England, or a Yahoo in Houyhnhnmland. The honest Portuguese were equally amazed at my strange dress, and the odd manner of delivering my words, which, however, they understood very well. They spoke to me with great humanity, and said, "they were sure the captain would carry me gratis to Lisbon, whence I might return to my own country; that two of the seamen would go back to the ship, inform the captain of what they had seen, and receive his orders; in the mean time, unless I would give my solemn oath not to fly, they would secure me by force. I thought it best to comply with their proposal. They were very curious to know my story, but I gave them very little satisfaction, and they all conjectured that my misfortunes had impaired my reason. In two hours the boat, which went laden with vessels of water, returned, with the captain's command to fetch me on board. I fell on my knees to preserve my liberty; but all was in vain; and the men, having tied me with cords, heaved me into the boat, whence I was taken into the ship, and thence into the captain's cabin.

His name was Pedro de Mendez; he was a very courteous and generous person. He entreated me to give some account of myself, and desired to know what I would eat or drink; said, "I should be used as well as himself;" and spoke so many obliging things, that I wondered to find such civilities from a Yahoo. However, I remained silent and sullen; I was ready to faint at the very smell of him and his men. At last I desired something to eat out of my own canoe; but he ordered me a chicken, and some excellent wine, and then directed that I should be put to bed in a very clean cabin. I would not undress myself, but lay on the bed-clothes, and in half an hour stole out, when I thought the crew was at dinner, and getting to the side of the ship, was going to leap into the sea, and swim for my life, rather than continue among Yahoos. But one of the seamen prevented me, and having informed the captain, I was chained to my cabin.

After dinner, Don Pedro came to me, and desired to know my reason for so desperate an attempt; assured me, "he only meant to do me all the service he was able;" and spoke so very movingly, that at last I descended to treat him like an animal which had some little portion of reason. I gave him a very short relation of my voyage; of the conspiracy against me by my own men; of the country where they set me on shore, and of my five years residence there. All which he looked upon as if it were a dream or a vision; whereat I took great offence; for I had quite forgot the faculty of lying, so peculiar to Yahoos, in all countries where they preside, and, consequently, their disposition of suspecting truth in others of their own species. I asked him, "whether it were the custom in his country to say the thing which was not?" I assured him, "I had almost forgot what he meant by falsehood, and if I had lived a thousand years in Houyhnhnmland, I should never have heard a lie from the meanest servant; that I was altogether indifferent whether he believed me or not; but, however, in return for his favours, I would give so much allowance to the corruption of his nature, as to answer any objection he would please to make, and then he might easily discover the truth."

The captain, a wise man, after many endeavours to catch me tripping in some part of my story, at last began to have a better opinion of my veracity. But he added, "that since I professed so inviolable an attachment to truth, I must give him my word and honour to bear him company in this voyage, without attempting any thing against my life; or else he would continue me a prisoner till we arrived at Lisbon." I gave him the promise he required; but at the same time protested, "that I would suffer the greatest hardships, rather than return to live among Yahoos."

Our voyage passed without any considerable accident. In gratitude to the captain, I sometimes sat with him, at his earnest request, and strove to conceal my antipathy against human kind, although it often broke out; which he suffered to pass without observation. But the greatest part of the day I confined myself to my cabin, to avoid seeing any of the crew. The captain had often entreated me to strip myself of my savage dress, and offered to lend me the best suit of clothes he had. This I would not be prevailed on to accept, abhorring to cover myself with any thing that had been on the back of a Yahoo. I only desired he would lend me two clean shirts, which, having been washed since he wore them, I believed would not so much defile me. These I changed every second day, and washed them myself.

We arrived at Lisbon, Nov. 5, 1715. At our landing, the captain forced me to cover myself with his cloak, to prevent the rabble from crowding about me. I was conveyed to his own house; and at my earnest request he led me up to the highest room backwards. I conjured him "to conceal from all persons what I had told him of the Houyhnhnms; because the least hint of such a story would not only draw numbers of people to see me, but probably put me in danger of being imprisoned, or burnt by the Inquisition." The captain persuaded me to accept a suit of clothes newly made; but I would not suffer the tailor to take my measure; however, Don Pedro being almost of my size, they fitted me well enough. He accoutred me with other necessaries, all new, which I aired for twenty-four hours before I would use them.

The captain had no wife, nor above three servants, none of which were suffered to attend at meals; and his whole deportment was so obliging, added to very good human understanding, that I really began to tolerate his company. He gained so far upon me, that I ventured to look out of the back window. By degrees I was brought into another room, whence I peeped into the street, but drew my head back in a fright. In a week's time he seduced me down to the door. I found my terror gradually lessened, but my hatred and contempt seemed to increase. I was at last bold enough to walk the street in his company, but kept my nose well stopped with rue, or sometimes with tobacco.

In ten days, Don Pedro, to whom I had given some account of my domestic affairs, put it upon me, as a matter of honour and conscience, "that I ought to return to my native country, and live at home with my wife and children." He told me, "there was an English ship in the port just ready to sail, and he would furnish me with all things necessary." It would be tedious to repeat his arguments, and my contradictions. He said, "it was altogether impossible to find such a solitary island as I desired to live in; but I might command in my own house, and pass my time in a manner as recluse as I pleased."

I complied at last, finding I could not do better. I left Lisbon the 24th day of November, in an English merchantman, but who was the master I never inquired. Don Pedro accompanied me to the ship, and lent me twenty pounds. He took kind leave of me, and embraced me at parting, which I bore as well as I could. During this last voyage I had no commerce with the master or any of his men; but, pretending I was sick, kept close in my cabin. On the fifth of December, 1715, we cast anchor in the Downs, about nine in the morning, and at three in the afternoon I got safe to my house at Rotherhith. {7}

My wife and family received me with great surprise and joy, because they concluded me certainly dead; but I must freely confess the sight of them filled me only with hatred, disgust, and contempt; and the more, by reflecting on the near alliance I had to them. For although, since my unfortunate exile from the Houyhnhnm country, I had compelled myself to tolerate the sight of Yahoos, and to converse with Don Pedro de Mendez, yet my memory and imagination were perpetually filled with the virtues and ideas of those exalted Houyhnhnms. And when I began to consider that, by copulating with one of the Yahoo species I had become a parent of more, it struck me with the utmost shame, confusion, and horror.

As soon as I entered the house, my wife took me in her arms, and kissed me; at which, having not been used to the touch of that odious animal for so many years, I fell into a swoon for almost an hour. At the time I am writing, it is five years since my last return to England. During the first year, I could not endure my wife or children in my presence; the very smell of them was intolerable; much less could I suffer them to eat in the same room. To this hour they dare not presume to touch my bread, or drink out of the same cup, neither was I ever able to let one of them take me by the hand. The first money I laid out was to buy two young stone-horses, which I keep in a good stable; and next to them, the groom is my greatest favourite, for I feel my spirits revived by the smell he contracts in the stable. My horses understand me tolerably well; I converse with them at least four hours every day. They are strangers to bridle or saddle; they live in great amity with me and friendship to each other.

CHAPTER XII.

[The author's veracity. His design in publishing this work. His censure of those travellers who swerve from the truth. The author clears himself from any sinister ends in writing. An objection answered. The method of planting colonies. His native country commended. The right of the crown to those countries described by the author is justified. The difficulty of conquering them. The author takes his last leave of the reader; proposes his manner of living for the future; gives good advice, and concludes.]

Thus, gentle reader, I have given thee a faithful history of my travels for sixteen years and above seven months: wherein I have not been so studious of ornament as of truth. I could, perhaps, like others, have astonished thee with strange improbable tales; but I rather chose to relate plain matter of fact, in the simplest manner and style; because my principal design was to inform, and not to amuse thee.

It is easy for us who travel into remote countries, which are seldom visited by Englishmen or other Europeans, to form descriptions of wonderful animals both at sea and land. Whereas a traveller's chief aim should be to make men wiser and better, and to improve their minds by the bad, as well as good, example of what they deliver concerning foreign places.

I could heartily wish a law was enacted, that every traveller, before he were permitted to publish his voyages, should be obliged to make oath before the Lord High Chancellor, that all he intended to print was absolutely true to the best of his knowledge; for then the world would no longer be deceived, as it usually is, while some writers, to make their works pass the better upon the public, impose the grossest falsities on the unwary reader. I have perused several books of travels with great delight in my younger days; but having since gone over most parts of the globe, and been able to contradict many fabulous accounts from my own observation, it has given me a great disgust against this part of reading, and some indignation to see the credulity of mankind so impudently abused. Therefore, since my acquaintance were pleased to think my poor endeavours might not be unacceptable to my country, I imposed on myself, as a maxim never to be swerved from, that I would strictly adhere to truth; neither indeed can I be ever under the least temptation to vary from it, while I retain in my mind the lectures and example of my noble master and the other illustrious Houyhnhnms of whom I had so long the honour to be an humble hearer.

- Nec si miserum Fortuna Sinonem
Finxit, vanum etiam, mendacemque improba finget.

I know very well, how little reputation is to be got by writings which require neither genius nor learning, nor indeed any other talent, except a good memory, or an exact journal. I know likewise, that writers of travels, like dictionary-makers, are sunk into oblivion by the weight and bulk of those who come last, and therefore lie uppermost. And it is highly probable, that such travellers, who

198

shall hereafter visit the countries described in this work of mine, may, by detecting my errors (if there be any), and adding many new discoveries of their own, justle me out of vogue, and stand in my place, making the world forget that ever I was an author. This indeed would be too great a mortification, if I wrote for fame: but as my sole intention was the public good, I cannot be altogether disappointed. For who can read of the virtues I have mentioned in the glorious Houyhnhnms, without being ashamed of his own vices, when he considers himself as the reasoning, governing animal of his country? I shall say nothing of those remote nations where Yahoos preside; among which the least corrupted are the Brobdingnagians; whose wise maxims in morality and government it would be our happiness to observe. But I forbear descanting further, and rather leave the judicious reader to his own remarks and application.

I am not a little pleased that this work of mine can possibly meet with no censurers: for what objections can be made against a writer, who relates only plain facts, that happened in such distant countries, where we have not the least interest, with respect either to trade or negotiations? I have carefully avoided every fault with which common writers of travels are often too justly charged. Besides, I meddle not the least with any party, but write without passion, prejudice, or ill-will against any man, or number of men, whatsoever. I write for the noblest end, to inform and instruct mankind; over whom I may, without breach of modesty, pretend to some superiority, from the advantages I received by conversing so long among the most accomplished Houyhnhnms. I write without any view to profit or praise. I never suffer a word to pass that may look like reflection, or possibly give the least offence, even to those who are most ready to take it. So that I hope I may with justice pronounce myself an author perfectly blameless; against whom the tribes of Answerers, Considerers, Observers, Reflectors, Detectors, Remarkers, will never be able to find matter for exercising their talents.

I confess, it was whispered to me, "that I was bound in duty, as a subject of England, to have given in a memorial to a secretary of state at my first coming over; because, whatever lands are discovered by a subject belong to the crown." But I doubt whether our conquests in the countries I treat of would be as easy as those of Ferdinando Cortez over the naked Americans. The Lilliputians, I think, are hardly worth the charge of a fleet and army to reduce them; and I question whether it might be prudent or safe to attempt the Brobdingnagians; or whether an English army would be much at their ease with the Flying Island over their heads. The Houyhnhnms indeed appear not to be so well prepared for war, a science to which they are perfect strangers, and especially against missive weapons. However, supposing myself to be a minister of state, I could never give my advice for invading them. Their prudence, unanimity, unacquaintedness with fear, and their love of their country, would amply supply all defects in the military art. Imagine twenty thousand of them breaking into the midst of an European army, confounding the ranks, overturning the carriages, battering the warriors' faces into mummy by terrible yerks from their hinder hoofs; for they would well deserve the character given to Augustus, *Recalcitrat undique tutus*. But, instead of proposals for conquering that magnanimous nation, I rather wish they were in a capacity, or disposition, to send a sufficient number of their inhabitants for civilizing Europe, by teaching us the first principles of honour, justice, truth, temperance, public spirit, fortitude, chastity, friendship, benevolence, and fidelity. The names of all which virtues are still retained among us in most languages, and are to be met with in modern, as well as ancient authors; which I am able to assert from my own small reading.

But I had another reason, which made me less forward to enlarge his majesty's dominions by my discoveries. To say the truth, I had conceived a few scruples with relation to the distributive justice of princes upon those occasions. For instance, a crew of pirates are driven by a storm they know not whither; at length a boy discovers land from the topmast; they go on shore to rob and plunder, they see a harmless people, are entertained with kindness; they give the country a new name; they take formal possession of it for their king; they set up a rotten plank, or a stone, for a memorial; they murder two or three dozen of the natives, bring away a couple more, by force, for a sample; return home, and get their pardon. Here commences a new dominion acquired with a title by divine right. Ships are sent with the first opportunity; the natives driven out or destroyed; their princes tortured to discover their gold; a free license given to all acts of inhumanity and lust, the earth reeking with the blood of its inhabitants: and this execrable crew of butchers, employed in so pious an expedition, is a modern colony, sent to convert and civilize an idolatrous and barbarous people!

But this description, I confess, does by no means affect the British nation, who may be an example to the whole world for their wisdom, care, and justice in planting colonies; their liberal endowments for the advancement of religion and learning; their choice of devout and able pastors to propagate Christianity; their caution in stocking their provinces with people of sober lives and conversations from this the mother kingdom; their strict regard to the distribution of justice, in supplying the civil administration through all their colonies with officers of the greatest abilities, utter strangers to corruption; and, to crown all, by sending the most vigilant and virtuous governors, who have no other views than the happiness of the people over whom they preside, and the honour of the king their master.

But as those countries which I have described do not appear to have any desire of being conquered and enslaved, murdered or driven out by colonies, nor abound either in gold, silver, sugar, or tobacco, I did humbly conceive, they were by no means proper objects of our zeal, our valour, or our interest. However, if those whom it more concerns think fit to be of another opinion, I am ready to depose, when I shall be lawfully called, that no European did ever visit those countries before me. I mean, if the inhabitants ought to be believed, unless a dispute may arise concerning the two Yahoos, said to have been seen many years ago upon a mountain in Houyhnhnmland.

But, as to the formality of taking possession in my sovereign's name, it never came once into my thoughts; and if it had, yet, as my affairs then stood, I should perhaps, in point of prudence and self-preservation, have put it off to a better opportunity.

Having thus answered the only objection that can ever be raised against me as a traveller, I here take a final leave of all my courteous readers, and return to enjoy my own speculations in my little garden at Redriff; to apply those excellent lessons of virtue which I learned among the Houyhnhnms; to instruct the Yahoos of my own family, is far as I shall find them docible animals; to behold my figure often in a glass, and thus, if possible, habituate myself by time to tolerate the sight of a human creature; to lament the brutality to Houyhnhnms in my own country, but always treat their persons with respect, for the sake of my noble master, his family, his friends, and the whole Houyhnhnm race, whom these of ours have the honour to resemble in all their lineaments, however their intellectuals came to degenerate.

I began last week to permit my wife to sit at dinner with me, at the farthest end of a long table; and to answer (but with the utmost brevity) the few questions I asked her. Yet, the smell of a Yahoo continuing very offensive, I always keep my nose well stopped with rue, lavender, or tobacco leaves. And, although it be hard for a man late in life to remove old habits, I am not altogether out of hopes, in some time, to suffer a neighbour Yahoo in my company, without the apprehensions I am yet under of his teeth or his claws.

My reconcilement to the Yahoo kind in general might not be so difficult, if they would be content with those vices and follies only which nature has entitled them to. I am not in the least provoked at the sight of a lawyer, a pickpocket, a colonel, a fool, a lord, a gamester, a politician, a whoremonger, a physician, an evidence, a suborner, an attorney, a traitor, or the like; this is all according to the due course of things: but when I behold a lump of deformity and diseases, both in body and mind, smitten with pride, it immediately breaks all the measures of my patience; neither shall I be ever able to comprehend how such an animal, and such a vice, could tally together. The wise and virtuous Houyhnhnms, who abound in all excellences that can adorn a rational creature, have no name for this vice in their language, which has no terms to express any thing that is evil, except those whereby they describe the detestable qualities of their Yahoos, among which they were not able to distinguish this of pride, for want of thoroughly understanding human nature, as it shows itself in other countries where that animal presides. But I, who had more experience, could plainly observe some rudiments of it among the wild Yahoos.

But the Houyhnhnms, who live under the government of reason, are no more proud of the good qualities they possess, than I should be for not wanting a leg or an arm; which no man in his wits would boast of, although he must be miserable without them. I dwell the longer upon this subject from the desire I have to make the society of an English Yahoo by any means not insupportable;

and therefore I here entreat those who have any tincture of this absurd vice, that they will not presume to come in my sight.

Footnotes:

{1} A stang is a pole or perch; sixteen feet and a half.

{2} An act of parliament has been since passed by which some breaches of trust have been made capital.

{3} Britannia.—Sir W. Scott.

{4} London.—Sir W. Scott.

{5} This is the revised text adopted by Dr. Hawksworth (1766). The above paragraph in the original editions (1726) takes another form, commencing:- "I told him that should I happen to live in a kingdom where lots were in vogue," &c. The names Tribnia and Langdon an not mentioned, and the "close stool" and its signification do not occur.

{6} This paragraph is not in the original editions.

{7} The original editions and Hawksworth's have Rotherhith here, though earlier in the work, Redriff is said to have been Gulliver's home in England.

NEUROLOGICAL DISORDERS
IN THE ELDERLY

Neurological Disorders in the Elderly

Edited by
F. I. Caird DM FRCP

David Cargill Professor of Geriatric Medicine, University of Glasgow

With a Foreword by
John A. Simpson MD FRCP (Lond, Glas & Edin)

Professor of Neurology, University of Glasgow; Physician in Charge of the Department of Neurology, Institute of Neurological Sciences, Southern General Hospital and Western Infirmary, Glasgow

WRIGHT · PSG
Bristol London Boston
1982

Published by:

John Wright & Sons Ltd, 42–44 Triangle West, Bristol BS8 1EX, England

John Wright PSG Inc., 545 Great Road, Littleton, Massachusetts 01460, U.S.A.

British Library Cataloguing in Publication Data
Neurological disorders in the elderly.
   1. Nervous system—Diseases
   2. Geriatrics
   I. Caird, F. I.
   618.97'68   RC346

ISBN 0 7236 0632 3

Library of Congress Catalog Card Number: 81-71454

Printed in Great Britain by John Wright & Sons (Printing) Ltd, at The Stonebridge Press, Bristol BS4 5NU

Preface

Disorders of the nervous system have long been recognized as of particular importance in old age. There are in the first place changes in the anatomy and function of the nervous system which are clearly age-related, and are very probably truly attributable to ageing. In addition, there are common diseases which constitute the most frequent causes of disability in the elderly, and pose major problems to those who are involved in the care of old people. The purpose of the present volume is to bring together the views of experts in the various fields in question, so as to give an account of the present state of scientific knowledge and to provide practical advice on the numerous considerations of diagnosis and management encountered in everyday practice. It is hoped that the attention given to modern non-invasive diagnostic measures and to the possibilities of judicious drug therapy and of surgical intervention will be of particular value.

It is a pleasure to thank numerous colleagues, especially in the Institute of Neurological Sciences, Glasgow, who have over the years helped in forming and sustaining my own views on the neurology of old age, and Mr Roy Baker of John Wright & Sons Ltd, for his assistance and guidance with the practical problems of a multi-author volume.

F.I.C.

Contributors

A. J. Akhtar FRCP
Consultant Physician in Geriatric Medicine,
Royal Victoria Hospital, Edinburgh

K. Andrews MRCP
Consultant Physician in Geriatric Medicine,
University Hospital of South Manchester

D. M. Bowen PhD
Senior Lecturer in Neurochemistry,
Miriam Marks Department of Neurochemistry, The National
Hospital, London

H. Brody PhD MD
Professor and Chairman, Department of Anatomical Sciences,
Center for the Study of Aging
State University of New York at Buffalo

G. A. Broe FRACP
Consultant Neurologist,
Lidcombe Hospital, Lidcombe, New South Wales

F. I. Caird DM FRCP
David Cargill Professor of Geriatric Medicine,
University of Glasgow

A. N. Davison BSc PhD DSc FRCPath
Professor of Neurochemistry,
Miriam Marks Department of Neurochemistry, The National
Hospital, London

J. Grimley Evans FRCP MFCM
Professor of Geriatrics (Medicine),
University of Newcastle upon Tyne

A. N. Exton-Smith CBE MA MD FRCP
Barlow Professor of Geriatric Medicine,
University College London

John S. Garfield MChir FRCP FRCS
Consultant Neurosurgeon,
Wessex Neurological Centre, Southampton General Hospital

W. M. Garraway MD MFCM
Senior Lecturer in Community Medicine,
The Usher Institute, University of Edinburgh

Marion Hildick-Smith MD FRCP
Consultant Physician in Geratric Medicine,
Nunnery Fields Hospital, Canterbury

N. M. Hyman MRCP
Consultant Neurologist,
The Radcliffe Infirmary, Oxford.

B. Isaacs MD FRCP
Charles Hayward Professor of Geriatric Medicine,
University of Birmingham

B. Jennett MD FRCS
Professor of Neurosurgery,
Institute of Neurological Sciences, Glasgow

J. G. McLeod DPhil FRACP FRCP
Bushell Professor of Neurology
Department of Medicine, University of Sydney

J. Marshall MD FRCP
Professor of Clinical Neurology,
Institute of Neurology, University of London

Margaret A. Roberts MRCP
Consultant Physician in Geriatric Medicine,
Victoria Infirmary, Glasgow

J. W. Turner FRCS
Consultant Neurosurgeon,
Institute of Neurological Sciences, Glasgow

Contents

Foreword

A neurologist does not require to be convinced of the benefits of specialization. Even within our discipline a striking development of the last thirty years has been the growth of centres with special expertise in limited aspects of neurology, such as neuromuscular diseases, disorders of higher nervous functions, epilepsy and disorders of movement, with corresponding acceleration of knowledge. This has been advantageous to our patients but has made it difficult for the general neurologist to remain expert in all aspects of his specialty.

Despite initial resistance from both neurologists and paediatricians, the role of paediatric neurology is now well established and it is in this area that most of the advances in clinical neurochemistry have taken place. Few general neurologists would now claim expertise in this field though it might be conceded that this is an inevitable result of removing an important group of diseases from the training and regular experience of the general neurologist. To repeat this limitation at the other end of life is a serious consideration, especially with the inexorable change of society towards a geriatric population. It would require the same sort of justification as paediatric neurology.

In previous years I have considered that the additional problems of old age consisted, in the main, of the cumulative loss of compensatory mechanisms of the nervous system, progressive loss of mental faculties including initiative, and skeletomotor and circulatory problems. The special problems of the aged are dementia and disorders of balance. Unquestionably, dementia is the most important neurological problem for the immediate future. Like the developmental age group, it is at this other extreme of life that neurochemistry is again the fundamental discipline with exciting prospects for diagnosis and treatment of neurotransmitter and receptor disorders. There will remain an important element of secondary disorders of ageing in every organ, including altered metabolism of drugs, and social problems with which the skilled geriatrician has become familiar. How these factors modify the response to familiar disorders and their management will be clear from the following chapters. The geriatric specialist will welcome this valuable compilation of source material and experienced advice on the management of the numerically greatest problems of old age, but it is my special pleasure to commend the book to my colleagues in neurology as the first systematic account of the practice of neurology in the aged and a challenge to look more carefully at those aspects of the failing nervous system which are not subsumed under conventional categories of disease.

John A. Simpson

1. EPIDEMIOLOGY OF NEUROLOGICAL DISORDERS IN OLD AGE

J. Grimley Evans and F. I. Caird

The aim of epidemiological studies is to illustrate the magnitude of a clinical problem and so provide data for the rational planning and organization of health care services, and to suggest causal mechanisms of disease, and thus potential preventive measures. Both these principles are evident in the epidemiology of neurological disorders in old age, and it is the purpose of this chapter to give a critical account of the present state of knowledge of the epidemiology of five common conditions in old age: cerebrovascular disease, Parkinson's disease, motor neurone disease, epilepsy and intracranial tumour.

CEREBROVASCULAR DISEASE

Stroke is a clinical syndrome of focal central nervous system damage of abrupt onset due to ischaemia or haemorrhage. The ischaemia may be due to thrombosis or embolism or to haemodynamic mechanisms in which blood flow is impaired even though the arteries remain patent. Prolonged systemic hypotension due to cardiac arrest or other major vascular catastrophe may produce diffuse cerebral neuronal loss or more localized damage in the watershed zones between the vascular fields supplied by the major cerebral arteries (Adams, 1979). By analogy, it is suspected that minor episodes of hypotension due to cardiac arrhythmias or localized disturbance of blood flow due to vasospasm (Loach and Benedict, 1980) or the impaired cerebral autoregulation observed in some old people may sometimes cause stroke. For obvious reasons it is difficult to obtain direct evidence on the importance of such mechanisms: the mere finding of ischaemic cerebral damage in the presence of patent arteries does not exclude the possibility of previous arterial obstruction by platelet aggregates which have subsequently dispersed.

A further complication may arise within the general category of thrombotic stroke. There is some evidence that there may be differences in the relative frequency of intracranial and extracranial arterial lesions in patients of different racial origins (Resch et al., 1969; Heyman et al., 1972). The variations may be associated with differences in the relative frequency of clinical syndromes of stroke but it is not clear whether they are primarily racial in origin or due to variation in the pattern of the precursors of atherosclerosis—hypertension, diabetes and hyper-cholesterolaemia (Heyden et al., 1970).

Thus the pathogenesis of stroke is heterogeneous. At first sight it might seem essential to consider the epidemiology of the different pathogenetic forms of stroke rather than the clinical syndrome as a whole. In the present state of knowledge, however, this is both impracticable and, in middle and late adult life, probably unhelpful. It is impracticable because the clinical distinction between haemorrhage and thromboembolism is notoriously unreliable, and CT scanning is not yet sufficiently widely available to provide epidemiologically sound data on the incidence of the different types of lesion in defined and representative populations. It is unhelpful because in later adult life all the common pathogenetic mechanisms of stroke are likely to have their major basis in age-associated arterial disease, although other con-ditions, such as mitral annulus calcification, contribute (de Bono and Warlow, 1979). The various forms of stroke may therefore differ in pathogenesis but be similar in aetiology to which the epidemiological method is primarily sensitive. At younger ages, when atherosclerotic arterial disease is less extensive, stroke will be in a higher proportion of cases due to specific causes, such as arteritis, coagulation defects or vascular anomalies which have distinct aetiologies. Specific causative agents, such as oral contraception or alcoholic debauch (Hillbom and Kaste, 1978), will be relatively more important at younger ages than at older. Mitral valve prolapse may also be a factor associated with stroke in younger but not in older subjects (Barnett et al., 1980).

In the epidemiology of stroke in childhood or early adult life separation of the different pathogenetic types is therefore essential. This chapter is concerned only with stroke in middle and older age and will make little attempt to discuss haemorrhagic and thromboembolic stroke separately. For what it is worth, published clinical data suggest that up to middle age infarctive and haemorrhagic strokes are approxi-mately equally common, and thereafter the incidence of cerebral infarction increases more steeply with age than does the incidence of haemorrhage (Abu-Zeid et al., 1975). It is, however, noteworthy that the incidence of stroke 'of undetermined type' increases even more rapidly with age, while age-associated trends in intensity of in-vestigation may be confusing the picture.

Overall the annual incidence of stroke is about 2 per 1000 at all ages and 18 per 1000 in persons aged over 65 among whom about 75 per cent of all strokes occur. Prevalence rates have been estimated as from 7 to 12 per thousand for all ages and 50–70 per thousand among persons aged over 65 (Baum and Robins, 1981). Baum (1981) has estimated that in the USA mortality data give a useful indication of the community frequency of stroke. One stroke death is regarded as corresponding to 15 prevalent cases and 3·5 hospital discharges with a primary diagnosis of stroke. These figures, particularly the second, would presumably need adjustment for varying patterns of care from country to country. They do, however, indicate that the consumption of health and social service resources by the disease is considerable (Weddell and Beresford, 1979), as are the economic consequences (Adelman, 1981).

Age and Sex

Mortality rates increase as an exponential function of age. In broad terms age-specific mortality rates double with every 5 or 6 years of age from around 1 per 100 000 per year at age 20 through around 1000 per 100 000 per year in the late 70s. Overall mortality rates are about 20 per cent higher in males than in females, but the sex ratio increases slightly with age from 1·1 in early adult life to 1·4 in the seventh decade. This is in striking contrast to the sex ratio of mortality rates from coronary heart disease, which declines over the same age range from 6·0 to 3·0.

There have been numerous studies of the incidence of cerebrovascular disease. The methodological problems include standardization of diagnostic criteria to reduce observer variation (Garraway et al., 1976) and the ascertainment of cases. Some studies have been restricted to hospitalized cases on the assumption that the great majority of stroke patients will receive acute hospital care (e.g. Abu-Zeid et al., 1975). This assumption would not hold in Great Britain where one-third (Wandless and Evans, 1982) to 60 per cent (Cochrane, 1970) of patients are treated at home.

Many of the reported studies are by themselves too small to provide stable estimates of incidence rates. *Fig.* 1.1 shows data on selected studies, seven from the USA (data in Report, 1972) and one each from Canada (Abu-Zeid et al., 1975), and Denmark (Marquardsen, 1976). Rates from a study in England were closely similar (Brewis et al., 1966). In selecting the USA studies we have used only data on white populations and have avoided those from the South-Eastern states where rates are higher than the national average.

The studies shown in *Fig.* 1.1 suggest a sex ratio (male to female) of about 1·3 in early middle age which may decline later. Over the age range depicted the rates in the various studies are broadly similar and follow a linear form on the double logarithmic plot, with the implication that the relationship between incidence and age is approxiately a power and not an exponential function. The distinction is made clear in *Fig.* 1.2, where for the sexes combined, age-specific mortality and incidence rates are both plotted semi-logarithmically. The exponential function of the mortality rates appears as a straight line while the

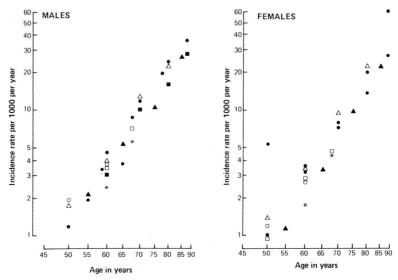

Fig. 1.1. Age-specific incidence rates of stroke from nine studies. *See* text for references.

power law function of incidence rates curves to converge onto it. The convergence of incidence rates onto mortality rates implies that the fatality of stroke must increase with age; this is undoubtedly true (Marquardsen, 1976; Baum and Robins, 1981).

The power law incidence function is similar to that of most adult cancers (Doll, 1970) while the exponential mortality curve is similar to that observed for all causes of death combined. Although at one time there was enthusiasm for interpreting such functions in terms of underlying aetiological or pathogenetic mechanisms (Burnet, 1974), this is unlikely to be profitable and at present the functions are best regarded as no more than empirical summaries of the data.

Although the great majority of strokes occur among elderly people most of our knowledge about associated risk factors relates to people aged below 60. This may have important consequences since the balance between intrinsic and extrinsic determinants of age-associated disease may be expected to vary with age (Evans, 1981), and the implications of neither observational nor interventive studies for stroke among younger adults can necessarily be extrapolated to the old.

Region and Race

Kurtzke (1969) reviewed the evidence for geographical variation in the incidence of stroke and concluded that alleged differences between regions were nothing more than artefacts due to varying standards and

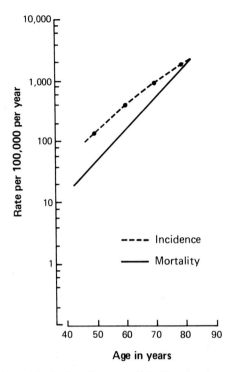

Fig. 1.2. Semi-logarithmic plot of age-specific incidence and mortality rates for stroke (both sexes combined). Incidence rates are estimated from *Fig.* 1.1, mortality rates from England and Wales, 1971.

criteria of diagnosis. At that time mortality statistics were the main source of data. At a national level age-specific mortality rates for the USA, England and Wales, Ireland, Norway, Sweden, Denmark and Canada all fitted the same exponential function. Analysis of mortality data within nations provided little evidence of clustering of high incidence areas. Kurtzke (1969) tentatively suggested that mortality rates from cerebrovascular disease tended to be higher where medical facilities were sparse. The explanation of such a trend might lie in the attribution of sudden deaths to stroke rather than the preferred modern convention of coronary heart disease.

Since the time of Kurtzke's review a number of studies have provided more convincing evidence that there are indeed genuine regional differences in stroke incidence. A series of studies in the USA suggested that the high mortality from stroke in the traditional 'stroke belt' of the South-Eastern and Central Eastern states, compared with the low mortality of the mountain, middle Atlantic, Pacific and New England areas did not reflect either variation in death certification practice or the accuracy of the stroke diagnosis on the death certificate (Kuller et al., 1969a, b). Incidence rates are higher than average in the Southern states of the USA, but data at later ages are too sparse to be sure whether this affects the elderly as clearly as the middle-aged and younger adult (Report of the Joint Committee for Stroke Facilities, 1972). Stolley et al. (1977) examined subjects from high, medium and low risk areas in the USA in a search for differences in the prevalence of conditions predisposing to stroke. They found compatible gradients for blood pressure in black females and white males, and for glucose intolerance in both races.

For many years Japan has been reputedly an area of high frequency of cerebrovascular disease. At one time this was thought to be due to excessively high rates of cerebral haemorrhage, but autopsy data, as distinct from death certification, suggest that the distribution of types of cerebrovascular disease is not strikingly different from that in occidental populations (Kurtzke, 1969). A co-ordinated international stroke registration programme by the World Health Organization included several Japanese centres (Lambo, 1979). This revealed that there were probably important differences in stroke incidence rates between regions in Japan with some centres reporting rates no higher than those in European populations. The regional differences in Japan were greater at younger than at older ages, and rates tended to converge at ages over 75.

Several studies have shown that stroke mortality rates show a correlation with the degree of softness of water supplies. The explanation for this association remains controversial but a preliminary study by Stitt et al. (1973) produced some evidence that blood pressures tend to be higher and to show steeper age-associated rises in middle-aged men living in soft water areas compared with men in hard water areas.

Mortality rates in the USA are consistently higher for stroke among Negroes than among Whites, although the magnitude of the difference has probably been declining in recent years. Incidence studies also suggest higher rates in both sexes in Negroes than in Whites up to the age of 75. At higher ages the picture is less certain (Report, 1972). The distribution of stroke types appears to be similar in Negro and White Americans (Bruun and Richter, 1973). The WHO registry in Ibadan (Osuntokun et al., 1979) suggests that up to the age of 74 incidence rates are similar to those of European populations. High rates in American Negroes are probably environmental rather than racial in origin.

In Great Britain regional mortality statistics show a gradient, with higher mortality rates from stroke in the North than in the South (OPCS, 1978). There have been no comparable studies on incidence to confirm this regional trend. The similar north–south gradients in Great Britain for a variety of other diseases raise the possibility that the phenomenon may be an artefact due to death certification practice or to a general effect on the fatality of disease, rather than its incidence.

Social Class and Occupation

In England and Wales there is a clear social class gradient for mortality from cerebrovascular disease at ages 15–64. Standardized mortality ratios increase monotonically from 76 and 80 in social class 1 males and females respectively to 139 and 136 in social class 5. Mortality ratios at higher ages do not show this relationship (OPCS, 1978). The social class difference in mortality is maximal in males in early adult life. A recent report has suggested social class differences in mean blood pressure in this sex and age group in Britain as in some studies from the USA (Evans and Tunbridge, 1981). More detailed examination of mortality data suggests high rates in men of working age in alcohol-related occupations.

Temporal and Seasonal Changes

Mortality rates from stroke in most Westernized countries have been falling at all ages and both sexes since before the Second World War (Reid and Evans, 1970; Stallones, 1979; Dobson et al., 1981). This is not entirely attributable to changes in certification practice or treatment, since longitudinal studies have shown that incidence rates, in recent years at least, have also been falling (Garraway et al., 1979; Ueda et al., 1981). The fall in incidence has involved both infarctive and haemorrhagic strokes, and there is no satisfactory evidence that there has been any trend in the relative frequencies of the two types of stroke (Anderson and McKay, 1968). The fall in mortality rates began before effective treatment for hypertension became available, and one possible explanation that has been advanced is a fall in the prevalence of hypertension and its related diseases (Reid and Evans, 1970) due to a change in some environmental factor such as dietary salt intake (Joossens, 1973). These temporal changes, which until recently were in the opposite direction to those of coronary heart disease, emphasize that the two conditions are not simply different consequences of the same causes.

There is evidence from both mortality and hospital admission data that there is a seasonal variation in stroke with higher rates in colder weather (McDowell et al., 1970). It is still not established whether this represents an effect of season on incidence or on the fatality and complications of stroke. Seasonal changes in blood pressure (Thulin et al., 1978) might provide a basis for an effect on incidence.

Blood Pressure

At younger ages it is clear that blood pressure is the dominant risk factor for stroke. This has been demonstrated in several prospective studies of incidence (Chapman et al., 1966; Heyman et al., 1971; Peacock et al., 1972). The relation is as clearcut with systolic as with diastolic pressures, but the two are so highly correlated within a given sex and age group that this is to be expected. Most controlled trials of treatment of high blood pressure in patients aged under 60 have shown a reduction in the incidence of stroke in the treated group. The situation is less clear in the elderly, because in studies such as those quoted they are included in only small numbers or are non-representative of general elderly populations. There is no evidence yet on whether control of high blood pressure in patients over the age of 60 confers any benefit.

Kannel (1976) presents data from the Framingham Study to show that up to the age of 75 stroke incidence is strongly correlated with blood pressure and that the magnitude of the association increases rather than diminishes with age. However, the elderly participants in the Framingham study were not a random sample of the original target population, and the longitudinal trends of blood pressure in the study cohort are notably different from what would be expected on the basis of cross-sectional studies. In the Chicago Stroke Study of 2772 welfare applicants aged 65–74, stroke incidence over 3 years was significantly related to blood pressure (Shekelle et al., 1974). More detailed analysis revealed that this was only true for a sub-group of the entry cohort. Among participants who were free at entry from all stigmata of peripheral, coronary or cerebral arterial disease, had a normal blood urea, were non-diabetic, and were not classified as ill in other ways, there was no relationship between blood pressure and subsequent stroke (Ostfeld et al., 1974). The participants in the Chicago Study were welfare applicants and thus not representative of a natural population.

Evans et al. (1980) provide a preliminary report from the Newcastle Age Research Group (NARG) Study on stroke incidence among 2800 persons aged 65 and over in a geographically defined population of North-East England. Blood pressures in this study were recorded in the respondent's own home by specially trained community nurses. There was no relationship between these pressures and subsequent stroke incidence, nor any relation between stroke incidence and blood pressures recorded in the respondent's primary care notes. A subsequent report on a much smaller Scottish study has also failed to find a relationship between blood pressure and subsequent stroke in an elderly population (Milne, 1981). In the NARG study stroke was significantly related to a history of diagnosed hypertension and to the use of antihypertensive medication at entry to the study.

There are a number of possible explanations for the differences in findings between the American and British studies. One possibility lies with methodology. There is evidence that the variability of blood pressure measurements may increase with age and so differences in measurement technique may have a more profound effect at older than at younger ages. Another possible explanation lies in the selection of the American study groups, or even conceivably, in true differences between the elderly of the two countries.

The NARG findings raised the interesting and potentially important issue that stroke in old age may be more related to blood pressure at earlier periods in life than in the year or so preceding the stroke. As discussed below the same may apply to obesity as a risk factor for stroke. There is evidence from the follow-up of undergraduate populations that high blood pressure in early adult life correlates with stroke incidence in middle and late middle age, but these studies have not extended into old age (Paffenbarger and Williams, 1967; Paffenbarger and Wing, 1971).

Obesity

Data on the relationship between obesity and stroke are inconsistent and related mainly to the young and middle-aged. It is also difficult to ascertain whether obesity has a direct relationship with stroke or acts through its association with hypertension, diabetes or physical inactivity. Heyden et al. (1971) suggested that both obesity and a history of weight gain after the age of 20 were risk factors for stroke. Paffenbarger and Williams (1967) and Paffenbarger and Wing (1971) found that high weight-for-height in early adult life was correlated with stroke later. In the NARG study of people aged 65 and over (Evans et al., 1980) respondents who subsequently developed stroke had similar mean values for height, weight and for Quetelet's Index (weight divided by the square of height) at the time of entry to the study. However, among the stroke group, remembered weights at age 25 were significantly greater than in the control group; differences at age 55 were in a similar direction but did not achieve statistical significance. Again, one interpretation would be that obesity in early adult life is a risk factor for stroke in old age, but obesity in old age is not. '

Serum Cholesterol

There is an association between stroke in early adult life and serum cholesterol but the relationship is much weaker than that between serum cholesterol and coronary heart disease. There does not appear to be a relationship between serum cholesterol and stroke in the middle aged and elderly.

Cigarette Smoking

Cigarette smoking appears to be associated with stroke in young men but not in women (Kannel et al., 1975), and this relationship in the Framingham Study also holds at age 65–74 (Kannel, 1976). No relationship was found in the Birmingham Study of respondents aged 50–69 (Peacock et al., 1972) nor in the NARG study of respondents aged 65 and over. The reason for these discrepancies is unknown.

Vascular Disease

It is well known that previous episodes of stroke or transient cerebral ischaemia are potent risk factors for stroke (Whisnant, 1976). Stroke has also been shown to be associated with coronary heart disease in the young and middle-aged adult (Kannel et al., 1975) and in the elderly with electrocardiographic changes of pathological Q-waves, ST-J depression and left bundle branch block (Evans et al., 1980). Atrial fibrillation is also associated with a 3–5 fold increase in risk of stroke in the elderly (Friedman et al., 1968; Evans et al., 1980). It is not known whether the excess strokes in atrial fibrillation are due to cerebral emboli or whether atrial fibrillation and stroke are independent manifestations of underlying vascular disease. In the NARG study there was a significant association between the presence of intermittent claudication and the subsequent incidence of stroke (Evans et al., 1980).

Haematocrit

The haematocrit is now recognized as being an important determinant of blood viscosity and cerebral blood flow (Willison et al., 1980) and high normal haemoglobin values have also been found to be correlated with stroke (Kannel et al., 1975). Cigarette smoking is a common cause of an above average haematocrit (Smith and Laidlaw, 1978). The value of haematocrit as a risk factor for stroke in the elderly, as distinct from the young and middle-aged, has not yet been adequately established.

Glucose Intolerance

Epidemiological studies confirm the findings of clinical series of a higher rate of stroke in diabetics. In general, findings of impaired glucose tolerance short of diagnosed diabetes are also associated with increased risk (Kannel, 1976). The relationship may be less strong at older ages when glucose intolerance becomes more common, and has not been found in some smaller studies in older age groups (Peacock et al., 1972). There is no clear evidence in older age groups on whether therapeutic control of glucose intolerance confers any benefit.

Comment

Although the epidemiology of stroke and coronary heart disease shows that the two conditions have some risk factors in common the difference in sex ratio, temporal trends and relative importance of the risk factors are considerable. In general, the epidemiology of stroke only closely resembles that of coronary heart disease at young ages when stroke is rare and when its aetiology may be different from that at later ages.

The importance of all recognized risk factors probably declines with age and the reasons for this are not yet established. There are a number of hints that an important reason may be a long latency in the effect of a causative influence so that for a stroke in old age the causes and their associated risk factors may lie long in the past. They may still be recognizable if the factors have remained stable for individuals within a population but will be attenuated in statistical significance. Further if this hypothesis is correct it can be predicted that the benefits of risk factor modification will be less in the old than in the young. Possibly prevention of disease in the elderly will need either to start in early adult life or to be more directly concerned with mechanisms than with causes of disease (Evans et al., 1980).

PARKINSON'S DISEASE

The epidemiology of Parkinson's disease raises a number of interesting problems, including the occurrence of three principal causes: post-encephalitic Parkinsonism, paralysis agitans or idiopathic Parkinsonism (Parkinson's disease proper), and arteriosclerotic Parkinsonism. Post-encephalitic Parkinsonism was recognized following the epidemics of encephalitis in the 10–15 years after the First World War. The diagnosis of arteriosclerotic Parkinsonism has gone out of fashion in recent years (Poskanzer and Schwab, 1963; Pallis, 1971), and most would now doubt whether it was ever a valid diagnostic category.

In a chronic disease such as Parkinsonism, incidence rates are of little significance, particularly in view of the very variable time interval between the first symptom and the establishment of the diagnosis, and the fact that this time is greatly affected by the availability of effective treatment (Poskanzer and Schwab, 1963). Mortality rates are also very difficult to interpret, partly because of the uncertainties of diagnostic categorization already mentioned, and partly because in a very chronic disease other causes of death are likely to appear on death certificates, the potential underlying cause being ignored. In one study (Kessler, 1972), Parkinson's disease was mentioned on only 39 per cent of death certificates of patients with the condition. Prevalence rates are thus likely to be the most informative. *Fig.* 1.3 shows that, in six studies, carried out by varying methods over several decades in different parts

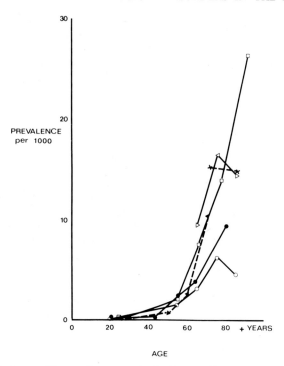

Fig. 1.3. Age-specific prevalence rates for Parkinson's disease.
□———□ Rochester (Minn.) (Kurland, 1958).
○———○ Carlisle (UK) (Brewis et al., 1966).
●———● Victoria (Aus.) (Jenkins, 1966).
△———△ Iceland (K. R. Gudmundsson, 1966).
▲ - - - ▲ Baltimore (Md) (Kessler, 1973).
× - - - × Glasgow (UK) (Broe et al., 1976).

of the world, there is reasonable agreement that at least for white populations, there is an exponential increase with age in the prevalence of Parkinson's disease, which averages about 15 per 1000 at age 70, and nearer 20 per thousand at age 80.

It has been suggested that most of the present cases of Parkinson's disease are the result of exposure to the encephalitis virus in the years after 1917. Poskanzer and Schwab (1963) found that the mean age at diagnosis of patients with Parkinson's disease at the Massachusetts General Hospital had increased by 27 years in the previous 35 years. Brown and Knox (1972) came to a similar conclusion. Marmot (1980) has suggested, on the basis of mortality data from the UK, that these findings may represent a true cohort phenomenon, though no allowance was made, or indeed could be made, for the vagaries of death certification mentioned above, which are especially likely to affect the elderly. There can be little doubt that the original suggestion by Poskanzer and Schwab, which was based on referral to a neurological clinic, reflects more the changing epidemiology of such referral than that of Parkinson's disease (Kurtzke and Kurland, 1976). Certainly Poskanzer and Schwab's hypothesis that there would be a precipitous drop in the prevalence of Parkinson's disease by 1980 has not been verified.

MOTOR NEURONE DISEASE

The epidemiology of motor neurone disease has been relatively little studied, apart from its incidence in peculiar populations on Pacific islands (Kurland, 1977). In the population of Rochester (Minn.), of about 37 000 people of all ages, there have been only 35 cases of motor neurone disease in the 52 years between 1925 and 1977 (Juergens et al., 1980). The overall age-specific incidence rate was $2 \cdot 3/10^5$/yr at age 50 and $19/10^5$/yr over the age of 75; there has possibly been a small increase in the average annual incidence over the period surveyed. The mean age at onset was 66 years, and 8 of the 35 patients (23 per cent) were over the age of 75 at diagnosis. This study, though of a small number of cases, is probably the most representative of a not uncommon and very puzzling condition.

EPILEPSY

The epidemiology of epilepsy has been the subject of a number of studies, well reviewed by Kurtzke (1968). He suggested that the incidence of primary (i.e. idiopathic) grand mal epilepsy shows an exponential fall with age, approximating to zero at age 70, while secondary seizures (i.e. those due to a definite cause) are approximately equally common at all ages, about 15 per 100 000 suffering their first such seizure per year. However, one study showed that first seizures were twice as common over the age of 65 as between the ages of 25 and 64 (Research Committee, 1960).

There is reasonable agreement that the prevalence of chronic epilepsy over the age of 60 is between 2 and 5 per 1000 (Research Committee, 1960; Brewis et al., 1966; G. Gudmundsson, 1966; Broe et al., 1976) though several of the studies mentioned are based on very few cases.

INTRACRANIAL TUMOUR

Most epidemiological studies of intracranial tumours suggest that their incidence, whether expressed as morbidity or mortality, increases with age to a peak in the range 60–70 years, and decline thereafter (Cohen and Modan, 1968; Kurtzke and Kurland, 1976; Schoenberg et al., 1976). Other studies, in which case ascertainment is very probably more complete, indicate that the incidence may remain unchanged, or continue to rise, after the age of 80 (Gudmundsson, 1970; Percy et al., 1972). If intracranial tumours diagnosed only at autopsy are included the continuing rise with age is even more striking (Annegers et al., 1980).

In the latter study 35 per cent of primary intracranial tumours were not diagnosed in life; three-quarters of these were meningiomas, and almost all were found in people over the age of 60. Although 70 per cent of undiagnosed tumours did not give rise to any symptoms in life, many significant intracranial tumours remain undiagnosed in the elderly (Schoenberg et al., 1978).

The incidence of metastatic intracranial tumours not unexpectedly increases with age, to a maximum between ages 50 and 80 (Gudmundsson, 1970). Nearly half of all metastatic tumours occur over the age of 60, as against about a quarter of primary tumours.

REFERENCES

Abu-Zeid H. A., Choi N. W. and Nelson N. A. (1975) *Canad. Med. Assoc. J.* **113**, 379.
Adams J. H. (1979) *Age Ageing* **8**, Suppl. 57.
Adelman S. M. (1981) *Stroke* **12**, Suppl. 1, 69.
Anderson T. W. and MacKay J. S. (1968) *Lancet* **1**, 1137.
Annegers J. F., Schoenberg B. S., Okazaki H. et al. (1980) In: Rose C. F. (ed.), *Clinical Neuroepidemiology*. Tunbridge Wells, Pitman Medical. p. 366.
Barnett H. J. M., Boughner D. R., Taylor D. W. et al. (1980) *N. Engl. J. Med.* **302**, 139.
Baum H. M. (1981) *Public Health (London)* **95**, 9.
Baum H. M. and Robins M. (1981) *Stroke* **12**, Suppl. 1, 59.
de Bono D. P. and Warlow C. P. (1979) *Lancet* **2**, 383.
Brewis M., Poskanzer D. S., Rolland C. et al. *Acta Neurol. Scand.* **42**, Suppl. 24, 1.
Broe G. A., Akhtar A. J., Andrews G. R. et al. (1976) *J. Neurol. Neurosurg. Psychiatry* **39**, 363.
Brown E. L. and Knox E. G. (1972) *Lancet* **1**, 974.
Bruun B. and Richter R. W. (1973) *Stroke* **4**, 406.
Burnet F. M. (1974) *Intrinsic Mutagenesis*. Leicester, MTP.
Chapman J. M., Reeder L. G., Borun E. R. et al. (1966) *Am. J. Public Health* **56**, 191.
Cochrane A. L. (1970) *Br. Med. J.* **3**, 105.
Cohen A. and Modan B. (1968) *Cancer* **22**, 1323.
Dobson A. J., Gibberd R. W., Wheeler D. J. et al. (1981) *Am. J. Epidemiol.* **113**, 404.
Doll R. (1970) *J. R. Stat. Soc. (A)*, **134**, 133.
Evans J. Grimley (1981) In: Dawson A. M., Compston N. and Besser G. M. (ed.) *Recent Advances in Medicine 18*. London, Churchill Livingstone. p. 17.
Evans J. Grimley and Tunbridge W. M. G. (1981) *Public Health (London)* **95**, 161.
Evans J. Grimley, Prudham D. and Wandless I. (1980) In: Barbagallo-Sangiorgi G. and Exton-Smith A. N. (ed.) *The Ageing Brain: Neurological and Mental Disturbances.* New York, Plenum. p. 113.
Friedman G. D., Loveland D. B. and Ehrlich G. P. (1968) *Circulation* **38**, 533.
Garraway W. M., Akhtar A. J., Gore S. M. et al. (1976) *Age Ageing* **5**, 233.
Garraway W. M., Whisnant J. P., Furlan A. J. et al. (1979) *N. Engl. J. Med.* **300**, 449.

Gudmundsson G. (1966) *Acta Neurol. Scand.* **43**, Suppl. 25.
Gudmundsson K. R. (1966) *Acta Neurol. Scand.* **43**, Suppl. 33.
Gudmundsson K. R. (1970) *Acta Neurol. Scand.* **46**, 538.
Heyden S., Hames C. G., Bartel A. et al. (1971) *Arch. Intern. Med.* **128**, 956.
Heyden S., Heyman A. and Goree J. A. (1970) *Stroke* **1**, 363.
Heyman A., Fields W. S. and Keating R. D. (1972) *J. A. M. A.* **222**, 285.
Heyman A., Karp H. R., Heyden S. et al. (1971) *Stroke* **2**, 509.
Hillbom M. and Kaste M. (1978) *Lancet* **2**, 1181.
Jenkins A. C. (1966) *Med. J. Aust.* **2**, 496.
Joossens J. V. (1973) *Triangle* **12**, 9.
Juergens S. M., Kurland L. T. and Mulder D. W. (1980) In: Rose F. C. (ed.) *Clinical Neuroepidemiology*. Tunbridge Wells, Pitman Medical. p. 409.
Kannel W. B. (1976) In: Caird F. I., Dall J. L. C. and Kennedy R. D. (ed.) *Cardiology in Old Age*. London, Plenum. p. 143.
Kannel W. B., Wolf P. A. and Dawber T. R. (1975) *Millbank Mem. Fund. Q.* **3**, 405.
Kessler I. I. (1972) *Am. J. Epidemiol.* **96**, 242.
Kuller L. H., Bolker A., Saslaw M. S. et al. (1969a) *Am. J. Epidemiol.* **90**, 545.
Kuller L. H., Bolker A., Saslaw M. S. et al. (1969b) *Am. J. Epidemiol.* **90**, 556.
Kurland L. T. (1958) In: Fields W. S. (ed.) *Pathogenesis and Treatment of Parkinsonism*. Springfield, Ill., Thomas. p. 5.
Kurland L. T. (1977) In: Rose F. C. (ed.) *Motor Neuron Disease*, Ch. 2. Tunbridge Wells, Pitman Medical.
Kurtzke J. F. (1968) *J. Chron. Dis.* **21**, 143.
Kurtzke J. F. (1969) *Epidemiology of Cerebrovascular Disease*. Berlin, Springer.
Kurtzke J. F. and Kurland L. T. (1976) In: Baker A. B. (ed.) *Clinical Neurology*, Vol. III, Ch. 48. New York and London, Harper & Row.
Lambo T. A. (1979) *Adv. Neurol.* **25**, 1.
Loach A. B. and Benedict C. R. (1980) *J. Neurol. Sci.* **45**, 261.
McDowell F. H., Louis S. and Monahan K. (1970) *J. Chronic Dis.* **23**, 29.
Marmot M. G. (1980) In: Rose C. F. (ed.) *Clinical Neuroepidemiology*. Tunbridge Wells, Pitman Medical. p. 391.
Marquardsen J. (1976) In: Gillingham F. J., Mawdsley C. and Williams A. E. (ed.) *Stroke*. London, Churchill Livingstone. p. 62.
Milne J. S. (1981) *J. Clin. Exp. Gerontol.* **2**, 135.
OPCS (1978) London, HMSO.
Ostfeld A. M., Shekelle R. B., Klawans H. et al. (1974) *Am. J. Public Health* **64**, 450.
Osuntokun B. O., Bademosi O., Akinkugbe O. O. et al. (1979) *Stroke* **10**, 205.
Paffenbarger R. S. and Williams J. L. (1967) *Am. J. Public Health* **57**, 1290.
Paffenbarger R. S. and Wing A. L. (1971) *Am. J. Epidemiol.* **94**, 524.
Pallis C. (1971) *Br. Med. J.* **3**, 683.
Peacock P. B., Riley C. P., Lampton T. D. et al. (1972) In: Stewart G. T. (ed.) *Trends in Epidemiology*. Springfield, Ill., Thomas. p. 231.
Percy A. K., Elveback L. R., Okazaki H. et al. (1972) *Neurology (Minn.)* **22**, 40.
Poskanzer D. C. and Schwab R. S. (1963) *J. Chronic Dis.* **16**, 961.
Reid D. D. and Evans J. Grimley (1970) *Br. Med. Bull.* **26**, 191.
Report of Joint Committee for Stroke Facilities (1972) I. *Epidemiology for Stroke Facilities Planning*. New York, American Heart Association.
Resch J. A., Okabe N. and Kimoto K. (1969) *Geriatrics* **24**(11), 111.
Research Committee (1960) *Br. Med. J.* **2**, 416.
Schoenberg B. S., Christine B. W. and Whisnant J. P. (1976) *Am. J. Epidemiol.* **104**, 499.
Schoenberg B. S., Christine B. W. and Whisnant J. P. (1978) *Neurology (Minn.)* **28**, 817.
Shekelle R. B., Ostfeld A. M. and Klawans H. L. (1974) *Stroke* **5**, 71.
Smith J. R. and Laidlaw S. A. (1978) *N. Engl. J. Med.* **298**, 6.
Stallones R. A. (1979) *Adv. Neurol.* **25**, 117.
Stitt F. W., Clayton D., Crawford M. D. et al. (1973) *Lancet* **1**, 122.

Stolley P. D., Kuller L. H., Nefzger M. D. et al. (1977) *Stroke* **8**, 551.

Thulin T., Bengtsson B. and Schersten B. (1978) *Postgrad. Med. J.* **54**, 10.

Ueda K., Omae T., Hirota Y. et al. (1981) *Stroke* **12**, 154.

Wandless I. and Evans J. Grimley (1982) In preparation.

Weddell J. M. and Beresford S. A. A. (1979) *Planning for Stroke Patients.* London, HMSO.

Whisnant J. P. (1976) In: Gillingham F. J., Mawdsley C. and Williams A. E. (ed.) *Stroke.* London, Churchill Livingstone. p. 21.

Willison J. R., Thomas D. J., Du Boulay G. H. et al. (1980) *Lancet* **1**, 846.

2. AGE CHANGES IN THE NERVOUS SYSTEM
Harold Brody

INTRODUCTION

An understanding of the changes which take place in the central nervous system with advancing age forms a basis for the appreciation of subtle and gross differences in the ageing individual. Up to this time it has not been possible to develop a 1:1 relationship between morphological change and behaviour and given the complexity of the central nervous system it should be apparent that this relationship may not be achieved. However, morphological change and its subsequent relation to physiological change forms the background against which ageing of the nervous system must be examined. The changes with time to be discussed in this chapter occur with normal ageing. This is not to deny that a number of these changes occur in certain neurological disorders. In fact, in dementias and diseases, specific morphological entities which are a normal concomitant of ageing may be exaggerated in number and location of incidence.

It has been emphasized earlier (Tomlinson, 1972; Brody and Vijaya-shankar, 1977) that 'normal' brains are usually selected for study without adequate information regarding the behaviour or intellect of the person while living. This is a basic difficulty with the examination of the brain in a cross-sectional series. It would be desirable were each study to develop from lifetime longitudinal studies but this is not available in most studies of the human central nervous system. Faced with this difficulty, specimens in such studies are obtained after death from individuals who had not previously demonstrated nervous system disease and had not been subject to neurological or psychiatric care. One should, however, be aware of a lack of information regarding nutritional status, pulmonary and cardiovascular function, drug inter-actions and their effect upon the ageing nervous system and finally the results of agonal changes accompanying death. It is at any rate generally accepted that based on the agreement of a number of studies and even in the absence of information regarding those factors cited in the previous sentence, there are typical changes in the normal ageing brain.

NEUROANATOMY

Changes in Gross Appearance and Structure

Brain Weight and Size

The earliest study of brain weight (Boyd, 1860), in a series from 3 months of age through the ninth decade, demonstrated that the brain reached a peak value of 1374 g between 14 and 20 years, followed by a loss of approximately 90 g or 6·6 per cent by weight. Similar related findings were present in both sexes. While Broca (1878) reported a maximum brain weight between 25 and 35 years of age, other studies (Pearl, 1922; Scammon and Dunn, 1922–23; ·Appel and Appel, 1942a, b; Pakkenberg and Voight, 1964), in which 1000–3000 specimens have been examined per study, indicate that maximum brain weight is attained by 20 years of age with a 7–10 per cent loss by the ninth decade. It should be kept in mind, however, that considering the direct correlation between body size and brain weight, and the fact that later generations tend to be larger in body size and weight, at any point in time the brain of a younger person should be expected to be larger than that of an older individual, considering the fact that most studies have dealt with a cross-sectional group of subjects. Information regarding body weight is not available in studies up to this time but should be included in further studies, particularly when performed with the examination of the brain within the closed skull as in computerized axial tomography (CT).

The examination of brain size as a concomitant of ageing is of interest since differentiation needs to be made between the moderate degree of brain atrophy in normal ageing and the severe atrophy which occurs in Alzheimer's disease and senile dementia of the Alzheimer type.

Using CT imaging, it has been demonstrated that with increasing age, there is a drastic atrophy of the brain, starting at about 50 years (Yamaura et al., 1980). The atrophy appears to be related to enlargement of the ventricles and sulci, a fact emphasized by other workers (Barron et al., 1976). Atrophy in old age may have a direct relationship to the degree of dementia (Richardson and Adams, 1975; Roberts and Caird, 1976) but one should be extremely cautious in diagnosing dementia only on the basis of a CT scan. It is imperative that the physician has information regarding the patient's mental status to aid in the diagnosis of this condition rather than to rely fully on the use of a laboratory technique, such as CT. In fact, a recent CT study of elderly patients with dementia demonstrated that cortical atrophy was related to age but not to dementia, while ventricular enlargement which was also related to age could be statistically correlated with dementia (Ford and Winter, 1981). The dangers of over-reliance upon CT have been reviewed in earlier literature (Wells and Duncan, 1977).

Changes in Cellular Structure

Neuronal Number

Certainly it is remarkable that the number of neurones in the central nervous system is relatively constant at a particular age. This is most apparent in examining nerve cell populations within restricted areas such as brainstem nuclear groups where one can quite readily count the number of neurones within a specific and well-demarcated region. It has been suggested that the number of neurones which reach maturity is the result of a balance between cell proliferation and cell death during neurogenesis (Jacobson, 1978). Since nerve cells are postmitotic and therefore not capable of reproducing themselves throughout life, a critical feature of ageing in the nervous system may be the degree of cell loss within specific brain regions. At the present time, it is not appreciated whether alteration in behaviour may be directly related to changes in the number or structure of neurones. With the loss of cells in normal ageing or as a result of neurological disease, changes in activity or behaviour may result from the decrease or structural alteration of their component parts, as well as to abnormal function of those neurones which remain. Any of these factors may play a role in the picture presented by the aged individual. That nerve cells are incapable of replication is probably advantageous since it would be extremely difficult for a later developing neurone to fit itself into the existing circuitry of the central nervous system. This is not to imply that possibilities of plasticity (continued proliferation of processes) do not exist in the older brain, for evidence for this has recently been reported in the normal aged human (Buell and Coleman, 1979).

Neuronal loss with ageing has been a controversial topic due primarily to a lack of appreciation by those working in this field that there may be species differences in the manner in which the neurone ages as well as differences between specific brain areas. The brain is not a single structure formed at one time, but is composed of separate units, each of which has its own sequence of development, fitting itself into a structural and physiological entity capable of integrating its disparate parts. Cell activity varies physiologically and biochemically and one should expect that neuronal reaction to disease, stress or passage of time will vary among cellular groups. It is incorrect to say that nerve cell numbers decrease with age. While this process does occur, it takes place within specific areas and is not a general occurrence within the entire nervous system. It appears that neuronal loss, while obvious in specific areas, may not be significant in other regions.

Cerebral Cortex

Examination of the neuronal population of the cerebral cortex requires careful sampling of specimens so that regions of cortex from many specimens may be compared.

When unit areas are examined quantitatively, specific cortical areas show significant loss. This is particularly apparent in the superior frontal gyrus (Brody, 1970), superior temporal gyrus, precentral gyrus and area striata and not significant in the postcentral or inferior temporal gyri (Brody, 1955). Although within unit areas of cortex there are some variations in cell number, these populations are clustered by decades and the decrease in number occurs in linear fashion with increasing age beginning at 20 years, which is used as a baseline for population studies in cerebral and cerebellar cortex (related to maximum brain weight at that age). The greatest loss is found in Golgi type II cells especially prominent in layers 2 and 4. These are cells with short processes which function as local circuit neurones that form central integrating circuits within the cortex and are characteristic of associational cells of this region. The loss of neurones in the areas described above has also been reported by other investigators using direct microscopic counting techniques (Colon, 1972; Shefer, 1973), as well as with use of an automatic counting device, the Quantimet (Tomlinson, 1976).

By means of a disruption and cell dispersion technique, it has also been demonstrated that there is approximately a 50 per cent loss of all neurones in the macular projection area of the human visual cortex (Devaney and Johnson, 1980). This may account for the loss in visual acuity which has been well documented as occurring with increasing age (Anderson and Palmore, 1974; Weale, 1975).

While studies of cell populations indicate neuronal decrease with age, it is critical that this approach be extended to changes in the morphological structure of nerve cells. Here it has been noted (Scheibel et al., 1975, 1976a, b) that in the normal ageing cortex there is a progressive loss of horizontal dendrites of pyramidal cells of layer 3 until these cells have finally lost their entire dendritic system. These authors are of the opinion that the loss of dendritic branching interrupts intracortical circuits, resulting in a modulation or inhibition of cortical activity. This may in turn result in a loss of stored programs within the horizontal dendritic system. The cells which contact these dendrites in the normal brain are located in layers 2 and 4. These have been shown to decrease in cell number to a larger extent than other cortical cells, indicating a possibility of mutual dependence of these cell groups. The cells of layers 2 and 4 are also formed last in the genesis of the cerebral cortex so it appears that within the cerebral cortex the very young small association cells are particularly sensitive to age change.

Is loss of dendrites an ultimate fate of all pyramidal cells in cortex? Examination of neurones and their processes demonstrate normal cells in close relation with denuded cells and in fact an increase and thickening in the branching of dendrites of some cells in the normal aged brain (Buell and Coleman, 1979), indicating the possibility of neuronal plasticity. While in normal specimens neurones lacking dendrites may be found alongside neurones with thickened branches, the latter type was not found in the brains of aged, demented individuals. It is obvious that these recent findings need to be replicated by other workers since the possibility of additional growth of fibre systems in the aged brain is an important finding.

Neurone Populations in other Central Nervous System Areas

Cerebellar Cortex

While neurones in the cerebral cortex decrease in number throughout life after 20 years, the Purkinje cells of the cerebellum do not show significant loss until the sixth decade of life (Hall et al., 1975). This may in part be related to the decreased co-ordinative ability which has been described in the elderly person and is of particular interest since there is no related decrease in cells of the inferior olive which projects its climbing fibres to the Purkinje cells.

Brainstem

An example of non-conformity with the concept of neuronal loss with ageing is found in the human brainstem where the facial nerve nucleus (Van Buskirk, 1945), the ventral cochlear nucleus (Konigsmark and Murphy, 1970, 1972), the inferior olive (Moatamed, 1966; Monagle and Brody, 1974), and the nuclei of the abducens and trochlear nerves (Vijayashankar and Brody, 1977a, b) show no significant difference in neurone number with age. The number of brainstem structures examined quantitatively in the human is small and up to this time only three areas have been found to decrease significantly in cell number. These are the cells of the locus coeruleus (Vijayashankar and Brody, 1979), the putamen (Bugiani et al., 1978) and the substantia nigra (McGeer et al., 1977). Neurone loss in these structures could have a significant effect upon function in the elderly, since the locus coeruleus projects widely in the central nervous system, influences REM sleep through its contact with the median raphe cells and influences catechol-amine balance through its noradrenaline secreting cells. The putamen and substantia nigra are critical structures involved in the basal ganglia system which has a major influence upon motor activity.

CYTOLOGICAL CHANGES

A number of cytological changes may occur to some extent in the brains of all ageing individuals but the frequency and distribution of these changes may distinguish the normal from the abnormal specimen. Unfortunately, little is known regarding these organelle changes in the human due to the difficulty in obtaining appropriate specimens. It is therefore necessary to include some descriptions in the rodent in discussing this area. Almost every cytoplasmic organelle has been described as demonstrating changes in its structure with increasing age. The Golgi complex which is a part of an extensive membrane system within the cell, fragments and dissolves. The cristae of mitochondria show an abnormal swelling, vacuolation and disruption and subsequent decrease in number. Endoplasmic reticulum is involved in synthetic activities and decreases with age. This may in turn result in a depression of cellular function and is observed by a progressive reduction in cytoplasmic basophilia.

The most consistent cytological change with increasing age is the deposition of lipofuscin within the cell's cytoplasm. This material, often termed 'wear and tear pigment', is gold-brown in colour, autofluorescent and is present in both dividing and non-dividing cells, such as those found in myocardium, spleen, adrenal gland and seminal vesicle. The material contains lipid, carbohydrate and protein and stains with a number of preparations, such as methyl green, PAS, Nile blue and ferric ferricyanide. Ultrastructurally, the pigment granules are electron-dense, osmiophilic, bound by a single membrane and with a probable lysosomal origin. The accumulation of this material has been considered to interfere with the metabolism of the cell, eventually resulting in that cell's death (Mann and Yates, 1974). However, this is unlikely since the cells of the inferior olive do not change numerically with age while they contain sufficient lipofuscin to fill the cell bodies almost completely, causing the nucleus to shift into a peripheral position. After the fourth decade, more than 90 per cent of all cells in the inferior olive contain this concentration of lipofuscin. At present, there is no clear acceptable explanation for the presence of this material. Recent evidence has been provided that 'intraneuronal lipofuscin has no measurable functional (electrophysiological) significance' (Rogers et al., 1980) and that its presence in Purkinje cells in the rat cerebellum is not a primary cause for dysfunction in that organ. While a good deal of information now exists in the literature regarding the distribution of lipofuscin within the central nervous system of animals, this is not available for the human. This could dispel some misconceptions gathered in non-quantitative studies. For example, the impression that large amounts of lipofuscin are collected by many cerebral cortical cells is not true. A quantitative study indicates that not more than 10 per cent of cells in cortex have an amount of lipofuscin sufficient to occupy one pole of a cell. The majority of cells contain scattered granules which occupy very little of the total volume of the cell (Brody, 1960).

SYNAPSES

The ultimate structure upon which attention needs to be focused is the synapse. Few studies have been performed, indicating the degree of difficulty in examining this area. Some animal work has demonstrated synaptic decrease in rats after 25 months of age in the dentate gyrus adjacent to the hippocampus (Bondareff and Geinisman, 1976), in the cerebellar cortex (Glick and Bondareff, 1979), in the visual cortex (Feldman, 1976) and in the cuneate and gracile nuclei (Fujisawa and Shiraki, 1978). However, an ultrastructural study of frontal and temporal cortex in man (Cragg, 1975) failed to demonstrate significant differences in synaptic density. Recalling the earlier reference to increased dendritic branching in cortex of normal aged individuals (Buell and Coleman, 1979), the possibility may exist that the density of synapses may remain unchanged if processes continue to proliferate. One could even consider the possibility of increased synaptic density if the replacement process is a reality (Pentney, 1981).

CONCLUSIONS

A great deal of attention needs to be directed toward the accumulation of data regarding normal ageing of the central nervous system. These should encompass all degrees of anatomical study from gross to ultrastructural levels. Even though the support of descriptive studies may not be attractive to granting agencies, it should be realized that an understanding of morphology creates a base upon which other basic science areas depend, eventually being transferred to information useful in the clinical management of the older person. The opportunity to study the human ageing nervous system is not available to many basic investigators and requires the co-operation of pathologists and other clinicians. The basic scientist should also be cognisant of the importance of obtaining good historical data regarding the patient in order to separate neurological or other clinical disorders from normal ageing. The acquisition of knowledge regarding the ageing process will require communication and transfer of information if eventually the medical community is to deal with the elderly in a knowledgeable and informed manner.

REFERENCES

Anderson B. and Palmore E. (1974) In: Palmore E. (ed.) *Normal Aging.* Durham, N.C., Duke University Press.
Appel F. W. and Appel E. M. (1942a) *Human Biol.* **14**, 48.
Appel F. W. and Appel E. M. (1942b) *Human Biol.* **14**, 235.
Barron S. A., Jacobs L. and Kinkel W. R. (1976) *Neurology* **26**, 1011.
Bondareff W. and Geinisman Y. (1976) *Am. J. Anat.* **145**, 129.

Boyd R. (1860) In: Schafer and Thane (ed.). Reference in *Quain's Anatomy*. London, Longman & Green, p. 219.
Broca P. (1878) *Rev. Anthrop.* **1**, 384.
Brody H. (1955) *J. Comp. Neurol.* **102**, 511.
Brody H. (1960) *J. Gerontol.* **15**, 258.
Brody H. (1970) In: Blumenthal H. T. (ed.) *Interdisciplinary Topics in Gerontology*, Vol. 7. New York, Academic Press.
Brody H. and Vijayashankar N. (1977) In: Finch C. E. and Hayflick L. (ed.) *The Biology of Aging*. New York, Van Nostrand Reinhold Co.
Buell S. J. and Coleman P. D. (1979) *Science* **206**, 854.
Bugiani O., Salvarani S., Mancardi G. L. et al. (1978) *Eur. Neurol.* **17**, 286.
Colon E. J. (1972) *Psychiat. Neurol. Neurochir.* **75**, 261.
Cragg B. G. (1975) *Brain* **98**, 81.
Devaney K. O. and Johnson H. A. (1980) *J. Gerontol.* **35**, 836.
Feldman M. L. (1976) In: Terry R. D. and Gershon S. (ed.) *Neurobiology of Aging*. New York, Raven Press.
Ford C. V. and Winter J. (1981) *J. Gerontol.* **36**, 164.
Fujisawa K. and Shiraki H. (1978) *Neuropath. Appl. Neurobiol.* **4**, 1.
Glick R. and Bondareff W. (1979) *J. Gerontol.* **34**, 818.
Hall T. C., Miller A. K. H. and Corsellis J. A. N. (1975) *Neuropathol. Appl. Neurobiol.* **1**, 267.
Jacobson M. (1978) *Developmental Neurobiology*. New York, Plenum Press.
Konigsmark B. W. and Murphy E. A. (1970) *Nature* **299**, 1335.
Konigsmark B. W. and Murphy E. A. (1972) *J. Neuropath. Exp. Neurol.* **31**, 304.
McGeer P. L., McGeer E. G. and Suzuki J. S. (1977) *Arch. Neurol.* **34**, 33.
Mann D. N. A. and Yates P. O. (1974) *Brain* **97**, 481.
Moatamed F. (1966) *J. Comp. Neurol.* **128**, 109.
Monagle R. D. and Brody H. (1974) *J. Comp. Neurol.* **155**, 61.
Pakkenberg H. and Voigt J. (1964) *Acta Anat.* **56**, 297.
Pearl R. (1922) *The Biology of Death*. Philadelphia, Lippincott.
Pentney R. B. (1981) Personal communication.
Richardson E. P. jun. and Adams R. D. (1975) In: Thorn G. W., Braunwald E., Isselbacher K. J. et al. (ed.) *Harrison's Principles of Internal Medicine*, 8th ed. New York, McGraw-Hill.
Roberts M. A. and Caird F. I. (1976) *J. Neurol. Neurosurg. Psychiatry* **39**, 986.
Rogers J., Silver M. A., Shoemaker W. J. et al. (1980) *Neurobiology of Aging* **1**, 1.
Scammon R. E. and Dunn H. L. (1922–23) *Proc. Soc. Exp. Biol. Med.* **19**, 114.
Scheibel M. E., Lindsay R. D., Tomiyasu U. et al. (1975) *Exp. Neurol.* **47**, 392.
Scheibel M. E., Lindsay R. D., Tomiyasu U. et al. (1976a) *Exp. Neurol.* **53**, 420.
Scheibel M. E., Tomiyasu U. and Scheibel A. B. (1976b) *Trans Am. Neurol. Assoc.* **101**, 23.
Shefer V. F. (1973) *Neurosci. Beh. Physiol.* **6**, 319.
Tomlinson B. E. (1972) In: Van Praag H. M. and Kalverbove A. F. (ed.) *Ageing of the Central Nervous System, Biological and Psychological Aspects*. Haarlem, DeErven F. Bohn, N.V.
Tomlinson B. E. (1976) In: Terry R. D. and Gershon S. (ed.) *Neurobiology of Aging*. New York, Raven Press.
Van Buskirk C. (1945) *J. Comp. Neurol.* **82**, 303.
Vijayashankar N. and Brody H. (1977a) *J. Comp. Neurol.* **173**, 433.
Vijayashankar N. and Brody H. (1977b) *Acta Anat.* **99**, 169.
Vijayashankar N. and Brody H. (1979) *J. Neuropathol. Exp. Neurol.* **38**, 490.
Weale R. A. (1975) *Trans. Ophthalmol. Soc. UK* **95**, 36.
Wells C. E. and Duncan G. W. (1977) *Am. J. Psychiatry* **134**, 811.
Yamaura H., Ito M., Kubota K. et al. (1980) *J. Gerontol.* **35**, 492.

3. CEREBRAL BLOOD FLOW
John Marshall

The metabolic needs of the brain are high and are met by an abundant cerebral blood flow (CBF). Although the brain contributes only 2 per cent to body weight it takes some 20 per cent of cardiac output. There is under normal circumstances close coupling between metabolic needs and CBF. The fine tuning of this mechanism has been elegantly demonstrated by Scandinavian workers (Olesen, 1971) who have shown in man that focal activation of the brain, such as occurs in hand movement, is accompanied by a focal increase in CBF in the appropriate region. Focal increase in CBF has also been demonstrated when mental rather than physical tasks were involved (Ingvar and Risberg, 1967; Risberg and Ingvar, 1973; Ingvar and Schwartz, 1974; Risberg et al., 1975).

The close relationship between brain function, metabolism and blood flow has naturally given rise to the question, 'Does cerebral blood flow decline with advancing years?' This is a question more easily put than answered. It really involves two questions. The first asks, 'Do measurements of CBF show it to be lower in older age groups than in younger?' The second—if the first is answered in the affirmative—is, 'To what is this reduction due? Is it an effect of the ageing process in itself or does it simply reflect the fact that vascular disease is more common among older people?' The question is further complicated by the close coupling between cerebral metabolism and CBF already mentioned. Primary cerebral degeneration, which again is commoner among the elderly, may reduce metabolic demands which will be reflected in a lowered CBF.

CEREBRAL BLOOD FLOW AND AGEING

The introduction by Kety and Schmidt of the nitrous oxide method of measuring cerebral blood flow (CBF) in man in 1945 was a milestone in the history of the physiology and pathophysiology of the cerebral circulation. Many conditions were subsequently studied by this technique, among them the effect of ageing upon CBF. Reviewing the data provided in papers published up to 1956 involving subjects aged 5–93 years, Kety (1956) concluded that CBF is high in the first decade of life, being of the order of 100 ml/100 g/min. During adolescence it falls rapidly, achieving the adult range of between 50 and 60 ml/100 g/min by the early twenties. Thereafter it declines slowly but perceptibly through the remaining years. The cerebral metabolic rate for oxygen ($CMRO_2$) follows a similar pattern indicating that the change in CBF is reflecting an underlying change in cerebral metabolism.

This was the accepted view of the relationship of CBF to ageing until 1963 when Dastur et al. (Kety being amongst the authors) re-examined the question. They observed that in the studies reviewed by Kety (1956) the subjects, whilst free from gross cerebrovascular disease, were not normal, being in hospital for a variety of conditions. In a new study strenuous effort was made to exclude in so far as possible subjects with any evidence of disease even though asymptomatic. Twenty-six normal old people had a CBF of 58 ml/100 g/min compared with 62/100 g/min in 15 normal young people which is not a significant difference. On the other hand, 10 elderly subjects without symptoms but with objective evidence of arteriosclerosis had a CBF of 49 ml/100 g/min which is significantly lower than in the young and old normal subjects (Dastur et al., 1963). Despite this reduction in CBF, $CMRO_2$ was unchanged indicating that the low CBF was not the result of reduced metabolic demands.

These results highlight the fundamental difficulty of determining normal parameters in older age groups. Absence of symptoms does not mean absence of disease of which there may indeed be objective evidence on careful examination in some instances. Even if the latter is meticulously excluded, there can be no guarantee that the person is free from disease as is often shown at autopsy.

Despite these difficulties continued efforts have been made to determine the effect of ageing upon CBF. Wang and Busse (1975) studied 48 elderly community volunteers of average age 79 years and found a CBF of only 47 ml/100 g/min which was 24 per cent lower than in a group of healthy young adults. More significantly, Thomas et al. (1979) studied 52 hospital patients in whom great care had been taken to exclude cerebral disease. The patients were suffering from conditions such as back pain, carpal tunnel syndrome and peripheral neuropathy and extensive neurological and psychological examination and investigation had been carried out to exclude intellectual deterioration, cerebral disorder, cardiopulmonary disease or diabetes mellitus. They measured flow through fast-clearing tissue only (this being mainly the grey matter) and found a highly significant negative correlation betweeen CBF and age (correlation coefficient -0.524, $P < 0.001$, *Fig. 3.1*).

The most recent evidence on the subject comes from the application of positron emission tomography following the inhalation of cyclotron produced radioactive oxygen (^{15}O). This enables cerebral blood flow and metabolism to be measured in man on a regional basis (Frack-owiak et al., 1980). Comparison of 14 elderly normal subjects with young normal adults showed a small reduction of both CBF and $CMRO_2$ in the former (Frackowiak et al., 1980).

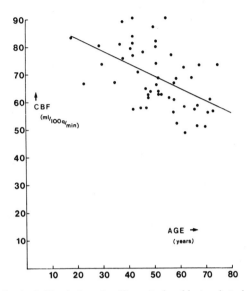

Fig. 3.1. Cerebral blood flow in 52 control subjects plotted against age. Correlation coefficient $= -0.524$, $P < 0.001$.

The conclusion to be drawn from the available evidence is that CBF does decline with age. This decline has been found in asymptomatic subjects and even amongst those in whom strenuous efforts have been made to exclude by clinical examination and investigation evidence of cerebral or vascular disease. This does not of course guarantee that there is no disease present; only pathological examination could do that. But from the practical standpoint when deciding whether a CBF measurement in an older person is normal, the fact that asymptomatic

Table 3.1. Effect of age upon cerebral blood flow. From Thomas et al. (1979)

Age	Mean CBF* (ml/100 g/min)
Under 45 years	77
45–54	68
55–64	64
Over 65 years	60

*Flow through fast clearing tissue.

and clinically normal old people often have a CBF below that found in middle age must be taken into account. Because slightly different CBF values are obtained by different laboratories universal norms cannot be given but an indication of the allowance required for the effect of ageing on CBF is given by the figures from the CBF laboratories at the National Hospital for Nervous Diseases (*Table* 3.1).

CEREBRAL UTILIZATION OF GLUCOSE

Although there has been difference of opinion about whether or not CBF declines as a result of normal ageing, there has been unanimity that a reduction in glucose metabolism occurs. Sokoloff (1966) found a significant reduction in CMRglu from 6·0 ml/100 g/min in normal young people to 4·6 ml/100 g/min in normal elderly subjects. This finding has been confirmed by Gottstein et al. (1972) who showed that the difference between the reduced CMRglu and the maintained $CMRO_2$ is accounted for by the utilization of ketone bodies in cerebral metabolism.

CEREBRAL BLOOD FLOW IN DEMENTIA

The relationship of CBF to ageing is highly relevant to the problem of CBF in dementia. Not long after the nitrous oxide technique of measuring CBF was introduced Freyhan et al. (1951) demonstrated a significant reduction in CBF in patients with organic dementia. Subsequently, Lassen et al. (1957, 1960) found a high correlation between psychological test scores and CBF in dementing patients.

With the introduction of isotope clearance techniques (Ingvar and Lassen, 1962) measurement of blood flow on a regional basis (rCBF) became possible. So-called senile dementia was characterized by a greater reduction in rCBF in the frontal and temporal areas than in the rest of the cortex (Ingvar and Gustafson, 1970; Obrist et al., 1970; Simard et al., 1971).

Dementia is a functional not a pathological term; it can be caused by a variety of pathological processes. The two commonest are the Alzheimer-type of change, which may occur in either the presenium or the senium, and vascular disease. Of the two, the Alzheimer type is the more common. The former tendency to label any elderly dement as suffering from cerebral arteriosclerosis was wrong; in terms of proba-bilities there is about a 60 per cent chance they have Alzheimer-type changes whatever their age and a 30 per cent chance they have vascular disease; some will have both.

Evidence has already been presented that cerebral arteriosclerosis, even when asymptomatic, is associated with a reduction in CBF. However, the fact that the condition may be asymptomatic indicates that reduced CBF alone does not usually cause dementia. Hachinski et al. (1974, 1975) put forward the view that it is the development of multiple small infarcts in the brain that produces the dementia. They also observed that the reduction in CBF was greater for a given degree of dementia in multi-infarct cases than in Alzheimer's dementia, confirming an observation originally made by O'Brien and Mallett (1970). However, Ingvar and Gustafson (1970) and Obrist et al. (1975) were not able to confirm this observation.

In summary, CBF is reduced in organic dementia and may help in those difficult diagnostic situations posed by the need to distinguish an early dementia from a mild depressive disorder. In deciding that the CBF is significantly reduced there is need to make allowance for the effect of age upon flow. The value of CBF in differentiating multi-infarct from Alzheimer's dementia is less certain; a reduction in CBF will be present in both but a very low measurement favours multi-infarct rather than Alzheimer's dementia.

CARBON DIOXIDE RESPONSIVENESS

The cause of the low CBF in Alzheimer's dementia is undoubtedly the reduced metabolic demands of the brain. The situation is not so clear cut in multi-infarct dementia. As already mentioned, asymptomatic cerebral arteriosclerosis is associated with some reduction in CBF. When the arteriosclerosis has led to multiple infarcts the reduction may be greater. The reduction before symptoms raises the question as to whether the low CBF is a response to reduced metabolism, as in Alzheimer's disease, or whether it reflects an inability of the vessels to supply more—a true cerebrovascular insufficiency.

The problem has been approached by study of the CO_2 responsiveness of the cerebral arteries. Carbon dioxide is the most powerful cerebral vasodilator known and norms for CO_2 reactivity in healthy adults are well established (Olesen et al., 1971; Illiff et al., 1974). Hachinski et al. (1975) studied a series of patients in whom considerable care had been taken to distinguish multi-infarct from Alzheimer's dementia by clinical means. They found a small, though not statistically significant, reduction in reactivity during lowering of P_{CO_2} by hyperventilation. Yamamoto et al. (1980) raised P_{CO_2} by inhalation of 5 per cent CO_2; they found reactivity to be normal in patients with Alzheimer's disease but reduced by one-third in those with multi-infarct dementia. The difference between the two studies may lie in the fact that in the one of Hachinski et al. it was the vasoconstrictor response to falling P_{CO_2} which was measured, whereas in the study of Yamamoto et al. the vasodilator response to rising P_{CO_2} was measured; the latter may be more sensitive than the former.

The vasodilator response to CO_2, though reduced, was not abolished. The low CBF in multi-infarct dementia cannot therefore be attributed in its entirety to the inability of the vessels, because of disease in the arterial wall, to supply more blood. It seems probable that the low CBF reflects a combination of reduced metabolic demand and reduced ability to supply.

CEREBROVASCULAR INSUFFICIENCY

Further light on this point is shed by the study of arteriovenous oxygen differences in the cerebral circulation. When blood supply falls in the presence of maintained metabolic demand, the brain responds by extracting more oxygen from the blood; the A–V O_2 difference becomes greater. If, on the other hand, metabolic demand falls, the reduction in CBF being in response to this, the A–V O_2 difference is maintained at the normal level.

Dastur et al. (1963), as mentioned earlier, found that patients with asymptomatic cerebrovascular disease had low CBF and that this was associated with increased A–V O_2 difference, indicating that supply was inadequate for the metabolic demands. $CMRO_2$ was unchanged. In patients with vascular dementia, on the other hand, the low CBF was associated with a normal A–V O_2 difference but reduced $CMRO_2$ indicating that metabolism had become depressed consequent on parenchymatous damage and that the CBF was now adequate to meet the reduced demands.

The thrust of this evidence is towards a concept of vascular dementia as a process involving both reduced blood supply and demand. The reduction in supply seems to be an early feature and may possibly be a contributory factor in producing the parenchymatous damage which reduces the metabolic demand which seems to come later. If this can be established as the pattern of evolution then it offers scope for early intervention to try and prevent the reduction in CBF.

CEREBRAL VASODILATORS

These reflections raise the question of the role of cerebral vasodilators in cerebral disease and in particular in vascular dementia. Not all substances which have beeen proffered as cerebral vasodilators do in fact increase CBF. It has however been clearly established by measurement of CBF in man that some do. The question whether raising CBF benefits the patient is less readily answered. The finding of a low CBF might suggest that vasodilators would be helpful but if the low CBF reflects reduced metabolic demand increasing the CBF would serve no purpose; it would simply create a state of luxury perfusion. But if the low CBF represents a combination of reduced demand and reduced capacity to supply as has been suggested, increasing the supply might have a marginal effect. Clinical trials of cerebral vasodilators do not suggest they have a major role in vascular dementia but on present evidence a marginal effect cannot be excluded.

EXTRACRANIAL VASCULAR DISEASE

The conditions so far considered have involved either diffuse cerebral parenchymal disease or diffuse involvement of small cerebral vessels. An important contributor to cerebrovascular disease is occlusive disease of the extracranial vessels. Atheroma of the carotid and vertebral arteries is common and frequently gives rise to stenosis leading to thrombotic occlusion. Before occlusion occurs, the stenosis might be thought to reduce blood flow. In general this is not the case; Brice et al. (1964) showed that an arterial lumen must be reduced by about 90 per cent before there is a significant reduction in blood flow. Stenoses of this degree occur but are uncommon. This does not mean that stenoses of lesser degree are innocuous; they contribute to cerebrovascular pathology by providing a source of emboli (Gunning et al., 1964). It is for this reason that surgical removal by endarterectomy or, failing this, anticoagulant therapy may prove beneficial in preventing strokes.

Stenoses of severe degree, especially if associated with occlusion of other vessels thus reducing the chance of adequate collateral supply, do reduce CBF. This may result in focal neurological defects or in an overall depression of higher cerebral function. Increasing CBF either by endarterectomy or by anastomosing an extracranial to an intracranial artery (Lumley, 1979) can produce dramatic improvement, demonstrating the importance of CBF for cerebral function.

CEREBRAL BLOOD FLOW IN POLYCYTHAEMIA

Polycythaemia is not an important numerical cause of cerebral dysfunction but it serves as an excellent illustration of the relationship between CBF and cerebral function. Thomas et al. (1977) showed that CBF in a group of patients with polycythaemia was reduced to $37.9 \, ml/100 \, g/min$ compared with $69 \, ml/100 \, g/min$ in controls. The CBF was improved to a level of $62.7 \, ml/100 \, g/min$ when the haematocrit was lowered by venesection.

Of particular relevance to the subject matter of this chapter was the observation that cerebral function as measured by psychological tests significantly improved as CBF rose (Willison et al., 1980). This confirmed the subjective experience of patients with polycythaemia who often complain of being 'thick headed' when their haematocrit is high and of being clearer when it has been lowered.

CONCLUSION

Measurement of CBF in man has greatly increased our understanding of the pathophysiology of the cerebral circulation. CBF and metabolism are closely linked and reduced CBF frequently reflects reduced metabolic demand caused by parenchymatous disease. In some situations the primary defect may be reduction in CBF; this is certainly the case when the haematocrit is high as in polycythaemia, and when extracranial occlusive vascular disease is very severe and involves more than one vessel. It may also be the case in the early stages of a vascular dementia. In all these instances there is the possibility of therapeutic intervention which in some may be beneficial.

REFERENCES

Brice J. G., Dowsett D. J. and Lowe R. D. (1964) *Lancet* **1**, 84.
Dastur D. K., Lane M. H. and Hansen D. B. (1963) In: *Human Aging: A Biological and Behavioral Study*. PHS Publication No. 986, pp. 57. Washington, DC, US Government Printing Office.
Frackowiak R. S. J. et al. (1980) *J. Comput. Assist. Tomogr.* **4**, 727.
Frackowiak R. S. J. et al. (1980) *Acta Neurol. Scand.* **62**, 336.
Freyhan F. A., Woodford R. B. and Kety S. S. (1951) *J. Nerv. Ment. Dis.* **113**, 449.
Gottstein U. et al. (1972) In: Meyer J. S. et al. (ed.) *Research on the Cerebral Circulation*; 5th International Salzburg Conference, 1970. pp. 137. Springfield, Ill., Thomas.
Gunning A. J., Pickering G. W., Robb-Smith A. H. T. et al. (1964) *Q. J. Med.* **33**, 155.
Hachinski V. C., Lassen N. A. and Marshall J. (1974) *Lancet* **2**, 207.
Hachinski V. C., Illiff L. D., Zilkha E. et al. (1975) *Arch. Neurol.* **32**, 632.
Illiff L. D., Zilkha E., du Boulay G. H. et al. (1974) *Stroke* **5**, 607.
Ingvar D. H. and Gustafson L. (1970) *Acta Neurol. Scand.* **43**, 42.
Ingvar D. H. and Lassen N. A. (1962) *Acta Physiol. Scand.* **54**, 325.
Ingvar D. H. and Risberg J. (1967) *Exp. Brain Res.* **3**, 195.
Ingvar D. H. and Schwartz M. S. (1974) *Brain* **97**, 273.
Kety S. S. (1956) *Res. Publ. Assoc. Res. Nerv. Ment. Dis.* **35**, 31.
Kety S. S. and Schmidt C. F. (1945) *Am. J. Physiol.* **143**, 53.
Lassen N. A., Feinberg I. and Lane M. H. (1960) *J. Clin. Invest.* **39**, 491.
Lassen N. A., Munck O. and Tottey E. R. (1957) *Arch. Neurol. Psychiatry* **77**, 126.
Lumley J. S. P. (1979) *Br. J. Surg.* **66**, 317.
O'Brien M. D. and Mallett B. L. (1970) *J. Neurol. Neurosurg. Psychiatry* **33**, 497.
Obrist W. D., Chivian E., Cronqvist S. et al. (1970) *Neurology* **20**, 315.
Obrist W. D., Thompson H. K., Wang H. S. et al. (1975) *Stroke* **6**, 245.
Olesen J. (1971) *Brain* **94**, 635.
Olesen J., Paulson O. B. and Lassen N. A. (1971) *Stroke* **2**, 519.
Risberg J., Halsey J. H., Wills E. L. et al. (1975) *Brain* **98**, 511.
Risberg J. and Ingvar D. H. (1973) *Brain* **96**, 737.
Simard D., Olesen J., Paulson O. B. et al. (1971) *Brain* **94**, 273.
Sokoloff L. (1966) *Res. Publ. Assoc. Res. Nerv. Ment. Dis.* **41**, 237.
Thomas D. J., du Boulay G. H. and Marshall J. et al. (1977) *Lancet* **2**, 161.
Thomas D. J., Zilkha E. and Redmond S. et al. (1979) *J. Neurol. Sci.* **40**, 53.
Wang H. S. and Busse, E. W. (1975) In: Harper M., Jennett B., Miller D. et al. (ed.) *Blood Flow and Metabolism in the Brain*. London, Churchill Livingstone.
Willison J. R., Thomas D. J. and du Boulay G. H. et al. (1980) *Lancet* **1**, 846.
Yamamoto M., Meyer J. S., Sakai F et al. (1980) *Arch. Neurol.* **37**, 489.

4. THE BIOCHEMISTRY OF THE AGEING BRAIN

David M. Bowen and Alan N. Davison

INTRODUCTION

With increasing age there is a shortened sleep cycle, flattening of mood, decreases in motor activity, altered endocrine function, as well as a reduction in cognitive ability. Short-term memory is especially affected. It is generally accepted that intellectual ability declines slowly from the third decade to the sixth, and more abruptly thereafter. However, as many as 10 per cent of the population over the age of 65 years suffers from a dementing process in which there is severe loss of memory and other mental changes. Commonly, this so-called 'senile dementia of the Alzheimer type' (SDAT) is not due to vascular disease, but is a degenerative condition of which the aetiology is unknown.

NORMAL AGEING

Structural Changes

There are extensive longitudinal studies (e.g. De Kaban and Sadowsky, 1978) on the wet weight of the ageing human brain. During the first three years of life, the brain increases four-fold in weight. Thereafter, there is a steady but slower increase in brain weight up to about 18 years of age. The first significant sign of decreasing wet weight is seen at about 45–50 years of age, and the lowest value occurs by about 86 years of age (De Kaban and Sadowsky, 1978). With increasing age, there is a narrowing of brain gyri and a widening and deepening of sulci with some increase in ventricular volume.

Loss of Nerve Cells

Although less well documented than for ageing human subjects, cognitive changes have been reported in other species, e.g. an age-related reduction in retention trial latencies and passive avoidance retention deficits have been found in rodents (Brizzee and Ordy, 1979; Lippa et al., 1980). These changes are not ascribed to reduced motor activity or altered pain threshold, which otherwise might influence such trials. There is some evidence that a small proportion of nerve cells is lost from the aged rat cerebral hemisphere and cerebellum (Peng and Lee, 1979). Particularly significant changes are seen in the hippocampus. Increased lipofuscin was found by Brizzee and Ordy (1979) with age, in both the hippocampus and visual area of the brain. Brizzee et al. (1980) have demonstrated gross morphological and cellular alterations in specific regions of the hippocampus and prefrontal cortex of aged (up to 29 years old) rhesus monkeys. Loss of hippocampus neurones was particularly evident in the CA-1 zone. In the ageing human brain, it seems that the population of certain groups of nerve cells remain unchanged, particularly in the brainstem and in selected nuclei (e.g. ventral cochlear nucleus; Konigsmark and Murphy, 1970). However, as was shown by Brody (1955 and pp. 19–21), there is a progressive loss of neurones from many parts of the cerebral cortex as well as cerebellum and spinal motor neurones (Tomlinson, 1980).

Changes in Nerve Cell Structures

In some regions (such as the cortex) of the ageing brain, examination by the Golgi method shows that there is loss of dendritic processes and synaptic contacts (Scheibel and Tomiyasu, 1978). Although in their study Buell and Coleman (1979) saw grossly atrophic dendritic arborization, the intensity of such change was no different in adult (mean age 52·1 years) compared to elderly (mean 79·6 years) subjects. In the normal ageing human parahippocampal gyrus, Buell and Coleman found continued growth of dendritic arborization. This suggests unexpected plasticity within the ageing brain. Possibly this reactive synaptogenesis is in response to neuronal loss. Currently available data suggest to Buell and Coleman a model in which there are two populations of neurones in normal ageing cortex: one a group of dying neurones with shrinking dendritic trees, the other larger group of surviving neurones with expanding dendritic trees. With increasing age, it is postulated that there is a shift of individual neurones from the surviving to the dying population. The rate at which this shift takes place may be a function of genetic and non-genetic or extrinsic (toxic, behavioural, infectious) factors. Even aged neurones have the capacity to grow new synapses following partial denervation, although the extent and rate of growth is diminished with increasing age (Cotman and Scheff, 1979). In the ageing rat, loss of synapses has been reported in the molecular layer of the dentate gyrus (Bondareff, 1978, 1980). Axonal transport of glycoproteins is significantly slowed in the septo-hippocampal pathway of the 25-month-old, compared to the 3-month-old animal (Geinisman et al., 1977). It is possible that with ageing, loss of synapses may be due to insufficient axonal transport, or, alternatively, to a decrease in the number of neurones.

Energy Metabolism in Ageing

With the reduction in numbers of nerve cells and such structural changes as accumulation of lipofuscin and formation of neuritic plaques, it may be anticipated that there would be reduction in glucose metabolism in ageing. This is of especial importance because, although the brain only accounts for some 2 per cent of body weight, it consumes about 20 per cent of the blood glucose and oxygen supply. However, on a wet weight basis, there is little indication of reduction in cerebral blood flow (CBF) to the brain of ageing healthy human subjects in whom vascular disease is absent. Dastur and his colleagues (1963) found the CBF of $62 \cdot 1 \pm 2 \cdot 9$ ml/100 g/min in young subjects (average age 21 years) to be relatively little reduced in normal old subjects (average age 71 years) where cerebral blood flow was $57 \cdot 9 \pm 2 \cdot 1$ ml/100 g/min. Neither was there any significant change in the oxygen consumption or the respiratory coefficient. The small decrease in glucose utilization in the elderly could be ascribed to replacement of glucose by ketone bodies as substrate. In our experience (Sims and Bowen, unpublished), there is no significant reduction with age in glucose utilization as measured by release of radioactive CO_2 from fresh brain tissue prisms incubated *in vitro* with [U-^{14}C]-glucose.

ENERGY METABOLISM IN EXPERIMENTAL ANIMAL BRAIN

As in humans, there is little to indicate that in other species, cerebral blood flow alters with age. Well-controlled *in vitro* studies on animal brain are obviously much more feasible and indeed some data indicates changes in regional oxygen and glucose consumption with age, in the rat. Peng et al. (1977) found that oxygen consumption in the rat cortex fell between the ages of 4–24 months, from 5·51 to 4·82 µl/mg of dry tissue/hour, there was a 21 per cent decrease in the hippocampus, and a 24 per cent decrease in the hypothalamus. As the authors pointed out, the various decreases in oxygen consumption depend on the functional state of the individual neurones. They do not attribute changes to reduced hormonal control, or to reduction in total neuronal number. However, it should be remembered that there is a continuous increase in rat brain wet weight during development, particularly up to the first 6 months. The augmentation in brain weight tapers off by a year. The presence of considerable amounts of relatively inert myelin in the white matter of 2-year-old animals may account for the decreased oxygen consumption in comparison to young rats. The same explanation may apply to data cited by Frolkis and Bezrukov (1979), where there are significant reductions in oxygen consumption in the hemispheres, cerebellum and particularly in the brainstem.

GLUCOSE METABOLISM

Experimental studies by Smith et al. (1980) on regional utilization of glucose (using the Sokoloff deoxyglucose method) in the rat brain, show reductions of about 20 per cent in glucose consumption of 26- and 36-month-old rat brains compared to that of 4–6-month-old animals. Reductions were greatest in structures associated with visual and auditory function. There seems, therefore, to be a small decline in overall metabolic activity within certain sensory regions of the central nervous system with increasing age. With increasing age, reductions are seen in the oxidation of glucose and 3-hydroxybutyrate by rat brain slices. Changes have been found in synaptic and non-synaptic mitochondrial oxidation of pyruvate and hydroxybutyrate. There seems to be an age-related decrease in activity of tricarboxylic acid cycle and glycolytic enzymes in many brain regions, which may relate to the regional changes in glucose utilization. Similar changes probably occur in the human brain, for example in the cortex phosphofructokinase seems to be particularly affected by ageing, with about a 30 per cent loss of activity from 20 to 80 years of age (Iwangoff et al., 1980).

NEUROTRANSMITTERS

Alterations in glucose metabolism do not appear to be accompanied by marked changes in neurotransmitter metabolism. It is of interest that although statistically non-significant, there is a reduction in transmitter concentration in the hypothalamus (Carlsson et al., 1980). This region controls neuroendocrine functions (releasing or inhibitory factors to the pituitary). The hypothalamus has been regarded as critical in determining the effects of ageing. Amongst the hormones of the hypothalamus (e.g. the releasing factors for gonadotrophins and thyrotrophin) are oxytocin and vasopressin. These peptides are stored in the pituitary and secreted from the pars nervosa. There is good evidence that vasopressin is involved in memory processes (Greidanus and De Weid, 1977). Unexpectedly, monoamine oxidase activity is increased in the ageing brain. This increase has been found to be due to enhanced activity in monoamine oxidase B (the isoenzyme preferentially utilizing phenylethylamine and benzylamine as substrates). In man, declines are seen in the brain catecholamine concentration with age, but monoamine oxidase A activity does not alter. Previous studies in which an age-related drop in the human post-mortem striatal dopamine concentration was found (Carlsson and Winblad, 1976), have been confirmed and extended (Carlsson et al., 1980). Reduction in noradrenaline has been found only in the hippocampus and for 5-hydroxytryptamine loss in the cingulate gyrus. McGeer et al. (1977) have examined some 55 areas from 28 control human brains, from individuals dying without signs of neurological disease. Analysis of the data showed that tyrosine hydroxylase, and to a lesser extent glutamate decarboxylase (GAD) and choline acetyltransferase (ChAT) activities generally showed a significant decrease with ageing in most regions studied (McGeer and McGeer, 1980). However, the marked drop in activity occurred from 5 years up to the age of 20 years. Thereafter, changes were less pronounced, e.g. in the caudate nucleus and putamen, only small decreases are seen in tyrosine hydroxylase and GAD and ChAT activity from the age of 20 to 80 years. In the same cases, the substantia nigra was examined histologically. In this region, about half the neuronal population was lost between 20 and 70 years of age. If comparable cell losses are seen in the striatum, then such cell loss could more than account for the decrement in ChAT, GAD and tyrosine hydroxylase activities from 50 years onwards. The serotoninergic, cholinergic and GABA-ergic systems in the striatum and hypothalamus, do not seem to undergo as marked declines with ageing as do the catecholaminergic systems (McGeer and McGeer, 1980). The major alterations found are loss (about 50 per cent) in dopamine and noradrenaline transmitter systems, possibly correlating with altered sleeping habits, depressive illness and dyskinesia (Winblad et al., 1978). In contrast, little decrease is seen in the activity of ChAT, the enzyme which catalyses the formation of acetylcholine, at least in the cerebral cortex and caudate nucleus. In the cortex, there is an age-related reduction in the concentration of the postsynaptic muscarinic cholinergic receptor protein (White et al., 1977; Perry, 1980). Some authors have found marked losses of cortical ChAT (Bowen et al., 1976) but not acetylcholinesterase activity (Perry and Perry, 1980). For example, Davies and Maloney (1977) find that ChAT activity in controls of 71 years or more have 90 per cent reductions in activity in the frontal cortex, parietal cortex and mid-temporal gyrus. The reasons for difference in these results with those of others is not known.

In rodents, transmitter-synthesizing enzymes show variable changes in activity with age. Probably, the dopaminergic system is more affected. Monoamine oxidase B activity increases with age. In the rat caudate nucleus, loss of tyrosine hydroxylase activity is more than due to generalized cell loss, but glutamate decarboxylase and ChAT activities show little change (McGeer et al., 1971). In mice, some loss of muscarinic receptor protein is found with age (Freund, 1980).

Since there is evidence that malfunctioning brain cholinergic mechanisms may be responsible in part for memory disturbance in the elderly, Lippa and his colleagues (1980) have evaluated the functional status of the hippocampal neurones in ageing rat brain. The hippocampus was chosen because of its central co-ordinating rôle in memory and apparent vulnerability to ageing. In addition, this region receives a major cholinergic input from cells originating in the medial septum.

The degree of memory impairment resulting from ageing was correlated with reduction of pre- and postsynaptic cholinergic functioning.
Glutamate-stimulated neuronal response does not alter with age.

SENILE DEMENTIA

Dementia is defined as the global impairment of higher cortical
functions. Memory is particularly affected. There is a reduction in
capacity to solve the problems of day-to-day living and the performance of learned perceptive-motor skills in the absence of gross
clouding of consciousness. The condition is usually irreversible and
progressive. Some causes of dementia are recognized (e.g. trauma,
multiple sclerosis, vitamin B_{12} or thyroxine deficiency, hydrocephalus,
etc.). Arteriosclerosis, leading to vascular or multi-infarct dementia
accounts for some 25 per cent of cases. However, the aetiology of the
largest group of patients with senile dementia of the Alzheimer's type
(SDAT) is unknown. In patients with senile dementia, there is generally
a reduction in cerebral blood flow by about 25 per cent (Grubb et al.,
1977). On intellectual testing, abnormal responses in regional cerebral
blood flow are found (Ingvar and Lassen, 1976). It is not clear if these
changes simply relate to brain atrophy, or if they are due to basic
defects in neuronal metabolism. The relationship between estimates of
brain ventricular dilatation by computerized axial tomography and
behaviour have in general been poor. Global assessments appear to be
the best predictors of ventricular and cortical pathology (De Leon et
al., 1980).

Pathology

Commonly, brain atrophy with enlarged ventricles is a feature of senile
dementia. Where there is vascular disease, areas of cerebral softening
and multi-infarcts are evident; but in SDAT there are more widespread
neuropathological changes, particularly in the temporal and frontal
cortex. There appears to be an enhanced loss of large cortical nerve
cells, and cells are lost from the hippocampus. Biochemical analysis of
the whole temporal lobe shows a loss of neuronal components
comparable to a reduction in cell number of about 30 per cent (Bowen
et al., 1979).

Histological examination shows that there are neurofibrillary tangles
containing paired helical filaments in the neuronal soma and neurites.
The tangles are found in highest concentration in the younger group of
patients (under 65 years old). There is considerable current interest in
the identification of the paired helical filaments, which appear to be
derived from a naturally-occurring filamentous protein. Wisniewski
and Iqbal (1980) have suggested that the tangles may be the result of a

structural shift to a β-pleated conformation of otherwise normal fibrous protein. Such changes may be induced by aluminium (De Boni and Crapper, 1978). However, tangles are not present in the brain of patients with renal dialysis encephalopathy, where there are raised brain concentrations of aluminium.

Neuritic plaques are found throughout the brain in SDAT. These plaques have a complex structure containing amyloid, degenerating synaptic terminals and neurites. Somewhat similar plaques have been seen in the slow virus disease of sheep, known as scrapie (Dickinson et al., 1980). Wisniewski et al. (1982) have shown that neuritic plaques and amyloid deposits can be induced in scrapie-infected mice along the line of the injection track into the brain.

A third feature of SDAT is the presence of granulovacuolar degeneration in the hippocampal neurones. This again points to degenerative changes occurring within the neurone. There is also evidence of deposition of amyloid and accumulation of the insoluble pigment—lipofuchsin—within some nerve cells. Since the main function of nerve cells is the propagation of an action potential with release of neurotransmitters, interest has focused on the possibility of some defect in this system being related to the functional change in dementia.

Neurotransmitters

Direct measurement of transmitter concentration in post-mortem tissue is subject to artefact. Nevertheless, useful information can be obtained by comparison of carefully matched post-mortem material for residual transmitter and metabolite concentration. Thus, remaining acetylcholine levels in the temporal cortex of SDAT cases was found by Richter et al. (1980), to be lower than in age-matched controls. Reduction in dopamine, homovanillic acid, noradrenaline and serotonin (5HT) have also been reported for some areas of post-mortem material (Winblad et al., 1978; Berger et al., 1980; Carlsson et al., 1980). Similarly, a reduction has been found in the concentration of the peptide somatostatin in the temporal cortex (Rossor et al., 1980a), but no alteration has been found in other peptides (Rossor et al., 1980b, c).

Receptor Binding

Receptor-binding proteins appear to be stable post-mortem. In SDAT no significant alteration has been observed in the concentration of the muscarinic cholinergic receptor (White et al., 1977; Perry et al., 1977a, b) except in the important area of the hippocampus (Reisine et al., 1978). Nevertheless, there are reductions in the concentration of some transmitter-binding proteins, such as GABA receptors in the caudate nucleus and frontal cortex (*Table* 4.1). An alternative method

Table 4.1. Neurotransmitter receptor binding in areas of control and SDAT post-mortem brain

		Mean percentage reduction			
Ligand	*For*	*Caudate nucleus*	*Putamen*	*Frontal cortex*	*Hippocampus*
QNB	Muscarinic cholinergic receptor	89%	75%	95%	43%
GABA	Inhibitory transmitter	57%*	77%	51%	59%
Spiro- peridol	Dopaminergic receptor	52%*	100%	70%	100%

Mean percentages in receptor binding in SDAT, compared to controls (mean age 69 years). Significant reductions are shown (*). (Reisine et al., 1978.)

for assessing the capability of brain tissue to synthesize neurotransmitter depends on the measurement of the activity of enzymes synthesizing neurotransmitters from precursor. Such a method led to the discovery of the dopaminergic defect in the basal ganglion of patients with Parkinson's disease (Lloyd and Hornykiewicz, 1970). In transmitter-synthesizing enzymes examined in post-mortem tissue from the brain of demented patients, the most notable change has been in the activity of choline acetyltransferase (the enzyme forming acetylcholine). Other enzymes, such as glutamate decarboxylase (which synthesizes the inhibitory transmitter GABA), do not change in activity in dementia or this cannot be convincingly demonstrated, as e.g. aromatic amino acid decarboxylase or tyrosine hydroxylase (enzymes involved in catecholamine biosynthesis). Choline acetyltransferase (ChAT) activity was found to be significantly reduced in SDAT in the frontal cortex and the reduction was found to be proportional to the degree of neuropathological change (Bowen et al., 1976). Similarly,

Table 4.2. Changes in acetylcholine synthesis and glucose metabolism in the neocortex of patients with senile dementia of the Alzheimer type (SDAT)

	Control	*SDAT* (% of control)	*Sample*
Choline acetyl- transferase (nmol/min/100 mg protein)	7·2 6·5	51 46	Post-mortem Biopsy
Stimulated acetylcholine synthesis (pmol/min/mg protein)	7·2	40	Biopsy
Carbon dioxide produced from glucose	390	125	Biopsy

Acetylcholine synthesis and glucose utilization was measured in fresh tissue prisms containing intact synaptic terminals. (Sims et al., 1980.)

Davies and Maloney (1976) and Perry et al. (1977a) found reduction in ChAT activity, especially in the memory co-ordinating areas, the hippocampus and mamillary bodies. Rather less reduction was found in the activity of the enzyme acetylcholinesterase. These observations suggested that there was a defect in cholinergic neuronal activity, possibly due to loss of precholinergic terminals. This conclusion was supported by observations on fresh biopsy material. We found reduction in ChAT activity in surgical samples from demented patients when there was neuropathological evidence for SDAT (*Table* 4.2). Glutamate decarboxylase activity was not affected.

The Cholinergic System

The ability of fresh biopsy tissue to synthesize acetylcholine under stimulated and resting conditions was studied by Sims and his colleagues (1980). For this purpose, tissue prisms were prepared, for these contain viable well-preserved synaptic endings free of intact cell bodies. The tissue prisms were incubated with $[U-^{14}C]$-glucose and release of radioactive carbon dioxide was measured. Synthesis of acetylcholine was determined by isolation of precipitated, labelled acetylcholine-reineckate. The data indicates that in SDAT there is reduction in synthesized acetylcholine, proportional to the reduction in choline acetyltransferase activity, under both resting and stimulated conditions. The most likely explanation of these findings is a selective loss of presynaptic cholinergic nerve endings. It has been proposed that choline transport is obligatorily coupled to acetylcholine synthesis and that ChAT is bound close to the choline transport sites on the membrane. However, Kessler and Marchbanks (1979) have shown experimentally that choline transport is not coupled to acetylcholine synthesis. There is evidence (Marchbanks et al., 1981) that acetylcholine immobilizes the choline carrier. It seems probable that acetylcholine synthesis is controlled by the activity of ATP citrate lyase and the acetyl CoA thereby released (Marchbanks and Wonnacott, 1979). Acetylcholine synthesis has been shown to be tightly linked to carbohydrate utilization and synthesis appears to be particularly sensitive to slight impairment of pyruvate oxidation (Blass et al., 1980). Thus, mild hypoxia could significantly inhibit acetylcholine synthesis.

CONCLUSION

In normal ageing some loss of neurones occurs, but there is evidence of compensatory synaptogenesis to remedy the reduction in neuronal interaction. There is relatively small alteration in metabolism, but some reduction in neurotransmitters. Catecholamines are particularly affected. In senile dementia of the Alzheimer's type, there is an increased loss of the larger neurones. There is significant loss of nerve cells in the hippocampus. Reduction in dendritic arborization is apparent. There is a significant loss of choline acetyltransferase activity and a parallel inability of the tissue to synthesize acetylcholine. These changes are proportional to neuropathological and intellectual deficit. Other changes in neurotransmitter concentration have been reported. The inter-relationship of these complex changes with the pathogenesis of dementia is not understood. Aluminium has been considered as one pathological factor, but in experimental animals aluminium does not cause reduction in choline acetyltransferase activity (Hetnarski et al., 1980). A primary defect in neuronal energy metabolism, if established, could explain the changes in neurotransmitter activity. Axonal flow of enzymes and substrates depends on energy as does synthesis of acetylcholine. Further work on glucose metabolism in the ageing and dementing brain should throw light on this interesting possibility.

REFERENCES

Berger B., Tassin J. P., Rancurel G. et al. (1980) In: Usdin E., Sourkes T. L. and Youdim M. B. H. (ed.) *Enzymes and Neurotransmitters in Mental Disease.* Chichester, John Wiley. p. 317.
Blass J. P., Gibson G. E., Shimada M. et al. (1980) In: Roberts P. J. (ed.) *Biochemistry of Dementia.* Chichester, John Wiley. p. 121.
Bondareff W. (1978) In: Katzman R., Terry R. D. and Bick K. L. (ed.) *Alzheimer's Disease. Senile Dementia and Related Disorders.* New York, Raven Press. p. 383.
Bondareff W. (1980) In: Adelman R. C., Roberts J., Baker G. T. III, Baskin S. I. and Cristofalo V. J. (ed.) *Neural Regulatory Mechanisms During Ageing.* New York, Alan R. Liss, Inc. p. 143.
De Boni U. and Crapper D. R. (1978) *Nature* 271, 566.
Bowen D. M., Smith C. B., White P. et al. (1976) *Brain* 99, 459.
Bowen D. M., White P., Spillane J. A. et al. (1979) *Lancet* 1, 11.
Brizzee K. R. and Ordy J. M. (1979) *Mech. Ageing Dev.* 9, 143.
Brizzee K. R., Ordy J. M. and Bartus R. T. (1980) *Neurobiol. Aging* 1, 45.
Brody H. (1955) *J. Comp. Neurol.* 102, 511.
Buell S. J. and Coleman P. D. (1979) *Science* 206, 854.
Carlsson A., Adolfsson R., Aquilonius S-M. et al. (1980) In: Goldstein M., Calne D. B., Lieberman A. and Thorner M. O. (ed.) *Ergot Compounds and Brain Function: Neuroendocrine and Neuropsychiatric Aspects.* New York, Raven Press. p. 295.
Carlsson A. and Winblad B. (1976) *J. Neural. Transm.* 38, 271.
Cotman C. W. and Scheff S. W. (1979) *Mech. Ageing Dev.* 9, 103.
Dastur D. K., Lane M. H., Hansen D. B. et al. (1963) In: Birren J. E., Butler R. N., Greenhouse S. W., Sokoloff L. and Yarrow M. R. (ed.) *Human Aging.* No. 986. Public Health Service Publication. p. 59.
Davies P. and Maloney A. J. F. (1976) *Lancet* 2, 1403.
Dickinson A. G., Fraser H. and Bruce M. A. (1980) In: Glen A. I. M. and Whalley L. J. (ed.) *Alzheimer's Disease.* Edinburgh and London, Churchill Livingstone. p. 42.
Freund G. (1980) *Life Sci.* 26, 371.
Frolkis V. V. and Bezrukov V. V. (1979) In: van Haln (ed.) *Interdisciplinary Topics in Gerontology.* Vol. 16. p. 17.
Geinisman Y., Bondareff W. and Telser A. (1977) *Brain Res.* 125, 182.

Greidanus T. B. and De Wied D. (1977) In: Davison A. N. (ed.) *Biochemical Correlates of Brain Structure and Function.* London, Academic Press. p. 215.

Grubb R. L. Jr., Richie M., Mokhtar H. C. et al. (1977) *Neurology (NY)* **27**, 971.

Hertnarski B., Wisniewski H. M., Iqbal K. et al. (1980) *Ann. Neurol.* **7**, 489.

Ingvar D. H. and Lassen N. A. (1976) In: Himwich H. E. (ed.) *Brain Metabolism and Cerebral Disorders.* New York, Spectrum Publications. p. 181.

Iwangoff P., Armbruster R., Enz. A. et al. (1980) *Mech. Ageing Dev.* **14**, 403.

De Kaban A. S. and Sadowsky D. (1978) *Ann. Neurol.* **4**, 345.

Kessler P. D. and Marchbanks R. M. (1979) *Nature* **279**, 542.

Konigsmark B. W. and Murphy E. A. (1970) *Nature* **228**, 1335.

De Leon M. J., Ferris S. H., George A. E. et al. (1980) *Neurobiol. Aging* **1**, 69.

Lippa A. S., Pelham R. W., Beer B. et al. (1980) *Neurobiol. Aging* **1**, 13.

Lloyd K. and Hornykiewicz O. (1970) *Science* **170**, 1212.

McGeer E. G., Fibiger H. C., McGeer P. L. et al. (1971) *Exp. Gerontol.* **6**, 391.

McGeer E. G. and McGeer P. L. (1980) In: Goldstein M., Calne D. B., Lieberman A. and Thorner M. O. (ed.) *Ergot Compounds and Brain Function (Advances in Biochemical Psychopharmacology, Vol. 23).* New York, Raven Press. p. 305.

McGeer P. L., McGeer E. G. and Suzuki J. S. (1977) *Arch. Neurol.* **34**, 33.

Marchbanks R. M. and Wonnacott S. (1979) In: Tucek S. (ed.) *Progress of Brain Research,* Vol. 49. Amsterdam, Elsevier. p. 77.

Marchbanks R. M., Wonnacott S. and Rubio M. A. (1981) *J. Neurochem.* **36**, 379.

Peng M. T. and Lee L. R. (1979) *Gerontology* **25**, 205.

Peng M. T., Peng Y. I. and Chen F. N. (1977) *J. Gerontol.* **32**, 517.

Perry E. K. (1980) *Age Ageing* **9**, 1.

Perry E. K., Gibson P. H., Blessed G. et al. (1977a) *J. Neurol. Sci.* **34**, 247.

Perry E. K. and Perry R. H. (1980) In: Roberts P. J. (ed.) *Biochemistry of Dementia.* Chichester, John Wiley. p. 135.

Perry E. K., Perry R. H. and Tomlinson B. E. (1977b) *Neurosci. Lett.* **4**, 185.

Reisine T. D., Yamamura H. I., Bird E. D. et al. (1978) *Brain Res.* **159**, 477.

Richter J. A., Perry E. K. and Tomlinson B. E. (1980) *Life Sci.* **26**, 1683.

Rossor M. N., Emson P. C., Mountjoy C. Q. et al. (1980a) *Neurosci. Lett.* **20**(3), 373.

Rossor M. N., Fahrenkrug J., Emson P. et al. (1980b) *Brain Res.* **201**, 249.

Rossor M. N., Iversen L. L., Mountjoy C. Q. et al. *Lancet* **2**, 1367.

Scheibel A. B. and Tomiyasu U. (1978) *Exp. Neurol.* **60**, 1.

Sims N. R., Smith C. C. T., Bowen D. M. et al. (1980) *Lancet* **1**, 333.

Smith C. B., Goochee C., Rapoport S. I. et al. (1980) *Brain* **103**, 351.

Tomlinson B. E. (1980) In: Roberts P. J. (ed.) *Biochemistry of Dementia.* Chichester, John Wiley. p. 15.

White P., Hiley C. R., Goodhardt M. J. et al. (1977) *Lancet* **1**, 668.

Winblad B., Adolfsson R., Gottfries C. G. et al. (1978) In: Frigerio A. (ed.) *Recent Developments in Mass Spectrometry in Biochemistry and Medicine,* Vol. 1. New York, Plenum Press. p. 253.

Wisniewski H. M. and Iqbal K. (1980) *Trends in Neurosci.* **3**, 226.

Wisniewski H. M., Moretz R. C. and Lossinsky A. S. (1982) In press.

5. EXAMINATION OF THE NERVOUS SYSTEM
F. I. Caird

Examination of the nervous system is of great importance in the elderly, because neurological disorders are the major cause of disability in old age (Akhtar et al., 1973), and because, as at any age, an exact diagnosis is an essential preliminary to rational decisions of management. The history, and especially the time scale of evolution of symptoms, is the principal guide to the pathology, while the examination points to the site of the lesion. In the elderly there should always also be an additional dimension, of particular importance in relation to rehabilitation. The functional capabilities of the patient require accurate assessment, and the presence of disorders of function of neurological or other origin which might constitute barriers to recovery must be determined (Adams and Hurwitz, 1963). The objectives of neurological examination thus differ somewhat in the elderly, as do a considerable number of methods, since these must be modified to allow for the frequent impairment of concentration and co-operation, and for those variations in physical signs which are possibly due to the ageing process itself (Critchley, 1931, 1956; Howell, 1949).

MENTAL STATE

The patient's mental state to a large extent determines how neurological examination is best conducted, in particular because of its relation to the level of co-operation likely to be achieved, and so to the credibility of some important physical signs. Mental impairment is also of crucial significance in overall functional ability and as a major barrier to recovery (Adams and Hurwitz, 1963). The principal problems are assessment of intellectual capacity, and of depression. Simple psychometric testing has much to recommend it. Which particular test is used is of less importance than a definite attempt to establish the presence and degree of what has been termed brain failure (Isaacs and Caird, 1976). Recent and remote memory, ability to carry out simple calculations, and orientation for time, place and person must all be tested. Simple guidelines for the diagnosis of depression in the elderly have been described (Caird and Judge, 1979).

The signs of impairment of consciousness in the elderly do not differ from those in younger patients. The Glasgow Coma Scale (Teasdale and Jennett, 1974) can be used in geriatric wards without difficulty.

MENINGEAL SIGNS

These may be difficult to interpret in the elderly because of the frequency of neck stiffness due to osteoarthritic changes in the cervical spine. The great majority of elderly patients with meningeal irritation show evidence of impairment of consciousness, and restricted forward flexion or rotation. Kernig's sign is also often difficult to interpret, and Brudzinski's is perhaps the more valuable.

THE CRANIAL NERVES

Tests of olfactory function are even more rarely used in the elderly than in the young, and there is good evidence of a substantial age-related decline in olfactory sensation (Prakash and Stern, 1973; *see* Bradley, 1979).

The visual fields may be reasonably accurately tested by confrontation in elderly patients who are co-operative, and by the menace reaction in those who are not. When competent observers differ about the presence of a hemianopia, confrontation using stimuli above and below the equator may detect a quadrantanopia. Simultaneous stimuli in the two visual fields will show the presence of a hemianopic attention defect. Visual neglect may be determined by the two-pen test (*see* Caird and Judge, 1979), or the patient may be asked to read a line of printed words, of which both halves are necessary to make sense (e.g. most newspaper headlines, or phrases such as 'Marks and Spencer'). Neglect of the left half of the visual field is shown by the patient reading only the right half of the line, and failing to recognize any problem.

Papilloedema is unusual in space-occupying intracranial lesions in the elderly. It has been reported in as many as 30 per cent of cases of intracranial tumour (Friedman and Odom, 1972; Cooney and Solitaire, 1974), but personal experience (*see* p. 232) indicates a much lower proportion. Papilloedema also becomes less common with age in subdural haematoma (Fogelholm et al., 1975; Luxon and Harrison, 1979) and over the age of 70 is virtually never due to high blood pressure (Kincaid-Smith et al., 1958). The absence of papilloedema is therefore no evidence of the absence of an expanding intracranial lesion.

Conjugate upward gaze is often impaired, and convergence limited in the elderly (Critchley, 1956). Abnormality of upward gaze is found in 30 per cent of neurologically normal old people, and perhaps twice as many elderly patients with dementia (Broe, unpublished). Impairment of upward gaze and bilateral ptosis may be a sign of raised intracranial pressure (Pennybacker, 1949). The doll's head manoeuvre is apparently unaltered in the elderly, and pupillary reactions to light are preserved, though the pupils are usually smaller than in the young, and may be slightly eccentric and irregular. Constriction on accommodation may be limited (Prakash and Stern, 1973).

Sensory functions in the face and corneal reflex are unaffected in old age, but the jaw jerk is present in only 50 per cent (Prakash and Stern, 1973).

Facial asymmetry, perhaps associated with absence of teeth, may be difficult to distinguish from upper motor neurone facial weakness, but help may be gained from separate testing of voluntary and emotional movement of the face, and demonstration of weakness of the platysma.

MOTOR FUNCTIONS

The simplest test of motor power in the upper limbs is to observe the outstretched hands, palms upwards. Proximal and distal weakness, drift associated with sensory loss, tremor, and the pronator sign may then be noted. Bradykinesia is best tested by observing serial flexion and extension movements of the fingers, as in playing the piano. Tone is difficult to assess, and rigidity associated with joint disease may mimic or complicate that due to neuromuscular disorders. The finger-nose-finger test is normally accurately performed provided its objectives are explained, and is adequate to demonstrate cerebellar ataxia. Wasting of the small muscles of the hands is commonly associated with arthritis in the small joints, or with generalized muscle wasting, and its value as a sign of neurological disease is thus limited (Prakash and Stern, 1973).

Power in the lower limb is most easily tested by asking the patient to lift his leg from the bed. A useful five-point grading system based on this simple test (Caird and Judge, 1979) has been validated (Garraway et al., 1976; *Table* 5.1). Tone can be difficult to assess in the presence of joint disease; co-ordination is never easy to test. Muscle bulk in the thigh is frequently affected by arthritis of the knee, but in the calf usually only suffers as part of generalized muscle wasting. Fascicula-

Table 5.1. A useful simple classification of power in the lower limb

0	No movement;
1	A flicker of movement, but the knee is not lifted from the bed;
2	The heel can be lifted off the bed but this cannot be sustained;
3	The heel can be held off the bed for 10 s or more;
4	Power better than 3, but not normal;
5	Normal power.

tion is not infrequently observed in the calf muscles, particularly when exposed to the cold, but only commonly in men; for some reason it is very rare in women. When there is also fasciculation in other muscle groups, the common cause is motor neurone disease, but benign fasciculation, perhaps best distinguished by its lesser extent and intensity, will occasionally be encountered. If there is doubt, electromyographic studies should be carried out (Ballantyne, 1981).

SENSORY FUNCTIONS

Sensory testing in old age is particularly limited by the patient's co-operation and mental state. In general, only simple tests of pain and touch are of value, and it is usually unprofitable to spend too much time over other sensory modalities. Simultaneous stimuli are useful in demonstrating lateralized sensory loss, since provided the patient can concentrate for short periods, it is usually possible to be certain of the presence or absence of sensory suppression. Position and vibration sense are of less significance, particularly in the lower limbs. There is an increase with age in vibration sense threshold (Cosh, 1953; Steiness, 1957), and vibration sense at least at the ankle is often absent (Himel and MacDonald, 1957; Skre, 1972; Prakash and Stern, 1973). Absence of vibration sense at the level of the knee is in need of an explanation other than age. The reason for these abnormalities, as for the reflex changes described below, is no doubt the so-called 'senile neuropathy', evident on neuropathological examination as segmental demyelination, and electrophysiologically as reduction in nerve conduction velocities (see McLeod, 1980).

Large-joint position sense and the phenomenon of neglect of the limbs are of more importance, as giving clues to functional impairment in patients with stroke. The former is most easily tested by the thumb-finding test (see Caird and Judge, 1979), and the latter by showing the patient his hand in his unaffected visual field. If the patient is at all uncertain of whose hand he is looking at, some degree of neglect is present. Denial of ownership of the hand is evidence of a more severe degree of abnormality. Left–right disorientation is also not infrequent, but is perhaps more often detected by the occupational therapist, than by the clinician.

REFLEXES

So-called primitive reflexes are not infrequently demonstrable in neurologically normal old people. The palmomental reflex increases in frequency with age (Dalby, 1970), while the glabellar tap is not specific to Parkinsonism, since it is present in one-third of neurologically normal old people (Prakash and Stern, 1973; Broe, unpublished), and is probably even more frequent in the various illnesses resulting in dementia in old age.

The second common reflex abnormality encountered in the elderly is reduction in tendon jerks, particularly the ankle jerk. Absence of the ankle jerks in 'normal' old people has been frequently documented (Howell, 1949; Mayne, 1965; Prakash and Stern, 1973). Broe et al. (unpublished) found that the frequency increases with age, and is greater in women than men (*Table* 5.2). The reason for the sex

Table 5.2. Prevalence of bilateral absence of ankle jerks in 'neurologically normal' old people (Broe et al., unpublished)

Age	Men	Women	Total
65–74	$11/96 = 11\%$	$29/156 = 19\%$	$40/252 = 16\%$
75+	$23/69 = 33\%$	$57/131 = 44\%$	$80/200 = 40\%$
	$34/165 = 21\%$	$86/287 = 30\%$	$120/452 = 27\%$

The differences between age groups are significant in each sex (t 3·6 and 4·7), but the differences between sexes are not.

difference is uncertain, but it is tempting to associate it with the greater degree of sway in elderly women (Overstall et al., 1977) Absence of the knee jerks (in the absence of osteoarthritis of the knees) and generalized reduction in reflexes in upper as well as lower limbs is much less common (Skre, 1972; Prakash and Stern, 1973), though the abdominal reflexes are more often absent than present.

The plantar responses remain flexor in normal old age, and are extensor only under the same circumstances as in the young.

ABNORMAL MOVEMENTS

So-called 'senile tremor' is now clearly recognized as a manifestation of essential or hereditary tremor (Critchley, 1956), which has the same prevalence in old age as Parkinsonism (Broe et al., 1976), from which it must be distinguished. Tardive dyskinesia, usually clearly due to phenothiazine therapy, and orofacial dyskinesia due to levodopa, are often seen in the elderly, but there remain choreiform movements which are not easily classified. For some the term senile chorea is appropriate; the observation (Bedford and Caird, 1960) that senile chorea seems to be associated with rheumatic heart disease is of interest.

FUNCTIONAL ASSESSMENT

Neurological examination of the elderly should include a number of simple assessments of function.

Lying

Examination of the lying patient is particularly important in Parkinson's disease, since the patient is often able to stand from sitting and walk from standing, but may be totally unable to turn when lying, or sit from lying. Thus a patient who is apparently independently mobile, may in fact be bed-bound because he cannot get out of bed. Examination of the ability to carry out these simple manoeuvres is thus an important part of the functional assessment of the patient with Parkinson's disease.

Sitting

Abnormalities of sitting posture are common in stroke, and are important in the assessment of the pace of rehabilitation, since patients who cannot sit unsupported cannot be expected to stand (Adams, 1974). Examination of the displacement reactions in the sitting position (Martin, 1976) may contribute to the diagnosis of Parkinson's disease. The patient sits on the bed with his feet off the ground and his hands on his knees. If he is suddenly displaced to his right, the normal integrated response consists of abduction of the left arm and extension of the elbow as a counterweight, and abduction of the right arm with flexion of the elbow to take the weight of the trunk. Loss of these reactions is associated with other well-recognized abnormalities, such as loss of arm swing on walking, and is no doubt important in contributing to postural instability in Parkinson's disease.

Standing

Examination of the patient standing from sitting will bring out proximal muscle weakness, and also the specific difficulty of the Parkinsonian. The flexed standing posture of some elderly people has been attributed to 'senile Parkinsonism'. This is unsatisfactory as a diagnosis, particularly if it attracts anti-Parkinson treatment; it is usually associated with diffuse brain disease and substantial intellectual impairment.

The backward-leaning syndrome is a second common abnormality of standing posture (Braverman, 1980). This may occur as part of the Parkinsonian syndrome, and also in diffuse or multifocal brain disease with bilateral pyramidal signs and intellectual impairment. The patient is unable to stand unsupported because he leans backwards beyond the point where his centre of gravity is inside his base. The neck may be extended, and there may be abnormal postures of the upper limbs, with the fingers hyperextended, and the arms abducted. A simple test shows the nature of the abnormality. If the patient is supported standing with eyes covered, and is moved slowly upright, and while this happens is asked 'Are you standing up straight?', a point will be reached when he will say he is standing straight and will prove that he feels that he is standing straight by starting to walk if he is pushed gently nearer the vertical. This condition may be exaggerated by prolonged bed rest, and often improves over a 10–14 day period after mobilization.

Walking

Every elderly patient with a neurological disorder who is capable of doing so should be examined while walking. The examination should include beginning to walk, at least 10 steps, a 180° turn, and return to the chair. The abnormalities of gait described in the standard textbooks will be observed, together with a substantial number which are not so described (Caird and Judge, 1979). In particular, the shuffling 'marche à petit pas' of the patient with diffuse brain disease must be distinguished from that of Parkinsonism. In the former there is no greater difficulty in turning and in starting to walk. If the patient stops after only a few steps, this is due to a restricted attention span rather than to any specific difficulty in walking.

Dressing

Dressing is a complicated sequence of learned acts, as anyone who has attempted to teach a small child to dress will immediately appreciate. It is not therefore surprising that it is frequently disordered in neurological disease. Two main types of difficulty may be distinguished, and the occupational therapist is often the best placed to make the distinction. There may be specific problems, such as hemiplegia, a stiff shoulder, inability to flex the trunk or hips, or left–right disorientation. Also commonly observed is dressing apraxia, in which the patient is unable to appreciate the sequence of acts required, and is uncertain where each garment should go. This is almost always accompanied by severe intellectual impairment, and to attribute it either to frontal or to parietal lobe disorder is not usually helpful.

REFERENCES

Adams G. F. (1974) *Cerebrovascular Disability and the Ageing Brain.* Edinburgh and London, Churchill Livingstone.
Adams G. F. and Hurwitz L. J. (1963) *Lancet* 2, 533.
Akhtar A. J., Broe G. A., Crombie A. et al. (1973) *Age Ageing* 2, 102.

Ballantyne J. (1981) In: Caird F. I. and Evans J. G. (ed.) *Advanced Geriatric Medicine*. Tunbridge Wells, Pitman Medical.

Bedford P. D. and Caird F. I. (1960) *Valvular Heart Disease in Old Age*. London, Churchill.

Bradley R. M. (1979) In: Han S. S. and Coons D. H. (ed.) *Special Senses and Aging*. University of Michigan, p. 3.

Braverman A. M. (1980) *J. Clin. Exp. Geront.* **2**, 99.

Broe G. A., Akhtar A. J., Andrews G. R. et al. (1976) *J. Neurol. Neurosurg. Psychiatry* **39**, 362.

Caird F. I. and Judge T. G. (1979) *Assessment of the Elderly Patient*. 2nd ed. Tunbridge Wells, Pitman Medical.

Cooney L. M. and Solitaire G. B. (1974) *Modern Geriatrics* **4**, 234.

Cosh J. A. (1953) *Clin. Sci.* **12**, 131.

Critchley M. (1931) *Lancet* **1**, 1119.

Critchley M. (1956) *J. Chron. Dis.* **3**, 456.

Dalby M. A. (1970) *Acta Neurol. Scand.* **46**, 601.

Fogelholm R., Heiskanen O. and Waltimo O. (1975) *J. Neurosurg.* **42**, 43.

Friedman H and Odom G. L. (1972) *Geriatrics* **27**, April, 105.

Garraway W. M., Akhtar A. J., Gore S. M. et al. (1976) *Age Ageing* **4**, 233.

Himel H. A. and MacDonald R. I. (1957) *Canad. Med. Assoc. J.* **77**, 459.

Howell T. H. (1949) *Br. Med. J.* **1**, 56.

Isaacs B. and Caird F. I. (1976) *Age Ageing* **4**, 241.

Kincaid-Smith P., McMichael J. and Murphy E. A. (1958) *Q. J. Med.* N.S. **27**, 117.

Luxon L. M. and Harrison M. J. G. (1979) *Q. J. Med.* N.S. **48**, 43.

McLeod J. G. (1980) *J. Clin. Exp. Geront.* **2**, 259.

Martin J. P. (1967) *The Basal Ganglia and Posture*. London, Pitman Medical.

Mayne N. (1965) *Lancet* **2**, 1313.

Overstall P. W., Exton-Smith A. N., Imms F. J. et al. (1977) *Br. Med. J.* **1**, 261.

Pennybacker J. (1949) *Edin. Med. J.* **56**, 590.

Prakash C. and Stern G. (1973) *Age Ageing* **2**, 24.

Skre H. (1972) *Acta Neurol. Scand.* **48**, 575.

Steiness I. (1957) *Acta Med. Scand.* **158**, 315.

Teasdale G. and Jennett W. B. (1974) *Lancet* **2**, 81.

6. INVESTIGATION OF NEUROLOGICAL DISORDERS
Margaret A. Roberts and F. I. Caird

Optimum management of a large number of elderly patients rests on the proper diagnosis of neurological disorders, and investigations play an important part in this. This chapter reviews some of the general considerations involved and the indications for various investigations, and outlines an approach to some specific diagnostic problems.

GENERAL CONSIDERATIONS

These are as follows:

1. The range of normal in the elderly must be known, so as to prevent both overdiagnosis, when normality is mistaken for abnormality, and underdiagnosis when the reverse occurs (Caird, 1973).

2. The potential hazards of individual investigations must be appreciated. If these increase with age, the need for a definite diagnosis likely to affect management must also be greater, if the investigation is to remain justifiable.

3. Particular investigations may or may not be easily accessible to the elderly. If they are effectively denied investigations of potential value to them, a situation of considerable difficulty results. The need to transfer frail or ill elderly patients from one hospital to another, to give them access to the investigations, is a further consideration of great practical importance.

4. The relationship between neurological disorders and extracranial disease is extremely close, so that the approach to an elderly patient with a neurological disorder must begin with a wide range of investigations that are not specifically neurological (e.g. the electrocardiogram, chest radiograph, and a wide range of biochemical measurements; Caird, 1979). To omit such elementary investigations will reduce the likelihood of reaching a correct diagnosis.

5. Clinical examination will define the probable site of a neurological lesion, and this will largely determine the investigations which will be helpful. Any attempt at 'blanket' investigation of the nervous system is totally inappropriate.

SPECIFIC INVESTIGATIONS AND INDICATIONS FOR THEIR USE

I. Neuroradiology

a. Plain Radiographs

The principal indications for a skull radiograph are suspected skull fracture, and the possibility of detection of pineal shift, and of abnormal calcification or decalcification (Du Boulay, 1977). However, even in the very elderly, the pineal is often not sufficiently calcified enough to be visible on straight skull radiographs (Macpherson and Mathieson, 1979), and therefore only the positive demonstration of a central or shifted pineal is of value. The skull radiograph not infrequently shows calcification in the carotid arteries at the syphon, and in the falx, and the changes of hyperostosis frontalis interna— conditions of no importance. Calcification in intracranial tumours such as meningioma may be detected.

Radiographs of the cervical spine are necessary when a cervical cord lesion is suspected. The virtually universal presence of radiological evidence of cervical spondylosis, with osteophyte formation resulting in foraminal encroachment and potential narrowing of the cervical canal (Nurick, 1972), make it best to regard as significant only radiologically very severe lesions, usually with subluxation of one vertebra upon another.

The diagnosis of the cause of cord compression at other sites requires radiographs of the spine of high quality, but these may be difficult to obtain if there is much kyphoscoliosis.

b. Radionuclide Imaging (RNI)

This has many advantages in the investigation of elderly patients. It is safe, and apart from intravenous injection, non-invasive. The patient must lie still, but RNI is much less movement-sensitive than computerized tomography (CT). The time taken for the procedure varies. A rectilinear scan may take up to 20 min—which is slower than most modern CT scans, but the gamma camera, now available in many centres, reduces the time to a few minutes for each position scanned. RNI procedures are widely available in many district general hospitals outwith neurosurgical centres.

Increased uptake of isotope is non-specific, and can be caused by any lesion in scalp, skull, or brain which rise to increased blood flow, or to breakdown in the blood–brain barrier. The scanner's resolution is limited and lesions smaller than about 2·5 cm are unlikely to be demonstrated. Lesions near the base of the skull may be masked by the high isotope activity of nearby bone (Burrows, 1972; *Table* 6.1). Despite these problems, detection rates are high (*Tables* 6.1 and 6.2),

Table 6.1. Detection rates by RNI of intracranial tumour (Baker et al., 1980)

Location	Type	Detection rate (%)	Comment
Supratentorial			
	Glioma	84	Rate for more
	Metastasis	85	differentiated
	Meningioma	93	tumours is lower (Butler et al., 1979)
Lateral infratentorial		62	
	Acoustic neuroma	67	(83%, Moody et al., 1972)
Central		46	Includes subfrontal, sellar and para-sellar, midbrain, vermis, and ventricular tumours

Table 6.2. Detection rate by RNI of other common intracranial lesions

Lesion	Detection rate (%)	Reference
Cerebral infarction	58	Campbell et al. (1978)
Cerebral haemorrhage	50	Shivers et al. (1974)
Subdural haematoma	90	Cowan and Maynard (1974)
Cerebral abscess	100	Crocker et al. (1974)

though a pathological diagnosis can only rarely be made. RNI is thus useful as a screening procedure. The major concern of the clinician is the exclusion of a mass lesion. RNI will detect over 80 per cent of such lesions when above the tentorium (*Table* 6.1; *Fig.* 6.1). A negative scan is particularly helpful in the elderly in excluding almost all such lesions (MacDonald, 1981).

Radionuclide cisternography may be of value in certain well-defined situations, in demonstrating patterns of cerebrospinal fluid flow, e.g. in communicating hydrocephalus, which is likely in the elderly to be of normal-pressure type. Unfortunately the test does not reliably predict the benefits of surgery (Stein and Langfitt, 1974), and the place of this investigation in the evaluation of hydrocephalus requires further assessment (Crockard et al., 1977).

c. Computerized Tomography (CT)

Computerized tomography is safe and accurate, and has virtually replaced many previous highly invasive procedures. Its advantages are

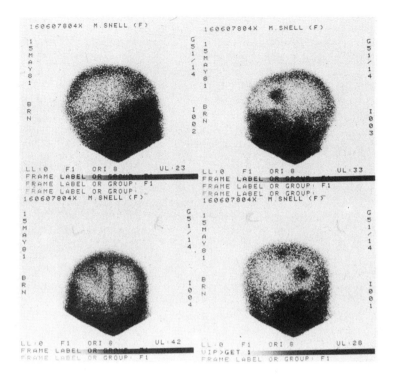

Fig. 6.1. Scintiscan of 78-year-old woman with progressive right hemiparesis and dysphasia. Area of increased uptake in left frontal region.

nowhere more apparent than in the investigation of elderly patients with neurological disorders.

Some practical points are relevant. The patient must lie flat and immobile for 5–10 min. Positioning of the head is of great importance in preventing distortion of the scan. Elderly patients with cardiac or respiratory disease may be unable to lie flat, and kyphosis may be sufficiently severe to prevent proper positioning of the head. Even slight movement of the head (e.g. due to talking or yawning) can cause interference. Patients who are confused or lack concentration may not be able to co-operate adequately, and sedation may be necessary; a small dose of intravenous diazepam is usually adequate, and a general anaesthetic is only very rarely necessary.

Contrast injection improves the identification of many lesions, but increases both the duration and the risk, with the occasional hypersensitivity and nephrotoxic reaction (Meeker et al., 1978).

CT scans in the normal elderly are essentially the same as those in younger patients, with some qualifications. Measurement of the ventricular system has shown that older normal subjects have larger ventricles than younger (Roberts and Caird, 1976; Gyldensted, 1977), with a trend towards increase in size with age (Jacobs et al., 1978; Jacoby et al., 1980). These differences are apparent without formal measurements. Cortical atrophy, shown by increased width of the cortical sulci (Gyldensted, 1977) and of the interhemispheric fissure (Haug, 1977), is also apparent in the normal elderly, but is more difficult to measure; again there is some relationship to age (Jacoby et al., 1980).

The detection rate by CT of intracranial tumours, wherever situated, is 94 per cent or better (Baker et al., 1980; *Fig.* 6.2). By contrast with RNI, a confident pathological diagnosis can be made in the great majority. The detection rate for cerebral abscess is 100 per cent (Neilsen and Gyldensted, 1977), and for subdural haematoma 90 per cent (Weichert et al., 1978). The possibility of a positive diagnosis of cerebral infarction is a major advantage. A low density area (cerebral

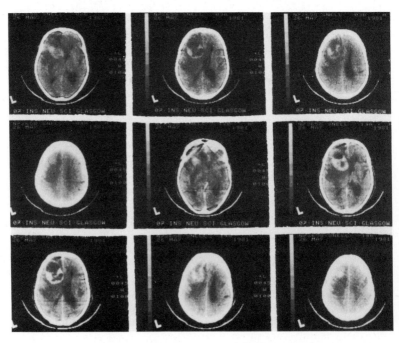

Fig. 6.2. CT scan of same patient as in *Fig.* 6.1. Multiple density space-occupying lesion in left frontal region, with compression of lateral ventricle, shift of midline structures, and extensive oedema (i to iv); increased density after contrast (v to viii); biopsy: metastatic papillary carcinoma.

softening) may be seen within 48 hours of the onset. There may initially be some mass effect due to oedema, but this usually disappears by the end of the third week (Yock et al., 1978). Some infarcts show enhancement with contrast, and may thus be confused with tumours, but this usually disappears from four weeks onwards (Norton et al., 1978). Low density areas may persist indefinitely. Other effects of cerebral infarction include focal cerebral atrophy, hemiatrophy of one hemisphere, and expansion of the ventricle on that side. In 20 per cent of cases CT scans are persistently normal despite good clinical evidence of a cerebral infarct presumably usually because a small lacunar infarct is strategically located, but is beyond the resolution of the method. Lesions near to bone, and some peripheral cortical infarcts near the vertex may not be detected.

CT scan contributes to the investigation of dementia, since it can show cerebral atrophy as ventricular dilatation and sulcal widening. Ventricular dilatation is greater in elderly patients with dementia than in those without (Roberts et al., 1976; Jacoby et al., 1980), but there is little or no discriminant value for the individual patient. However, if the ventricles are normal in size, an extracerebral cause for the intellectual impairment should be considered (Fox et al., 1975; Roberts and Caird, 1976). Cerebral infarcts can be demonstrated in multi-infarct dementia (Roberts et al., 1978). The major contribution of CT to the diagnosis of the cause of dementia is the exclusion of underlying remediable lesions. If there is gross ventricular dilatation without cortical atrophy, further investigation for normal-pressure hydrocephalus is indicated (Crockard et al., 1977).

d. Angiography

The overall complication rate of this investigation has recently been put at 26 per cent (Olivecrona, 1977), though the majority of complications are local (e.g. haematoma at the site of puncture). Generalized reactions (nausea, vomiting, hypersensitivity) occurred in 4 per cent, and permanent neurological damage in 0·2 per cent; this is more likely to occur in the elderly, particularly those with cerebrovascular disease (Eiken and Gormsen, 1962). There remain specific indications for angiography in the elderly, in the investigation of thrombo-embolic disease and suspect intracranial aneurysm, but it should not be contemplated unless surgical intervention or positive medical treatment can be offered.

e. Pneumoencephalography

This is an unpleasant procedure, though its major danger (subdural haematoma) is rare (Peterson and Kieffer, 1972). Patients with dementia are often made noticeably worse, and may take several days to recover (White et al., 1973). It remains a standard procedure for the identification of sellar and suprasellar masses, but its dangers in the elderly must be weighed against the likely benefits of any diagnosis revealed.

f. Myelography

This remains important in the demonstration of the site and nature of cord compression, and may therefore be indicated in elderly patients with paraplegia, and in some cases of cervical myelopathy, if there is a prospect of operative treatment. The procedure is unpleasant, but carries few dangers.

g. Other Techniques

Computerized emission tomography, which combines CT with RNI, may show some improvement in detection rates over standard RNI, and can certainly locate lesions more precisely, but will not necessarily result in a positive pathological diagnosis (Ell et al., 1980).

Positron emission tomography (PET) combines the uptake of isotopes into cerebral metabolic pathways with CT, and can measure local cerebral blood flow and metabolism. It may prove to be a useful research technique in the study of stroke, epilepsy and dementia (Jones et al., 1980).

II. Electrophysiology

a. The Electroencephalogram

The EEG has an important place in neurological investigation in the elderly, because it is relatively widely available, completely non-invasive, and capable of producing useful recordings from almost every patient. McGeorge (1981) has provided an excellent brief review.

Age changes in the EEG are well documented (see Busse and Wang, 1979). The frequency of the basic alpha rhythm declines by about 1 Hz per decade over the age of 60, though the dominant frequency does not fall below 8 Hz, the lower limit of normality (Obrist, 1954; Silverman et al., 1955; Friedlander, 1958). Many elderly individuals also show episodic, irregular slow wave activity, in the theta and delta frequency bands (4–7 Hz and 0–3 Hz respectively), in the temporal areas, particularly the left (Busse et al., 1956). If changes of this type are the only abnormality in the EEG, and there are no physical signs (especially hemianopia) to suggest a structural disorder in the temporal lobes, further investigation is unnecessary.

The EEG may provide evidence of focal hemisphere lesions, but can only rarely suggest their cause. Generalized fast rhythms may indicate drug effects, and slow rhythms a metabolic disorder. In illnesses resulting in dementia, the basic frequency slows, and the degree of slowing and severity of intellectual impairment are broadly related (see Roberts et al., 1978), but this is of no discriminant value. In dementia of vascular origin, localized slow wave abnormalities are often superimposed on slow background rhythms, and represent the EEG consequences of cerebral infarction.

b. Sensory Evoked Responses

The techniques for study of sensory evoked responses are less widely available than the EEG, but are equally non-invasive. Useful reviews are provided by Starr (1978) and McCutcheon and Iraqui-Madoz (1980). Both the latencies of the auditory and visual evoked responses, and their wave forms, are affected by ageing (Dustman and Beck, 1969; Celesia and Daly, 1977; Goodin et al., 1978b; Rowe, 1978). The visual evoked responses can be of great value when there is a possibility of chiasmal involvement by a pituitary tumour (Halliday et al., 1976; Holder, 1978). The significance of changes in the visual and auditory evoked responses in dementia is uncertain (Visser et al., 1976; Goodin et al., 1978a).

The somatic and somatosensory evoked responses are perhaps of greater value, though the latter show an increase in latency with age (Luders, 1970). They are useful particularly when there is uncertainty about the level of a lesion causing glove and stocking sensory loss, or when there are pyramidal signs involving the lower limbs. Thus delay in the somatic evoked responses, if peripheral nerve conduction velocities are normal, strongly supports a lesion in the spinal cord.

c. Electrophysiological Studies of Peripheral Nerve and Muscle

If the diagnostic problem is clearly posed, the neurophysiological investigation of peripheral nerve and muscle can give very valuable information in elderly patients (Ballantyne, 1981). This is particularly the case in ischaemic or entrapment neuropathy, in polyneuritis, in confirming by objective means the sinister diagnosis of motor neurone disease, and in assisting in the diagnosis of primary disorders of muscle, such as polymyositis.

III. Miscellaneous Investigations

a. Lumbar Puncture

The indications for lumbar puncture are now relatively few. Examination of the CSF is mandatory, as a matter of urgency, if meningitis is suspected. Except in the presence of papilloedema, lumbar puncture should never be delayed by other investigations, since bacterial meningitis in old age is a grave emergency (Sanderson and Denham, 1980). Confirmation of a clinical diagnosis of subarachnoid haemorrhage is also important.

b. Ultrasound

Ultrasonic techniques have two potential applications, in the detection of shift of midline structures (echoencephalography), and of occlusive disease of the large neck vessels. Echoencephalography can detect midline shift in space-occupying lesions, but the technique is difficult and requires continuous practice if it is to be reliable. Such practice is unlikely in geriatric units, and the diagnosis of potentially remediable conditions should now be made by other means.

Doppler ultrasonic techniques can show stenosing lesions of the carotid arteries, and may be of value, since the haemodynamic significance of bruits in the neck in elderly people is often uncertain, and it is a non-invasive alternative to arteriography. The value of the technique is difficult to assess (Lewis, 1981), and vascular surgeons are still likely to require the greater precision given by arteriography.

THE APPROACH TO SOME COMMON DIAGNOSTIC PROBLEMS

A logical approach to the problems presented by elderly patients with neurological disease is essential, particularly so that transfer to specialized centres is undertaken only when necessary. In this section, the investigation of four common neurological problems will be discussed: focal brain disease, epileptic seizures, impaired consciousness and confusional states. The views expressed are based on studies carried out in the University Department of Geriatric Medicine at the Southern General Hospital, to which elderly patients are referred from other geriatric units for neurological investigations; all patients involved had a CT scan, together with other appropriate investigations. The outcome of the investigations has been related to the major presenting feature.

I. Focal Cerebral Disease

The clinical examination should indicate involvement of a specific part of the brain. Although vascular disease is the most common cause of a focal hemisphere lesion, tumour, subdural haematoma, and, rarely, abscess may be encountered. The most important factor determining the need for intensive investigation is the temporal onset of the lesion.

Sixty-seven patients presenting with the sudden onset of hemiplegia, whose neurological deficit reached its maximum within 24 hours, were investigated, and none found to have a mass lesion. Of 45 patients with a longer onset (almost all with lesions progressive over many weeks), 25 (55 per cent) had an intracranial tumour. Although both intracranial tumour (Knox and Adams, 1969) and subdural haematoma (Feldman et al., 1963) have been reported with an acute presentation in the elderly, and transient improvement following an acute onset has been described in a proportion of patients with meningioma (Daly et al., 1961), there is little support for a general policy of investigation of acutely developing focal lesions in elderly patients.

Extracranial causes must always be excluded, in particular a cardiac source of embolism, inflammatory arteritis and hypoglycaemia. A skull radiograph is unlikely to be of value, and EEG and RNI are rarely indicated, if the onset is acute. In progressive lesions RNI indicates the need for a CT scan (see above), but a normal RNI is powerful evidence against a remediable mass lesion, and further investigation should only be undertaken in the presence of compelling clinical and EEG signs (Suberviola and Gregson, 1975; MacDonald, 1981). Similar general considerations apply to infra- as to supratentorial lesions, but if further investigation is justifiable, a CT scan should be carried out, as RNI may well be negative (see Table 6.1).

Endocrine disorder and visual disturbance are the indications for investigation of lesions in the region of pituitary. Further investigation of an enlarged pituitary fossa is not necessary unless careful examination of the visual fields, and/or visual evoked responses (see above) are abnormal.

2. Epileptic Seizures

Unless they occur in the setting of a severe intercurrent illness, epileptic seizures beginning for the first time in old age are likely to be due to underlying intracranial disorder (Roberts et al., 1982). Such seizures may be a symptom of an intracranial tumour, but review of the literature suggests that this is the case in only 10–15 per cent (Hildick-Smith, 1974; Roberts et al., 1982). The cause of seizures in 58 patients, in all of whom a CT scan was carried out, is shown in Table 6.3.

The diagnosis of epileptic seizures is essentially clinical, since the EEG is only likely to be diagnostic for 24 hours or so after a seizure. It is important to determine whether the seizure is partial or grand mal in type.

Once a clinical diagnosis of an epileptic seizure has been established, the following suggestions for investigation are put forward:

a. If there are no focal signs, and no evidence of mental impairment, extracerebral disorders (e.g. uraemia, hypoglycaemia and hypocal-

Table 6.3. Final diagnosis in 58 patients presenting with seizures

	No.	%
Cerebrovascular disease	28	48
Tumour	10	17
Idiopathic	7	12
Non-vascular dementia	5	9
Subdural haematoma	4	7
Extracranial	3	5
Post-traumatic	1	2
Total	58	

caemia; postural hypotension; cardiac arrhythmia) should be excluded. A realistic approach is then to gain control of the fits with anticonvulsants, and to proceed to an EEG and RNI scan. If these are abnormal, a CT scan should be carried out. If they are normal the patient should be observed. If focal signs have not developed within 2–3 years, the patient is unlikely to have a tumour which will cause significant problems in his lifetime.

b. If there are no focal signs, but evidence of mental impairment, the latter requires detailed assessment. If it is chronic and global in type, senile dementia is likely to be the cause of the seizures (Hildick-Smith, 1974; Roberts et al., 1982), and there is little to be gained by further investigation. If, however, the disturbance of mental function is of a type which could represent a specific frontal lobe syndrome, then this is a sign of focal rather than diffuse brain disease, and investigations should be instituted as indicated below.

c. If there are focal signs, cerebrovascular disease is the most common cause of seizures (see Roberts et al., 1982). Further investigation is only rarely justifiable in patients who have had a definite cerebral infarct either at the time of onset of the seizures, or in the previous 1–2 years, but if there are indications of a progressive lesion, RNI and CT scan are indicated.

3. Alteration in Conscious Level

The spectrum of alteration of consciousness is due to brain dysfunction related to a wide variety of intra- and extracranial disorders, and the prevention of irreversible damage is crucial. In unselected series of patients of any age, alteration in conscious level is most often due to alcohol or head injury, but even in selected series referred for neurological investigation, metabolic and diffuse cerebral disorders are the most important causes (Plum and Posner, 1980).

In the present study 60 patients showed impaired conscious level (Table 6.4); 18 had a mass lesion (either tumour or subdural haema-

Table 6.4. Final diagnosis in 60 patients with altered conscious level

	As primary abnormality	With other abnormalities	Total
Tumour	2	10	12
Subdural haematoma	5	1	6
Intracerebral haemorrhage	5	0	5
Cerebrovascular disease	20	5	25
Dementia	3	5	8
Other	4	0	4
Total	39	21	60

toma) and 5 more an intracerebral haematoma. Almost half had cerebral vascular disease, and in both these and those with dementia, impairment of consciousness was almost always due to metabolic causes (disorders of water and electrolyte balance, or infection). Investigation of impaired conscious level must start with the exclusion of extracranial factors. Those with the simultaneous onset of focal signs are likely to have a vascular cause. EEG and RNI studies must be interpreted in this light (see above). CT should be reserved for those in whom there is a high index of clinical suspicion of tumour of subdural haematoma.

4. The Confused Elderly Patient

Disturbance of higher mental functions is very common among patients admitted to geriatric units (Lloyd, 1970). Most can be relatively easily placed into one or other of the categories of delirium and dementia, but there is often doubt, especially when both states may be present. Most episodes of delirium are found to be due to infections, cardiac failure, etc., and most elderly patients with delirium will recover and can be discharged (Hodkinson, 1973). The value of investigation of more chronic mental impairment in the elderly has not been shown (Marsden, 1978). Although in younger patients potentially remediable lesions may often be present (Marsden and Harrison, 1972; Pearce and Miller, 1973; Smith and Kiloh, 1981), the main impetus for investigation has come from accounts of mental change associated with intracranial tumour (Hunter et al., 1968), the frequent occurrence of mental symptoms as the first evidence of subdural haematoma in the elderly (see Luxon and Harrison, 1979), and the description of the potentially remediable condition of normal pressure hydrocephalus (Adams et al., 1965).

In 179 patients referred for investigation of a confusional state, this was persistent and established (i.e. over 1 year in duration) in 97 cases, and of more recent onset in 82 (Table 6.5). In the former group, only one was thought to have a potentially remediable condition (normal

Table 6.5. Final diagnosis in 179 patients investigated for confusion

	Confusion		
	Recent	Established	
	(less than 1 yr)	(over 1 yr)	Total
Final diagnosis	No. (%)	No. (%)	No. (%)
Senile dementia	34 (42)	70 (72)	104 (58)
Vascular dementia	15 (18)	25 (26)	40 (22)
Recent cerebral infarct	3 (4)	0	3 (2)
Tumour	9 (11)	0	9 (5)
Subdural haematoma	3 (4)	0	3 (2)
? Normal pressure hydrocephalus	2 (2)	1 (1)	3 (2)
Functional disorder	5 (6)	0	5 (3)
Other: Intracerebral	4⎫ 11 (13)	1⎫ 1 (1)	12
Extracerebral	7⎭	0⎭	
Total	82	97	179

pressure hydrocephalus), but this was not subsequently confirmed. Three-quarters had non-vascular, and one-quarter vascular dementia.

Of the 82 patients presenting with a more recent onset of confusion, 27 (33 per cent) had potentially remediable conditions (*Table* 6.5). The initial problem is to establish whether confusion is due to a focal or diffuse cerebral disturbance. The common focal disorders simulating a confusional state are dysphasia, parietal and frontal lobe disorder. Of the 82 patients, 11 had focal cerebral lesions, 10 with dysphasia which had gone unrecognized, most commonly because it was purely receptive in type. One patient diagnosed as having dementia showed apathy and self-neglect, but no impairment of memory, symptoms which were due to a frontal lobe tumour.

It is also important to be certain that the patient does not have an affective disorder; 5 of the 82 patients suffered from depression.

In 11 patients there was an extracerebral cause for the confusional state (e.g. hypercalcaemia, inappropriate ADH secretion, infections), and, in addition, a significant number finally diagnosed as having dementia, also had evidence of infection, or drug toxicity, whose correction led to some improvement.

Thus in the elderly patient with the recent onset of confusion, attention should first be paid to extracerebral causes. If there are no focal neurological signs, there is little to be gained by detailed investigation for an intracranial lesion, although the EEG may be helpful (Obrecht et al., 1979). It may demonstrate an unsuspected focal lesion, particularly perhaps in the territory of a posterior cerebral artery, in a patient whose lack of co-operation makes it difficult to demonstrate a hemianopia; it may also suggest a metabolic disorder if there is slow-wave activity, or drug toxicity if fast (beta) activity is present. The need to investigate those with focal signs will depend upon the time-relations of the onset (*see above*). RNI and CT should be reserved for those who present with the gradual onset of focal signs and confusion. At present only those with the classic triad of gait distur-bance, incontinence and mental change should be investigated for possible normal-pressure hydrocephalus and the first step should be CT.

CONCLUSION

Careful clinical assessment, supplemented by appropriately chosen investigations, remains the mainstay of diagnosis of neurological disorders in the elderly.

REFERENCES

Adams R. D., Fisher C. M., Hakim S. et al. (1965) *N. Engl. J. Med.* **273**, 117.
Baker H. L., Houser O. W. and Campbell J. K. (1980) *Radiology* **136**, 91.
Ballantyne J. P. (1981) In: Caird F. I. and Evans J. G. (ed.) *Advanced Geriatric Medicine 1*, Tunbridge Wells, Pitman Medical.
Burrows E. H. (1972) *Br. Med. J.* **1**, 473.
Busse E. W., Barnes R. H., Friedman E. L. et al. (1956) *J. Nerv. Ment. Dis.* **124**, 135.
Busse E. W. and Wang H. S. (1979) *J. Clin. Exp. Geront.* **1**, 145.
Butler A. R., Passalaqua A. M., Berenstein A. et al. (1979) *Am. J. Roentgenol.* **132**, 607.
Caird F. I. (1973) *Br. Med. J.* **4**, 348.
Caird F. I. (1979) *Age Ageing* **8**, Suppl. 44.
Campbell J. K., Houser O. W., Stevens J. C. et al. (1978) *Radiology* **126**, 694.
Celesia G. G. and Daly R. F. (1977) *Arch. Neurol.* **34**, 403.
Cowan R. J. and Maynard C. D. (1974) *Semin. Nucl. Med.* **4**, 319.
Crockard H. A., Hanlon K., Duda E. E. et al. (1977) *J. Neurol. Neurosurg. Psychiatry* **40**, 736.
Crocker E. F., McLaughlin A. F., Morris J. G. et al. (1974) *Am. J. Med.* **56**, 192.
Daly D. D., Svien J. H. and Yoss R. E. (1961) *Arch. Neurol.* **5**, 287.
du Boulay G. H. (1977) *Br. J. Hosp. Med.* **17**, 272.
Dustman R. E. and Beck E. C. (1969) *Electroencephalogr. Clin. Neurophysiol.* **26**, 2.
Eiken M. and Gorsmen J. (1962) *Acta Med. Scand.* **172**, 151.
Ell P. J., Deacon J. M., Ducasson D. et al. (1980) *Br. Med. J.* **1**, 438.
Feldman R. G., Pincus J. H. and McEntee W. J. (1963) *Arch. Intern. Med.* **112**, 966.
Fox J. H., Topel J. L. and Huckman M. S. (1975) *J. Neurol. Neurosurg. Psychiatry* **38**, 948.
Friedlander W. J. (1958) *Geriatrics* **13**, 29.
Goodin D. S., Squires, K. C., Henderson B. H. et al. (1978b) *Electroencephalogr. Clin. Neurophysiol.* **44**, 447.
Goodin D. S., Squires K. C. and Starr A. (1978a) *Brain* **101**, 635.
Gyldensted C. (1977) *Neuroradiology* **14**, 183.
Halliday A. M., Halliday E., Kriss A. et al. (1976) *Brain* **99**, 357.
Haug G. (1977) *Neuroradiology* **14**, 201.
Hildick-Smith M. (1974) *Age Ageing* **3**, 203.
Hodkinson H. M. (1973) *J. R. Coll. Physicians Lond.* **7**, 305.
Holder G. E. (1978) *Electroencephalogr. Clin. Neurophysiol.* **45**, 278.
Hunter R., Blackwood W. and Bull J. (1968) *Br. Med. J.* **2**, 9.
Jacobs L., Kinkel W. R. and Painter F. (1978) In: Katzman R., Terry R. D. and Bick K. L. (ed.) (Aging, Vol. 7) *Alzheimer's Disease: Senile Dementia and Related Disorders*. New York, Raven Press. p. 241.
Jacoby R. J., Levy R. and Dawson J. M. (1980) *Br. J. Psychiatry* **136**, 249.

Knox E. W. and Adams G. F. (1969) *Gerontol. Clin.* **11**, 1.
Lewis R. R. (1981) MD Thesis, University of London.
Luders, H. (1970) *Electroencephalogr. Clin. Neurophysiol.* **26**, 2.
Luxon L. M. and Harrison M. J. G. (1979) *Q. J. Med. N.S.* **48**, 43.
McCutcheon C. B. and Iraqui-Madoz V. J. (1980) In: Tyler H. R. and Dawson D. M. (ed.) *Current Neurology,* Vol. 2. Boston, Houghton Mifflin.
MacDonald J. B. (1981) In: Caird F. I. and Evans J. G. (ed.) *Advanced Geriatric Medicine 1.* Tunbridge Wells, Pitman Medical.
McGeorge A. (1981) In: Caird F. I. and Evans J. G. (ed.) *Advanced Geriatric Medicine 1.* Tunbridge Wells, Pitman Medical.
Macpherson P. and Mathieson M. (1979) *Neuroradiology* **18**, 67.
Marsden C. D. (1978) In: Isaacs A. D. and Post F. (ed.) *Studies in Geriatric Psychiatry.* New York, Wiley. p. 95.
Marsden C. D. and Harrison M. J. G. (1972) *Br. Med. J.* **2**, 249.
Meeker T. C., Ludwig S. and Glimp R. (1978) *JAMA* **240**, 2247.
Moody R. A., Olsen J. O., Gottschalk A. and Hoffer B. (1972) *J. Neurosurg.* **36**, 148.
Neilsen H. and Gyldensted C. (1977) *Neuroradiology* **12**, 207.
Norton G. A., Kishore P. R. and Lin J. (1978) *Am. J. Roentgenol.* **131**, 881.
Nurick S. (1972) *Brain* **95**, 87.
Jones T. (1980) *Br. Med. Bull.* **36**, 231.
Lloyd C. M. (1970) Royal College of Physicians of London. Study of Mental Impairment in the Elderly: Report of a Pilot Survey.
Obrecht R., Okhomina F. O. A. and Scott D. F. (1979) *J. Neurol. Neurosurg. Psychiatry* **42**, 75.
Obrist W. D. (1954) *Electroencephalogr. Clin. Neurophysiol.* **6**, 235.
Olivecrona H. (1977) *Neuroradiology* **14**, 175.
Pearce J. and Miller E. (1973) *Clinical Aspects of Dementia.* London, Baillière Tindall.
Peterson H. O. and Kieffer S. A. (1972) *Introduction to Neuroradiology.* New York, Harper & Row.
Plum F. and Posner J. B. (1980) *The Diagnosis of Stupor and Coma*, 3rd ed. Philadelphia, Davis.
Roberts M. A. and Caird F. I. (1976) *J. Neurol. Neurosurg. Psychiatry* **39**, 986.
Roberts M. A., Caird F. I., Grossart K. W. et al. (1976) *J. Neurol. Neurosurg. Psychiatry* **39**, 909.
Roberts M. A., McGeorge A. and Caird F. I. (1978) *J. Neurol. Neurosurg. Psychiatry* **41**, 903.
Roberts M. A., Godfrey J. B. W. and Caird F. I. (1982) *Age Ageing* **11**, 24.
Rowe M. J. (1978) *Electroencephalogr. Clin. Neurophysiol.* **44**, 459.
Sanderson P. J. and Denham, M. J. (1980) In: Denham M. J. (ed.) *The Treatment of Medical Problems in the Elderly.* Lancaster, MTP. p. 35.
Shivers J. A., Adcock D. F., Guinto F. C. et al. (1974) *Radiology* **111**, 211.
Silverman A. J., Busse E. W. and Barnes R. H. (1955) *Electroencephalogr. Clin. Neurophysiol.* **7**, 67.
Smith J. S. and Kiloh L. G. (1981) *Lancet* **1**, 824.
Starr A. (1978) *Ann. Rev. Neurol. Sci.* **1**, 103.
Stein S. C. and Langfitt T. W. (1974) *J. Neurosurg.* **41**, 463.
Suberviola P. D. and Gregson N. D. (1975) *J. Neurol. Neurosurg. Psychiatry* **38**, 52.
Visser S. L., Stam F. C., van Tilburg W. et al. (1976) *Electroencephalogr. Clin. Neurophysiol.* **40**, 385.
Weichert H. C., Lohr E., Clar H. E. et al. (1978) *Neuroradiology* **16**, 467.
White Y. S., Bell D. S. and Mellick R. (1973) *J. Neurol. Neurosurg. Psychiatry* **36**, 146.
Yock D., Norman D. and Newton D. H. (1978) In: Bories J. (ed.) *The Diagnostic Limitations of Computerised Axial Tomography.* Berlin, Springer-Verlag. p. 90.

7. PATHOLOGY OF CEREBROVASCULAR DISEASE
N. M. Hyman

Cerebrovascular disease pathology is essentially the study of cerebral arterial disease. Its association with ageing means that it occurs in association with extracranial vascular disease, hypertension and perhaps additional pathological disease of the heart and kidneys. The two major pathological processes causing strokes are due to either *infarction,* in which brain tissue is deprived of sufficient blood supply, or *haemorrhage.* Both processes produce damage to brain parenchyma and, in addition, there is disease of the blood vessel itself.

About 80 per cent of all strokes are due to cerebral infarction, about 10 per cent are due to primary intracerebral haemorrhage and about 10 per cent are due to aneurysmal subarachnoid haemorrhage.

CEREBRAL INFARCTION

A cerebral infarct is an area of brain in which the blood flow has fallen below the critical level necessary to maintain the viability of the tissue (Adams, 1967). This frequently results from arterial occlusion and in turn, this is due to either thrombosis or embolism. In over 90 per cent of cases the cause of either the primary cerebral arterial thrombi or the extracranial arterial source of the emboli is atherosclerosis. The distribution of the major sites of this process tend to be localized to sites of turbulent blood flow and mechanical stress on the arterial wall (*Fig.* 7.1). The detailed pathogenesis of atheroma will not be considered but it appears that as the lumen of the vessel narrows with the condition, so fibrin-platelet mural thrombi form and over a variable period of time complete occlusion of the lumen results. Atheroma is undoubtedly exacerbated by hypertension and atheromatous plaques may ulcerate due to either ischaemic necrosis or intraplaque haemorrhage. Recanalization with re-endothelialization may occur at a later date but the factors governing this development are poorly understood.

Fibrin-platelet aggregates overlying more proximal atheromatous sites may embolize into distal smaller vessels and, in addition, larger emboli consisting of entire thrombi may be responsible. The two

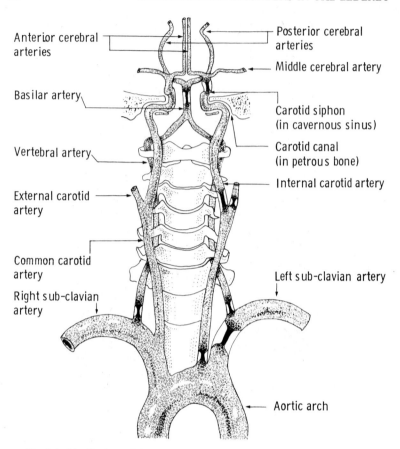

Fig. 7.1. Distribution of the major sites of atherosclerosis. (From *Textbook of Medicine*, ed. D. J. Weatherall, 1981, Oxford University Press, by kind permission.)

important extracranial sites are the origin of the internal carotid artery (Hutchinson and Yates, 1957) (*Fig.* 7.2) and the heart.

Both primary cerebral arterial thrombosis and cerebral arterial embolism may be due to other causes in addition to atheroma and the principal conditions are summarized in *Tables* 7.1 and 7.2.

Types of Cerebral Infarction: Gross Examination

Primary thrombotic occlusion typically results in a *bland* or *anaemic* infarct. In the first 6 hours no change is visible although the tissue is irreversibly damaged. Between 6 and 48 hours, the normal sharp demarcation between the grey and white matter is lost and there is

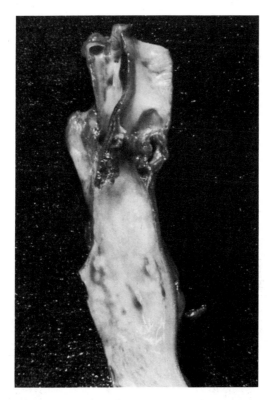

Fig. 7.2. Atheroma and stenosis at origin of internal carotid artery. (By kind permission of Dr M. Esiri, Neuropathology Department, Radcliffe Infirmary, Oxford.)

associated oedema. Following formalin fixation this area of infarction can be recognized by palpation due to the soft consistency. In the next 10 days the oedematous reaction remains and the softened tissue becomes more friable. After 10 days the boundaries of the infarcted

Table 7.1. Main causes of cerebral arterial thrombosis in the elderly

1. *Atheroma*	
2. *Vasculitis*	Giant-cell (temporal) arteritis, polyarteritis nodosa, endarteritis obliterans due to tuberculosis, syphilis etc.
3. *Haematological disorders*	Polycythaemia rubra vera, essential thrombocythaemia, thrombotic thrombocytopenic purpura, hyperviscosity syndromes, e.g. myeloma

Table 7.2. Main causes of cerebral arterial embolism in the elderly

1. *Sites of extracranial arterial atheroma*: principally the common carotid bifurcation; the origins of the innominate, common carotid, subclavian and vertebral arteries.

2. *Sites of intracranial arterial atheroma*: principally the carotid syphon, vertebral arteries near junction with basilar artery and basilar artery itself.

3. *Cardiac origin*:
   i. Left atrium: thrombi or myxoma.
   ii. Mitral valve: vegetation in bacterial and marantic endocarditis; prosthesis; mitral annulus calcification.
   iii. Left ventricle: mural thrombi from myocardial infarction and cardiomyopathy.
   iv. Aortic valve: sclerosis and calcification; prosthesis; vegetations in bacterial and marantic endocarditis.

4. *Trauma*: Cervical manipulation; direct trauma to neck; cervical fracture-dislocation.

territory are more easily defined (*Fig.* 7.3). The necrotic white matter liquefies and the area of necrosis is replaced by grey tissue causing a depression within the cortex (*Fig.* 7.4). In the next few months a cystic, loculated cavity results, intersected by vascular strands.

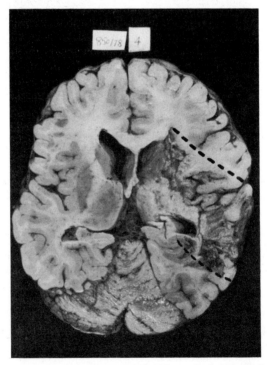

Fig. 7.3. Cerebral infarction (within right middle cerebral artery territory).

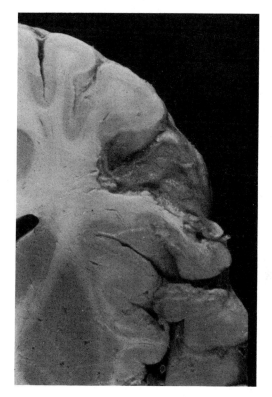

Fig. 7.4. Old cortical infarct.

Haemorrhagic infarcts consist of petechial zones, often confluent, and frequently involving the cortex (*Fig.* 7.5). They are linked to embolic disease (Fisher and Adams, 1951) and it is postulated that capillary blood vessels are damaged by anoxia following embolic occlusion and if that embolus should lyse then secondary cortical irrigation occurs with associated haemorrhage.

Lacunar infarcts (*Fig.* 7.6) consist of small, irregular softenings, up to 1·5 cm in diameter (Fisher, 1965) and are seen with greatest frequency in the deeper parts of the brain, particularly the basal grey nuclei and the anterior pons. It is likely that the majority are secondary to occlusion of deep penetrating arteries (Fisher, 1969), although some may reflect old haemorrhage. They are usually multiple and are characteristically found in the elderly with longstanding hypertension. There may be failure to correlate these lesions retrospectively, following post-mortem examination of the brain, with clinical aspects of the case even if the history is well documented.

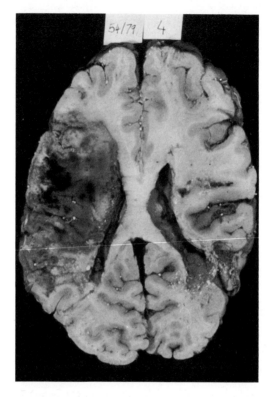

Fig. 7.5. Haemorrhagic infarct within left middle cerebral artery territory.

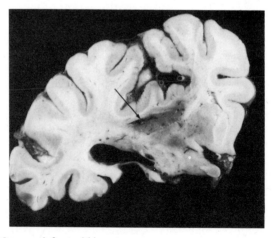

Fig. 7.6. Lacunar infarct within putamen.

Watershed (boundary-zone) infarcts result from failure of perfusion to the 'last fields of irrigation' which in turn are the most distal branches of each major artery (*Fig.* 7.7). The boundary between the

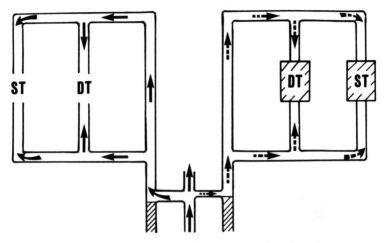

Fig. 7.7. Watershed infarction. Arterial occlusion on left with adequate anastomosis and on right with inadequate anastomosis and subsequent watershed 'infarction' in both superficial (ST) and deep (DT) arterial territories.

middle and anterior cerebral territories is particularly vulnerable but other potential watershed zones are the middle and posterior, anterior and posterior cerebral arterial boundaries or the superior, anterior inferior and posterior inferior cerebellar arterial territories. Watershed infarction may be unilateral as in some cases of internal carotid artery occlusion or bilateral following generalized hypoperfusion, such as prolonged hypotension.

Of particular importance, when considering the elderly, is the question of the ability of various cells within the central nervous system to survive ischaemia. The *rate* of reduction of blood is of importance; generally the more rapid the obstruction of blood flow, the more likely is infarction to occur. In addition, the *type* of vessel involved by the pathological process is of importance. For instance, if obstruction occurs at an arteriolar level then diffuse small cortical lesions occur as found in patients with atheroma and hypertensive disease. Cortical pallor with scarring results. A condition known as *granular atrophy of the cortex* probably results from more severe ischaemia perhaps due to prolonged systemic hypotension or bilateral internal carotid thromboses. Small, punched-out foci of scar tissue are situated within the cortex producing the bilateral and symmetrical appearance characteristic of the disorder.

Topography of Cerebral Infarcts

Differences in individual anastomotic pathways in association with diffuse atheromatous disease and flow patterns are all responsible for the variations in numbers and size of cerebral infarction. Anastomoses occur at the following sites:

1. Cortico-meningeal anastomoses connect the cortical branches of the main cerebral arteries across their border zones.

2. Within the circle of Willis.

3. Between the external and internal carotid arteries via the ophthalmic artery and meningohypophyseal branch.

4. Between the external carotid and the vertebral arteries via the occipital artery.

Infarction classically occurs within the territory of the whole or part of a cerebral artery (*Fig. 7.8*).

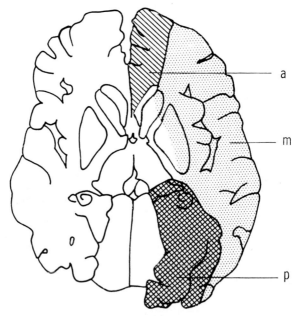

Fig. 7.8. Distribution of anterior (a), middle (m) and posterior (p) cerebral arterial territories in horizontal section (to simulate the CT scan) at level of internal capsule.

1. *Middle Cerebral Artery Territory*

This territory includes the lateral surfaces of the majority of the frontal and parietal lobes, insula, superior and middle temporal gyri and deep striatum. Infarction usually involves only part of the vascular territory due to either carotid artery occlusion with partial vascular anastomoses at the base of the brain or terminal middle cerebral branch occlusion. Complete proximal middle cerebral artery occlusion is frequently embolic and results in extensive infarction within the arterial territory due to inadequate available anastomoses (*see Fig. 7.5*). Internal capsular infarctions result from primary thrombotic occlusion of the deep penetrating branches of the middle cerebral artery.

2. *Anterior Cerebral Artery Territory*

This territory consists of the superior frontal gyrus, inferior and medial aspects of the frontal lobe back to the precuneus, corpus callosum and anterior basal ganglia. The anterior cerebral artery is rarely occluded in isolation due to the anastomosis provided by the anterior communicating artery. In addition, embolic lesions from the internal carotid artery are more likely to take a middle cerebral rather than an anterior cerebral arterial route.

3. *Posterior Cerebral Artery Territory*

Infarction includes the inferomedial surfaces of the occipital lobe, the cuneus, the calcarine cortex and, importantly, the thalamo-geniculate territory. The infarcts may be bilateral due to basilar artery occlusion or ipsilateral secondary to probable embolic disease (*Fig. 7.9*).

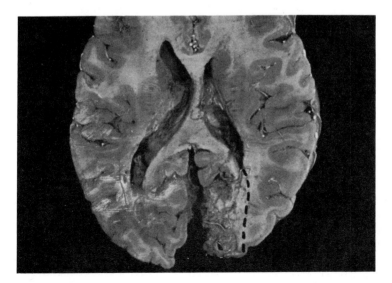

Fig. 7.9. Infarct within right posterior cerebral artery territory.

4. *Massive Hemisphere Infarct*

Sudden occlusion of the internal carotid artery with associated failure of the anastomotic channels produces this type of infarction. In addition, the swollen temporal lobe may occlude the posterior cerebral artery increasing the area of destruction (*Fig.* 7.10).

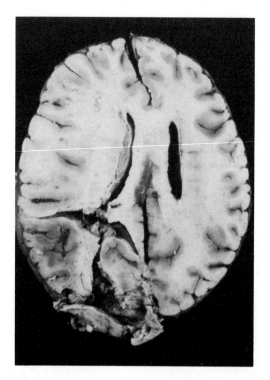

Fig. 7.10. Massive hemisphere infarct following sudden occlusion of left internal carotid artery.

5. *Brainstem Infarcts*

A large number of possible infarction sites within the brainstem can occur due to the wide variation in vascular anatomy with associated anastomoses. In practice, infarction of the dorsolateral medulla is common but primary thrombosis of the posterior inferior cerebellar artery is less important than primary thrombotic disease of the vertebral artery with secondary occlusion of the ostium of the posterior inferior cerebellar artery. The basilar artery may be occluded by either primary thrombotic or embolic disease.

PRIMARY INTRACEREBRAL HAEMORRHAGE

Primary intracerebral haemorrhage occurs frequently in association with systemic hypertension. The size of the haemorrhage varies between those causing massive hemisphere destruction and death within a few hours to small lesions only several millimetres in diameter. At least some lacunar 'infarcts' are secondary to small old haemorrhage. The principal sites of massive haemorrhage are within the basal ganglia (*Fig.* 7.11), particularly involving the putamen. Other sites include the subcortical parieto-occipital region, thalamus, pons (*Fig.* 7.12) and within the cerebellar hemispheres (McKissock et al., 1961).

The lenticulostriate vessels supply the putamen and the pathological basis for the haemorrhage is arterial bleeding from such a vessel. It is postulated that arteries of the size 50–200 μm in diameter form microaneurysms secondary to ageing and hypertension (Ross Russell, 1963). The walls of these lesions are composed of a thin layer of connective tissue alone, predisposing them to rupture.

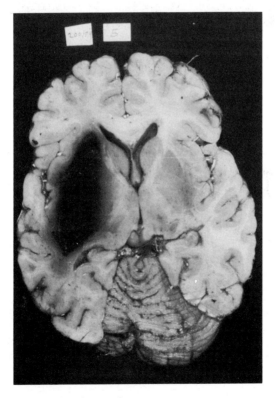

Fig. 7.11. Left hemisphere haemorrhage.

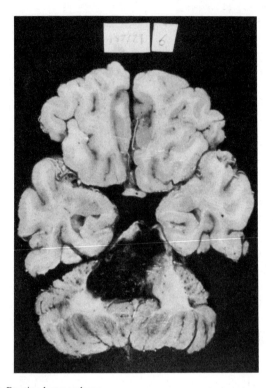

Fig. 7.12. Pontine haemorrhage.

The post-mortem gross appearance of the hypertensive brain is characterized by small cystic softenings in the internal capsule, basal ganglia and brainstem; these 'infarcts' may reflect old tiny haemorrhages or, alternatively, a combination of small haemorrhages and associated thromboses of typical perforating vessels. In addition, yellow linear scars arise in the subcortical white matter and are almost certainly the result of so-called 'slit-haemorrhages'.

After a major intracerebral haemorrhage the blood extends typically into the ventricular system and survival is rare if the ventricles are 'flooded' in such a way. It is more unusual for the blood to extravasate into the subarachnoid space unless the underlying lesion proves to be a small berry aneurysm.

Major haemorrhage into the pons, thalamus and midbrain is usually rapidly fatal. Primary cerebellar hemisphere haemorrhage (McKissock et al., 1960) with associated obstructive hydrocephalus is now increasingly recognized in life due to CT scanning facilities, with therapeutic implications.

Intracerebral bleeds displace and compress adjacent tissue and this produces fibre separation rather than ischaemic infarction. Therefore, if survival occurs, the potential for functional recovery is better than following primary infarction.

INTRACRANIAL ARTERIAL ANEURYSMS

The vast majority of intracranial aneurysms are so-called berry aneurysms. They consist of thin-walled saccular dilatations and the larger ones are frequently multiloculated. The aneurysms themselves are not congenital and rarely present before teenage life. The commonest size is that of a pea and unruptured aneurysms are seen in between 1 and 2 per cent of routine autopsies.

Histologically, the walls consist simply of a thin layer of connective tissue lined by endothelium; importantly, the normal muscular and elastic components of the arterial wall are absent. At the neck of the sac the muscle of the media of the parent artery ends abruptly. The pathogenesis of these lesions is partly due to the congenital deficiency of the muscle of the arterial media at sites of arterial branching. However, additional factors are necessary to disrupt the internal elastica and age, atheroma and arterial hypertension are all implicated (Crompton, 1966). Nevertheless although these three factors are of obvious importance in an ageing population, rupture can occur without their association.

Aneurysms arise from the distal angle of points of arterial division and are situated chiefly on the vessels that constitute the circle of Willis (*Fig.* 7.13); 90 per cent are situated in the carotid territory and 10 per cent in the vertebrobasilar territory (*Fig.* 7.14); 15 per cent of aneurysms are multiple and are frequently symmetrical.

Blood from a ruptured aneurysm usually spreads into the subarachnoid space. Localized Sylvian haematomas may result from rupture of middle cerebral artery aneurysms (*Fig.* 7.15). Anterior communicating aneurysms may rupture into both the subarachnoid space and into the medial aspects of the adjacent frontal lobe (*Fig.* 7.16). Occasionally, blood passes from a ruptured aneurysm into the subdural space.

Subarachnoid blood itself is rarely, if ever, the cause of mortality but over 60 per cent of deaths, following aneurysmal rupture, result from secondary intracerebral or intraventricular haemorrhage. An additional complication of subarachnoid haemorrhage, associated with berry aneurysms, is that of cerebral infarction secondary to arterial 'spasm' (Crompton, 1964). This phenomenon is particularly common between the third and seventh day after the bleed and the arteries involved are usually close to the offending aneurysm. The term 'spasm' suggests a reversible muscular mechanism which is not necessarily the case as an inflammatory reaction initially takes place within the arterial

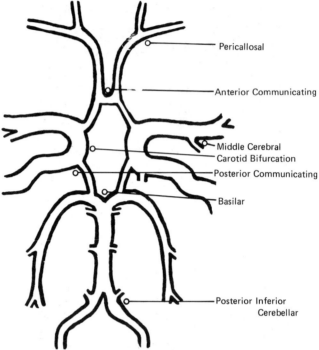

Fig. 7.13. Location of principal sites of aneurysm formation in the circle of Willis.

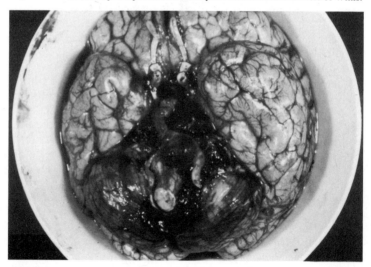

Fig. 7.14. Saccular aneurysm arising from left vertebral artery near bifurcation with basilar artery.

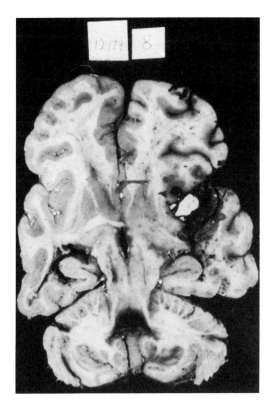

Fig. 7.15. Right middle cerebral artery aneurysm (filled with dye) and associated Sylvian haematoma.

wall and the round-cell infiltration is later replaced by fibrous organization after the third week (Hughes and Schianchi, 1978). A further complication of a ruptured aneurysm is communicating hydrocephalus due to the presence of blood within the subarachnoid space. The clinical correlate of this process may be evident shortly after the bleed or may be apparently delayed for several weeks.

ATHEROSCLEROTIC FUSIFORM ANEURYSMS

Large fusiform aneurysms of either the internal carotid artery or the basilar artery are not infrequently present in the elderly secondary to atherosclerosis. Those on the internal carotid territory may present as a compressing lesion within the cavernous sinus. These aneurysms rarely rupture but may thrombose and calcify.

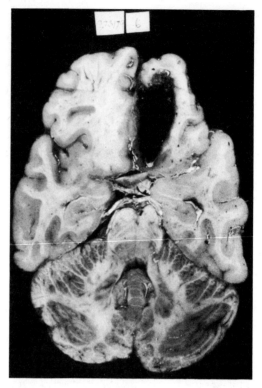

Fig. 7.16. Right frontal lobe haematoma secondary to rupture of anterior communicating aneurysm.

ARTERIOVENOUS MALFORMATIONS

These malformations are due to abnormal communication between arteries and veins without an intermediary capillary network. The vascular components are often hugely dilated and tortuous and the majority are sited on the cerebral hemispheres. Their chief complication is that of rupture to produce either intracerebral haemorrhage or subarachnoid haemorrhage.

However, they rarely produce morbidity in the elderly as rupture is rare over the age of 60 years.

STROKE AND OEDEMA

The oedema resulting from massive acute hemisphere infarction or haemorrhage produces herniation of the cingulate gyrus under the falx and lateral displacement of the midline structures. However, significantly, there is *downward* displacement of the mamillary bodies and herniation of the hippocampal gyrus in the tentorial notch. This downward thrust results in the final and usually fatal corollary of massive hemisphere oedema, that is secondary brainstem haemorrhage (*Fig. 7.17*).

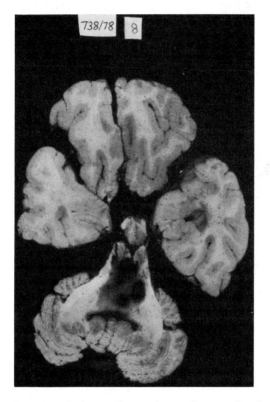

Fig. 7.17. Secondary brainstem haemorrhages after massive hemisphere infarction.

VASCULAR PATHOLOGY OF VENOUS ORIGIN

Thrombosis of a dural venous sinus leads to circulatory stagnation with haemorrhages proximal to the site of the occlusion. The resulting venous infarcts are characteristically haemorrhagic and involve both the cortex and the subcortical white matter.

The prime example of this type of lesion is the superior sagittal sinus thrombosis with symmetrical haemorrhagic infarction (*Fig.* 7.18).

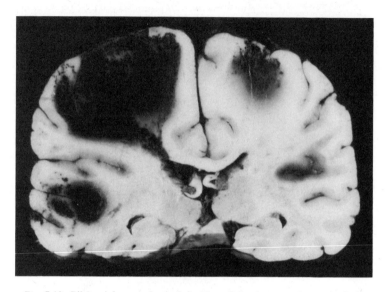

Fig. 7.18. Bilateral haemorrhagic infarctions following superior sagittal sinus thrombosis. (By kind permission of Dr M. Esiri, Neuropathology Department, Radcliffe Infirmary, Oxford.)

Primary thrombosis of any of the dural venous sinuses may complicate malnutrition, dehydration, infectious fevers, tuberculosis, head injury, leukaemia and polycythaemia rubra vera. Secondary thrombosis is usually found as a complication of pyogenic infection due to either local disease (e.g. mastoid air space infection) or a more remote lesion (e.g. infection of the face).

REFERENCES

Adams J. H. (1967) *Scott. Med. J.* **12**, 335.
Crompton M. R. (1964) *Brain* **87**, 491.
Crompton M. R. (1966) *Brain* **89**, 797.
Fisher C. M. (1965) *Neurology (Minn.)* **15**, 774.
Fisher C. M. (1969) *Acta Neuropathol. (Berl.)* **12**, 1.
Fisher C. M. and Adams R. D. (1951) *J. Neuropath. Exp. Neurol.* **10**, 92.
Hughes J. T. and Schianchi P. M. (1978) *Neurology* **48**, 515.
Hutchinson E. C. and Yates P. O. (1957) *Lancet* **1**, 2.
McKissock W., Richardson A. and Walsh L. (1960) *Brain* **83**, 1.
McKissock W., Richardson A. and Taylor J. (1961) *Lancet*, 221.
Ross Russell R. W. (1963) *Brain* **86**, 425.

8. CLINICAL FEATURES OF STROKE
K. Andrews

Stroke by its very nature produces a whole variety of clinical features depending on the site and volume of the brain damage. The more obvious motor features are emphasized in the terms 'hemiplegia' and 'stroke' whereas the equally, if not more, important sensory components often receive little attention.

Clinical features should give guidance to the underlying pathology, the problems requiring management and the prognosis. However, although certain features (*Table* 8.1.) may point towards the underlying

Table 8.1. Clinical features of stroke associated with the underlying pathology

Feature	Thrombosis	Embolism	Haemorrhage	Tumour
Prodromal symptoms	+	±	−	±
Onset	Step-like	Sudden	Sudden	Gradual
Recovery	Slow	Rapid	Rapid deterioration	Gradual deterioration
Headache	±	Unusual	+	+
Coma	−	−	+	−
Neck rigidity	−	−	+	−
CSF blood	−	±	+	−
Carotid bruit	+	±	−	−
Hypertension	±	−	+	−
Symptoms localized to arterial territory	+	+	±	−

pathology, diagnosis on clinical presentation is notoriously unreliable (Dalsgaard-Nielsen, 1955; Bladin, 1963).

CONSCIOUS LEVEL

A disturbed conscious level implies widespread damage of the cerebral cortex or the brain stem and as such is an unfavourable sign. Mortality associated with coma varies from 30 per cent (Robinson et al., 1968;

Kuller et al., 1970) to over 90 per cent (Cooper et al., 1963) compared to about 17 per cent of those who remain mentally alert.

The severity of the stroke is also associated with a disturbed conscious level (Melville and Renfrew, 1961) but the depth of the coma seems to be less important than its duration, with coma lasting for longer than 24 hours having a very bad prognosis.

MOTOR FEATURES

Weakness of one or more limbs is the most obvious sign of stroke, being present in 92 per cent of stroke patients admitted to hospital (Marquardsen, 1969) with the upper limb being more often involved, and usually more severely, than the leg. Anterior cerebral artery lesions, producing predominantly leg weakness, are present in only about 3 per cent of strokes (Held, 1975).

Although at first power loss is usually diffuse, in incomplete deficits the extremities show the greatest degree of weakness. Recovery takes place from the proximal muscles towards the extremity (Twitchell, 1951) and occurs first in the flexors of the arm and extensors of the leg.

Recovery of muscle power depends on the severity at the onset. In our own study 79 per cent of those starting with a moderate paresis, but only 16 per cent of those with paralysis, reached levels of minimal weakness. Very little recovery of muscle power occurs after the first three months (Stern et al., 1971; Licht, 1975) and useful recovery of the arm is unlikely if there is no improvement within one month of the stroke (Bard and Hirschberg, 1965). In those cases of pure motor deficit associated with lesions of the internal capsule prognosis is usually very good though it may take up to one year for maximum recovery to be achieved (Fisher and Curry, 1965).

Although motor features predominantly affect one side of the body, the normal side may show inco-ordination when both sides are used together (Belmont et al., 1971). The intact side moves faster and out of phase with the affected side, producing an alternating pattern of dominance. This results in abnormal walking patterns and inco-ordination when both hands are used together.

TONE

At the onset of the stroke there is usually an initial decrease in tone with absent reflexes followed, within a few days, by hypertonicity and brisk reflexes.

Hypertonicity is found in 22–59 per cent of stroke patients (Marquardsen, 1969; Sylvain, 1972; Held, 1975) and produces the classic spastic hemiplegic posture of retraction and adduction of the shoulder, flexion of the elbow and fingers with pronation of the wrist; and in the leg there is extension and adduction at the hip and extension of the knee. Functional recovery of the limb depends on the type of tone present. Although Moskowitz et al. (1972) found that functional recovery of the limbs was inversely proportional to the degree of spasticity we found that only 14 per cent of patients with persistent flaccidity (one-fifth of our patients) became mobile outside their home compared to 29 per cent of those with hypertonicity and three-quarters of those with normal tone. Peszczynski (1961), on the other hand, claims that patients with prolonged flaccidity almost always learn to walk but that they require prolonged periods of rehabilitation. This poor prognosis for flaccidity is probably because of its association with sensory loss and parietal lobe damage (Hurwitz and Adams, 1972).

REFLEXES

In addition to the hyperactive deep reflexes and clonus in the quadriceps, gastrocnemius and finger flexors of the affected side, there are a large number of tonic and labyrinthine reflexes. These result in synergic movements of the limbs with various patterns of gross extensor and flexor movements produced by turning the head or moving parts of a limb (Kottke, 1975). These reflex patterns have been utilized in rehabilitation programmes (Brunnstrom, 1970).

SENSATION

Sensation is essential to normal activity. There are two functional levels of sensation (*Fig.* 8.1), the transmission of information along nerve

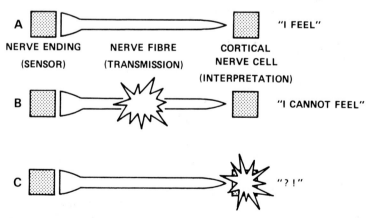

Fig. 8.1. Sensory dysfunction in stroke. *a*, Normal sensation; *b*, Nerve fibre damage—anaesthesia; *c*, Cortical damage—anosognosia.

fibres, and the interpretation of that information by the cerebral cortex.

Damage to the transmitting nerve fibres produces sensory loss but with awareness that the anaesthetized part exists. Infarction of the thalamus or its connections may produce sensory loss without motor involvement (Fisher, 1965) or the more distressing 'thalamic syndrome' in which there is sensory loss, affecting all or only a few modalities, associated with excessive and extremely unpleasant sensations when the sensory threshold is reached. Bouts of spontaneous intractable pain may also occur.

Damage to the cerebral cortex (*Fig.* 8.1*c*) results in a variety of clinical features of disturbed interpretation of sensation. Luria (1973) has described three hierarchical functions. At the lowest level, the primary sensory cortex situated in the postcentral gyrus, differentiates between the various modalities of sensation. Damage to this area does not produce anaesthesia since awareness of sensation takes place in the thalamus. However, the patient does have difficulty in interpreting whether an object in touch with the body is hot or cold, rough or smooth, sharp or blunt and light or heavy.

Information from this primary cortex is further analysed by the parietal lobe (secondary—association cortex) to build up an image of the opposite side of the body and of objects in touch with it. Damage to this area results in difficulty in determining the shape of objects by touch alone and since there is damage to the area representing parts of the body image the affected limbs cease to exist as far as the patient is concerned (unilateral neglect). In milder forms the patient may only be aware of the affected limb when attention is drawn to it but neglects it when distracted (inattention). These patients present with gross disturbances in the performance of activities of daily living.

About one-third of patients have significant sensory loss (Marquardsen, 1969; Anderson, 1971; Gresham et al., 1975), though Lascelles and Burrows (1965) found a higher incidence (80 per cent) when the cerebral cortex was involved.

Although sensory loss usually occurs on the affected side of the body bilateral impairment of sensation is found in up to 30 per cent of unilateral cortical lesions (Carmen, 1971; Corkin et al., 1973; Essing et al., 1980).

There is little information available about recovery of sensory loss but Buskirk and Webster (1955) found that two-point discrimination returned to normal in half of their patients in about 6 weeks, whereas tactile and vibration sense loss improved in only about one-quarter.

Sensory loss is associated with poor functional improvement even when motor recovery is good (Moskowitz et al., 1972) especially when there is concomitant cortical damage such as visual field defects (Stern et al., 1971).

VISION

Vision depends on information from one side of visual space being transmitted to the contralateral occipital cortex (*Fig.* 8.2). A unified picture of both visual fields is obtained by communication between the two occipital lobes through the corpus callosum.

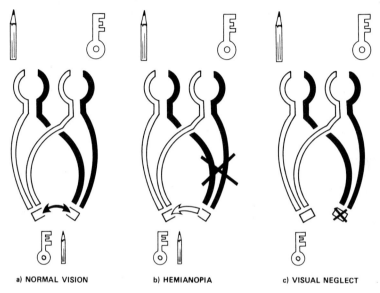

a) NORMAL VISION   b) HEMIANOPIA   c) VISUAL NEGLECT

Fig. 8.2. Visual pathway dysfunction.

Obstruction of the internal carotid artery below the ophthalmic branch produces blindness in that eye with a contralateral hemiplegia.

Damage to the nerve fibres as they pass back through the brain (*Fig.* 8.2*b*) produces a homonymous hemianopia for which the patient can compensate by turning the head or eyes. This is not the case when the occipital cortex is damaged since the cells which interpret the existence of the opposite visual field do not function and therefore to all intents that visual space does not exist (*Fig.* 8.2*c*) and scanning does not occur (unilateral visual neglect). Thus when two objects, such as a pen and a key, are held up, one in each visual field, only the one in the normal field will be recognized. When the objects are exchanged there is no visual memory for the first object and the patient does not seem concerned at its sudden disappearance. All activities in the affected visual territory do not 'exist'—food on only one side of the plate is eaten, time is read on only one side of a clock, one side of a newspaper column is read and when asked to draw a simple picture only half of it will be drawn (*Fig.* 8.3). Other problems arise when the patient is unable to concentrate on two objects at the same time (simultaneous agnosia). Since there is no visual memory of an object as soon as it moves out of the centre of vision the patient draws pictures with their

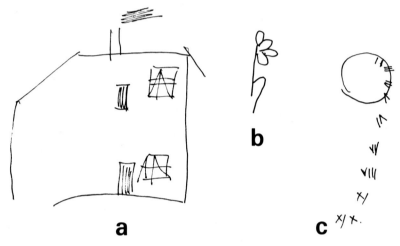

Fig. 8.3. Picture drawings in unilateral visual neglect.

component parts out of context (*Fig.* 8.4) or dressing becomes difficult since the position of one part of the clothing is forgotten as soon as attention moves to another part.

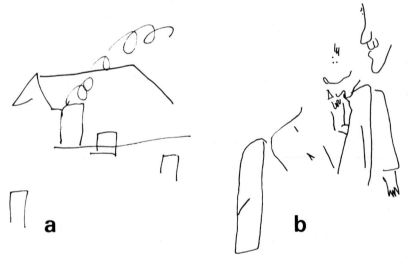

Fig. 8.4. Picture drawings in simultaneous agnosia.

Homonymous hemianopia occurs in 20–40 per cent of patients (Waylonis et al., 1973; Gresham et al., 1975) and has been associated with high mortality (Waylonis et al., 1973; Brust et al., 1976) and poor functional recovery (Miller, 1973). These findings are probably related to the high incidence (90 per cent in our study) of cortical deficits in patients with hemianopia.

Structural abnormalities of picture drawing, such as those described, were found in half of the patients who survived the first two weeks following the stroke and was associated with a high mortality and poor prognosis for functional recovery (Andrews et al., 1980).

CEREBRAL HEMISPHERE DIFFERENCES

Although each hemisphere is basically responsible for interpreting information from, and initiating action on, the opposite side of the body, each seems to have a large degree of specialization (Dimond and Beaumont, 1974; Wexler, 1980). Information is analysed in different ways by each hemisphere. The left brain 'shuffles' information around to carry out detailed analysis whereas the right brain is more efficient at instant recognition of pictures.

The analytical skills of the left hemisphere make it more successful than the right in dealing with problems of mathematics and language whereas the right brain is more efficient in recognizing spatial relationships.

Damage to the so-called 'dominant' hemisphere produces a variety of dysphasias of which there are two functional types (Butler and Benson, 1974). Those due to damage to the posterior part of the brain produce problems of interpreting language either for the spoken work alone (pure word deafness) or for spoken and written language (Wernicke's aphasia); the patient may be able to repeat words (echolalia) or speak fluently but without comprehension (transcortical sensory aphasia). On the other hand comprehension may be intact but the patient may be unable to find names (anomic aphasia) or have more widespread expressive language difficulties (Broca's aphasia). Since both the receptive and motor speech areas are supplied by the middle cerebral artery mixed pictures are very common.

Dysphasia is found in about one-third of survivors of stroke (Marquardsen, 1969) and is associated with a high mortality (Baker et al., 1968; Waylonis et al., 1973). Although most studies associate dysphasia with poor functional recovery, at least two authors (Peszczynski, 1961; Cain, 1969) did not find this association.

As with most other symptoms in stroke there seems to be little recovery of dysphasia after the first 6 months (Douglass, 1953; Vignolo, 1964; Sarno et al., 1971; Kurtesz and McCabe, 1977) though Sands et al. (1969) have found recovery continuing for several years.

Damage to the 'non-dominant' hemisphere produces features of the various agnosias with unilateral neglect of the body and visual space. Difficulties arise in locating the position of objects and in estimating their size and in judging distances. Mobile patients may have difficulty finding their way through familiar routes, even within their own home (topographoagnosia). Some patients also have difficulty in recognizing familiar faces (Hecaen and Angelergues, 1962; De Renzi and Spinnler, 1966; Warrington and James, 1967; Meadows, 1974) though they may recognize the person when they hear the spoken voice (prosopagnosia).

BLADDER FUNCTION

Incontinence of urine following a stroke is usually of the uninhibited neurogenic bladder type but since the lesion is unilateral there may be partial control of the bladder with good prospects for recovery. Immobility of the patient and his reticence, or inability, to ask for help also leads to incontinence as does apathy (Adams and Hurwitz, 1963) and perceptual disorders (MacLeod and Williamson, 1967).

Our own findings suggest that continence returns in half of the incontinent patients within the first 6 months, and in a further 18 per cent during the second 6 months, following the stroke. Functional outcome is poor when incontinence is present (Lorenze et al., 1959; Marquardsen, 1969), and in our study only 55 per cent of incontinent stroke patients progressed beyond a chairfast state compared to 88 per cent of those who were continent throughout.

BOWEL FUNCTION

Constipation is found in any cause of immobility due to a slowing of the food transit time through the bowel. A poor intake of fluid and roughage along with physical difficulties with toileting contribute to the incidence of constipation.

Faecal incontinence was found in about one-quarter of our patients and continence returned in 83 per cent of these within the first 6 months but 11 per cent were still incontinent at the end of the first year. In Peszczynski's opinion (1961) faecal incontinence is the most important prognostic symptom especially if present for longer than four weeks.

DEPRESSION

Depression is a difficult symptom to assess. It is important to distinguish between depression due to neurological damage and that due to the state of unhappiness at the change in lifestyle. When depression is present at the onset of the stroke it is usually associated with other evidence of cerebral cortical dysfunction, especially of the right hemisphere (Folstein et al., 1977), and has a poor prognosis for morbidity and mortality.

The depression occurring after the first few months is correlated with the most changes in lifestyle (Court et al., 1979) such as restricted social activity, awareness of being at risk and a loss of independence, self-respect and self-esteem. Brain damage is associated by many patients with insanity and therefore it is not surprising that they become anxious or depressed (Davidson, 1973).

CONFUSION

Although there have been several studies describing localized cerebral lesions which produce confusion, in stroke its presence implies widespread cerebral damage and the size of the lesion is more important than its site. It is important that dysphasia, poor concentration and depression should not be misdiagnosed as confusion.

Marked confusion is found in about one-quarter of patients but this settles in about two-thirds of those who survive the first year. However, only about one-third of the confused patients in our study showed significant functional recovery compared to two-thirds of those who were not confused.

EMOTIONAL PROBLEMS

There is an emotional response to any illness but in stroke the brain damage may release pre-existing conflicts, drives or fantasies which have previously been contained by social inhibitions (Robinson, 1976). The response of a patient to his illness is important and Grossman (1953) has suggested that there are no medical stumbling blocks in rehabilitation other than those created by the patients' emotional problems.

Adverse emotional reactions were common in the 29 patients discharged from a Stroke Unit (Isaacs, 1976): 3 showed aggression, 3 regressive behaviour and 10 were excessively irritable and uncooperative. The commonest pattern was that of gloomy silence and withdrawal of any effort to maintain sociability and only 4 patients accepted their disability with stoicism.

Hurwitz and Adams (1972) have pointed out that patients may be accused of not making an effort when there is a genuine lack of capacity. Unrecognized perceptual disorders, depression and dysphasia are often interpreted as lack of motivation. It must also be recognized that poor motivation may be due to the patient not being allowed to do things for himself (Andrews and Stewart, 1979).

Emotional lability is a common feature in generalized cerebrovascular disease but also occurs in localized brain damage. In this condition the patient easily shows his emotion in response to circumstances and can very quickly move from expressions of happiness to those of sadness. It is basically a lack of the tight control normal individuals keep on their emotions and is not of prognostic significance. Emotional incontinence is a more serious barrier to recovery (Adams, 1974). In this condition there are outbursts of weeping, and less commonly laughter, which is inappropriate to the circumstance and often occurs with the slightest provocation. Since insight is often preserved the patient becomes extremely embarrassed and depressed. Unfortunately this condition is almost always refractory though it may gradually lessen over a period of several months (Adams and Hurwitz, 1963).

Both of these conditions have been associated with brainstem lesions (Clarke, 1975) and with the thalamic syndrome (Barr, 1974; Carpenter, 1974) probably because of the impairment of control which the higher centres normally exercise over the thalamus and the hypothalamus (Walton, 1977).

Catastrophic reactions are an excessive form of anxiety which occur in a patient who is doing his best to conceal his defects and is suddenly confronted with a situation beyond his powers. When faced with a problem he cannot solve or he is stressed beyond a limited capacity he becomes excessively anxious, agitated, mute and unable to respond. There may be autonomic disturbances with irregular pulse and changes in the respiratory rate (Fisher, 1961). Outbursts of aggression or a loss of consciousness may be other expressions of this reaction. Fisher (1961) has pointed out that this state is related to fear of being unable to complete the task rather than a response to failure, and Allison (1962) suggests that it is influenced by the patient's premorbid temperament.

BRAINSTEM STROKES

Most of the features so far described are associated with carotid artery territory strokes but vertebrobasilar artery infarcts account for up to 15 per cent of all strokes (Currier et al., 1958; Carter, 1964).

Complete obstruction of the main trunk of the basilar artery results in coma associated with small but reactive pupils, flaccid quadriplegia, bulbar palsy and disturbance of lateral gaze. Since the vital functions of respiration, pulse and temperature control are involved death usually occurs within a few days. Soft palate paralysis and disturbed conscious level are associated with high case fatality (Fogelholm and Aho, 1975). Patrick et al. (1980) found that all of their patients (5) in coma died, that when symptoms fluctuated beyond 24 hours the mortality rate was 27 per cent compared to only 5 per cent of those whose symptoms had stabilized within 24 hours.

One-third of Patrick's patients with brainstem infarction had weakness, ataxia, vertigo, nausea, vomiting or dysarthria and 15 per cent had dizziness, diplopia, dysphagia and loss of consciousness. Involvement of the posterior cerebral arteries results in a bilateral homonymous hemianopia with cortical blindness. Infarction of the small perforating branches to the internal capsule may produce pure motor hemiplegia with dysarthria (Fisher, 1967). Although sensation is usually bilaterally lost it may be preserved even in the presence of complete paralysis.

Infarction of the cerebellum is uncommon because of its good anastomotic blood supply. Cerebellar signs are more likely to be due to damage to the connections with the brainstem rather than an intracerebellar infarction. It is, however, important to recognize a cerebellar haemorrhage since it is amenable to surgery. In this, death may occur rapidly with signs of an acutely expanding tumour in the posterior fossa associated with bilateral corticospinal tract signs, oculomotor disturbances, nystagmus and signs of raised intracranial pressure. Early symptoms are usually those of vomiting, ataxia and to a lesser extent headache (Fisher et al., 1965; Ott et al., 1974) but loss of consciousness was uncommon in both of these studies.

The mode of onset is variable with about 20 per cent presenting with a rapid progressive deterioration to death within forty-eight hours; a few present with a gradual onset but most have an intermediate pattern (McKissock et al., 1960).

Although Ott et al. (1974) found ataxia to be common, Fisher et al. (1965) found ataxia and nystagmus in about one-third of cases and McKissock et al. (1960) noted that cerebellar signs were often absent.

AGE AND STROKE

The incidence of stroke rises disproportionately with age from about 0·35/1000 of those in the 35–44 age group to 9/1000 in the 65–74 group and 25/1000 of those 75–84 (Goldner et al., 1967; Wylie, 1970; Whisnant et al., 1971; Matsumoto et al., 1973; Gibson, 1974). The mortality rate also rises with age (Baker et al., 1968; Richter et al., 1977) as does the severity of the stroke (Rogoff et al., 1964; Robinson et al., 1968; Lehann et al., 1975). Aho et al. (1980) found that the elderly were more likely than the younger age groups to have a hemiplegia rather than a monoplegia.

The final outcome is also poorer in the older age groups (Wylie, 1968; Shafer et al., 1974; Haerer and Woosley, 1975; Richter et al., 1977) with only 8 per cent of Carroll's patients (1962) over 80 years of age reaching full independence compared to 38 per cent of those under the age of 50 years. However, Lehann et al. (1975) could find no significant difference between the age groups and found that recovery correlated more with the severity of symptoms on admission. This is in keeping with our own findings which showed that the elderly were more limited in action prior to the stroke and that the older severely affected patients did as well (or as badly) as the younger severely disabled patients.

Elderly patients are also more prone to perceptual disorders (Andrews et al., 1980) and incontinence of urine (Bhattacharyya et al., 1979).

Some workers (Vignolo, 1964; Kertesz and McCabe, 1977) have found that dysphasia recovers less well in elderly patients but others (Culton, 1971; Sarno et al., 1971) could not find this correlation.

In general, recovery of the different features of stroke depends more on the severity at the onset rather than the age of the patient. However, it must be recognized that a greater number of elderly patients are more severely affected in stroke than those in younger age groups.

REFERENCES

Adams G. F. (1974) In: *Cerebrovascular Disability and the Ageing Brain.* Edinburgh, Churchill Livingstone.
Adams G. F. and Hurwitz L. J. (1963) *Lancet* **2**, 533.
Aho K., Harmsen P., Hatano S. et al. (1980) *Bull WHO* **58**, 113.
Allison R. S. (1962) In: *The Senile Brain.* London, Arnold.
Anderson E. K. (1971) *Arch. Phys. Med. Rehabil.* **52**, 293.
Andrews K., Brocklehurst J. C., Richards B. et al. (1980) *Rheumatol. Rehabil.* **19**, 180.
Andrews K. and Stewart J. (1979) *Rheumatol. Rehabil.* **18**, 43.
Baker R. N., Schwartz W. S. and Ramseyer J. C. (1968) *Neurology* **18**, 933.
Bard G. and Hirschberg G. G. (1965) *Arch. Phys. Med. Rehabil.* **46**, 567.
Barr M. L. (1974) In: *The Human Nervous System,* 2nd ed. New York, Harper & Row.
Belmont I., Karp E. and Birch H. G. (1971) *Brain* **94**, 337.
Bhattacharyya A. K., Beck C. and Nork J. G. (1979) *Arch. Phys. Med. Rehabil.* **60**, 528.
Bladin P. F. (1963) *Med. J. Aust.* **2**, 773.
Brunnstrom S. (1970) In: *Movement Therapy in Hemiplegia.* New York, Harper & Row.
Brust J. C., Shafer S. C., Richter R. W. et al. (1976) *Stroke* **7**, 167.
Buskirk C. V. and Webster D. (1955) *Neurology* **5**, 407.
Butler R. B. and Benson D. F. (1974) *Br. J. Hosp. Med.* **12**, 211.
Cain L. S. (1969) *J. Am. Geriatr. Soc.* **17**, 595.
Carmen A. (1971) *Cortex* **7**, 83.
Carpenter M. B. (1974) In: *Core Text of Neuroanatomy.* Baltimore, Williams & Wilkins.
Carroll D. (1962) *J. Chronic Dis.* **15**, 179.
Carter A. B. (1964) In: *Cerebral Infarction.* London, Pergamon.
Clarke R. G. (1975) *Essentials of Clinical Neuroanatomy and Neurophysiology,* 5th ed. Philadelphia, Davis.
Cooper E. S., Ipsen J. and Brown H. D. (1963) *Geriatrics* **18**, 3.
Corkin S., Milner B. and Taylor L. (1973) *Trans. Am. Neurol. Assoc.* **98**, 118.
Court C., Capildeo R. and Rose F. C. (1979) In: Greenhalgh R. M. and Rose F. C. (ed.) *Progress in Stroke Research 1.* London, Pitman Medical.
Culton G. L. (1971) *J. Speech Hear. Disord.* **36**, 563.
Currier R. D., Giles C. L. and Westerberg M. R. (1958) *Neurology (Minn.),* **8**, 664.
Dalsgaard-Nielsen T. (1955) *Acta Psychiat. Neurol. Scand.* **30**, 169.
David N. J. and Heyman A. (1960) *J. Chronic Dis.* **11**, 394.

Davidson R. (1973) *Geriatrics* **18**, 151.
Dimond S. J. and Beaumont J. G. (ed.) (1974) In: *Hemisphere Function in the Human Brain*. New York, Halsted Press.
Douglass E. (1953) *Can. Med. Assoc. J.* **69**, 376.
Essing J. P., Gerten J. W. and Yarnell P. (1980) *Stroke* **11**, 528.
Fisher C. M. (1961) *Am. J. Cardiol.* **7**, 379.
Fisher C. M. (1965) *Neurology* **15**, 76.
Fisher C. M. (1967) *Neurology* **17**, 614.
Fisher C. M. and Curry H. B. (1965) *Arch. Neurol.* **13**, 30.
Fisher C. M., Pickard E. H., Polak A. et al. (1965) *J. Nerv. Ment. Dis.* **140**, 38.
Fogelholm R. and Aho K. (1975) *Stroke* **6**, 328.
Folstein M. F., Marberger R. and McHugh P. R. (1977) *J. Neurol. Neurosurg. Psychiatry* **40**, 1018.
Gibson C. J. (1974) *Arch. Phys. Med. Rehabil.* **55**, 398.
Goldner J. C., Payne G. H., Watson F. R. et al. (1967) *Am. J. Med. Sci.* **253**, 129.
Gresham G. E., Fitzpatrick T. E., Wolf P. A. et al. (1975) *N. Engl. J. Med.* **293**, 954.
Grossman M. (1953) *Am. J. Psychiatry* **109**, 849.
Hecaen H. and Angelergues R. (1962) *Arch. Neurol.* **7**, 92.
Haerer A. F. and Woosley P. C. (1975) *Stroke* **6**, 543.
Held J. P. (1975) In: Licht S. (ed.) *Stroke and its Rehabilitation*. Baltimore, Waverly Press.
Hurwitz L. J. and Adams G. F. (1972) *Br. Med. J.* **1**, 94.
Isaacs B. (1976) In: Gillingham F. J., Mawdsley C. and Williams A. E. (ed.) *Stroke*. Edinburgh, Churchill Livingstone.
Kertesz A. and McCabe P. (1977) *Brain* **100**, 1.
Kottke F. J. (1975) In: Licht S. (ed.) *Stroke and its Rehabilitation*. Baltimore, Waverly Press.
Kuller L., Anderson H., Peterson D. et al. (1970) *Stroke* **1**, 86.
Lascelles R. G. and Burrows E. H. (1965) *Brain* **88**, 85.
*Lehann J. F., Delateur B., Fowles R. S. et al. (1975) *Arch. Phys. Med. Rehabil.* **56**, 383.
Licht S. (1975) In: *Stroke and its Rehabilitation*. Baltimore, Waverly Press.
Lorenze E. J., Simon H. B. and Linden J. L. (1959) *JAMA* **169**, 1042.
Luria A. R. (1973) In: *The Working Brain*. Harmondsworth, Middlesex, Penguin.
McKissock W., Richardson A. and Walsh L. S. (1960) *Brain* **83**, 1.
MacLeod R. D. M. and Williamson J. (1967) *Scott. Med. J.* **12**, 384.
Marquardsen J. (1969) *Acta Neurol. Scand.* **45**, Suppl. 38.
Marshall J. and Kaeser A. C. (1961) *Br. Med. J.* **2**, 73.
Matsumoto N., Whisnant J. P., Kurland L. T. et al. (1973) *Stroke* **4**, 20.
Meadows J. C. (1974) *J. Neurol. Neurosurg. Psychiatry* **37**, 489.
Melville I. D. and Renfrew S. (1961) *J. Neurol. Neurosurg. Psychiatry* **24**, 346.
Miller L. S. (1973) *Arch. Phys. Med. Rehabil.* **54**, 592.
Moskowitz E., Lightbody F. E. H. and Freitag N. S. (1972) *Arch. Phys. Med. Rehabil.* **53**, 167.
Ott K. H., Kase C. S., Ojemann R. G. et al. (1974) *Arch. Nuerol.* **31**, 160.
Patrick B. K., Ramirez-Lassepas M. and Snyder B. D. (1980) *Stroke* **11**, 643.
Peszczynski M. (1961) *Am. J. Cardiol.* **7**, 365.
De Renzi E. and Spinnler H. (1966) *Neurology* **6**, 145.
Richter R. W., Bengen B., Bruun B. et al. (1977) *Arch. Phys. Med. Rehabil.* **58**, 224.
Robinson R. A. (1976) In: Gillingham F. J., Mawdsley C. and Williams A. E. (ed.) *Stroke*. Edinburgh, Churchill Livingstone.
Robinson R. W., Demirel M. and Le Beau R. J. (1968) *J. Chronic. Dis.* **21**, 221.
Rogoff J. B., Cooney D. V. and Kutner B. (1964) *J. Chronic Dis.* **17**, 539.
Sands E., Sarno M. T. and Shankweler D. (1969) *Arch. Phys. Med. Rehabil.* **50**, 202.
Sarno J. E., Sarno M. T. and Levita E. (1971) *Arch. Phys. Med. Rehabil.* **52**, 73.
Shafer S. Q., Brunn B., Brown R. et al. (1974) *Arch. Phys. Med. Rehabil.* **55**, 264.

Stern P. H., McDowell F., Miller J. M. et al. (1971) *Stroke* **2**, 213.
Sylvain C. (1972) In: Licht S. (ed.) *Stroke and its Rehabilitation.* Baltimore, Waverly Press.
Twitchell J. E. (1951) *Brain* **74**, 443.
Vignolo L. A. (1964) *Cortex* **1**, 344.
Walton J. N. (1977) In: *Brain's Diseases of the Nervous System*, 8th ed. London, Oxford University Press.
Warrington E. K. and James M. (1967) *Cortex* **3**, 317.
Waylonis G. W., Keith M. W. and Aseff J. N. (1973) *Arch. Phys. Med. Rehabil.* **54**, 151.
Wexler B. E. (1980) *Am. J. Psychiatry* **137**, 279.
Whisnant J. P., Fitzgibbons J. P., Kurland L. T. et al. (1971) *Stroke* **2**, 11.
Wylie C. M. (1968) *J. Am. Geriatr. Soc.* **16**, 428.
Wylie C. M. (1970) *Stroke* **1**, 385.

9. MANAGEMENT OF THE ELDERLY PATIENT WITH STROKE

A. J. Akhtar and W. M. Garraway

INTRODUCTION

Stroke is a nightmare neurological disorder which may not only cause severe physical handicap but may also impair the patient's perception of his own illness and the world about him, in the absence of any familiar symptoms of ill health. This change in cognitive processes causes the patient and the caring relatives much anguish and bewilderment. It is a disease which often deprives the victim of the capacity for contentment and enjoyment of life and may also bring about a serious personality change so as to make him unrecognizable to his family. The management of patients with stroke is a complex and sometimes lengthy process requiring sustained effort, enthusiasm and optimism on the part of the staff, the patient and the caring relatives. The patient suffering from stroke requires much individual attention from those treating him and a plan of management suited to his individual needs must be devised and, if necessary, changed as the pattern of recovery or deterioration unfolds. This flexibility of approach demands vigilance and frequent reappraisal of the patient's neurological and functional status by the rehabilitation team, but permits the rational and optimal use of resources. Despite the very considerable challenge it poses to the health care professions stroke, unlike myocardial infarction, pathogenetically a very similar disorder, has not inspired widespread interest and research activity. This is especially true of studies designed to evaluate and compare different approaches to treatment (Hewer, 1976). This chapter describes the care of acute stroke in older people and reviews some of the relevant literature.

THE SIZE OF THE PROBLEM

Stroke is a major burden on the community (Acheson and Fairbairn, 1970). This manifests itself in several ways including the burden on the families of stroke patients living at home and on the community health and social services who have an important part to play in providing support to the families of stroke patients. Whilst these are important aspects of the problem the real impact of stroke occurs in relation to the hospital service. Stroke is the second commonest cause of hospital admission in Britain after myocardial infarction, comprising 1 in every 40 admissions. But the actual use of hospital beds is proportionally much greater. In Scotland 1 in every 8 hospital beds (excluding maternity beds and beds in psychiatric hospitals) is occupied by a stroke patient.

The prospects for the future are not promising. The trend over the past few years in Scotland shows a relative increase in the proportion of hospital bed days being devoted to the care of stroke patients in relation to total available resources, particularly in the elderly age groups (Garraway, 1976). If the average annual percentage increase in bed occupancy experienced by stroke patients during the past decade is projected and present policies regarding hospital admission, discharge and management of stroke remain the same, patients with stroke will occupy no less than 18 per cent of all available hospital bed days by the end of this century.

THE CONTROVERSY ABOUT STROKE UNITS

Developments in special diagnostic procedures applied to stroke have ensured better anatomical localization of lesions, made more specific diagnosis possible, or allowed the correct underlying pathological process to be identified, but have not been shown to improve the natural history of the disease for the better. Despite numerous therapeutic trials, the indications for medical treatment remain few. Surgical intervention has given promising results following subarachnoid haemorrhage from ruptured aneurysm, but this group only comprises a very small proportion of stroke. Changing the organization of stroke care to provide intensive care equipment, facilities and staffing has no impact on overall mortality during the immediate period following onset.

Thus, the focus has shifted to those patients who survive the immediate period of mortality, and attempts have been made to determine the most effective means of organizing their rehabilitation. In particular, several studies have been carried out to assess the effectiveness of stroke rehabilitation units. The conclusions reached by these studies are confusing. Opinion is divided. On the one hand, Waylonis et al. (1973) found that a stroke rehabilitation team introduced into a community hospital had no effect on the functional outcome of patients. A randomized controlled trial conducted as part of the Birmingham Stroke and Rehabilitation Study compared University Hospital care with intensive multidisciplinary rehabilitation (Peacock et al., 1972). Numbers admitted to the study were small and a high proportion of post-randomization dropout was encountered in the control group. The conclusion reached was that although the results of intensive rehabilitation were encouraging, the relative effectiveness of lengthy and expensive rehabilitation had not been proven.

On the other hand, Isaacs and Marks (1973) in an account of the work of a stroke unit at Lightburn Hospital, Glasgow concluded that severely disabled stroke patients can respond to prolonged rehabilitation in a suitably organized unit. This was a descriptive study with no patients available for comparison. A stroke rehabilitation unit was established in Portland, Oregon in 1969 (Dow et al., 1974). It was claimed that the proportion of patients with strokes of equal severity going home rose from 13 per cent to 56 per cent as a result of being admitted to the stroke unit, with no corresponding increase in the proportion of controls going home from other hospitals. Another comparison of two groups of patients treated 'before' and 'after' a stroke rehabilitation unit had been commissioned was reported by Adams (1974). During the period 1948–56 when elderly patients with stroke were rehabilitated in the geriatric wards of the City Hospital in Belfast, approximately 40 per cent of patients regained sufficient functional independence to enable them to be discharged home. During the period 1956–58, a stroke rehabilitation unit was established and stroke patients transferred there from medical units once they had proved their ability to survive, usually 1 or 2 weeks following onset. Thereafter, the proportion of patients discharged home rose to 60 per cent, with a consequent lowering of both the proportion of patients requiring long stay care and those dying within two months of onset. McCann and Culbertson (1976) compared the effectiveness of a stroke rehabilitation unit with the medical service of a general hospital in Rhode Island. Comparison was made between 224 patients treated in the stroke unit with 110 patients approved for stroke unit admission who were accommodated and treated in medical wards because the stroke unit was full at the time. A patient was considered to have improved if his condition decreased in severity between the time of admission to therapy and the time of discharge. Functional status of patients on admission was expressed as mild, moderate and severe disability. No significant difference was found between the two treatment systems for mild or severe disability gradings. But the stroke unit attained statistically significant better results for patients presenting with moderate disability.

An attempt to resolve the controversy surrounding stroke rehabilitation units has recently been made through a randomized controlled trial which compared the management of elderly patients with acute stroke in a stroke unit and medical units (Garraway et al., 1980). The stroke unit was created by changing the function of a ward of 15 beds within a geriatric unit and had evolved an operational policy that was initially based on the work of Isaacs (1977). Almost all general practitioners serving a catchment population of 470 000 notified patients aged 60 years and over, using as the definition of stroke, a focal neurological deficit of presumed vascular origin that had been present for at least 6 hours but no longer than 3 days. Medical staff were on call 24 hours a day to undertake home visits to confirm the practitioners' diagnosis. The outcome of the acute phase of rehabilitation was assessed when discharge was imminent or at a cut-off point of 16 weeks after admission. A higher proportion of patients discharged from the stroke unit were assessed as independent (62 per cent of survivors) compared with patients discharged from medical units (45 per cent of survivors). The study concluded that the stroke unit improved the natural history of stroke during the acute phase of rehabilitation by increasing the proportion of patients who were returned to functional independence. But it must be emphasized that because of the limitations which apply to the conduct of such trials in the working of health services, the results of this study need to be replicated in other centres before a policy to establish stroke units could be implemented (Garraway and Prescott, 1977).

One cause of difficulty has been due to the absence of any clearly defined and agreed method of evaluating functional capacity in terms of activities of daily living. Such a method requires to be objective, comprehensive, concise and simple (Nichols, 1976), and these ideals are incompatible. The more comprehensive the index, the more difficult and time consuming it is, the simpler the less specific and sensitive. Some progress has been made recently. A modification of the ADL indices of Katz et al. (1963) has been shown by Sheikh et al. (1979) to be repeatable, subject to low intra-observer variation, and give scores in hospital which correlated well with those obtained at home. Smith et al. (1977) have described a purpose-built ADL unit designed to reproduce the patient's home environment; they used and demonstrated the validity of a different type of index, in which patients were classified as independent if they could get in and out of bed, dress, were mobile indoors, could perform toileting and personal hygiene, cook a simple meal, feed themselves, and control their environment without human assistance; they were considered dependent if they needed human aid to carry out one of the functions listed or failed to carry it out altogether.

SELECTION OF PATIENTS FOR STROKE UNITS

The humanitarian spirit in medicine is to support the course of maximum effort for all patients, even when a proportion of patients will respond poorly to such efforts. This is an appropriate approach when services and facilities are abundant. But when time or resources are scarce, it is more rational to concentrate on those patients who are likely to respond most readily, while providing less intensive care to those persons who are likely to be poor responders or whose condition does not warrant intensive treatment (Wylie, 1968). This concept of triage (or literally, a 'sorting out') has been widely used by military surgeons and in civilian practice and has been suggested as a way of sorting out casualties after a major disaster (Irving, 1976). It has now been used as the basis for selecting patients for admission to a study which examined the effectiveness of a stroke rehabilitation unit in rehabilitating acute strokes in the elderly (Garraway et al., 1981).

Stroke presentations were divided into three bands: 'upper', 'middle' and 'lower', using selection criteria derived from previous studies of the natural history of stroke. Patients placed in the 'middle' band of strokes were eligible for the study. The 'upper' band contained patients who were likely to do poorly whether they were rehabilitated or not. The 'lower' band contained patients who were likely to recover spontaneously and would not require a sustained period of rehabilitation. Concentration on the 'middle' band of strokes allowed a more realistic comparison to be obtained of the relative effectiveness of a stroke unit and medical units in rehabilitating those patients whose prognosis in terms of years of life was good, but who were likely to have residual disability which would require ongoing support. The development of the triage which defined a middle band of stroke was probably an important factor in being able to accept the hypothesis in this study that a stroke unit could return a higher proportion of patients to independence following onset of acute stroke than could medical units. This could have important implications for the management of acute stroke in clinical practice.

ASSESSMENT OF REHABILITATION POTENTIAL

There is no certain way of predicting potential for recovery in the early stages after a stroke, but it is possible to arrive at some estimate of potential for rehabilitation during the first few weeks. It is important for the clinician to assess the stroke patient at regular intervals so that scarce rehabilitation resources may be directed where they are likely to be of greatest benefit. This is not to say that patients with an apparent poor outlook for functional recovery should be abandoned. All patients should receive enough treatment to ensure the prevention of contractures and the exploitation of any unexpected recovery which may occur.

The presence of a second disabling condition may adversely affect the level of independence finally achieved. Pre-existing blindness, amputation of a leg, rheumatoid arthritis or severe osteoarthrosis of the hips or knees may lead to the need for long-term hospital care in a stroke patient who might otherwise have gone home (Lorenze et al., 1958).

Patients with little or no intellectual impairment who are continent of urine merit intensive and protracted rehabilitation even in the presence of gross physical disability due to motor or sensory loss. Patients with serious intellectual impairment and with gross urinary incontinence which persists for 8 weeks or more are unlikely to regain independence and do not justify the protracted utilization of intensive therapy.

MEDICAL MANAGEMENT

Acute stroke may not occur as an isolated event in the elderly and is often associated with other disorders such as myocardial infarction, which may even cause it, or dehydration due to self-neglect or an intercurrent gastrointestinal illness. It is important therefore to perform an electrocardiogram on every patient and to treat dehydration and its cause if this is present. Intravenous therapy may be necessary if the patient is seriously dehydrated or is unable to swallow. In some it may be more appropriate to give fluids by means of a fine nasogastric tube which can be tolerated for several weeks at a time. Dysphagia is unusual after a stroke for more than a week, unless there is impairment of consciousness or there has been a previous stroke affecting the opposite side.

Most stroke patients admitted to hospital will have some degree of urinary incontinence. Catheterization should not be resorted to for reasons of nursing expediency. The patient must be given a chance to become continent even if this involves the nursing staff in laborious regular and frequent toileting. Permanent catheterization should only be considered if it is clear that urinary incontinence is unlikely to recover, is causing the patient discomfort, and is likely to damage the skin. It is not possible to be certain of this for at least 8 weeks after the stroke. A further reason for permanent catheterization is to allow the ambulant stroke patient with persistent severe urinary incontinence to be discharged home.

DRUG TREATMENT

In spite of much research no treatment has been shown significantly to influence the progression of acute cerebral infarction. Attempts to increase cerebral blood flow by keeping the patient supine (Steers, 1976), and by CO_2 inhalation (Millikan, 1955) have not been shown to be of value. The use of naftridrofuryl (Admani, 1978) has not been confirmed as beneficial. Reduction in oedema surrounding the infarct has been attempted with glycerol (Meyer et al., 1971, 1972) and dexamethasone (Patten et al., 1972; Bauer and Tellez, 1973; Mulley et al., 1978); again there is no convincing evidence of benefit. Dextran has been given intravenously for its effects on plasma volume and platelet behaviour (Gilroy et al., 1969); it was found by Matthews (1976) to reduce immediate but not late mortality in severe stroke, and to have no effect on functional recovery. Anticoagulants have been advocated in order to halt thrombus formation but their place in the elderly is very limited (Millikan, 1971). They may be of benefit in embolic stroke, where they do not restrict infarct size but prevent further embolization. Treatment should be delayed until it is apparent that there is reasonable neurological recovery, as this reduces the risk of haemorrhage from the site of infarction or from a wrong diagnosis (Whisnant, 1976).

The drug treatment of systemic arterial hypertension in the elderly is fraught with hazards and calls for judgement and moderation (Britton et al., 1980). This is particularly so in elderly stroke patients who are found to have raised arterial pressure shortly after the stroke. A diastolic pressure of 110 mmHg is acceptable in the absence of fundal signs worse than grade 2 and evidence of left ventricular strain. If the diastolic pressure is substantially greater than this, drug treatment must be tentative and gradual. In the first instance a thiazide diuretic should be tried and if this fails to reduce the diastolic pressure to around 100–110 mmHg a beta-adrenergic blocking drug may be added and gradually increased until a satisfactory pressure is achieved. The early morning diastolic should not be lowered much below 110 mmHg. It is also important to remain vigilant for symptoms of postural hypotension. The vasodilator hypotensive drugs, like hydralazine, are, in the elderly, especially prone to cause a large systolic fall in pressure on assuming the upright posture. If in doubt it is best to be guided by the fall in systolic pressure on standing and by symptoms of postural hypotension than by the diastolic pressure. It must be borne in mind, however, that some patients are ultrasensitive to a postural fall and a small drop in blood pressure may produce symptoms of unsteadiness and a fear of falling. The over-enthusiastic treatment of raised blood pressure may cause a further stroke or the extension of one that has already occurred.

Sophisticated investigations are rarely needed in elderly stroke patients. A brain scan may be required if the diagnosis is in doubt and in particular if a cerebral tumour or a subdural haematoma is suspected (Heiser and Quinn, 1966). Computerized tomography is a useful non-invasive radiological technique which can distinguish between cerebral infarction and brain tumour or subdural haematoma and also between cerebral infarction and intracerebral haemorrhage. This technique is of value if the diagnosis is in doubt and if the findings will alter the management of the patient. Lumbar puncture may be required if subarachnoid haemorrhage is suspected. Cerebral angiography is justifiable in patients who make a good functional recovery and are found to have a bruit over either carotid artery, because it may be possible to prevent further infarction by timely endarterectomy (Eastcott et al., 1954). The chances of finding an operable lesion are greatly diminished in the absence of a bruit.

It is important to recognize depression in stroke patients and not to attribute emotional behaviour to reduced inhibition unless a tendency to weep is matched by a tendency to laugh. If in doubt the patient should be given an antidepressant in a small dose, which should be continued for at least 3 weeks.

Deep venous thrombosis of the paralysed leg is a recognized complication after stroke (Warlaw et al., 1976) but does not appear to be related to the degree of paralysis. Early rehabilitation may prevent this complication although Warlaw and his associates were unable to identify any predisposing factors.

The medical management of some stroke patients poses difficult ethical problems. This is especially true of the severely disabled who either suffer an extension or a second stroke with resulting uncon-sciousness. It must be emphasized that patients who suffer their first stroke, however severe, must be given the benefit of resuscitative measures considered to be appropriate for such a patient in the absence of a stroke. It is most important to begin treatment early when this is indicated, especially for instance for a respiratory infection, so that rehabilitation does not have to be deferred for longer than necessary. In patients with severe mental impairment before their stroke the rel-evance of treatment of a respiratory infection with antibiotics must be carefully considered by the team; in many cases the patient's comfort is of greater importance than the prolongation of life. In many instances the giving of fluids by drip may be necessary as a palliative measure in the conscious patient with swallowing difficulty, even if the chances of recovery seem remote.

STROKE NURSING

The contribution of expert nursing in the management of acute stroke cannot be overemphasized. The unconscious patient and those with severe disability and incontinence require standard traditional nursing care (Sahs et al., 1979). In the elderly patient the nurse can make additional contributions to management in rehabilitation and in communication with relatives (Murray et al., 1982). In many respects the ward sister is the most important member of the stroke re-habilitation team. She is not only responsible for creating an at-mosphere of optimism and hope, but the performance in the ward of members of the rehabilitation disciplines depends very much on how she sees their role. She must be hospitable and not overconcerned about questions of professional boundaries. She must bridge the gulf between the purely medical and nursing management of the patient and the management of functional impairment and social circumstances.

Enthusiastic nurses who are prepared to learn the rudiments of physiotherapy and occupational therapy will reinforce the efforts of the occupational therapist and the physiotherapist round the clock. The observations of the nurse regarding the physical and mental performance of the patient in the ward are of very considerable importance when deciding the patient's placement.

STROKE REHABILITATION

The aim of stroke rehabilitation is to restore to the patient the highest level of physical, emotional and social capability possible. In the elderly one has usually to be satisfied with a less than perfect result. For best results it is important for rehabilitation to begin early (Anderson, 1966; Garraway et al., 1980; Steinmann, 1975) which means that the patient must be assessed by the rehabilitation team with a view to the commencement of treatment as soon after the stroke as possible. Delay on the part of junior hospital staff in referring patients for rehabilitation may adversely influence outcome (Garraway et al., 1980). It is equally important for patients who are managed at home to begin domiciliary rehabilitation early. They should not be left languishing for days or weeks before the need for treatment is recognized by the medical attendant as by this time irreparable harm may have occurred.

Table 9.1. Barriers to recovery after stroke

Exercise tolerance	Cardiorespiratory disease
Motivation	Ability to persevere. Drive
Sensory deficit	Loss of proprioception. Loss of spatial appreciation
Mental capacity	Receptive language disorder. Denial of disability. Perseveration. Loss of recent memory
Motor loss	Severe persistent weakness in the leg
Postural control	Ataxia. Spasticity. Loss of proprioception. Neglect

How far a patient may be pushed during rehabilitation must be determined by the doctor, the physiotherapist and the occupational therapist. Effort tolerance and the presence of cardiac disease will largely determine this. Before treatment is started a programme of rehabilitation tailored to the needs of the individual patient must be worked out (Hewer, 1976). Adams (1974) listed six prognostic indicators in stroke patients at the onset of a programme of rehabilitation (*Table* 9.1). These must be assessed in every stroke patient so that scarce rehabilitation resources are directed where they are likely to be most successful.

Patients with left hemiplegia and a disorder of spatial appreciation are among the most difficult to rehabilitate because of the lack of insight and denial of disability which are a frequent accompaniment of severe non-dominant hemisphere infarcts (Adams and Hurwitz, 1963; Isaacs, 1971). The doctor should explain this disorder to the other members of staff (Adams, 1971) so that the patient's behaviour is not taken to reflect his pre-stroke personality. Patients with a severe disorder of spatial orientation (neglect) are often garrulous, facile and demanding. Occasionally they may have to be moved into a side room in order to spare other patients being subjected to a stream of inappropriate verbosity.

Physiotherapy is one of the cornerstones of stroke rehabilitation. Its primary aim is to re-establish the patient's ability to walk. There is considerable disagreement among physiotherapists about which method of treatment is best and there is also a lack of controlled trials comparing different approaches. Feldman et al. (1972) compared treatment received by stroke patients in a department of physical medicine with 'functionally orientated' medical care given by non-physical medicine experts. He concluded that there was no advantage in having a formal rehabilitation programme. Brunnstrom (1964) developed a method of treatment based on the premise that voluntary movement springs from primitive reflexes which may be modified by the patient in a particular sequence. Bobath (1970) uses 'reflex-inhibiting' postures which facilitate the normal reflexes and inhibit the abnormal. Proprioceptive neuromuscular facilitation (PNF) is also used in the treatment of stroke and is described by Manning (1974) and by Knott (1967). Some therapists believe that attempts at walking should be made even before the acquisition of balance to increase the self-confidence of the patient (Dunbar, 1981); others do not (Isaacs, 1978). All are agreed, however, that physiotherapy should begin early and should involve nursing staff and relatives in whatever programme of treatment is selected for the patient. Skilled rehabilitation not only improves the patient's physical capacity, but also gives him a feeling of security and confidence in his future. The experienced therapist will by her very approach to the patient diminish his fear. Her cheerful, tranquil and unhurried behaviour has a soothing effect which is often evident in the patient's appearance soon after treatment is started.

The prevention of a painful shoulder is a part of physiotherapy. The education of other members of the team in how best to prevent this, by careful positioning and by frequent gentle passive movements is an important function of the physiotherapist (Smith et al., 1982).

The occupational therapist trains the patient to perform daily tasks (Ford, 1971) and is able to discern the existence of neurological deficits which may not be apparent on clinical examination. A minor disorder of spatial appreciation may be evident to the occupational therapist and may explain the patient's inability to perform as well as expected. The contribution of the occupational therapist comprises not only the re-education of the patient but also the assessment of the patient's ability to perform activities essential to self-care (*see below*). Language impairment with consequent difficulty with communication is common in patients with right hemiplegia. Such patients must be assessed by the speech therapist as soon as possible so that treatment appropriate to the needs of the individual patient may be started (Hewer, 1976). The patient's family and the nursing staff (Patterson, 1971) can make a major contribution to the patient's treatment by stimulating him to use his residual language to the full. Even the other patients can help by talking to the dysphasic patient. It is important that the approach to the patient's treatment is properly co-ordinated by the speech therapist so that it is not contradictory and confusing. Material presented to the patient by the therapist must be relevant to the patient in his immediate environment (Ellams, 1974).

THE MULTIDISCIPLINARY TEAM

Acute stroke is an example of a disease requiring the multidisciplinary approach (Macleod and Williamson, 1967; Steinmann, 1975; Pathy, 1975). Those who survive are often seriously disabled, both mentally and physically, with relatives in need of much support, guidance and reassurance. It is an illness which usually marks a turning point in the patient's life, requiring painful readjustments and changes of attitude in the patient and the caring relative. It is not possible for any single discipline to offer all the skills and guidance required for this purpose. The stroke team comprising the nurse, physiotherapist, occupational therapist, speech therapist, social worker and doctor should meet at least once a week to discuss one or two patients in detail. Such meetings not only allow the team to decide about the next move in the patient's management, but are also of educational value for members of the team. Each member is able to educate the others, so that the doctor learns about stroke nursing and the nurses about social work. The patient should be allowed to participate in these meetings and also the caring relative. It is important that the relative should speak freely, ask questions and express fears—this is only possible after the patient has been returned to the ward. The multidisciplinary meeting is not to the liking of every relative or patient and in some instances it is preferable for each team member to talk to the relative separately. The team can keep the relative informed of progress and dispel any expectations of long-term care in patients with a reasonable prognosis. The general practitioner should be invited to these meetings so that he is kept informed of developments and is able to contribute to the planning of the patient's future management after discharge from hospital.

TALKING TO PATIENTS AND RELATIVES

It is important that stroke patients should be treated in an atmosphere of informality and approachability. Ideally, nursing staff should have the time to sit down with patients and talk to them in a relaxed unhurried atmosphere. The patient should be allowed to take the initiative and to direct conversation whenever possible, and the member of staff should avoid patronizing the patient and encourage self-expression. Many stroke patients have to rely on a caring relative for support once they leave hospital (Brocklehurst et al., 1981) and the chances of successful discharge are greatly increased when the relative has easy access to team members. The social worker can make a very worthwhile contribution by seeing the relative at regular intervals as the time for the patient's discharge approaches.

PREPARATION FOR DISCHARGE

The timing of the patient's discharge from hospital and the preparation of the relatives is crucial if it is to be successful. To 'sell' a severely incapacitated patient to relatives who will be unable to cope is not only dishonourable but also lacking in foresight. If such a patient has to be readmitted to the same unit or elsewhere, a second discharge becomes difficult even if it is reasonable, because the caring relative, scarred after the first let down, will mistrust the hospital and will be reluctant to have the patient home again. The trust and co-operation of the relative is of vital importance because the majority of stroke patients are looked after by a near relative (Brocklehurst et al., 1981).

A predischarge home visit by the physiotherapist and occupational therapist can do much to enhance the morale of the patient and relatives. It can show the relative what the patient is capable of doing at home and it gives the patient confidence in his own ability. It may be advantageous to underwrite precarious discharges by guaranteeing readmission if the patient deteriorates or the relative is unable to cope. This assurance from the consultant will often overcome reluctance in the relative and may result in an unexpectedly successful discharge. Some units have a room the patient inhabits for a few days before discharge in which his ability to cope without the support available in the ward may be judged. If the patient requires pads or Kanga pants for urinary incontinence he must be given a supply which will last until the general practitioner is able to prescribe them.

THE STROKE CLUB

This is a relatively recent development in the postdischarge management of stroke. It is usually organized by voluntary bodies or volunteers and encouraged by the Chest, Heart and Stroke Association (Isaacs, 1978). Stroke Clubs are as much for the benefit of the relative as of the patient. In some instances it is only the relative who attends, and finds the opportunity to discuss problems in common with other relatives a source of relief and enlightenment (Owen, 1981). Caring relatives isolated from people in the same predicament as themselves come to believe that their own circumstances are unique and that no one can know what it is like to be trapped in a stressful and strenuous situation not of their own making, with no prospect of relief. To be able to discuss private and personal difficulties with someone also a victim, and to identify with their problems is a source of comfort and encouragement. For the patient it offers the opportunity of rudimentary social contact, since a visit to the Club may be the only time that he is able to go out of doors. It has also the very considerable advantage of lessening intolerable domestic tensions by giving the relative and the patient greater insight and the opportunity of speaking freely. The organizers should encourage discussion and contact between individuals, but should remain inconspicuous and let patients and relatives run the show as far as possible.

THE DAY HOSPITAL

Day care facilities for geriatric patients in need of continuing rehabilitation after discharge from hospital have existed for over 20 years (Brocklehurst and Tucker, 1980). The pattern of day hospital usage varies considerably in different units, but the trend since its inception has been for the day hospital to provide physical rehabilitation for disabled patients in need of treatment and not simply to offer club facilities to 'old people who have nothing to do'. It is staffed by nurses and to be effective it must be closely allied to occupational therapy and physiotherapy departments. The day hospital is eminently suited to the needs of many stroke patients, who require continuing rehabilitation after discharge from hospital to maintain walking, and whose relatives may be in need of a brief period of freedom once or twice a week. It is not surprising that Brocklehurst (1964) found stroke to be the common diagnosis in one Day Hospital. The criteria for the selection of elderly stroke patients into the day hospital are similar to those used in the selection of other geriatric patients (Brocklehurst, 1973).

MANAGEMENT OF STROKE IN THE COMMUNITY

The great majority of stroke patients are cared for in the community and the statutory services which exist for the elderly disabled make it possible for many patients to live in their own homes for much longer than would be so in their absence. For the severely disabled, however, the lynch pin of support is often a near relation or neighbour. In these, if the chief carer dies, becomes ill or is unwilling to continue, the statutory services cannot cope for longer than a few days, if that, and the patient must be admitted to hospital. It is not possible for the statutory services, as they are at present, to offer physical support and supervision for most of the day and night to severely disabled patients in the community. Any moves in the future to reallocate funds from an increasingly depleted hospital service to the community services will have to recognize the need for greater physical support for the disabled by the community services so that a viable alternative exists in the community to long-term care in hospital.

The general practitioner leads the community team which consists primarily of the district nurse, health visitor and home help. The function of the district nurse should extend beyond basic nursing and the giving of injections. Her rôle in the rehabilitation of stroke patients in the community is not always appreciated by the medical profession (Kratz, 1978) and like her hospital counterpart the district nurse has much to offer in the mobilization and general rehabilitation of the patient in the community and also in supporting the family morale. The health visitor, who is a trained nurse, is not merely an observer of unmet need, but is able to follow up patients after discharge and report back to the general practitioner or hospital consultant depending on whether she is based in the community or in hospital. Her contribution is especially important in patients discharged from hospital on a trial basis when she is able to keep the hospital informed of how the patient is coping at home. The home help, an extremely valuable member of the community team, provides domestic support. She comes nearest to substituting for a caring relative actually living with the patient. Many home helps do much more than is demanded of them by their official remit. They often help with basic nursing, rehabilitation, the giving of drugs, cooking meals and shopping. Some even visit after hours or during the weekend to see if all is well. No other community service adversely affects the discharge of patients from hospital as much as a reduction in the home help service.

The general practitioner when faced with an acute stroke must decide whether to treat the patient at home or in hospital (Mulley and Arie, 1978). The degree of functional incapacity and domestic support very often determine which is most suitable. Patients in the lower band of stroke triage (Garraway et al., 1981) with minor neurological deficit are often managed at home, while those in the middle and upper bands require hospital admission. The availability of nursing, physiotherapy and occupational therapy in the community is important in deciding the best course. It is important that patients in the middle band be referred to hospital for early rehabilitation whatever the social circumstances, unless of course the domiciliary rehabilitation service is able to offer daily treatment at home and is able to fully exploit the patient's potential for recovery.

It is most important for the morale of the patient and caring relative and also for the appropriate management of the patient that the general practitioner should visit the stroke patient at home soon after discharge from hospital.

REFERENCES

Acheson R. M. and Fairbairn A. S. (1970) *Br. Med. J.* I, 621.
Adams G. F. (1971) *Geront. Clin.* 13, 181.
Adams G. F. (1974) *Cerebrovascular Disability and the Ageing Brain.* Edinburgh, Churchill Livingstone.
Adams G. F. and Hurwitz L. J. (1963) *Lancet* 2, 533.
Admani A. K. (1978) *Br. Med. J.* 2, 1678.
Anderson W. F. (1966) *Physiotherapy* 1, 34.
Bauer R. B. and Tellez H. (1973) *Stroke* 4, 547.
Bobath B (1970) *Adult Hemiplegia: Evaluation and Treatment.* London, Heinemann.
Britton M., de Faire U. and Helmers C. (1980) *Acta Med. Scand.* 207, 253.
Brocklehurst J. C. (1964) *Geront. Clin.* 6, 151.
Brocklehurst J. C. (1973) *Br. Med. J.* 4, 223.
Brocklehurst J. C., Morris P. and Andrews K. et al. (1981) *Soc. Sci. Med.* 15a, 35.
Brocklehurst J. C. and Tucker J. S. (1980) *Progress in Geriatric Day Care.* London, King Edwards Hospital Fund.
Brunnstrom S. (1964) *Movement Therapy in Hemiplegia, a Neurophysiological Approach.* New York, Harper & Row.
Dow R. S., Dick H. L. and Crowell F. A. (1974) *Stroke* 5, 40.
Dunbar S. (1981) Personal communication.
Eastcott H. H. G., Pickering G. W. and Rob C. G. (1954) *Lancet* 2, 944.
Ellams J. (1974) *Nurs. Mirror* 1, 66.
Feldman B. E., Lee B. R. et al. (1972) *J. Chronic Dis.* 15, 297.
Ford J. (1971) *Mod. Geriatrics* 1, 414.
Garraway W. M. (1976) In: Gillingham F. J., Mawdsley C. et al. (ed.) *Stroke.* Proceedings of the Ninth Pfizer International Symposium. London, Churchill Livingstone.
Garraway W. M., Akhtar A. J., Prescott R. J. et al. (1980) *Br. Med. J.* 280, 1040. •
Garraway W. M., Akhtar A. J., Smith A. L. et al. (1981) *J. Epidemiol. Community Health* 35, 39.
Garraway W. M. and Prescott R. (1977) *Health Bull. (Edinb.)* 35, 131.
Gilroy J., Barnhart M. I. and Meyer J. S. (1969) *JAMA* 210, 293.
Heiser W. J. and Quinn J. L. (1966) *Arch. Neurol.* 15, 125.
Hewer L. R. (1976) In: Ross Russell R. W. (ed.) *Cerebral Arterial Disease.* London, Churchill Livingstone.
Irving M. (1976) *Br. J. Surg.* 63, 731.
Isaacs B. (1971) *Mod. Geriatrics* 1, 390.
Isaacs B. (1977) *Health Bull.* 35, 93.
Isaacs B. (1978) In: Brocklehurst J. C. (ed.) *Textbook of Geriatric Medicine and Gerontology.* Edinburgh, Churchill Livingstone.
Isaacs B. and Marks R. (1973) *Age Ageing* 2, 139.
Katz S., Ford A. B., Moskowitz R. W. et al. (1963) *JAMA* 185, 914.
Knott, M. (1967) *Physiotherapy* 53, 2.
Kratz R. C. (1978) *Care of the Long-term Sick in the Community.* Edinburgh, Churchill Livingstone.
Lorenze E. J., DeRosa A. J. and Keenan E. L. (1958) *Arch. Phys. Med. Rehabil.* 39, 366.

McCann C. and Culbertson R. A. (1976) *J. Am. Geriatr. Soc.* **24**, 211.
MacLeod R. D. M. and Williamson J. (1967) *Scott. Med. J.* **12**, 384.
Manning J. (1974) *Neurology for Physiotherapists.* London, Faber & Faber.
Matthews W. M. (1976) In: Gillingham F. J., Mawdsley C. et al. (ed.) *Stroke.* Proceedings of the Ninth Pfizer International Symposium. London, Churchill Livingstone.
Meyer J. S., Charney J. Z., Rivera V, M. et al. (1971) *Lancet* **2**, 993.
Meyer J. S., Fukuuchi Y., Shimaza J. et al. (1972) *Stroke* **3**, 168.
Millikan C. H. (1955) *Arch. Neurol. Psychiatry* **73**, 324.
Millikan C. H. (1971) *Stroke* **2**, 501.
Mulley G. and Arie T. (1978) *Br. Med. J.* **2**, 1321.
Mulley G., Wilcox R. J. and Mitchell J. R. A. (1978) *Br. Med. J.* **2**, 994.
Murray S. K., Garraway W. M., Akhtar A. J. et al. (1982). In preparation.
Nichols P. J. R. (1976) *Occup. Therapy* **39**, 160.
Owen G. G. O. (1981) *Br. Med. J.* **1**, 1310.
Pathy J. (1975) *Geront. Clin.* **17**, 161.
Patten B. M., Mendell, J., Bruun B. et al. (1972) *Neurology* **22**, 377.
Patterson A. (1971) *Mod. Geriatrics* **1**, 403.
Peacock P. B., Riley C. P., Lampteon T. D. et al. (1972) In: Stewart G. J. (ed.) *Trends in Epidemiology.* Springfield, Ill., Thomas.
Sahs A. L., Hartman E. C. and Aronson S. N. (1979). *Stroke.* Tunbridge Wells, Castle House Publications Ltd.
Sheikh K., Smith D. S., Meade T. W. et al. (1979) *Int. Rehabil. Med.* **1**, 51.
Smith M. A., Garraway M. W., Akhtar A. J. et al. (1977) *Br. J. Occup. Therapy* **40**, 51.
Smith R. G., Cruickshank J. C., Dunbar S. et al. (1982) In preparation.
Steers A. J. W. (1976) In: Gillingham F. J., Mawdsley C. et al. (ed.) *Stroke.* Proceedings of the Ninth Pfizer International Symposium. London, Churchill Livingstone.
Steinmann B. (1975) *Age Ageing.* Supplementary Issue, 31.
Warlow C., Ogston D. and Douglas A. J. (1976) *Br. Med. J.* **1**, 1178.
Waylonis G. W., Keith M. W. and Aseff J. N. (1973) *Arch. Phys. Med. Rehabil.* **54**, 151.
Whisnant J. P. (1976) In: Gillingham F. J., Mawdsley C. et al. (ed.) *Stroke.* Proceedings of the Ninth Pfizer International Symposium. London, Churchill Livingstone.
Wylie C. M. (1968) *J. Am. Geriatr. Soc.* **16**, 428.

10. PARKINSONISM AND RELATED DISORDERS
G. A. Broe

Parkinsonism is a clinical syndrome characterized by the combination of rigidity and bradykinesia and frequently including the following clinical features: resting tremor; a disorder of posture and balance; autonomic dysfunction; dementia.

The presence of rigidity and bradykinesia is essential to the diagnosis. Resting tremor completes the classic triad. However, the presence of tremor is not essential to the diagnosis and indeed resting tremor is commonly absent in senile or late-onset Parkinsonism, i.e. over 70 years of age. Posture and balance defect, autonomic dysfunction and dementia are all more common in senile Parkinsonism.

Parkinsonism is a disorder of ageing with a prevalence of about 2000 per 100 000 above 70 years of age; under 50 years of age the prevalence is only 8 per 100 000 (Broe et al., 1976; Nobrega et al., 1976). A clinicopathological continuum exists between a younger group of patients having the classic disorder and a much larger group over 70 years of age having a different clinical picture, an altered therapeutic response, and more widespread neuropathological changes.

CLASSIFICATION AND CLINICAL FEATURES

Parkinsonism is commonly classified into idiopathic Parkinson's disease and symptomatic Parkinsonism. 'Arteriosclerotic Parkinsonism' is no longer considered a true entity. Parkinsonism may also complicate a number of multisystem disorders of the brain seen with ageing (*Table* 10.1).

Idiopathic Parkinson's disease itself is not an homogeneous entity either clinically or pathologically. In senile Parkinsonism (*Table* 10.2) resting tremor is less common, and senile or essential tremor is relatively more frequent. Rigidity and bradykinesia are essential diagnostic features for both varieties of Parkinsonism; in the elderly group they tend to be bilateral and symmetrical from onset, whereas in the younger subject they are more typically unilateral at onset and asymmetrical in progression. In senile Parkinsonism the disorder of posture and balance occurs earlier and tends to dominate the clinical

Table 10.1. Classification of extrapyramidal disorders in the elderly

A. Idiopathic Parkinsonism
   Classic paralysis agitans
   Senile Parkinsonism
   Striatonigral degeneration

B. Symptomatic Parkinsonism
   Postencephalitic (viral)
   Drug-induced
   Toxic

C. Multisystem disorders with Parkinsonism
   Progressive supranuclear palsy
   Shy–Drager syndrome
   Alzheimer's dementia

D. Hyperkinetic syndromes
   Senile chorea
   Huntington's chorea
   Dyskinesias
   Senile dystonia

Table 10.2. Idiopathic Parkinson's disease

Clinical feature	Classic idiopathic Parkinson's disease (40–65 years)	Senile Parkinsonism (70 + years)
Tremor	Diagnostic Resting in type	Uncommon Essential or senile in type
Rigidity	Diagnostic Asymmetrical	Diagnostic Symmetrical
Bradykinesia	Diagnostic Asymmetrical	Diagnostic Symmetrical
Posture and balance defect	Mild and late	Early and progressive
Autonomic defect	Mild	Moderate to severe
Dementia	Mild and late	Early and progressive
Progression	Variable— slow or rapid	Slow
Chronic levodopa response	'On–off' at 2–5 years common (20%)	'On–off' rare and late

picture to a greater degree. Postural hypotension is more frequent in the elderly Parkinsonian as are defective bladder control and distressing constipation. These symptoms reflect autonomic dysfunction due to the disease rather than age changes alone. A slowly progressive dementia is more frequent in the older age group.

Senile Parkinsonism differs also in its rate of progression which is slow and its response to levodopa therapy which tends to be steady and sustained for many years. Fluctuations in response are correspondingly rare in the aged provided low-dose therapy is used.

Striatonigral degeneration is a rare disorder that can be distinguished pathologically but not clinically from idiopathic Parkinsonism in the aged.

Symptomatic Parkinsonism includes the post-encephalitic (viral) form which is rare and the drug-induced form which is common. Both occur predominantly in the older age group and are discussed further below.

'*Arteriosclerotic Parkinsonism*' was the label applied inaccurately to two groups of predominantly elderly patients. First, the group with senile Parkinsonism who were more demented and had coincidental vascular disease were wrongly labelled 'arteriosclerotic'. Secondly, patients with 'état lacunaire' or multiple small hypertensive end-vessel strokes were wrongly labelled 'Parkinsonian'. In fact this latter group have bilateral corticospinal signs without significant extrapyramidal disorder. The term 'arteriosclerotic Parkinsonism' should be abandoned as there is no clinical or pathological evidence for a vascular cause of Parkinsonism in old age (Eadie and Sutherland, 1964; Selby, 1968).

Progressive supranuclear palsy is a not uncommon multisystem disorder in the elderly that may present as Parkinsonism. The classic features include the eye movement disorder with early involvement of downward gaze, rather than the involvement of upward gaze seen almost universally in idiopathic Parkinsonism. This is associated with nuchal and axial rigidity, bradykinesia, gait disorder out of proportion to other findings with frequent falls, a characteristic dysarthria and progressive dementia. Corticospinal and cerebellar signs may occur. This syndrome may develop in a patient with quite typical senile Parkinsonism; however, more commmonly it develops in a patient with an atypical extrapyramidal disorder which is initially hard to classify and which progresses more rapidly. Anti-Parkinsonian drugs are not of any consistent value in this disorder.

The Shy–Drager syndrome and olivo-pontocerebellar degeneration are multisystem disorders with Parkinsonian features that typically commence in late middle life and will not be considered further here. The subject of Parkinsonism, dementia and ageing is of such importance that it will be discussed in a separate section (*see below*).

A number of hyperkinetic extrapyramidal disorders occur with ageing although, with the exception of tardive dyskinesia, these are epidemiologically and clinically of far less importance than the Parkinsonian syndromes.

Senile chorea is rare and usually attributable to a specific aetiological factor such as polycythaemia vera, vascular disease, or Alzheimer's disease. In the author's experience true bilateral symmetrical chorea with gradual onset in the seventh or eighth decade is most commonly Huntington's disease of late onset. Chorea as a result of cerebral infarction in the basal ganglia is always of sudden onset and usually asymmetrical or unilateral. The onset of bilateral symmetrical chorea has been seen by the author as a manifestation of a small unilateral infarct involving the region of the caudate nucleus in a patient with a previous infarct involving the opposite caudate.

Mild *orofacial dyskinesia* may occur in elderly edentulous subjects in the absence of any precipitating drug. However, this is rare and tardive dyskinesia is essentially a drug-induced disorder and will be discussed under that heading (*see below*).

Dystonias other than spasmodic torticollis with onset in the seventh or eighth decade are rare; however, slowly progressive *senile dystonia* does occur with asymmetrical involvement predominantly of the upper limbs. This clinical picture may be associated with progressive dementia and in the author's experience with the development of progressive supranuclear palsy.

PATHOLOGY AND PATHOGENESIS

The primary biochemical defect in idiopathic Parkinsonism is a deficiency of dopamine in the striatum of the basal ganglia. In idiopathic Parkinsonism the degree of this deficiency correlates with the severity of symptoms (Lloyd and Hornykiewicz, 1972). Striatal dopamine deficiency is secondary to a loss of dopamine production from the pigmented cells of the substantia nigra associated with the pathological finding of a loss of over 75 per cent of nigral cells. In idiopathic Parkinsonism the post-synaptic receptors of the striatum remain substantially intact and therefore responsive to dopamine or dopamine agonists (Klawans et al., 1977). This explains the success of exogenous levodopa, converted to dopamine in the striatum, in correcting the biochemical defect and clinical features of idiopathic Parkinsonism in a majority of cases.

Dopamine in the nigrostriatal pathway is an inhibitory neurotransmitter. Dopamine receptors in the striatum are located on cholinergic striatal interneurones. As dopaminergic transmission to the striatum decreases with fallout of substantia nigra cells, the intact striatal cholinergic neurones become hyperactive and the clinical features of Parkinsonism appear. This concept of an altered balance between dopaminergic and cholinergic transmission in the striatum may explain the effectiveness of anticholinergic agents on the one hand and dopaminergic agents on the other in treating the symptoms of Parkinsonism.

In younger Parkinsonian subjects with relatively selective damage to the nigrostriatal pathway this simplistic explanation of the biochemistry and treatment of Parkinsonism has some validity. Even in the younger age group deficiencies and imbalances occur in other neurotransmitter systems, including noradrenaline, serotonin and gamma-aminobutyric acid, and pathology is not confined to the nigrostriatal pathway (Greenfield and Bosanquet, 1953; Ehringer and Hornykiewicz, 1960; Eadie, 1963; Curzon, 1977; Carlssen, 1978; Rinne, 1978).

In the older age group clinical and neuropathological studies indicate more widespread neuronal loss and neurotransmitter alterations, although the major pathology in senile Parkinsonism involves the substantia nigra (Carlssen, 1978; Lieberman et al., 1978; Broe and Huang, 1981). This may in part reflect the superimposition of Parkinsonism on normal age changes in the brain. Normal ageing is accompanied by a progressive loss of nigral neurones (McGeer and McGeer, 1978). There is also fallout of other specific neuronal populations, including cerebellar Purkinje cells, noradrenergic neurones of the locus coeruleus, and cholinergic neurones of the superior temporal gyrus and of the frontal lobe (Brody, 1976; Corsellis, 1976; Bondareff, 1977; Carlssen, 1978).

The clinical features and drug therapy of senile Parkinsonism must be considered on the basis of these widespread neuropathological changes as quite different from classic idiopathic Parkinson's disease in younger age groups.

Striatonigral degeneration presents clinically as idiopathic Parkinsonism in the elderly but is unresponsive to dopaminergic therapy. The pathogenesis of Parkinsonism in this disorder, as in the Shy–Drager syndrome, lies in damage to the postsynaptic dopaminergic receptors with the brunt of the pathology falling on the striatal neurones rather than the nigrostriatal pathway. Exogenous levodopa therapy is consequently ineffective.

Drug-induced Parkinsonism is most common in elderly subjects. It tends to occur in the elderly with low doses of the offending drug and with short-duration therapy. The clinical picture resembles senile Parkinsonism rather than classic paralysis agitans in the predominance of bilateral symmetrical bradykinesia followed by rigidity, with resting tremor occurring less commonly.

In general the predilection of the elderly to develop drug-induced Parkinsonism reflects the high incidence of the disease in the over 70 age group and the progressive loss of substantia nigra cells with the normal ageing process. McGeer and McGeer (1978) have shown a loss of 50 per cent of nigral neurones in normal ageing from the seventh decade onwards. Such nigral cell loss remains compensated without clinical Parkinsonism until the remaining cells are depleted of dopamine by drugs such as reserpine and tetrabenazine, or postsynaptic receptor block occurs with the phenothiazines and butyrophenones.

These drugs should only be used in elderly subjects for the treatment of major functional psychoses or for the hyperactivity of dementia when this is unresponsive to other measures.

A wide variety of drugs may produce extrapyramidal movement disorders, varying from acute dystonic and hyperkinetic reactions, seen more commonly in younger subjects, to chronic movement disorders, seen with prolonged drug therapy more commonly in the elderly. The latter group of movement disorders are known collectively as the tardive dyskinesias. It is now well recognized that following removal of the offending drug these movement disorders may continue for many months or indeed may be permanent.

Buccolingual or orofacial dyskinesia is the common form seen in elderly subjects. These facial movements, consisting of involuntary mouthing, chewing, sucking and licking, may occur in edentulous elderly subjects without drug therapy, particularly in association with senile dementia of the Alzheimer type or generalized evidence of neurological ageing. With neuroleptic medication these movements are more commonly severe and distressing and may spread to include limbs and trunk with grunting and irregular respiration.

Tardive dyskinesias are most commonly caused by the phenothiazines, particularly the fluorinated compounds, and by the butyrophenones. They may occur in association with drug-induced Parkinsonism in the elderly or occur independently. The predilection of tardive dyskinesia for the elderly reflects the high incidence of abnormality of the central nervous system in elderly subjects (Broe and Huang, 1981).

In the author's experience prolonged anticholinergic therapy alone, when used for the treatment of essential tremor with the misdiagnosis of Parkinsonism, may cause permanent buccolingual dyskinesia. Similarly, Stemetil, commonly misused as a labyrinthine suppressant in the elderly with non-specific giddiness, may produce tardive dyskinesia.

The prime aim of therapy is to prevent tardive dyskinesia by avoiding the misuse not only of the major tranquillizers in the elderly but of agents such as Stemetil, methyldopa and anticholinergics. Management of the established disorder is complex in the short term but essentially involves removal if possible of the offending drug.

Patients with postencephalitic Parkinsonism show clinical and pathological evidence of more widespread neuronal damage than is seen in senile Parkinsonism; however, the substantia nigra is predominantly involved. These patients are extremely sensitive to levodopa in small doses with high toxicity and poor overall therapeutic response (Hunter et al., 1970; Krasner and Cornelius, 1970). This disorder is now exceedingly rare, affecting the few aged survivors of the epidemic of encephalitis lethargica of the 1920s.

DIFFERENTIAL DIAGNOSIS OF SENILE PARKINSONISM

The diagnosis of Parkinsonism remains a clinical one. In the younger patient the classic features of resting tremor and asymmetrical rigidity and bradykinesia are unmistakable. When hemi-Parkinsonism occurs in this age group without tremor a progressive focal lesion may initially be suspected.

Parkinsonism in the aged, characterized by subtle onset, absence of tremor, and bilateral symmetrical slowing, is commonly misdiagnosed as arthritis in its early stages. Generalized psychomotor slowing may lead to diagnoses of depression or hypothyroidism in the elderly Parkinsonian patient (*Table* 10.3).

Table 10.3. Differential diagnosis of senile Parkinsonism

Arthritis
Depression
Hypothyroidism
Etat lacunaire
Essential tremor
Senescent gait disorder
Senile dementia of the Alzheimer type

The disorder most commonly mistaken for Parkinsonism is benign essential tremor (Duvoisin, 1977). Essential, senile or heredofamilial tremor is common in old age with a prevalence approaching that of Parkinsonism in the age group 65–74 years and affecting some 4 per cent of the over 75 year age group (Broe et al., 1976). It is an action tremor and disappears with complete relaxation, whereas the resting tremor of Parkinsonism occurs while the limb is at rest and is inhibited by action. In addition, only essential tremor involves the jaw, face and voice.

Despite these marked differences between the two types of tremor diagnostic confusion frequently arises and for a variety of reasons. First, essential tremor in the elderly is usually slow at 4–6 Hz, unlike most action tremor in younger subjects with a frequency of 10–12 Hz; it also has a pill-rolling character. Secondly, the elderly patient has to be completely relaxed for essential tremor to disappear and this is often difficult to achieve. Thirdly, essential tremor is associated with accelerated neurological ageing in the elderly and in particular with a disorder of gait and balance termed 'senescent gait disorder' (Broe, 1980, 1981; Broe and Huang, 1981). Finally, essential tremor is not uncommonly seen in association with true Parkinsonism in elderly subjects.

For these reasons the diagnosis of Parkinsonism should only be made in the elderly when tremor, whatever its form, is accompanied by significant rigidity and bradykinesia. Patients with monosymptomatic essential tremor are not improved or are made worse by anti-Parkinsonian therapy and are exposed to needless risk of adverse side effects. In particular anticholinergics given to these patients may result in tardive dyskinesia which may indeed be permanent.

The second common neurological disorder to be misdiagnosed as Parkinsonism in the elderly is the syndrome of 'état lacunaire'—multiple small cerebral infarcts resulting from hypertensive cerebrovascular disease. This disorder which has a clear-cut clinical picture and distinctive neuropathology has carried numerous diagnostic labels including arteriosclerotic Parkinsonism (Critchley, 1929), multiple lacunes, cerebral arteriosclerosis, and multi-infarct dementia (Hachinski et al., 1974). The clinical syndrome is due to repeated small strokes resulting from occlusion of penetrating end-vessels in the central grey and white matter, the internal capsules and within the brainstem. Postural defect, hypertonia, impaired fine movements and impaired facial movements occur, but these result from bilateral corticospinal lesions with brisk reflexes and extensor plantars. Severe gait disorder of the marche-à-petit-pas type and pseudobulbar crying are important diagnostic features differentiating this disorder from Parkinsonism. Anti-Parkinsonian drugs are ineffective unless a true extrapyramidal disorder is coincidentally present.

PARKINSONISM, DEMENTIA AND AGEING

An association between Parkinsonism and dementia seems undoubted on the clinical and pathological evidence (Loranger et al., 1972b; Sweet et al., 1976; Lieberman et al., 1978; Hakim and Mathieson, 1979; Broe, 1981; Broe and Huang, 1981). This association was described prior to the levodopa era (Selby, 1968) and is more obvious with longer survival due to levodopa therapy. Debate continues as to the nature of Parkinsonian dementia and it is probable that it is multifactorial in origin.

The weight of evidence suggests that the increasing frequency and severity of dementia seen during chronic levodopa therapy is due to disease progression and is not a toxic effect of long-term therapy (Broe, 1981). First, dementia may be due to a dopaminergic defect perhaps within the mesolimbic pathway. This is suggested by a number of clinical trials which have shown initial improvement in Parkinsonian dementia with levodopa therapy to a similar extent to other Parkinsonian symptoms. This improvement is not sustained after the first year of therapy (Maier and Martin, 1970; Loranger et al., 1972a; Broe and Caird, 1973; Drachman and Stahl, 1975). Secondly, a number of factors suggest a cholinergic mechanism in Parkinsonian dementia: the fact that dementia progresses after the first year of levodopa therapy without deterioration in other Parkinsonian symptoms suggests involvement of another neurotransmitter system; pathological involvement of cholinergic neurones occurs in longstanding Parkinsonism; in elderly and demented Parkinsonian subjects anticholinergics cause more neuropsychiatric toxicity than appropriate doses of levodopa (Duvoisin, 1977; Caird and Williamson, 1978; Broe, 1981).

Thirdly, Hakim and Mathieson (1979) have noted the frequent occurrence of Alzheimer changes (plaques and tangles) in the brains of patients with Parkinsonism and dementia. Their assumption that Parkinsonian dementia may be explained by the simultaneous presence of Alzheimer's disease is not supported by a clinical study of the incidence of dementia in Parkinson's disease (Lieberman et al., 1979). It is inevitable that two such common disorders of ageing as Parkinsonism and Alzheimer dementia will coincide occasionally in the one patient. However, senile plaques and neurofibrillary tangles are not specific for Alzheimer's disease. In conclusion, the weight of evidence suggests that there is a dementia specific to Parkinsonism, although it is probably multifactorial.

Senile dementia of the Alzheimer type (SDAT) in its classic form is clinically, pathologically and biochemically distinct from Parkinson's disease. However, a number of studies have noted that SDAT is not uncommonly accompanied by clinical evidence of rigidity and bradykinesia and by gait disorder (Parkes et al., 1974; Pearce, 1974a, b; Bowen and Davison, 1975; Drachman and Stahl, 1975; Broe, 1980). It is possible that SDAT with motor deficit represents the superimposition of Alzheimer dementia on elderly subjects with senile gait disorder or accelerated neurological ageing (Broe and Huang, 1981). Conversely SDAT without motor deficit would represent the superimposition of Alzheimer dementia on an aged population with an otherwise normal brain.

Alternatively, it is possible that SDAT is a syndrome of multiple aetiology, one variety being associated with extrapyramidal features and defective monoamine metabolism in addition to the documented cholinergic defect (White et al., 1977; Davies, 1978). The association between SDAT, senile Parkinsonism and senile gait disorder requires further study by accurate clinical definition of aged populations in neurological terms prior to neuropsychological and neurophysiological examination and ultimately neuropathological and neurohistochemical studies. In therapeutic terms the presence of mild to moderate dementia in a patient with significant Parkinsonism is not a contraindication to a cautious trial of low dose levodopa, and a favourable outcome may be expected at least in the short term provided concurrent anticholinergic therapy is avoided (Broe and Caird, 1973).

THERAPY OF SENILE PARKINSONISM

Levodopa remains the drug of choice for the treatment of Parkinsonism in old age. Levodopa therapy should not be delayed until the elderly patient is significantly disabled as long-term sequelae are rare with appropriate dosage. It should be used in preference to anticholinergics and amantadine which are both less effective and more toxic in the elderly. Levodopa should not in general be used in combination with other antiparkinsonian drugs. In terms of late neuropsychiatric complications it is preferable to commence levodopa alone and not to use combined therapy with a peripheral dopa decarboxylase inhibitor (PDI) (carbidopa or benserazide) unless levodopa alone is ineffective or poorly tolerated. Finally, levodopa therapy should be initiated gradually in the elderly and low maintenance doses used to avoid toxicity and to achieve maximum long-term therapeutic benefit.

Parkinsonism is essentially a disorder of ageing yet levodopa dosage levels and modes of initiating therapy have been standardized on relatively young groups of patients (*Table* 10.4).

Table 10.4. Early levodopa trials

Trial	Number of subjects	Average age	Average daily dose (g)
Barbeau (1969)	86	60	4·8
Cotzias et al. (1969)	17	51	5·8
Godwin-Austen et al. (1969)	18	56	3·0–8·0*
Klawans and Garvin (1969)	105	65*	2·0–6·0*
Mawdsley (1970)	32	61	4·0–6·0*
Mones et al. (1970)	152	55*	3·0–4·0*
Peaston and Bianchine (1970)	22	65	3·0
Stellar et al. (1970)	91	60*	3·0–5·0*

* Estimated.

These trials have recommended starting doses in the range of 0·5–1·0 g of levodopa and maintenance doses in the range of 3·0–6·0 g daily as applicable to all age groups. These doses would not be regarded as 'high' by the majority of neurologists; yet geriatricians are aware that elderly Parkinsonian patients are at great risk with such dose regimes. Drug therapy of Parkinsonism in the elderly requires a major difference in approach in terms of lower, starting doses, incremental doses, frequency of increments and maintenance dosage of levodopa (*Table* 10.5). The need for this altered approach lies in both central and peripheral aspects of levodopa metabolism in the elderly. Senile Parkinsonism is characterized by more widespread neuropathological changes in the brain producing a more diffuse neurological disorder (Carlssen, 1978; Broe, 1980; Broe and Huang, 1981). The

Table 10.5. Levodopa trials in the elderly

Trial	Number of subjects	Average age	Average daily dose (g)
Broe and Caird (1973)	16	76*	1·7
Grad et al. (1974)	15	76	1·9
Sutcliffe (1973)	50	70	1·0–2·0*
Vignalou and Beck (1973)	122	70–90*	2·4

* Estimated.

ageing brain is more vulnerable to the neuropsychiatric toxicity of levodopa. Peripherally, ageing brings about an altered absorption and metabolism of levodopa increasing the bioavailability of the drug and reducing the oral dose required (Evans et al., 1980; Evans, Broe et al., 1981). In treating senile Parkinsonism levodopa should be commenced in a dosage of 50–100 mg daily. Increments should be no higher than 100 mg and should be made at intervals of no less than 4 days as an inpatient or 7 days as an outpatient. The occasional patient will commence improvement or show toxicity on as little as 50 mg of levodopa daily. An initial dose of 0·5–1 g in such a patient could produce the syndrome of 'acute agitated hallucinatory delirium' described by Sacks and co-workers which may be of days, weeks or months duration (Sacks et al., 1970; 1972). Average daily maintenance dosage varies from 1 to 2 g although a satisfactory therapeutic response may be seen with 300–750 mg of levodopa daily. Using this regime the maintenance dosage of 1–2 g daily will be reached in 2 months to 4 months but may take longer if increments need to be reduced because of early toxicity.

Evans, Broe et al. (1981) have shown in elderly subjects (aged 71–86 years) a threefold increase in levodopa absorption following oral administration of levodopa in comparison to a group of young controls (Fig. 10.1). Both elderly patients with Parkinsonism on a low-dose regime of levodopa and elderly controls showed the same increase in absorption calculated in terms of the computed area under the plasma levodopa concentration versus time curve (Fig. 10.2) (Evans et al., 1980; Evans, Broe et al., 1981).

Other workers have noted the same phenomenon in single case absorption studies in elderly Parkinsonian subjects (Granerus et al., 1974; Mearrick et al., 1974).

Levodopa is an aromatic amino acid and is absorbed primarily in the small bowel by an active transport mechanism (Wade et al., 1973). In younger subjects the majority of orally administered levodopa is metabolized to dopamine in the stomach by the enzyme dopa decarboxylase, which has a high gastric activity, and is therefore not

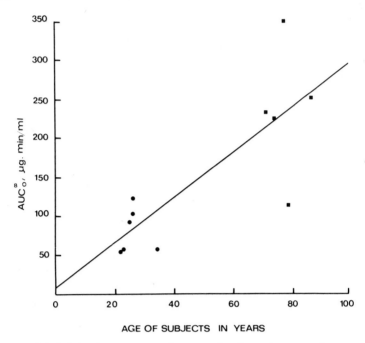

Fig. 10.1. Relation between age and areas under observation curves in young normals (●) and elderly Parkinsonian subjects (■) (Evans et al., 1980).

presented to the small bowel as levodopa for absorption (Rivera-Calimlim et al., 1970a, b). Gastric emptying rate was measured in three groups—elderly Parkinsonian subjects, elderly controls and young controls—and a threefold delay in gastric emptying was noted in the elderly (Evans, Triggs et al., 1981). The increased levodopa absorption in the elderly therefore occurred despite a much prolonged gastric emptying rate which has been shown to increase levodopa decarboxylation and to reduce levodopa absorption in younger subjects (Rivera-Calimlim et al., 1970b; Mearrick et al., 1974; Bianchine and Shaw, 1976). It is postulated from these recent studies that elderly subjects 70 years and over have a low gastric activity of dopa decarboxylase, resulting in markedly reduced gastric metabolism of levodopa; hence presentation of much higher concentrations of levodopa to the small bowel for absorption (Broe, 1981). It is felt that these changes in pharmacokinetics of levodopa in the elderly are in part responsible for lower dosage requirements and for the tolerance of levodopa therapy without severe nausea and vomiting seen in the elderly. Dopa decarboxylase activity is also decreased by a statistically significant amount in the liver and kidney of older animals (Awapura

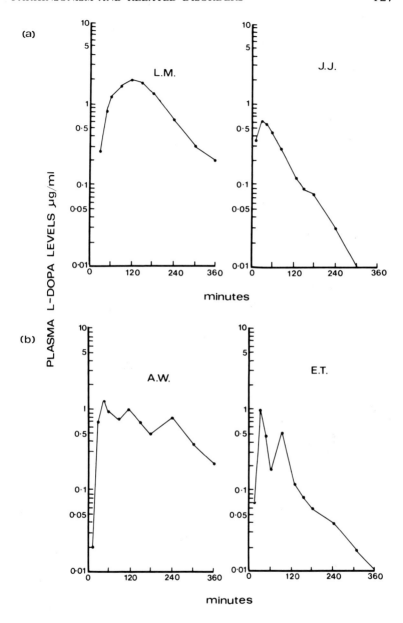

Fig. 10.2. Plasma levodopa levels following oral doses in 2 elderly Parkinsonian subjects (LM and AW), and 2 young normal subjects (JJ and ET): note multiple peaks (AM and ET) and greater areas under the curves (LM and AW) (Evans et al., 1980).

and Saine, 1975). It is probable that systemic as well as gastric decarboxylation of levodopa is reduced in the elderly, decreasing systemic dopamine levels which contribute to nausea and increasing bioavailability of levodopa to the brain.

Levodopa improves the major symptoms of Parkinsonism in approximately 70–80 per cent of elderly patients. Resting tremor (when present), rigidity, and bradykinesia improve to a similar degree (Broe and Caird, 1973). Failure of tremor to improve occurs when there is a significant component of essential tremor. Dementia improves with other Parkinsonian symptoms but only during the first year of treatment (Maier and Martin, 1970; Loranger et al., 1972a; Drachman and Stahl, 1975). Dysphagia, constipation and urinary symptoms may not improve to the same degree as other features, and very occasionally worsen with anti-Parkinsonian therapy (Duvoisin, 1977). Similarly, postural hypotension may increase significantly when therapy with levodopa is initiated (Broe and Caird, 1973).

The significant early toxic effects of levodopa include anorexia, nausea, vomiting, postural hypotension, mental changes and involuntary movements. All of these are uncommon or mild using the recommended regime and can be overcome by further reducing or slowing increments. Despite the theoretical possibility of inducing cardiac arrythmias, significant cardiac toxicity is rare in elderly subjects even with a high rate of coincident heart disease and ECG abnormality (Broe and Caird, 1973). Improved mobility due to levodopa therapy may, however, precipitate congestive failure or angina (Broe and Caird, 1973; Duvoisin, 1977).

The proper therapy of dose-limiting anorexia, nausea and vomiting in the elderly is to reduce the dose increments of levodopa until tolerance occurs, or to use measures aimed at lowering absorption, e.g. taking the drug with food including a significant protein content. Phenothiazine anti-emetics and anticholinergics to slow gastric emptying are contraindicated. Combination therapy with carbidopa or benserazide (Sinemet, Madopar) is rarely necessary as tolerance commonly develops with the above measures. Madopar with a higher ratio of benserazide to dopa (1:4) may be more helpful than Sinemet (carbidopa to dopa 1:10), when gastrointestinal side effects occur at a low dosage of levodopa (50–100 mg), as may occur with elderly patients. The effective dose of carbidopa to prevent decarboxylation of dopa to dopamine is in the region of 50–70 mg daily, and this is not achieved until Sinemet doses of 500–750 mg are given. Mild postural hypotension is almost universal during early treatment. If it becomes symptomatic which is unusual it is managed by ceasing increments for several weeks until tolerance occurs.

Neuropsychiatric toxicity is the major danger of levodopa therapy in the elderly but severe mental disturbances are not seen with the low dose regime unless anticholinergics are used in combination (Broe and Caird, 1973). Early reports of severe mental disturbance made levodopa therapy suspect in the elderly. 'Severe psychotic reaction' (Jenkins and Groh, 1970) and a syndrome of 'agitated hallucinatory delirium accompanied by severe chorea and motor unrest' were described (Sacks et al., 1970, 1972). These reactions were related to the relatively high average doses of levodopa (2·5–5·0 g daily) used in these elderly and deteriorated subjects.

Confusion, delirium, visual hallucinations and psychosis are the dose-related neuropsychiatric side effects of levodopa and these are common with high-dose levodopa, with combined therapy using a PDI, with amantadine in average dosage, and with anticholinergics.

The commonest dose-related side effect in 'high-dose' trials on younger subjects is the development of abnormal involuntary movements (AIM). The development of AIM in elderly subjects means overdosage. Vignalou and Beck (1973) have shown that a satisfactory therapeutic response can be obtained in the elderly with a significantly lower incidence of AIM than in a younger control group.

Finally, an unusual early side effect of levodopa therapy in the elderly is the development of incontinence while other parameters of physical and mental function are improving. This occurred in one-third of elderly subjects from 1–7 weeks after initiation of therapy and was not associated with worsening of confusion or dementia. In all cases it responded to a temporary reduction in dosage (Broe and Caird, 1973).

The long-term benefits of levodopa in Parkinsonism have been remarkable for all age groups. Good symptomatic relief occurs for a period of years and clear-cut evidence for this lies in the significantly reduced mortality from the disease (Marttila and Rinne, 1979). However, experience with long-term therapy has shown that the underlying disease process progresses steadily despite good relief of symptoms. Progression is slower in senile Parkinsonism than in Parkinson's disease in younger age groups (Pearce, 1978), and this is important in the better long-term response of elderly patients to levodopa therapy (Broe, 1981).

The results of long-term 'high-dose' therapy over a period of 5 or more years have now been thoroughly assessed in younger subjects by a number of workers (Sweet and McDowell, 1975; Barbeau, 1976; Marsden and Parkes, 1977). Marsden and Parkes (1977) have found that approximately one-third of their surviving patients at 5 years are essentially worse than prior to commencing levodopa. This phenomenon, described with chronic levodopa therapy by all major workers, is generally referred to as 'late deterioration'. However, it takes a number of distinctive forms. First, abrupt fluctuations may occur during the day after several years of chronic levodopa therapy. This is most commonly referred to as the 'on–off' effect. It appears to be related to high-dose levodopa therapy and is commoner in younger patients. Secondly, a progressive physical deterioration may occur while on chronic levodopa therapy. This is usually a progressive disorder of gait and balance rather than a return of the major Parkinsonian symptoms although either may occur. Thirdly, and particularly in elderly subjects, a progressive deterioration of mental function may occur without symptoms of levodopa toxicity and despite continuing benefit of levodopa on other Parkinsonian symptoms. Some controversy continues as to the role of disease progression or levodopa therapy in causing late deterioration and this can only be resolved by considering the three distinct forms of deterioration individually.

The 'on–off' effect is uncommon in elderly Parkinsonian patients on low-dose levodopa therapy alone. In young and old patients 'on–off' is clinically more frequent and severe following long-term 'high-dose' levodopa (Barbeau, 1976; Birkmeyer, 1976) and occurs earlier with combination therapy using a PDI, possibly because this achieves higher striatal concentrations of levodopa (Marsden and Parkes, 1976; Pinder et al., 1976; Barbeau, 1978; Broe, 1981). The pathogenesis of the 'on–off' phenomenon is unknown, though several factors appear to contribute, including high striatal dopamine concentrations and progression of the underlying disease process with loss of 'storage' capacity for dopamine in the brain (Broe, 1981).

Senile Parkinsonism has a typically slow progression. The clinical effect of levodopa is steady and non-fluctuating and levodopa effect continues for several days after therapy is ceased. This is termed by Muenter et al. (1977) the 'long-duration response' to levodopa. It continues for many years of low-dose therapy in the elderly. Loss of this 'long-duration response' is due in part to progression of the disease. It is gradually replaced by an increasing reliance on 'short-duration response' which tends to correlate with plasma dopa levels (Shoulson et al., 1975; Mueneter et al., 1977; Papavasiliou et al., 1979). 'Short-duration response' is an integral part of the 'on–off' effect and appears to be far more common in the younger patient. Levels of the metabolite 3-O-methyldopa may also play a role in producing 'short-term response' and 'on–off' phenomena (Rivera-Calimlim et al., 1977).

The present empirical management of 'on–off' is unsatisfactory and reflects the complexity of its pathogenesis. Importantly the elderly on low-dose levodopa maintain a 'long-duration response' to the drug for many years and have a low incidence of 'on–off'. It appears that 'on–off' can be delayed or reduced by the use of lower doses of levodopa at all ages and by avoiding combination therapy with a PDI (Broe, 1981).

Progressive physical deterioration while on levodopa appears to be due to progression of the underlying disease process. The elderly patient develops a progressive disorder of gait and balance without return of rigidity or worsening of bradykinesia and without fluctuation in response to therapy. Clinically this is a worsening of the gait and balance disorder which characterizes senile Parkinsonism, indicating possible involvement of non-dopaminergic pathways. In terms of therapy it is important to exclude levodopa toxicity by reducing dosage as gait disorder, particularly episodes of freezing, may occur with high levodopa levels (Ambani and Van Woert, 1973; Barbeau, 1976). Dementia occurs and progresses during chronic levodopa therapy in elderly patients, primarily because of progression of the underlying disease process (Sweet and McDowell, 1975; Sweet et al., 1976; Lieberman et al., 1978). While levodopa is associated with a variety of acute and chronic mental disturbances in elderly and demented subjects there is no good evidence that it causes a progressive dementia (Broe, 1981).

The mental disturbances associated with chronic levodopa therapy consist of an increasing incidence of vivid nightmares, visual hallucinations and paranoid delusions as well as acute confusional states. These are essentially toxic effects of the drug and are more likely with 'high-dose' therapy; however, they do occur with chronic low-dose therapy. They initially subside when levodopa is ceased or the dosage further reduced but may recur later at lower levodopa dosage. Eventually they may occur off all therapy and in this respect appear to be part of the Parkinsonian syndrome in the elderly. These neuropsychiatric symptoms are more common with anticholinergics and amantadine in the elderly, particularly when used in combination with levodopa. They are also more common with the use of a PDI, with bromocriptine and it seems with the newer dopamine agonists, lisuride and pergolide.

The benefits of combined therapy are limited in the elderly and its use carries increased risk of neuropsychiatric toxicity. It is also possible that combined therapy leads to earlier onset of the 'on–off' effect in all age groups although this risk seems lower in the elderly. It would seem reasonable to commence elderly patients on levodopa alone, reserving the use of a PDI for those who have gastrointestinal side effects which do not respond to the simple measures outlined; remembering that the low-dose combination of benserazide or carbidopa are not ideal for the elderly who develop nausea and vomiting on low doses of levodopa (Broe, 1981). Combined therapy should also be used in elderly subjects who have a less than adequate response to levodopa alone as undoubtedly some older patients obtain a greater degree of benefit from combined therapy than from an equivalent or maximal tolerated dose of levodopa.

Anticholinergic agents should not in general be used in elderly Parkinsonian patients either alone or in combination with levodopa (Broe and Caird, 1973; Duvoisin, 1977; Caird and Williamson, 1978). Acute neuropsychiatric disturbances are the major toxic effects of these drugs. However, anticholinergics clinically interfere with memory, apart from inducing visual hallucinations and acute confusional states. There is also no evidence that antihistamine agents produce less toxicity in elderly subjects, as has been claimed (Bianchine, 1976; Cohen and Scheife, 1977).

Amantadine is a moderately effective anti-Parkinsonian agent with a relatively low toxicity in younger subjects. It also causes visual hallucinations and acute confusional states in elderly subjects. The elderly with frequent subclinical impairment of renal function are at particular risk from this agent in average doses (200 mg daily) as it has a relatively long duration of action and is excreted unchanged in the urine. Combined therapy with low-dose amantadine (100 mg daily) and low-dose levodopa occasionally has some advantages in elderly subjects.

Bromocriptine carries a higher incidence of neuropsychiatric toxicity than levodopa, including toxic confusional states and paranoid ideation (Calne et al., 1978; Lees et al., 1978; Pearce and Pearce, 1978; Lieberman et al., 1979). Its major use has been in younger subjects with the 'on–off' phenomenon and it has been of only marginal benefit. It should not in general be used in senile Parkinsonism where the 'on–off' phenomenon is rare and potential risk of neuropsychiatric complications high. The same restrictions will probably apply to the use of newer dopamine agonists (pergolide and lisuride) which have a high potency, a long half-life but a high incidence of neuropsychiatric toxicity in younger subjects (Gopinathan et al., 1980; Lieberman et al., 1980).

REFERENCES

Ambani L. M. and Van Woert M. H. (1973) *N. Engl. J. Med.* **288**, 1113.
Awapura J. and Saine S. (1975) *J. Neurochem.* **24**, 817.
Barbeau A. (1969) *Can. Med. Assoc. J.* **101**, 791.
Barbeau A. (1976) *Arch. Neurol.* **33**, 333.
Barbeau A. (1978) In: Lipton M. A., Di Mascio A. and Killam K. F. (ed.) *Psychopharmacology: A Generation of Progress*. New York, Raven Press. p. 771.
Bianchine J. R. (1976) *N. Engl. J. Med.* **295**, 814.
Bianchine J. R. and Shaw G. M. (1976) *Clin. Pharmacokinet.* **1**, 313.
Birkmeyer W. (1976) In: Birkmeyer W. and Hornykiewicz O. (ed.) *Advances in Parkinsonism*. Basle, Editions Roche. p. 407.
Bondareff W. (1977) In: Birren J. E. and Schaie K. W. (ed.) *Handbook of the Psychology of Aging*. New York, Van Nostrand Reinhold. p. 157.
Bowen D. M. and Davison A. N. (1975) *Lancet* **1**, 1199.
Brody H. (1976) In Terry R. D. and Gershon S. (ed.) *Aging. (Vol. 3): Neurobiology of Aging*. New York, Raven Press. p. 177.
Broe G. A. (1980) In: Molloy M., Stanley G. V. and Walsh K. W. (ed.) *Brain Impairment*. Proceedings of the 1979 Brain Impairment Workshop. University of Melbourne, Department of Psychology.
Broe G. A. (1982) In: Triggs E., Stevenson I. H. and Swift C. (ed.) *Clinical Pharmacology in the Elderly*. New York, Marcel Dekker.

Broe G. A., Akhtar A. J. et al., (1976) *J. Neurol. Neurosurg. Psychiatry* **39**, 362.
Broe G. A. and Caird F. I. (1973) *Med. J. Aust.* **1**, 630.
Broe G. A. and Huang C. Y. (1981) Excerpta Medica International Congr. Series. No. 546, 254.
Caird F. I. and Williamson J. (1978) *Lancet* **1**, 986.
Calne D. B., Williams A. C. et al. (1978) *Lancet* **1**, 735.
Carlssen A. (1978) *Adv. Exp. Med. Biol.* **113**, 1.
Cohen M. M. and Scheife R. T. (1977) *Am. J. Hosp. Pharm.* **34**, 531.
Corsellis J. A. N. (1976) In: Terry R. D. and Gershon S. (ed.) *Aging (Vol. 3): Neurobiology of Aging.* New York, Raven Press, p. 205.
Cotzias G. C., Papavasiliou P. S. and Gellene R. (1969) *N. Eng. J. Med.* **280**, 337.
Critchley M. (1929) *Brain* **52**, 23.
Curzon G. (1977) *Postgrad. Med. J.* **53**, 719.
Davies P. (1978) *Adv. Exp. Med. Biol.* **113**, 251.
Drachman D. A. and Stahl S. (1975) *Lancet* **1**, 809.
Duvoisin R. C. (1977) *Adv. Exp. Med. Biol.* **90**, 131.
Eadie M. J. (1963) *Brain* **86**, 781.
Eadie M. J. and Sutherland J. M. (1964) *J. Neurol. Neurosurg. Psychiatry* **27**, 237.
Ehringer H. and Hornykiewicz O. (1960). *Klin. Wochenschr.* **38**, 1236.
Evans M. A., Broe G. A. et al. (1981) *Neurology* **32**, 1288.
Evans M. A., Triggs E. J., Broe G. A. et al. (1980) *Eur. J. Clin. Pharmacol.* **17**, 215.
Evans M. A., Triggs E. J., Cheung M. et al. (1981) *J. Am. Geriatr. Soc.* **29**, 201.
Godwin-Austen R. B., Tomlinson E. B. et al. (1969) *Lancet* **2**, 165.
Gopinathan G., Teravainen H. et al. (1980) *Neurology* **30**, 366.
Grad B., Wener J. et al. (1974) *J. Am. Geriatr. Soc.* **22**, 489.
Granerus A. K., Jagenburg R. et al. (1974) *Acta Med. Scand.* **196**, 459.
Greenfield J. G. and Bosanquet F. D. (1953) *J. Neurol. Neurosurg. Psychiatry* **16**, 213.
Hachinski V. C., Lassen N. A. and Marshall J. (1974) *Lancet* **2**, 207.
Hakim A. M. and Mathieson G. (1979). *Neurology* **29**, 1209.
Hunter K. R., Stern G. M. and Sharkey J. (1970) *Lancet* **2**, 1366.
Jenkins R. B. and Groh R. H. (1970). *Lancet* **2**, 177.
Klawans H. L. and Garvin J. S. (1969) *Dis. Nerv. Syst.* **30**, 737.
Klawans H. L., Goetz C. (1977). *Adv. Exp. Med. Biol.* **90**, 21.
Krasner N. and Cornelius J. M. (1970). *Br. Med. J.* **2**, 496.
Lees A. J., Haddad S. et al. (1978) *Arch. Neurol.* **35**, 503.
Lieberman A., Dziatolowski M. et al. (1978). *Ann. Neurol.* **6**, 355.
Lieberman A. N., Kupersmith M. et al. (1979) *Neurology* **29**, 363.
Lieberman A., Liebowitz M. et al. (1980) *Neurology* **30**, 366.
Lloyd K. and Hornykiewicz O. (1972) *J. Neurochem.* **19**, 1544.
Loranger A. W., Goodell H. et al. (1972a) *Arch. Gen. Psychiatry* **26**, 163.
Loranger A. W., Goodell H. et al. (1972b) *Brain* **95**, 405.
McGeer P. L. and McGeer E. G. (1978) *Adv. Exp. Med. Biol.* **113**, 41.
Maier M. J. and Martin W. E. (1970) *JAMA* **213**, 465.
Marsden C. D. and Parkes J. D. (1976) *Lancet* **1**, 292.
Marsden C. D. and Parkes J. D. (1977) *Lancet* **1**, 345.
Marttila R. J. and Rinne U. K. (1979) *Acta Neurol. Scand.* **59**, 80.
Mawdsley C. (1970). *Br. Med. J.* **1**, 331.
Mearrick P. T., Wade D. N. et al. (1974) *Aust. N.Z. J. Med.* **4**, 144.
Mones R. J., Elizan T. S. and Siegal G. J. (1970) *N.Y. State J. Med.* **70**, 2309.
Muenter M. D., Sharpless N. S. et al. (1977) *Mayo Clin. Proc.* **52**, 163.
Nobrega F. T., Glattre E. et al. (1976). In: *Excerpta Medica International Congress Series No. 175.* p. 474.
Papavasiliou P. S., McDowell F. H. et al. (1979) *Neurology* **29**, 194.
Parkes J. D., Marsden C. D. et al. (1974) *Q. J. Med.* **53**, 19.
Pearce I. and Pearce J. (1978) *Br. Med. J.* **1**, 1402.

Pearce J. (1974a) *Eur. Neurol.* **12**, 94.
Pearce J. (1974b) *Br. Med. J.* **1**, 445.
Pearce J. M. S. (1978) *Br. Med. J.* **2**, 1664.
Peaston M. J. T. and Bianchine J. R. (1970) *Br. Med. J.* **1**, 400.
Pinder R. M., Brogden R. N. et al. (1976) *Drugs* **11**, 329.
Rinne U. K. (1978) *Acta Neurol. Scand.* **57** (Suppl. 67) 77.
Rivera-Calimlim L., Dujoune C. A. et al. (1970a) *Pharmacologist* **12**, 269.
Rivera-Calimlim L., Dujoune C. A. et al. (1970b) *Br. Med. J.* **4**, 93.
Rivera-Calimlim L., Tandon D. et al. (1977) *Arch. Neurol.* **34**, 228.
Sacks O. W., Kohl M. S. et al. (1972) *Neurology* **22**, 516.
Sacks O. W., Messeloff C. et al. (1970) *Lancet* **1**, 1231.
Selby G. (1968) In: Vinken P. J. and Bruyn G. W. (ed.) *Handbook of Clinical Neurology* Vol. 6. Amsterdam, North Holland Publishing Co., p. 173.
Shoulson I., Glaubiger G. A. and Chase T. N. (1975). *Neurology* **25**, 1144.
Stellar S., Mandell S. et al. (1970) *J. Neurosurg.* **32**, 275.
Sutcliffe R. L. G. (1973) *Age Ageing* **2**, 34.
Sweet R. D. and McDowell F. H. (1975) *Ann. Intern. Med.* **83**, 456.
Sweet R. D., McDowell F. H. et al. (1976) *Neurology* **26**, 305.
Vignalou J. and Beck H. (1973) *Gerontol. Clin.* **15**, 50.
Wade D. N., Mearrick P. T. and Morris J. L. (1973) *Nature* **242**, 463.
White P., Goodhardt M. J. et al. (1977) *Lancet* **1**, 668.

11. DISORDERS OF BALANCE
B. Isaacs

THE CONCEPT OF BALANCE

All that can be said with confidence about balance in old people is that many of them have lost it.

The term 'loss of balance' is employed in two different senses: first to describe a single fall in a well person not otherwise explained by a trip, slip or faint; and second to describe recurrent falls in a disabled person who cannot maintain an upright posture unsupported. In neither case is it clear what is lost when balance is lost, and whether what is lost can be regained. These questions are discussed in this chapter.

WHAT IS BALANCE?

Balance is the set of functions which maintains man upright during stance and locomotion by detecting and correcting displacements of the line of gravity beyond the support base.

The centre of mass of the human body lies in the neighbourhood of the second sacral vertebra, although its exact position varies with the relative positions of the body segments. For a rigid object, such as a manikin, stability would require that the vertical line through the centre of mass should always fall within the support base. However, the human body in movement is composed of many segments which are in constantly changing relationship to one another and which are supported on a small shifting base. The maintenance of stability during movement is achieved only if the sum of the ground reaction forces on the support base is equal and opposite to the algebraic sum of the dynamic forces generated by the muscles (Eberhardt, 1976). All willed movements of the body, such as rising from a chair or walking, which involve rapid and repeated alterations in the relation of the body segments to one another and in the ground forces, are kept under continuous surveillance so that the required adjustments of muscle tension are made with speed and accuracy (Murray et al., 1967). The 'balance mechanism' is the sum of the neurological activities which control self-initiated displacements of the body.

This would be sufficient in a predictable environment. But human locomotion is conducted at a range of speeds, over a variety of surfaces,

at various levels of illumination, through many expected and unexpected obstacles, and the 'balance mechanism' has to take account of
all these circumstances. Unexpected displacements may be imposed on
those which have been initiated, requiring rapid modification of the
planned activity. The success of human balance in an extraordinary
range of conditions argues for the presence of rapid, precise mechanisms capable of detecting displacement and of selectively adjusting
muscle tension.

THE COMPONENTS OF THE BALANCE MECHANISM

Balance comprises:

1. *Afferent mechanisms* which detect displacement;
2. *Central mechanisms* which receive and integrate the inflow and
issue corrective instructions; and
3. *Efferent mechanisms* which transmit the instructions for execution
by muscles.

A summary of the main mechanisms involved is given in *Table* 11.1.
A certain amount is known about how these mechanisms operate in
healthy young people, although there is virtually no information on
their integration (Welford, 1974). Something is also known about

Table 11.1. Mechanisms involved in balance

Afferent
Vision
Vestibular
          semicircular canals
          otoliths
Proprioception
          neck   ⎫   ⎧ joint capsule mechanoreceptors
          trunk   ⎬ involving ⎨ Golgi tendon organs
          lower limbs ⎭   ⎩ muscle spindles
Touch and pressure   soles of feet
Physical transients   foot, ankle, knee
                   hip, pelvis, spine

Central
Myotatic stretch relexes   ⎫   ⎧ spinal cord
'Long loop' responses   ⎬ involving ⎨ brain stem
'Pre-programmed' responses   ⎬   ⎨ cerebellum
Voluntary command   ⎭   thalamus
                                basal ganglia
                                midbrain nuclei
                                sensorimotor cortex
                              ⎩ and their connections

Efferent
Betz cell outflow to antigravity muscles
Other pyramidal outflow
Spinal motoneurone pool
Motor units
Muscle fibres

failure of these mechanisms in disease. However, there is only very scanty information about disturbances of balance in old people who fall.

Afferent Mechanisms

Vision

While vision and vestibular function participate in balance (Dornan et al., 1978), neither is critical to its successful maintenance (Cody and Nelson, 1978). When visual stimuli conflict with information from other sources, balance judgements are based correctly on the proprioceptive inflow (Cody and Nelson, 1978). Reduction of proprioception, as in the amputee, leads to increased dependence on vision. In tracking experiments, where stability is not at risk, vision tends to predominate over proprioception (Klein and Posner, 1974). The interdependence of the two systems is complex (Bles et al., 1977) and old people in whom both systems may fail concurrently doubtless show variable patterns. In old age falls may result from a conflict between visual and proprioceptive or vestibular information.

Vestibular Function

The vestibules signal linear and angular acceleration of the head, and their inflow contributes to balance. Labyrinthine function is impaired in old age (Bruner and Norris, 1971; van der Laan and Oosterveld, 1974). In ordinary circumstances normal balance is consistent with loss of labyrinthine function (Martin, 1967)—a striking instance of the redundancy of afferent information.

Proprioception

The mechanorecptors of the spinal joints of the neck are probably even more important in conveying information about the position and movement of the head in space than are the vestibules (Wyke, 1979). Disease of the neck joints with loss of the mechanoreceptors is common in old age and is a possible source of 'loss of balance'. 'Vertigo' is often described in association with cervical spondylosis, and is said to be sometimes relieved by cervical decompression (Mangat and McDowell, 1973). Anaesthesia of cervical joints causes ataxia in normal volunteers but no impairment of kinaesthesia (de Jong et al., 1977). However, cervical spondylosis is an almost universal finding in old people; and no study has been made of the relation of pathological changes in the mechanoreceptors to disturbances of balance. Stabilization of the neck by a cervical collar has not been conclusively shown to benefit balance disturbances.

Afferent discharges from muscle spindles and tendon organs (Houk et al., 1980; Rymer and D'Almeida, 1980), provide knowledge of the current state of the muscles, as a background against which changes in muscle tension are made.

Central Mechanisms

Until recently the main central mechanisms of balance were thought of as the stretch reflexes and the righting reflexes.

Stretch reflexes are rapid and are believed to follow a monosynaptic pathway (Melvill Jones and Watt, 1971a; Burke et al., 1980). But these remain at the segmental level from which they originate and make only a limited contribution to stabilization (Burke and Eklund, 1977). Their abolition by regional anaesthesia does not affect postural responses (Traub et al., 1980).

Righting reflexes originate in the vestibular system. They control head turning and reflex eye movements. Their contribution to correction of the whole body during displacement is incompletely understood.

In the past decade knowledge of balance mechanisms has been extended by experiments in which displacing forces are applied to the body and electromyographic responses are detected in distant muscles. The experimental conditions allow precise control of the postural set and of the displacing force, and accurate timing of the electromyographic response. The repetition of these tests in different conditions (e.g. in the absence of vision or in subjects with known neurological lesions) gives further information about the possible pathways involved.

Experiments of this type have demonstrated the existence of a number of 'long loop' reflexes or responses (Grimm and Nashner, 1978) whose latency exceeds that of the stretch reflex but is less than that of a voluntary response to displacement. These 'long loop' reflexes have a 'servo' function, that is they tend to restore conditions to those which existed before the displacement. 'Long loops' are deployed in the execution and control of gait, posture, load-compensation to unexpected disturbances, oculovestibular reflexes and voluntary movements. They thus might be the functional units of which the balance mechanism is built; and it is from study of their disorders that better understanding of failing balance in old age may come. An analysis of the disturbance of these 'long loops' in patients with cerebellar disorders is given by Nashner and Grimm (1978).

A response whose latency lies between that of the stretch reflex and of voluntary movement which has been extensively studied is the response of the supporting muscles of the lower limbs and trunk to a sudden unexpected change in tension in the arm (Marsden et al.,

1976a, b, 1978). This response truly anticipates the effects of load changes and tends to minimize them. The anticipatory postural response was normal in 2 patients with cerebellar ataxia; but there was no clear-cut relationship between its presence and the clinical state of balance in a number of patients with Parkinson's disease and persistent postural instability. Nashner (1976) described a patient with cerebellar ataxia in whom a rather similar 'long loop' reflex, which he called the 'functional stretch response', was absent; his subject showed inappropriate responses to displacement. In the presence of vestibular lesions, Bussel et al. (1980) found that the response was reduced but not abolished; and concluded that the detection of displacement alone did not determine the response, but that some mechanism existed for integrating this with the postural demands on the body at the time. While these studies may well have uncovered a mechanism of great importance in the detection and response to unexpected displacements, Traub et al. (1980) warn that the responses to small displacements demonstrated in the experiments may not be the same as those required to maintain balance during large shifts of body position.

Experiments on Free Fall etc.

A different approach to the uncovering of balance responses has been studies of the events which follow stepping up and down and falling. The best known and most dramatic were those of Greenwood and Hopkins (1976a, b, 1980) who suspended volunteers above the ground by a parachute harness connected to a solenoid. EMG electrodes were attached over various muscles and the subjects were then allowed to fall with eyes open or closed and over various distances with and without knowledge of the height from which they were to be dropped. They demonstrated an initial 'startle' response involving electrical activation of all the muscles of the body and dependent on vestibular stimulation; and a later response of the leg extensors which was dependent on knowledge of the height of the fall and was evidently related to preparation for landing. Less dramatic experiments on stepping and hopping confirmed the existence of a pre-programmed pattern of leg extension designed to facilitate ground contact and dependent on adequate warning (Greenwood and Hopkins, 1976a, b, 1980). Melvill Jones and Watt (1971a, b) explained the jolt which results from short unexpected downward steps as being due to lack of time to bring this response into operation.

Nashner (1977) stood his subjects on a platform which he was able to rotate, and demonstrated a pre-programmed response among related leg and trunk muscles. By varying the conditions he was able to show that subjects differed in whether they used information from vision, vestibules or afferent muscles as a basis for modifying the programme as a result of learning. Spinal reflexes are also involved in corrections after this type of displacement. Burke and Eklund (1977) stressed the importance of the alpha-gamma linkages, while Gottlieb and Agarwal (1979) noted that the myotatic reflex was also involved.

Summary of Central Mechanisms

In experimental conditions both short and long loop mechanisms of various types contribute to stabilization after trunk displacement. Visual, vestibular and proprioceptive contributions interact unpredictably. Pre-programmed patterns of movement are available to deal with expected situations and these can be modified and updated in the light of continuing experience. In the infinitely more complex circumstances of real life, such factors as attention and experience colour the responses. Several workers believe that transcortical pathways are involved in these 'long loop' reflexes, which are abolished by lesions of the sensorimotor cortex; but as Hultborn and Wigström (1980) point out, this does not necessarily mean that the pathways are themselves traversed by these reflexes. The latency suggests that as many as 70 neurones may be involved in any one response.

Efferent Mechanisms

The efferent pathway consists of the cells of the motor cortex and their monosynaptic outflow to the spinal motor neurones; the peripheral motor nerves and their neuromuscular junctions; and the muscles themselves.

The spinal motor neurone pool is no mere assembly of relay stations; but it is acted upon by segmental and suprasegmental influences which modify its output (Phillips, 1978). Muscle strength diminishes with age, endurance of contractions is prolonged and co-ordination diminishes (Aviansson et al , 1978). These functional changes are accompanied by loss of muscle cells and diminution of the proportion of small type 2b fibres in the muscle (Kakulas and Mastaglia, 1966; Serratrice et al., 1968). Not only do these changes weaken the efferent activity of the muscles; but they diminish the contribution of muscle afferents to the subjective awareness of joint position and movement (Houk et al., 1980; Matthews, 1980).

BALANCE IN OLD AGE

The frequency of falls in old age provides stark but indirect evidence of disturbance of the balance mechanism (Gryfe et al., 1977; Brocklehurst et al., 1978; Evans et al., 1979; Wild et al., 1980). Falls are particularly common beyond the age of 75 and are commoner in females than in males, for reasons which are not understood. Walking has been defined as 'a series of catastrophes narrowly averted' (Rasch and Burke, 1978); and it is not surprising that a high proportion of falls in old age occur during quiet walking (Wild et al., 1980). Falls represent failure to detect and correct displacement. Many falls occur during displacements of ordinary intensity which are initiated by the subject himself, e.g. on rising from a chair or during walking; and suggest a grave disturbance of the balance mechanism. Other falls, such as those which result from encounter with a hazard, imply failure to correct an unexpected displacement imposed upon the subject, as distinct from one which he himself has initiated. This suggests a less severe but still abnormal loss of responsiveness. Falls which occur in the absence of circulatory causes therefore give a clue to the severity of the underlying disturbance according as to whether the displacement was of ordinary or extraordinary intensity and whether it was imposed or initiated by the subject.

The complex investigations which have revealed the 'long loop' and similar mechanisms have not as yet been conducted on subjects in the age group 75 and over who are at most risk of falling; and such studies are eagerly awaited. Spontaneous sway during quiet standing has, however, been frequently observed since its first description by Dr Mitchell of Philadelphia (Hinsdale, 1887). The frequency of sway reflects the constant fine adjustment of postural muscles (Soames et al., 1976) and is said to be controlled by a 'discontinuous interrogation of the degree of stretch in the neuromuscular fibres' (Bonnet et al., 1976). The swaying movements are induced by displacement of the centre of mass, and may employ 'long loop' pathways (Ligvinses, 1973). Sway is increased in the very old (Sheldon, 1963; Murray et al., 1975; Hasselkus and Shambes, 1975; Black et al., 1977). Sway was not significantly increased in old people who fell as a result of imposed displacements; but was greater in those whose falls were attributed to initiated displacements (Overstall et al., 1977). Sway was also increased in those with brain injuries (Seliktar et al., 1978).

Guimaraes and Isaacs (1980) sought indirect evidence of balance disorder by studying the variability in length of successive steps during quiet walking. Old people admitted to hospital after suffering a fall had greatly increased variability of stepping.

PATHOGENESIS OF BALANCE DISORDERS

The structures which participate in the balance responses are notoriously susceptible to age-related changes. Particularly striking is the loss of dendrites from the Betz cells of the motor cortex which relay by monosynaptic pathways to the spinal motor neurones innervating the anti-gravity muscles (Scheibel, 1979). Smaller pyramidal cells and spinal motor neurones undergo similar but less drastic age-related changes. Unfortunately, no studies relate these pathological findings to functional disturbances observed in life; but Scheibel speculated that the observed changes might cause decreasing ability to relax anti-gravity tone across weight-bearing joints prior to patterned motor activity, deterioration in precision and strength, and increased fatigua-bility. These are all possible accompaniments of difficulty in main-taining balance during locomotion.

In the presence of damage to the neuronal circuitry of the balance mechanism and of altered physical properties of muscles, ligaments and joints, the complex movements of locomotion and change of posture might be subject to random cumulative error. During walking, foot placement might deviate from the intended position; and the resulting difference between the planned and the achieved position of the centre of mass of the body might not be detected. This in turn might result in a subsequent step being more inaccurate than the first; and so on. The resulting gait pattern would be irregular and unpredictable; and an unexpected fall might result. The findings of Guimaraes and Isaacs (1980) on the gait of old people who have fallen are consistent with this hypothesis.

CIRCULATORY MECHANISMS

This review has concentrated on neuromuscular mechanisms of im-paired balance, but it is widely held by clinicians that circulatory factors are often responsible. Transient reduction of cardiac output, by reducing the oxygen supply to critical areas of the brain or spinal cord, might retard or arrest neuronal traffic for a sufficient time for tone to be lost in the anti-gravity muscles and for a fall to result without loss of consciousness. Proposed mechanisms include: postural hypotension; vertebral basilar ischaemia; and cardiac dysrhythmia. Direct evidence is difficult to obtain since this necessitates measurement at the time of the fall.

Postural Hypotension

Blood pressure undoubtedly falls in many people on change of posture (Johnson et al., 1965; Caird et al., 1973; Wild et al., 1980). This is not necessarily associated with a fall. The very act of changing posture creates circumstances in which susceptible persons are at risk of falling. Substantial drops in the blood pressure were registered by intra-arterial traces in elderly patients who had previously fallen but without any symptoms occurring (Rowlands, 1982). It may therefore be the case that postural hypotension is over-diagnosed as a cause of falls. However, it is likely that this mechanism is responsible for some falls; and Wild et al. (1980) found that old people taking hypotensive drugs were over-represented amongst those who fell on change of position.

Vertebro-basilar Ischaemia

The account of a 'dizzy' attack or a fall on head turning does not of itself implicate the vertebral artery; since this manoeuvre causes stimulation of the sensitive neck mechanoreceptors and of the semicircular canals. Direct evidence of vertebrobasilar occlusion is difficult to obtain; and this might be thought more likely to cause transient ischaemic attacks rather than symptomless falls.

Cardiac Dysrhythmia

Severe disturbances of heart rhythm cause Stokes–Adams attacks; and shorter bursts may be associated with transient ischaemic attacks (Luxon et al., 1980). Less serious rhythm disturbances are extremely common; and a convincing association with falls or even with dizzy attacks does not seem to have been established (Clee et al., 1979; Camm et al., 1980).

Cardiovascular disturbances are probably not a common cause of isolated falls in old age and are not associated with permanent disturbances of the balance mechanisms.

REHABILITATION

Rehabilitation of balance on neurophysiological principles is not yet established. Little heed is paid to the statement of Rasch and Burke (1978) that 'a highly developed awareness of the occurrence of unbalancing movements is essential to expert performance'. The popular four-legged walking frame perpetuates an unphysiological concept. It deprives the nervous system of its normal sensory input and turns the faller into a hexapod, replacing the proprioceptive information from the subject's legs with that obtained through the legs of the frame. The result is a grotesque start-stop travesty of normal gait. Patients become addicted to this apparently safe mode of progression, but are highly vulnerable when they are parted from their frame.

In approaching the patient, Grimm and Nashner (1978) advocated asking 'What's wrong with the programme?' By describing an individual's difficulties as a specific disorder of movement control commensurate with perceived dysfunction they believe that the possibility of future therapy would become more clear. It is hoped that clinicians and physiotherapists will accept the challenge.

CONCLUSION

The maintenance of the upright position through the wide range of human movements requires an infinitely complex array of control mechanisms. Ageing man compensates for his decreasing skill by restricting the more extreme encounters with his environment. Advanced old age is accompanied by an enhanced probability of falling even in quiet domestic surroundings. This argues major disruption of the elements of balance. Recent studies, however, show a high degree of redundancy and hold out the possibility that, even with advanced structural change, relatively intact elements of the mechanism may remain functionally efficient and enable balance to be effective and safe.

REFERENCES

Aviansson A., Grimby G. et al. (1978) *Scand. J. Rehabil. Med. (Suppl.)* **6**, 43.
Black F. O., O'Leary D. P. et al. (1977) *Trans. Am. Acad. Ophthalmol. Otolaryngol.* **84**, 549.
Bles W., Kapteyn T. S. and de Wit G. (1977) *Adv. Otorhinolaryngol.* **22**, 111.
Bonnet M., Gurfinkel S. et al. (1976) *Aggressologie* **17b**, 35.
Brocklehurst J. C., Exton-Smith A. N. et al. (1978) *Age Ageing* **7**, 7.
Bruner A. and Norris T. W. (1971) *Acta Otolaryngol.* [*Suppl.*] (*Stockh*) 282.
Burke D. and Eklund G. (1977) *Acta Physiol. Scand.* **100**, 187.
Burke D., Hagbarth K. E. et al. (1980) *Prog. Clin. Neurophysiol.* **8**, 243.
Bussel B., Katz R. et al. (1980) *Prog. Clin. Neurophysiol.* **8**, 310.
Caird F. I., Andrews G. R. and Kennedy R. D. (1973) *Br. Heart J.* **35**, 527.
Camm A. J., Evans K. E. et al. (1980) *Am. Heart J.* **99**, 598.
Clee M. D., Smith N. et al. (1979) *Age Ageing* **8**, 173.
Cody K. A. and Nelson A. J. (1978) *Phys. Ther.* **58**, 35.
Dornan J., Fernie C. R. and Holliday P. J. (1978) *Arch. Phys. Med. Rehabil.* **59**, 586.
Eberhardt H. P. (1976) In: Herman R. M., Grillner S. et al. (ed.) *Neural Control of Locomotion.* New York, Plenum Press.
Evans J. G., Prudham D. and Wandless I. (1979) *Public Health* **93**, 235.
Gottlieb G. L. and Agarwal G. C. (1979) *J. Neurophysiol.* **42**, 91.
Greenwood R. J. and Hopkins A. P. (1976a) *J. Physiol. (Lond.)* **254**, 507.
Greenwood R. J. and Hopkins A. P. (1976b) *Brain* **99**, 375.
Greenwood R. and Hopkins A. (1980) *Prog. Clin. Neurophysiol.* **8**, 294.
Grimm R. J. and Nashner L. M. (1978) *Prog. Clin. Neurophysiol.* **4**, 70.
Gryfe C. I., Amies A. and Ashley M. J. (1977) *Age Ageing* **6**, 201.
Guimaraes I. M. and Isaacs B. (1980) *Int. J. Rehabil.* **2**, 177.
Hasselkus B. R. and Shambes G. M. (1975) *J. Gerontol.* **30**, 661.
Hinsdale G. (1887) *Am. J. Med. Sci.* **93**, 478.
Houk J. C., Crago P. O. and Rymer W. Z. (1980) *Prog. Clin. Neurophysiol.* **8**, 33.
Hultborn H. and Wigström H. (1980) *Prog. Clin. Neurophysiol.* **8**, 99.
Johnson R. H., Smith A. C. et al. (1965) *Lancet* **1**, 731.
De Jong P. T. V. M., De Jong J. M. B. V. et al. (1977) *Ann. Neurol.* **1**, 240.
Kakulas B. A. and Mastaglia F. L. (1966) *Proc. Aust. Assoc. Neurol.* **4**, 35.
Klein R. M. and Posner M. I. (1974) *Brain Res.* **71**, 401.
Van der Laan F. L. and Oosterveld W. J. (1974) *Aerosp. Med.* **45**, 540.
Ligvinses A. I. (1973) *Aggressologie* **14B**, 17.
Luxon L. M., Crowther A. et al. (1980) *J. Neurol. Neurosurg. Psychiatry* **43**, 37.
Mangat K. S. and McDowall G. D. (1973) *J. Laryngol. Otol.* **87**, 555.
Marsden C. D., Merton P. A. and Morton H. B. (1976a) *J. Physiol.* **257**, 1.
Marsden C. D., Merton P. A. and Morton W. B. (1976b) *J. Physiol.* **259**, 531.
Marsden C. D., Merton P. A. and Morton H. B. (1978) *J. Physiol.* **275**, 47.
Martin J. P. (1967) In: De Reuck A. V. S. and Knight J. (ed.) *Myotatic, Kinaesthetic and Vestibular Mechanisms.* London, Churchill. p. 92.

Matthews P. B. C. (1980) *Prog. Clin. Neurophysiol.* **8**, 12.
Melvill Jones G. and Watt D. G. D. (1971a) *J. Physiol.* **219**, 709.
Melvill Jones G. and Watt D. G. D. (1971b) *J. Physiol.* **219**, 727.
Murray M. P., Seireg A. and Scholz R. C. (1967) *J. Appl. Physiol.* **23**, 831.
Murray M. P., Seireg A. and Sepic S. B. (1975). *J. Bone Joint Surg.* **57A**, 510.
Nashner L. M., (1976) *Exp. Brain Res.* **26**, 59.
Nashner L. M. (1977) *Exp. Brain Res.* **30**, 13.
Nashner L. M. and Grimm R. J. (1978) *Prog. Clin. Neurophysiol.* **4**, 300.
Overstall P. W., Exton-Smith A. N. et al. (1977) *Br. Med. J.* **1**, 261.
Phillips C. G. (1978) *Prog. Clin. Neurophysiol.* **4**, 1.
Rasch P. J. and Burke R. K. (1978) (ed.) *Kinesiology and Applied Anatomy: the Source of Human Movement.* Philadelphia, Lea & Febiger.
Rowlands D. (1982) Communication to British Geriatrics Society (to be published).
Rymer W. Z. and D'Almeida A. (1980) *Brain* **103**, 1.
Scheibel A. B. (1979) In: Ordy J. M. and Brizzee K. R. (ed.) *Sensory Systems and Communication in the Elderly.* New York, Raven Press. p. 297.
Seliktar R., Susak Z. et al. (1978) *Scand. J. Rehabil. Med.* **10**, 59.
Serratrice G., Roux H. and Aquaron R. (1968) *J. Neurol. Sci.* **7**, 275.
Sheldon J. H. (1963) *Geront. Clin.* **5**, 129.
Soames R. W., Atha J. and Harding R. H. (1976) *Aggressologie* **17B**, 15.
Traub M. M., Rothwell J. C. and Marsden C. D. (1980) *Brain* **103**, 393.
Welford A. T. (1974) *Brain Res.* **71**, 381.
Wild D., Nayak U. S. L. and Isaacs B. (1980) Report to the DHSS.
Wyke B. (1979) *Age Ageing* **8**, 251.

12. EPILEPSY
Marion Hildick-Smith

DEFINITION AND CLASSIFICATION OF SEIZURES

An epileptic seizure occurs as a result of an abnormal paroxysmal discharge of cerebral neurones. The extent and the location of the discharging neurones determine the type and extent of the seizure. Generalized seizures arise more or less symmetrically with no evidence of focal onset, whereas partial seizures start by activation of a group of neurones limited to part of a single hemisphere.

The classification of epileptic seizures was considered in detail in 1969 by the Commission of the International League Against Epilepsy, and its suggestions were later adopted by the World Health Organization. Unfortunately, the resultant classification was far too cumbersome for everyday use, and the League is now reconsidering the matter, but has not yet published its views. It is believed that the classification will be similar to the one detailed below:

A. Generalized seizures (22 per cent of classifiable adult seizures, according to Gastaut et al. (1975))
  —absence attacks (petit mal)
  —myoclonic attacks
  —tonic-clonic (grand mal)
  —tonic
  —akinetic

B. Partial seizures (75 per cent of classifiable adult seizures, half of these arising in the temporal lobes)
  —simple without impairment of consciousness (including Jacksonian, temporal lobe and psychomotor attacks)
  —complex, with impairment of consciousness
  —secondarily generalized (leading to grand mal)
  —generalized but with EEG focus

C. Unclassifiable (these may account for 18 per cent of all seizures)

It is difficult to be certain where epilepsy of the elderly fits into this classification since the question of epilepsy of very late onset has excited little interest until the last decade. Previously late-onset epilepsy had often been taken to refer to epilepsy starting after the age of 20 or so (Berlin, 1953; Livingston, 1956) and in 1974 the number of papers dealing with epilepsy starting after the age of 60 was limited to seven (Fine, 1966; Carney et al., 1969; Feuerstein et al., 1970; Bancaud, 1970; Bonduelle et al., 1970; Courjon et al., 1970; Vercellato and Delobel, 1970). Six of these papers based their observations on patients referred to neurosurgical units who were likely to be relatively fit. Hildick-Smith (1974) studied 50 patients with epilepsy starting after the age of 60 among new patients admitted to a geriatric unit. These were a relatively ill and disabled group, of whom 56 per cent had grand mal, 24 per cent had focal attacks, and 14 per cent had both. In a later study by neurologists (Schold et al., 1977) of 50 elderly epileptics living at home, 56 per cent had focal (partial) motor seizures, and in 44 per cent the seizures were generalized.

The variation in selection among the groups of elderly epileptics studied makes all aspects of comparison difficult, but there does seem some agreement that grand mal (among the generalized attacks) and all variants of the partial attacks occur in the elderly. Other types of seizures, such as petit mal, are almost unknown in the old. The temptation to call a partial seizure, especially the relatively common temporal lobe attack, a 'minor' fit or 'small' fit should be avoided because of the danger of confusion with petit mal which is rare in the old and requires quite different drugs in its treatment.

Annual incidence rates of epilepsy (discussed elsewhere in this volume (p. 13)) vary from 30 per 100 000 population in Carlisle (Brewis et al., 1966) to 73 per 100 000 in South-East England (Pond et al., 1960), while Hauser and Kurland (1975) give a figure of 48·7 per 100 000 for Rochester (Minn) after a careful study over 33 years in association with the Mayo Clinic. Their study is probably the most reliable, and gives a prevalence rate of 5·7 per 1000 over the whole population, and 10·2 per 1000 for those over 60. They also confirm the importance of partial seizures in the elderly.

CAUSES OF EPILEPSY IN THE OLD (*Table* 12.1)

Searching for a removable cerebral lesion may be very important in younger patients, but its importance in the elderly has been overstated. It may not be possible to determine the cause at all in up to 50 per cent of those with late onset epilepsy (Schold et al., 1977) and the success rate in finding a cause has not seemed to improve greatly when more sophisticated investigations have been employed (Carney et al., 1969; Bancaud, 1970). However, if CT scanning, with its greater diagnostic

Table 12.1. Causes of epilepsy in the elderly

1. Vascular, especially post-hemiplegic
2. Associated with dementia (primary neuronal or 'multi-infarct')
3. Cerebral tumours
   Secondary, especially bronchus, breast
   Primary
4. Metabolic e.g.
   Renal failure
   Hypoglycaemia
   Hyperventilation
   Hypocalcaemia
5. Idiopathic
   Recurrence of childhood epilepsy
6. Cardiac
   Arrhythmias, especially Stokes–Adams attacks
7. Trauma
8. Drug
   Overdosage, e.g. of tricyclic antidepressants
   Interactions
   Withdrawal, e.g. alcohol
9. Unknown causes

specificity, becomes more readily available, this situation may change.

Until recently some neurologists affirmed that 'cerebrovascular disease, either focal or general, only occasionally causes epilepsy' (Gibberd, 1973)—and this view may reflect the fact that they do not see many patients of advanced age. Later neurologists (Schold et al., 1977) give cerebrovascular disease as the cause of epilepsy in 30 per cent of those aged 70 or more. Hauser and Kurland (1975) found cerebral thrombosis or haemorrhage a frequent cause of epilepsy among those aged 70 or more; and 21 out of 50 of Hildick-Smith's (1974) cases had their epilepsy following hemiplegias or other cerebrovascular episodes. As hemiplegias are common in the old, and some 5 per cent (Marquardsen, 1969) or 8 per cent (Webster et al., 1956) of hemiplegics go on to develop epilepsy, it would be surprising if hemiplegia were not a frequent condition predisposing to epilepsy in the elderly.

Fits in association with slow-onset dementia are likely to present an increasingly common diagnostic problem as the population ages. The value of the CT scan in this situation in showing cerebral atrophy or, for example, in excluding an olfactory groove meningioma, will be increasingly apparent in the future.

Most tumours found as the cause of epilepsy over the age of 60 are malignant, only one series containing any number of benign tumours (Bonduelle et al., 1970). Over the age of 70 tumours become increasingly rare as a cause of fits (Carney et al., 1969). Although McKeown (1965) found 14 meningiomas out of the 21 primary cerebral tumours in 1500 post-mortem examinations of elderly people, 11 of these had been silent lesions and had not revealed their presence by causing fits. Thus the indications for investigation of elderly epileptics to discover a primary intracranial tumour are not very strong. Now that we have the non-invasive CT scan, patients with focal signs whose health would justify craniotomy ought however to be investigated. A number of metabolic and drug causes of epilepsy (*see Table* 12.1) are included in various series, as are occasional cardiac causes, making it important that all aspects of the patients' health, metabolism and medication be considered when epilepsy occurs for the first time in old age.

DIAGNOSIS OF SEIZURES IN THE ELDERLY (*Table* 12.2)

As in the younger age groups it is vital to obtain a clear history of epileptic attacks, and if possible to confirm the story from a reliable witness. The elderly patient may be frightened and confused and may be accompanied by an equally anxious and elderly relative. Alternatively, the fit may have occurred in an old person living alone. It is important to ask direct questions about any warning symptoms, about

Table 12.2. Differential diagnosis of 'turns'

A. *With impairment of consciousness*
   Postural
      Syncope, including cough, micturition
      Postural hypotension
   Non-postural
      Epilepsy
      Transient ischaemic attacks
      Cardiogenic, e.g. Stokes–Adams, carotid sinus attacks
      Spontaneous hypoglycaemia
      Migraine
      Psychogenic
B. *Without impairment of consciousness*
   Drop attacks
   Vertebrobasilar insufficiency

a focal onset, about impairment or loss of consciousness, incontinence and later muddled thinking. Any residual symptoms, such as temporary paralysis, may point to a transient ischaemic attack (though Todd's paralysis after an epileptic seizure is a confusing alternative). In a syncopal attack there is a more gradual onset, with pallor and sweating, and without confusion on recovery of consciousness. Apparently obvious predisposing situations (as in cough or micturition syncope) may not be mentioned unless direct questions are asked. It is also important to ask whether the 'turns' are precipitated by a sudden change of posture—suggesting postural hypotension which may occur in 14 per cent of old people (Exton-Smith, 1977) or by palpitations, suggestive of significant arrhythmia. Turns accompanied by sinking sensations and sweating may suggest spontaneous hypoglycaemia. Drop attacks, which may occur in as many as 3·5 per cent of adult women (Stevens and Matthews, 1973), do not lead to impairment of consciousness, and the patient can usually get up again immediately, although some patients experience difficulty in rising until their feet can be put in contact with the floor or a wall. Attacks due to vertebrobasilar insufficiency (perhaps overdiagnosed in the past) may occur when the head is extended.

Another aspect of history-taking which may be important is to note any drugs currently being taken, or recently withdrawn. Tricyclic antidepressants, steroids, etc. may provoke seizures, while rapid alcohol withdrawal will have the same effect.

It is often difficult to be sure, even after careful questioning of patient and relative, whether attacks are epileptic or not. In the elderly, as with younger patients, the majority of epileptics presenting between attacks will show no neurological abnormality on physical examination. The position is further complicated in the elderly by the likelihood of coexistent pathology. Is the minor arrhythmia or the aortic systolic murmur, for example, an irrelevant finding or vital to the diagnosis? The 'norms' of neurological examination in the elderly are not yet well-established. In 100 non-neurological patients in a geriatric ward, the fundus could be seen clearly in only 44 patients, 34 had irregular pupils and 3 had equivocal plantars (Prakash and Stern, 1973). In another study Carney et al. (1969) found papilloedema in only 3 out of 20 elderly patients with cerebral tumours. Thus the interpretation of the physical signs may be difficult.

Despite these difficulties a well-documented neurological examination will be useful as a baseline for future testing, while examination of the blood pressure lying and standing, careful checking for aortic stenosis or arrhythmia and examination of chest and breasts for neoplasm should not be omitted.

EXTENT OF INVESTIGATION IN THE ELDERLY

Potentially helpful tests include estimation of haemoglobin, white cell count, ESR, urea, creatinine, electrolytes and glucose. A VDRL test may be indicated and a chest radiograph will help to exclude a neoplasm.

A carefully-positioned skull radiograph can show pineal shift or perhaps localized calcification or erosion of the skull vault. The dorsum sellae may be poorly calcified in old age, and may misleadingly suggest raised intracranial pressure.

A single electrocardiogram may give an equivocal result, and it may be necessary to embark on long-term monitoring (Schott et al., 1977), while the patient goes about his normal activities, to see whether the attacks of arrhythmia coincide with the 'turns'.

A low serum calcium (after correcting to a serum albumin level of 40 g/l) may be associated with the fits, and could be due to renal impairment, osteomalacia, chronic diarrhoea, etc. Rarely (Graham et al., 1979) idiopathic hypoparathyroidism can be the cause, in which case the fits may respond to 1α-hydroxycholecalciferol, together with daily calcium supplements.

THE PLACE OF THE EEG AND CT SCAN IN DIAGNOSIS

In the majority of hospitals, without easy access to CT scanning, the next step in diagnosis of epilepsy is usually by electroencephalography, though some neurologists (Hopkins and Scambler, 1977) feel that this is often done unnecessarily.

An EEG record will require careful interpretation in the elderly. In a study of 266 normal volunteers aged 60–94 years, Busse and Obrist (1963) showed that 51 per cent of the group had normal EEG tracings by young standards. However, about 37 per cent showed an abnormal EEG record of focal type consisting primarily of theta or delta (slow) waves over the anterior temporal regions. When such characteristic waves occur independently over both hemispheres, they are now thought to provide strong presumptive evidence of vasculodegenerative disease. When they occur unilaterally (usually over the left hemisphere) serial EEGs might be needed to distinguish the possible vascular focus from an expanding intracranial lesion.

A further useful finding in the EEG is a combination of the anterior temporal slow wave foci with spike discharges or sharp waves. Although these findings do not prove that attacks are epileptic in origin, they do add weight to the possibility when confronted with a rather ambiguous history, i.e., of dizzy turns with some weakness of a limb afterwards—tending to support a diagnosis of epilepsy (from cerebrovascular disease) rather than one of transient ischaemic attacks.

Another characteristic but uncommon EEG finding is the presence of a continuous focal discharge over some area, usually the temporal lobe, in a patient presenting with a fit, who is left with a hemiparesis and with confusion. These patients are usually diagnosed as having had a stroke but may make a complete recovery on anticonvulsants.

A unilateral abnormality elsewhere than in the temporal area suggests a non-vascular pathology, and this suggestion is strengthened if the focus is in the post-central, frontal or parasagittal regions. Multiple foci on the EEG could result from multiple metastases or from other pathology, but the patient usually has other abnormalities apart from the fits.

It has long been difficult to separate the normal changes of ageing on the EEG (slowing of alpha frequency, diffuse theta waves, and less fast activity) from those of dementia or other pathology (van der Drift and Magnus, 1962; Rizvi, 1978). Mathews (1973) pointed out the problem of interpreting a single EEG tracing which 'departs from accepted standards of normality'; this difficulty is worsened when the patient is elderly.

The EEG can help in establishing a diagnosis, but since the EEG can be normal in 30 per cent of those who undoubtedly have epilepsy, a normal record cannot be said to exclude the condition.

It seems likely that the value of EEG in epilepsy will diminish as CT scanning becomes more readily available (Hopkins, 1980). The CT scan can show significant abnormalities in 69 per cent of patients who have simple partial seizures, and in 35 per cent of those with generalized seizures (Janz, 1978). The CT scan can not only show the size and location of a lesion, but also its nature. It can distinguish between a benign and a malignant tumour, between haemorrhage and infarct. It can demonstrate normal anatomy and hence can readily show the cerebral atrophy which may accompany dementia and fits in the old. It is a non-invasive and safe investigation in the aged, though it may be difficult for some restless or osteoarthritic elderly patients to lie still for the requisite four periods of $4\frac{1}{2}$ minutes while the scan is taken. The CT scan is more reliable than the scintiscan, whose accuracy is impaired by bloodflow to muscles, and which cannot readily demonstrate lesions less than 2 cm in diameter (*Br. Med. J.*, 1975a).

It seems likely that the CT scan will become the investigation of choice for partial seizures, and will replace serial EEGs in demonstrating an expanding intracranial lesion. At present the availability of CT scans is limited, but those elderly epileptic patients who are well, alert and give symptoms or signs of a focal lesion (particularly a progressive or disabling one) should have this investigation, if they are fit to proceed to craniotomy should the scan indicate this. Elderly patients who show no suggestion of a focus (on history, examination, EEG) should not be referred, in the author's view, but should be re-examined in 3 months. Malignant lesions rapidly reveal themselves; benign or non-progressive lesions allow time for re-examination.

If a potentially removable and accessible tumour is demonstrated, the decision whether to operate is still not easy. Many elderly people, even those who have been previously well, fare badly after craniotomy, and have increased liability to chest infections, deep vein thrombosis and pressure lesions in the postoperative period. The decision to operate will depend on the viewpoint of the patient and relatives and on the presence of other progressive disabilities arising from the tumour, but operation will probably not be advised solely for fits or headaches which can be controlled by medication.

MANAGEMENT OF EPILEPSY

It is now known that epilepsy can be satisfactorily controlled using one drug alone (Reynolds et al., 1976; Shorvon et al., 1978) using carefully monitored doses. Previous treatment was by combinations of drugs on the grounds that their therapeutic effects were additive while their individual toxicity was reduced, but there is no evidence for this. Trials of new anticonvulsants were not done on previously untreated patients, but on those who had continuing seizures on existing drugs— thus perpetuating polypharmacy. Shorvon and Reynolds (1979) have stated that it is more difficult to stop polypharmacy than to avoid it in the first place. They suggested (Shorvon et al., 1978) that polypharmacy is largely and perhaps totally unnecessary in newly-diagnosed adult epileptics. Only 10 per cent of Reynolds' patients (Reynolds et al., 1976) needed a second anticonvulsant, though without the help of serum drug levels, 54 per cent might have done so. If seizures are not controlled on one drug at optimum serum concentrations, this is now regarded (*Br. Med. J.*, 1980) as an indication for changing to a different drug rather than adding a second (or third), as has been done until recently.

Fortunately, both grand mal and the varieties of partial (focal) seizures which occur in the old are usually controllable with phenytoin (Epanutin), which has been available since 1938. Dosage regimes will be described later in the section on drug monitoring. An alternative treatment for grand mal, and perhaps now the first choice for partial attacks, would be carbamazepine (Tegretol), which has been in use since 1962. Phenobarbitone is not a satisfactory drug to use for epilepsy in the elderly. It may cause excitement and aggression instead of sedation in this age group, and its serum levels are unreliable for monitoring. A combination of phenobarbitone (30–60 mg t.d.s.) and phenytoin (100 mg t.d.s.) was particularly widely prescribed in the past. Hopkins and Scambler (1977) found that 43 out of 89 epileptics they investigated in 17 London practices were on this combination of drugs. It now appears that phenobarbitone provokes induction of an enzyme which increases the rate of metabolism of phenytoin and hence lowers the blood levels of this drug. Replacement of phenobarbitone by primidone (Mysoline) in the combination therapy was not a very logical step, since primidone was converted to phenobarbitone in the body.

Most of the foregoing remarks apply mainly to newly-diagnosed epileptics. Elderly patients who have been under treatment for long periods and who are well-controlled, e.g. on phenobarbitone and phenytoin, should perhaps be left on their existing medication. Advantage could, however, be taken of a period of hospital admission, if it occurs, to withdraw their phenobarbitone gradually and monitor their serum phenytoin levels more effectively.

DRUG MONITORING (*Table* 12.3)

There has been a great improvement in the drug treatment of epilepsy since the monitoring of serum levels of anticonvulsants became possible, and whole books are now devoted to the complications of monitoring (Johannessen et al., 1980). Phenytoin has been studied pharmacologically more intensively than any other drug (Parsonage, 1980) and there is a close relationship between its serum range and therapeutic effect. There is disagreement about the therapeutic range; some work on a 10–25 µg/ml (40–100 µmol/l) range, but the majority (Lund, 1974; Reynolds et al., 1976; Richens, 1979) use the narrower range of 10–20 µg/ml (40–80 µmol/l) which is now more generally accepted.

Table 12.3. Doses of anticonvulsants in the elderly

Drug	Approximate dosage	Therapeutic range µg/ml	µmol/l
Phenytoin (Epanutin)	300 mg/day divided into 2 or 3 doses, or as a single dose, preferably at night	10–20	40–80
Carbamazepine (Tegretol)	600 mg/day divided into 2 or 3 doses	4–10	17–42
Phenobarbitone (not recommended)	90–180 mg/day preferably as a single dose at night	85–170 (unreliable)	

Phenytoin is 90 per cent protein-bound, mostly to albumin, and it is only the free drug which exerts a pharmacological action. There is controversy whether binding, and hence dosage required to give a certain serum level, varies with age and sex and between individuals (Sherwin et al., 1974; Hayes et al., 1975; Furlanut et al., 1978).

The metabolism of phenytoin, by enzymes in the liver, is to 5-*p*-hydroxyphenyl-5-phenylhydantoin (pHPPH) which is conjugated with glucuronic acid, and 70–80 per cent is excreted in the urine. The enzyme system concerned in this reaction can become saturated, and it follows that very small increases in daily dose of phenytoin above a certain level can result in toxic accumulation of the drug. The kinetics of phenytoin (saturation kinetics of Michaelis-Menten type) can be defined in terms of the serum concentration at which metabolism is half-saturated (K_m) and the maximum rate of metabolism (V_{max}). Both these values are very similar in the elderly to those in the young (Lambie and Caird, 1977) and it seems true that the elderly, like the young, need daily dosages of 300 mg or so of phenytoin to achieve therapeutic serum levels. 'Fine tuning' of phenytoin levels is possible now that phenytoin (Epanutin) is available in 100, 50 and 25 mg sizes. It is not recommended to vary the preparation used, since the bioavailability of the drug depends on particle size, which in turn varies between different preparations.

In practice, it is now suggested that a new patient should be started on 200 mg/day of phenytoin, and the steady-state serum level measured in 2–3 weeks, when further cautious increases in dosage can be made to achieve a therapeutic serum level, perhaps using the revised nomogram calculated by Rambeck et al. (1979) (*Fig. 12.1*). Increasing the dose of phenytoin by one-fifth can double the serum level in 2–3 weeks, since in the steady-state the half-life of phenytoin can be as long as 140 hours (Lehtovaraa et al., 1980). It may take a month to show the full effect of a dose change. With increased knowledge it is also clear that once daily dosage is enough to give satisfactorily smooth blood levels of the drug, and that this regime does not increase the incidence of side effects (Reynolds et al., 1976; Mucklow and Dollery, 1978).

Once a patient is established on phenytoin, too rigid reliance on the therapeutic range is not advised. In particular, a single low serum level in a patient who has not had any fits, need not necessarily lead to an increase in dosage. It must be remembered that there is a variation between laboratories, and that the 95 per cent confidence limits for a blood specimen which contains 60 µmol/l of phenytoin range from 45·2 to 74·8 µmol/l. It is always preferable to take blood for monitoring mid-morning (and not fasting) to avoid introducing a further variable factor.

Some experts now suggest that the lower limit of the therapeutic range can be abandoned if the patient is fit-free, since some mild epileptics are controlled with serum levels below 40 µmol/l, whereas other patients can tolerate over 80 µmol/l.

Kidney and liver disease may both lead to decreased protein-binding of phenytoin. In kidney disease the result is that a lower serum level of phenytoin may be compatible with therapeutic control of epilepsy. In liver disease there may also be delayed metabolism of the drug, and this might overcome the lower binding effect, and result in a toxic accumulation of phenytoin on a previously therapeutic dosage.

Where there is doubt, estimation of the free (unbound) phenytoin would be valuable. Such a measure may be available in the salivary phenytoin, since the salivary gland acts as a simple dialysis membrane allowing only the free fraction to pass through. Some experts (Mucklow and Dollery, 1978) advocate the use of salivary phenytoin, and assume that the normal range for this is one-tenth of that of plasma phenytoin. However, these measures are not yet generally available nor reliable enough for routine use (*Br. Med. J.*, 1980).

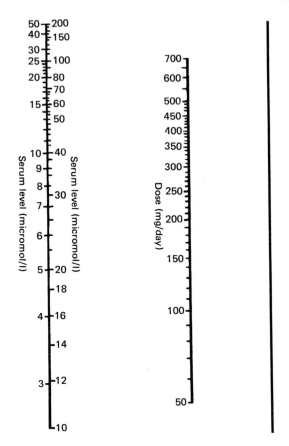

Fig. 12.1. Nomogram for adjusting the phenytoin dosage. Given a single reliable serum level on a given daily dose of phenytoin, the dose required to achieve a desired serum level can be predicted. A line is drawn connecting the observed serum level (left hand scale) with the dose administered (centre scale) and extended to intersect the right hand vertical line. From this point of intersection, another line is drawn back to the desired serum level (left hand scale). The dose to produce the desired level can be read off on the centre scale.

Notes: This monogram will give misleading predictions if the serum level measurement is inaccurate, if the patient's compliance is in doubt, or if a change in concurrent treatment has been made since the measurement of the serum level. It may take 2–3 weeks for steady state to be achieved after a change in phenytoin dose.

Nomograms on a tear-off pad are available from Parke-Davis.

The metabolism of carbamazepine has been less well studied, but the drug is known to be effective alone in 70 per cent of partial seizures. (Strandjord and Johannessen, 1980). It has a short half-life, so must be given at least twice a day. As it is initially sedating, dosage should be started at night. There is a poor correlation between the dosage and the serum level, but mean daily doses of 9.7 ± 3.3 mg/kg have been suggested, with a daily range of 200–1100 mg.

DRUG INTERACTIONS

Anticonvulsants, including phenytoin, can give rise to so many drug interactions that the individual physician cannot remember them all, and this group of drugs figures prominently in the numerous interaction wall-charts and pocket-discs which are now available. Phenytoin is a potent inducer of hepatic enzymes which increase the metabolism of many drugs. This is the probable mechanism by which phenytoin reduces the plasma concentration and therapeutic effect of the oral anticoagulants, of other anticonvulsants such as carbamazepine, of benzodiazepines such as diazepam (Valium), of phenothiazines, and of tricyclic antidepressants. In younger patients the effect of phenytoin in decreasing the effectiveness of contraceptive steroids may result in an unexpected pregnancy, fortunately not a hazard that needs to be considered in the elderly. Contrariwise the serum phenytoin concentration may itself be reduced if the patient begins to take another anticonvulsant (e.g. carbamazepine or phenobarbitone) or a benzodiazepine. A tricyclic antidepressant may, by the same mechanism, increase the risk of fits, so it is suggested that another type of antidepressant (e.g. viloxazine or mianserin) should be used (Hopkins, 1980).

Giving sulthiame (Ospolot) to a patient on phenytoin greatly increases the serum level of phenytoin (by inhibiting its metabolism) and may precipitate toxicity; while adding an anticholinergic or antidiarrhoeal agent may have the same effect by increasing absorption time (Neuvonen et al., 1980). Phenytoin metabolism is also thought to be inhibited by coumarin anticoagulants, pheneturide, and in slow acetylators of isoniazid.

The interaction of phenytoin and alcohol is not clear, one author stating that phenytoin-treated patients are more alcohol intolerant, and another that chronic alcohol ingestion can reduce the serum phenytoin concentration. Excess beer drinking may increase fits because of the volume of fluid ingested.

Phenytoin can be displaced from its plasma protein-binding sites (and hence give rise to more free phenytoin on the same dose) by valproic acid, salicylic acid and phenylbutazone.

Many of these interactions are still being discovered, and may explain some contradictory results in past reports on the drug control of epilepsy. Some of the interactions give rise to little difficulty so long as the physician is alert to the risk and prescribes the drugs concerned only when absolutely necessary.

TOXICITY AND LONG-TERM DRUG COMPLICATIONS

Rashes arising in patients on phenytoin are rarely severe or persistent enough to warrant reduction and removal of the drug. Acne and hirsutism have been reported in some patients. Overgrowth of collagen is said to be the basis for the gingival hyperplasia and for the long-term coarsening of the features which may occur. Other toxic effects include fever, hepatitis, lupus erythematosus, erythema multiforme and lymphadenopathy.

On long-term treatment some patients develop folate deficiency which may lead in turn to anaemia (Bonduelle et al., 1970; Grant and Stores, 1970). Routine supplements of folic acid are thought by some (Shaw and Hoffbrand, 1970) to increase the frequency of epileptic fits; however, most physicians would watch for and treat any folate-deficiency anaemia if it arose. Leucopenia, thrombocytopenia, agranulocytosis and aplastic anaemia are rare.

There is increased hydroxylation of calciferol in patients on long-term anticonvulsants, and this effect may lead to hypocalcaemia and osteomalacia. In theory this would be worsened in the elderly who have inadequate dietary calcium and poor exposure to sunlight. However, Ray and Rao (1974), in a study of 36 elderly patients on long-term phenytoin and phenobarbitone, found no hypocalcaemia, perhaps because many of their patients were bedfast or chairfast, so that their bone calcium was being mobilized into the blood and masking any drug-induced hypocalcaemia.

The long-term effects of phenytoin treatment are rarely serious. The severe toxic effects of overdosage consist of cerebellar signs (ataxia and slurred speech with nystagmus), accompanied by confusion. In the past it was very difficult to distinguish such toxic effects in the elderly from the effects of unrelated neurological conditions. The position is now clearer, since it seems to be unusual for serious toxicity to occur below serum levels of 120 µmol/l (30 µg/ml)(Lund 1974).

Toxicity of carbamazepine has been less intensively studied but there are reports of hyponatraemia and of water intoxication, reversible by decreasing the dosage of the drug (Parsonage, 1980). Side-effects of dizziness and diplopia are frequently dose-limiting (*British National Formulary*, 1981). A generalized erythematous rash may occur in about 3 per cent of patients; leucopenia and other blood disorders have occurred rarely.

In status epilepticus the danger of cerebral damage from repeated periods of anoxia, and the cardiorespiratory exhaustion from repeated seizures may be worse in the old patient. Intravenous (not intramuscular) diazepam (10 mg) should be given slowly, over a period of 2–3 min to avoid respiratory depression, followed by a second injection later if the treatment fails, or by an intravenous infusion of chlormethiazole (Heminevrin).

The unusual condition of epilepsia partialis continua consists of continuous motor jactitation. This has been observed by the author in elderly stroke patients and in some in renal failure, but its incidence is unknown. Occasionally a complex partial status epilepticus may give rise to a confusional state.

COMPLIANCE

There is increasing awareness of the importance of patient compliance in epilepsy. Richens (1978) reported that 40 per cent of outpatients with epilepsy did not take all the anticonvulsant drugs prescribed for them. Mucklow and Dollery (1978) found no phenytoin in the saliva of 11 out of 86 epileptic patients supposedly taking the drug, and concluded that these 11 patients could clearly be identified as non-compliant. Reynolds et al. (1976) found that the serum phenytoin gradually declined in 14 out of 31 new epileptics on constant or increased dosage, and suggested that this was partly due to changing drug metabolism and partly due to poor compliance.

Hopkins and Scambler (1977) in a study of 94 adult epileptics living at home in London, found that medical supervision of the condition was not as good as it should be, both by general practitioners and by hospital specialists. Only 10 patients were currently under outpatient supervision, and in half of these it seemed unnecessary. On the other hand 3 patients had been discharged from outpatient supervision when the frequency of their attacks was weekly or more frequently. Many patients saw a different (and often junior) doctor at each visit to outpatients. The authors concluded that medical supervision was not related to patient need. Though the hospital doctor usually told the patient the diagnosis, in 18 per cent even this communication failed, and it is unlikely that proper instruction leading to good compliance can occur on the basis of the random supervision being provided.

The doctor must tell the patient the diagnosis and explain that tablets must be taken for life. It helps the patient to comply if the drug regime can be stabilized on a once-daily basis, and if the introductory doses of sedating drugs are given at bedtime. Old people need drug bottles that are easy to open. However, there has recently been agreement at national level to provide childproof containers for all drugs, unless an elderly person specifically asks for an easily-openable one. This rule is likely to lead to further non-compliance, either because the elderly person has not made the request, or because the prescription has been collected by a younger relative or home help, and the pharmacist has therefore not been alerted to the problem.

Clear large print or type for the instruction label on the bottle is another aid to compliance. Many doctors are now advising a reminder similar to the one we use, a treatment card with instructions, drug name and specimens of the tablets attached with Sellotape.

SOCIAL ASPECTS AND RISKS OF EPILEPSY

There are risks associated with epilepsy at all stages of life, old age being no exception, and advice to live as normal a life as possible, while being careful about medication, continues to apply. Sensible precautions include guarding of fires and stairwells, and not bathing while alone in the house. Unfortunately there is still some community intolerance of the condition, and this results in difficulty in placing even a well-controlled epileptic in some old people's homes. If the old person can continue to live at home with help from relatives, neighbours, home helps or district nurses (any of whom can check that drugs are being taken regularly), then this is often the best solution while the patient continues otherwise well.

In retirement it may be a social necessity to drive a car (Pond and Bidwell, 1959/60), so that the decision to prohibit driving should be taken only after careful consideration. In Great Britain it is necessary to be fit-free (during waking hours) for 3 years, with or without treatment, in order to be declared fit to drive. An elderly person who develops epilepsy for the first time must inform the Licensing Centre, who may require information from the family doctor or request a specialist examination. When pronounced fit to drive, a licence will be issued up to the age of 70 or for 3 years (whichever is the longer), or, after the age of 70, for 3 years. If treatment is changed, the patient must remain fit-free for 6–12 months before driving again. It is sensible for the elderly epileptic not to engage in driving for prolonged periods, and not to go without food or sleep. Even small amounts of alcohol interact with anticonvulsants and the patient should be warned about this.

Difficult decisions have to be made if an elderly driver has a single fit. The outcome will depend on whether there is evidence of a continuing liability to epileptic attacks. If confirmation is obtained of this liability (by neurological examination, EEG, etc.) the 3 year rule will apply. If there is no evidence after full investigation of a cerebral lesion, but positive evidence of a metabolic cause for the single fit then the patient may drive again in 6 months (Raffle, 1976).

CONCLUSION

In the elderly, epilepsy may be only part of a complex disease process, and often only a subsidiary part. It is essential to examine all aspects of the patient's condition (medical, psychological, social, etc.) before coming to a balanced conclusion about the best treatment. Instead of concentrating on the possibility of finding a removable tumour, doctors should turn their attention to better control of the fits —and in this aim they are greatly helped by the advances recently made in monitoring of drug treatment.

I should like to acknowledge with grateful thanks the helpful advice given by Dr Bidi Evans, FRCP, on EEG interpretation.

REFERENCES

Bancaud J. (1970) *Sem. Hôp. Paris* **46**, 3138.
Berlin L. (1953) *JAMA* **152**, 794.
Bonduelle M., Sallou C. and Guillard J. (1970) *Sem. Hôp. Paris* **46**, 3141.
Brewis M., Poskanzer D. C., Rolland C. et al. (1966) *Acta Neurol. Scand.* **42**, (Suppl. 24) 1.
British Medical Journal (1975a) **2**, 295.
British Medical Journal (1975b) **2**, 524.
British Medical Journal (1980) **281**, 1087.
British National Formulary (1981) London, Br. Med. Ass. & Pharm. Soc. G.B.
Busse E. W. and Obrist W. D. (1963) *Postgrad. Med.* **34**, 179.
Carney L. R., Hudgins R. L., Espinosa R. E. et al. (1969) *Arch. Intern. Med.* **124**, 707.
Courjon J., Artru F. and Zeskov P. (1970) *Sem. Hôp. Paris* **46**, 3129.
Exton-Smith A. N. (1977) In: Exton-Smith A. N. and Grimley Evans J. (ed.) *Care of the Elderly*. London, Academic Press, p. 48.
Feuerstein J., Weber M., Kurtz D. et al. (1970) *Sem. Hôp. Paris* **46**, 3125.
Fine W. (1966) *Br. Med. J.* **1**, 199.
Furlanut M., Benetello P., Testa G. et al. (1978) *Pharmacol. Res. Commun.* **10**, 85.
Gastaut H., Gastaut J. L., Goncalves e Silva G. E. et al. (1975) *Epilepsia* **16**, 457.
Gibberd F. (1973) *Br. J. Hosp. Med.* **9**, 152.
Graham M., Williams B. O. and Rowe M. J. (1979) *Br. Med. J.* **1**, 1460.
Grant R. H. E. and Stores O. P. R. (1970) *Br. Med. J.* **4**, 644.
Hauser W. A. and Kurland L. T. (1975) *Epilepsia* **16**, 1.
Hayes M. J., Langman M. J. S. and Short A. H. (1975) *Br. J. Clin. Pharmacol.* **2**, 73.
Hildick-Smith M. (1974) *Age Ageing* **3**, 203.
Hopkins A. (1980) *Medicine* **32**, 1632.
Hopkins A. and Scambler G. (1977) *Lancet* **1**, 183.
Janz D. (1978) In: Meinardi H. and Rowan A. J. (ed.) *Advances in Epileptology*. Amsterdam, Swets & Zeittinger.
Johannessen S. I., Morselli P. L., Pippenger C. E. et al. (ed.) (1980) In: *Antiepileptic Therapy: Advances in Drug Monitoring*. New York, Raven Press.
Lambie D. C. and Caird F. I. (1977) *Age Ageing* **6**, 133.
Lehtovaara R., Bardy A. and Neuvonen P. (1980) In: Johannessen S. I., Morselli P. L., Pippenger C. E. et al. (ed.) *Antiepileptic Therapy: Advances in Drug Monitoring*. New York, Raven Press.
Livingston S. (1956) *N. Engl. J. Med.* **254**, 1211.
Lund L. (1974) *Arch. Neurol.* **31**, 289.
McKeown F. (1965) *Pathology of the Aged*. London, Butterworths.
Marquardsen J. (1969) *Acta Neurol. Scand.* **45**, Suppl. 38, 150.
Matthews W. B. (1973) *J. R. Coll. Phys. Lond.* **7**, 207.
Mucklow J. C. and Dollery C. T. (1978) *Br. J. Clin. Pharmacol.* **6**, 75.
Neuvonen P. J., Lehtovaara R. and Bardy A. (1980) In: Johannessen S. I., Morselli P. L., Pippenger C. E. et al. (ed.) *Antiepileptic Therapy: Advances in Drug Monitoring*. New York, Raven Press.
Parsonage M. (1980) In: Tyler J. H. (ed.) *The Treatment of Epilepsy*. Lancaster, MTP.
Pond D. A. and Bidwell B. H. (1959/60) *Epilepsia* **1**, 285.
Pond D. A., Bidwell B. H. and Stein L. (1960) *Psychiatr. Neurol. Neurochirurg. (Amst.)* **63**, 217.
Prakash C. and Stern G. (1973) *Age Ageing* **2**, 24.

Raffle A. (ed.) (1976) *Medical Aspects of Fitness to Drive*. 3rd ed. London, Medical Commission on Accident Prevention.

Rambeck B., Boenigk H. E., Dunlop A. et al. (1979) *Ther. Drug Monitoring* 1, 325.

Ray A. K. and Rao D. B. (1974) *J. Am. Ger. Soc.* 22, 222.

Reynolds E. H., Chadwick D. and Galbraith A. W. (1976) *Lancet* 1, 923.

Richens A. (1978) *Prescrib. J.* 18, 125.

Richens A. (1979) *Clin. Pharmacokinet.* 4, 153.

Rizvi C. A. (1978) *Va. Med.* 105, 637.

Schold C., Yarnell P. R. and Earnest M. D. (1977) *JAMA* 238, 1177.

Schott G. D., McLeod A. A. and Jewitt D. E. (1977) *Br. Med. J.* 1, 1454.

Shaw M. T. and Hoffbrand A. V. (1970) *Practitioner* 204, 795.

Sherwin A. L., Loynd J. S. et al. (1974) *Epilepsia* 15, 507.

Shorvon S., Chadwick D. et al. (1978) *Br. Med. J.* 1, 474.

Shorvon S. and Reynolds E. H. (1979) *Br. Med. J.* 2, 1023.

Stevens D. L. and Matthews W. B. (1973) *Br. Med. J.* 1, 439.

Strandjord R. E. and Johannessen S. I. (1980) In: Johannessen S. I., Morselli P. L., Pippenger C. E. et al. (ed.) *Antiepileptic Therapy: Advances in Drug Monitoring*. New York, Raven Press.

van der Drift J. H. A. and Magnus O. (1962) *Electroencephalogr. Clin. Neurophysiol.* 14, 664.

Vercellato P. and Delobel R. (1970) *Sem. Hôp. Paris* 46, 3133.

Webster J. E., Gurdjian E. S. et al. (1956) *Neurol. (Minn.)* 6, 491.

13. NEUROPATHIES AND MYOPATHIES
J. G. McLeod

Diseases of the lower motor neurone include anterior horn cell degenerations, particularly amyotrophic lateral sclerosis or motor neurone disease; root lesions, or radiculopathies; peripheral neuropathies; diseases affecting the neuromuscular junction, such as myasthenia gravis and myasthenia secondary to malignancy; and diseases of muscle, or myopathies. The distinction between these different types of lower motor neurone disorder can usually be made clinically by careful neurological examination, aided by electromyography (EMG) and nerve conduction studies, and in some cases by nerve or muscle biopsy. The present chapter will be devoted to describing the diseases of peripheral nerve, muscle and the neuromuscular junction.

PERIPHERAL NEUROPATHY

Peripheral nerve trunks are composed of motor and sensory fibres and the postganglionic axons of the sympathetic nervous system. All three components may be affected in diseases of the peripheral nerves, giving rise to motor and sensory symptoms. Motor symptoms are wasting and weakness, mainly in distal muscles; the patient may notice difficulty in climbing stairs, stumbling while walking, difficulty in turning keys in locks, undoing buttons or unscrewing the lids of bottles or jars. Common sensory symptoms are numbness, tingling, feelings of pins and needles in the hands and feet, burning sensations, pain in the extremities, sensations of walking on cotton wool, or band-like constrictions around the wrists or ankles. Autonomic disturbances, such as dryness or excessive sweating of the extremities, postural hypotension, impotence and sphincter disturbances, and nocturnal diarrhoea or constipation, may also occur.

On physical examination weakness and wasting are usually more pronounced in the distal muscle groups although when the spinal roots are predominantly affected (radiculopathies) proximal muscles may be mainly involved. Reflexes are usually depressed but in mild cases the abnormalities may be confined to the ankle jerks. Sensory changes are pronounced distally and commonly have a 'glove and stocking distribution'. In mild cases of peripheral neuropathy diagnostic difficulties may be encountered in elderly patients in whom ankle jerks may be normally depressed or absent (Critchley, 1931; Howell, 1949) and in whom vibration sense and tactile sensation may be impaired (Newman and Corbin, 1936; Dyck, 1975).

In Western communities, the most frequent causes of peripheral neuropathy in elderly patients are diabetes, alcoholism and malignancy (Huang, 1981). In the present review, only those peripheral neuropathies that may be expected to occur in elderly patients will be considered. For more detailed accounts the reader is referred to Dyck et al. (1975).

Pathology

Nerve trunks consist of large numbers of parallel nerve fibres which receive their blood supply from small nutrient blood vessels that are branches of larger regional vessels. In some diseases, e.g. diabetes and polyarteritis nodosa, the nutrient vessels may become occluded and result in infarction of part or the whole of the nerve trunk. Vascular occlusions of this nature are a cause of mononeuritis multiplex in which several isolated nerves are affected in an asymmetrical fashion (*Table* 13.1).

Two major pathological processes affect peripheral nerves—axonal degeneration and segmental demyelination, In axonal degeneration the axis cylinder dies first and the myelin disintegrates secondarily. This degenerative process may result from crush or injury or from disease of the cell body; when the metabolism of the cell is affected, the most distal portions of the axon may die back from the periphery (dying-back neuropathy). In segmental demyelination the myelin sheath is affected but there is little associated degeneration of the axon (*Table* 13.2).

Table 13.1 Causes of mononeuritis multiplex

Vascular
  Diabetes
  Polyarteritis nodosa
  Rheumatoid arthritis
  Systemic lupus erythematosus
  Wegener's granulomatosis

Inflammatory
  Leprosy
  Sarcoidosis

Infiltrations
  Malignancy
  Amyloid

Trauma

Injections, Vaccinations

Inoculations

Table 13.2. Major pathological changes associated with certain types of peripheral neuropathy

Axonal Degeneration
Alcohol
Vitamin B_1 or B_{12} deficiency
Neoplasms
Uraemia
Arsenic
Thallium
Gold
Vincristine
Nitrofurantoin
Acromegaly
Diabetes
Tuberculoid leprosy
Amyloid disease

Segmental Demyelination
Diphtheria
Guillain–Barré syndrome
Relapsing polyneuritis
Déjérine–Sottas syndrome
Hypertrophic Charcot–Marie–Tooth disease
Lepromatous leprosy
Refsum's disease
Diabetes

Degeneration of peripheral nerves is part of the normal ageing process and therefore the pathological changes seen in nerve biopsies must be related to the age of the subject. It has been shown that there is a significant decrease in the density of myelinated fibres with age (Swallow, 1966; O'Sullivan and Swallow, 1968; Tohgi et al., 1977). Studies of teased single fibres indicate an increasing number of abnormalities with age, such as axonal degeneration, variability of internodal length and short internodes (Lascelles and Thomas, 1966; Arnold and Harriman, 1970). On electron microscopy, increasing degeneration of myelinated and unmyelinated fibres associated with evidence of active regeneration may be observed (Ochoa and Mair, 1969).

Genetically Determined Neuropathies

Charcot–Marie–Tooth Disease

A number of different types of neuropathy are genetically determined and an important part of the approach to a patient with peripheral neuropathy is to enquire about a family history. The most common hereditary disorder of the peripheral nerve that is seen in older patients is Charcot–Marie–Tooth disease which is compatible with a normal life span and may cause little serious disability. There is distal wasting of the lower limbs with foot drop and pes cavus is usually present. Wasting of the intrinsic hand muscles occurs and mild distal sensory loss is usually apparent. The reflexes in the lower limbs are depressed or absent. The condition progresses very slowly over many years. The most common mode of inheritance is autosomal dominant (Dyck and Lambert, 1968).

Primary Amyloid Disease

Although primary amyloid disease is genetically determined, sporadic cases may present in the elderly with a painful predominantly sensory neuropathy in which there is a selective loss of pain and temperature sense. Amyloid deposits may be seen in peripheral nerves in which there is a marked loss of small myelinated and unmyelinated fibres (Thomas and King, 1974).

Neuropathies Associated with Metabolic and Endocrine Disturbances

Diabetes Mellitus

Peripheral neuropathy is a common complication both in early-onset insulin-dependent diabetes and in maturity-onset diabetes. The most common form is a symmetrical, predominantly sensory, polyneuropathy. Numbness, tingling and burning pain in the feet are common symptoms, and sometimes aching and lancinating pains in the calves may occur. When there is severe sensory impairment, perforating ulcers of the feet and neuropathic joints may occur with associated sensory ataxia (diabetic pseudotabes). Symptoms of autonomic dysfunction are common and include diarrhoea, constipation, dysphagia, retention and incontinence or urine, impotence, sphincter disturbances, impaired sweating and postural hypotension.

Diabetic amyotrophy is a syndrome of asymmetrical proximal muscular weakness and wasting of the lower limbs often associated with pain in the thighs. The condition occurs predominantly in patients over the age of 50 and it seems to improve spontaneously if the control of the diabetes is good. It is considered to be a form of proximal motor neuropathy.

Isolated peripheral nerve lesions are common, particularly carpal tunnel syndrome, ulnar nerve lesions at the elbow and radial, femoral and lateral popliteal nerve palsies.

Uraemia

A distal symmetrical peripheral neuropathy occurs in uraemia and is present in the majority of patients receiving dialysis. The symptoms are mainly sensory and patients complain of pain, numbness, restless legs, burning feet, cramps and paraesthesiae. Sometimes severe muscle wasting occurs. Reflexes are depressed, particularly in the lower limbs.

Peripheral neuropathy progresses slowly but occasionally it may have an acute onset with rapid progression. Improvement usually occurs with more effective dialysis but more consistently after renal transplantation (Asbury, 1975).

Acromegaly

Carpal tunnel syndrome is well recognized as a complication of acromegaly. Less commonly, a generalized symmetrical sensorimotor neuropathy may occur, even in patients without associated diabetes (Low et al., 1974).

Thyroid Disease

Peripheral neuropathy may be secondary to myxoedema. Rarely, it may also occur in thyrotoxicosis.

Connective Tissue Diseases

Rheumatoid Arthritis

Patients with severe longstanding disease and significant titres of rheumatoid factor are the ones most likely to develop peripheral neuropathy. There are several different types of peripheral neuropathy in rheumatoid arthritis; a mild distal sensory neuropathy is common and a more florid mixed sensorimotor neuropathy may also occur.

Mononeuritis multiplex due to necrotizing angiitis and entrapment neuropathies are also well-recognized complications of rheumatoid disease (Pallis and Scott, 1965).

In *polyarteritis nodosa*, mononeuritis multiplex, often with acute onset, associated with paraesthesiae, is the most common peripheral nerve manifestation but a symmetrical sensorimotor neuropathy may also occur. Similar peripheral nerve complications also occur less often in other collagen disorders such as *systemic lupus erythematosus*, *Wegener's granulomatosis* and *Sjögren's syndrome*.

Neuropathy in Malignancy

Malignant tumours may cause direct compression or infiltration of peripheral nerves or roots. Clinical peripheral neuropathy also occurs as a remote manifestation in about 5 per cent of cases with *carcinoma*, and the incidence is higher in carcinoma of the lung and stomach. Electrophysiological and pathological studies, however, indicate that subclinical neuropathy may occur in up to 50 per cent of cases. A predominantly sensory neuropathy occurs particularly in association with carcinoma of the lung, but a sensorimotor type of neuropathy is more common.

The onset of the neuropathy is usually subacute and may precede other symptoms of malignant neoplasm by a period ranging from 2 months to 5 years. In occasional cases the onset may be acute with respiratory paralysis and bulbar symptoms similar to those seen in the Guillain–Barré syndrome. Symptoms and signs of neuropathy usually involve the lower limbs to a greater extent than the upper limbs. Remitting and relapsing neuropathies have also been described in association with malignancy. The cerebrospinal fluid protein may be elevated or normal in carcinomatous neuropathies of different types. Impairment of sensory conduction and mild slowing of motor conduction are usually found (McLeod, 1975).

Peripheral neuropathies are associated with the *lymphomas and other reticuloses*. Clinical neuropathies occur in about 5–10 per cent of patients with lymphomas but with the aid of electrophysiological techniques in diagnosis, the incidence is about 35 per cent (Walsh, 1971a; McLeod and Walsh, 1975a).

In *acute leukaemia* there may be haemorrhage into or direct infiltration of the peripheral nerve. In *chronic lymphatic* and *chronic myeloid leukaemia* peripheral neuropathy may occur as a remote manifestation of the condition (McLeod and Walsh, 1975a).

Paraproteinaemias and Dysproteinaemias

There is clinical evidence of peripheral neuropathy in about 13 per cent of patients with multiple myeloma but electrophysiological studies reveal evidence of a subclinical neuropathy in about 50 per cent of cases (Walsh, 1971b). There have been reports of peripheral neuropathy complicating solitary plasmacytomas as well as more generalized form of multiple myeloma. There seems to be a higher incidence of polyneuropathy in the osteosclerotic type of myeloma. Peripheral neuropathies may also be associated with macroglobulinaemia, cryoglobulinaemia, polyclonal gammopathies and 'benign' monoclonal gammopathy (McLeod and Walsh, 1975b).

Serum Sickness, Injections and Vaccinations

Peripheral neuropathy may occur in association with serum sickness induced by injections of antisera, antibiotics and other drugs; smallpox vaccination; typhoid-paratyphoid vaccination; tetanus toxoid; anti-rabies vaccination and other injections and inoculations. The most common complication is an acute brachial neuritis but a more generalized acute polyneuritis of the Guillain–Barré type may also occur. These polyneuropathies presumably have an immune basis and the brachial neuritis is probably a localized form of a more generalized condition.

Inflammatory Neuropathies

Acute Idiopathic Polyneuritis (Guillain–Barré Syndrome)

This can affect all age groups. Huang (1981) reported 2 patients, one aged 81 and another aged 77 with the Guillain–Barré syndrome who made excellent recoveries, in a series of 59 patients with different causes of polyneuropathy in old age. The disease has an acute onset and is potentially fatal. The most common initial symptoms are paraesthesiae or pain in the lower limbs which are followed usually by weakness. Proximal muscles may be affected to the same or even greater extent than the distal muscle groups. Facial and bulbar paralysis are common and weakness of the extra-ocular muscles may also occur. Reflexes are usually depressed or are absent and there is a variable degree of sensory loss. Within a period of 3 weeks this predominantly motor neuropathy progresses to a maximum disability often with complete quadriparesis and respiratory paralysis. Recovery with significant residual disability occurs in 80 per cent of patients. Subsequent relapses occur in about 5 per cent of cases (McLeod et al., 1976). Typically the CSF protein is elevated and the cell concentration is not increased but in some patients the protein may not be raised and the cell count may be greater than 30 cells/cmm. Nerve conduction studies are usually abnormal with marked slowing of motor conduction consistent with the underlying pathology of segmental demyelination. It is likely that the pathogenesis of the disorder is a cell-mediated immune response directed to normal peripheral myelin and this may be provoked in some way by certain virus infections.

Chronic Relapsing Polyneuritis

Some demyelinating neuropathies have a subacute onset and may run a slow relapsing and remitting course. CSF protein is nearly always elevated and marked slowing of motor conduction occurs in the majority of cases. In contrast to the Guillain–Barré syndrome, the HLA-B8 antigen is associated with this condition, suggesting that it is in part genetically determined. The chronicity may be related to the immune response of the host (Prineas and McLeod; 1976; Dyck et al., 1975).

Alcoholic and Nutritional Neuropathies

Alcohol is one of the most common cause of peripheral neuropathy in urban populations. The patient may be asymptomatic but on neurological examination signs of peripheral neuropathy, such as distal muscle wasting, depressed or absent ankle jerks and distal sensory impairment will be apparent. Symptoms are usually those of distal muscle weakness, paraesthesiae and pain. Objective sensory examination usually reveals loss of all modalities. Excessive sweating or impairment of sweating over the extremities may be noted due to involvement of the sympathetic nerve fibres. Postural hypotension is uncommon except in the most severe cases. The pathological changes are those of axonal degeneration. The electrophysiological findings are usually those of mild impairment of motor and sensory conduction with more pronounced involvement of distal sensory fibres. Alcoholic neuropathy is caused by vitamin deficiency, particularly of thiamine rather than by the direct effects of alcohol on the nervous system (Walsh and McLeod, 1970; Victor, 1975).

Vitamin deficiencies causing beri-beri, pellagra, pernicous anaemia, pyridoxine and folic acid deficiency may all cause a predominantly sensory neuropathy. Peripheral neuropathy can also occur as a complication of intestinal malabsorption even when there are no demonstrable vitamin deficiencies.

Toxic Neuropathies

Peripheral neuropathy may be caused by a variety of drugs, heavy metals and industrial agents (*Table* 13.3).

Table 13.3. Agents causing peripheral neuropathy

Heavy Metals and Industrial Agents
Arsenic
Lead
Mercury
Thallium
Gold
Acrylamide
n-Hexane, methyl *n*-butyl ketone
Tri-orthocresyl phosphate
Carbon disulphide

Drugs
Isoniazid
Ethambutol
Nitrofurantoin
Vincristine
Phenytoin
Disulfiram
Dapsone
Chloroquine
Perhexiline
Hydralazine
Metronidazole
Clioquinol
Thalidomide

Diagnosis

A careful history with attention to details of alcohol and drug intake, diet, possible exposure to industrial and environmental toxins, family history, symptoms of systemic disease and a clinical search for underlying malignancy and other medical conditions are essential. Certain clinical types of peripheral neuropathy are recognized which may assist in the diagnosis (*Table* 13.4).

Table 13.4. Clinical types of peripheral neuropathy

Acute Onset
Guillain–Barré syndrome
Porphyria
Diphtheria
Toxic
Serum sickness, postvaccinial
Malignancy

Predominantly Motor
Guillain-Barré syndrome
Porphyria
Diphtheria
Lead
Charcot–Marie–Tooth disease

Predominantly Sensory
Leprosy
Diabetes
Vitamin B_{12} or thiamine deficiency
Malignancy
Hereditary sensory neuropathy
Amyloid
Uraemia

Investigations

Urinalysis, full blood count, erythrocyte sedimentation rate (ESR), fasting blood glucose, glucose tolerance test, serum electrolytes, serum proteins, serum creatinine, liver function tests and chest radiographs are basic investigations which should be performed in all patients with peripheral neuropathy of undetermined aetiology. Other investigations, such as urinary porphyrins and heavy metals, plasma electrophoresis, serum cholesterol and triglycerides, CSF examination and radiological and endoscopic investigation for underlying malignancy may be indicated in other cases.

Electrophysiological Studies

In generalized symmetrical neuropathies electrophysiological studies usually demonstrate an impairment of motor and/or sensory conduction; gross slowing of conduction may indicate underlying segmental demyelination (*see Table* 13.2).

Nerve Biopsy

After electrophysiological and other studies have been performed biopsy of the sural or radial nerve may be helpful in diagnosis, particularly if electron microscopy and quantitative studies of the numbers and diameters of myelinated and unmyelinated fibres are undertaken.

In spite of all investigations, the cause in a proportion of patients remains undetermined. In Huang's study (1981) the aetiology remained undetermined in about 20 per cent.

Management

Acute Neuropathies

In the Guillain–Barré syndrome and other peripheral neuropathies with acute onset the vital capacity should be measured every 2–4 hours in the initial stages. Tracheostomy and artificial ventilation may be necessary. Careful nursing is very important and particular attention should be paid to the care of the skin, bladder, bowels, mouth, pharynx and trachea. Lung and urinary tract infections require prompt treatment. Intravenous or intragastric feeding may be necessary. Splints to prevent foot and wrist drop may be necessary and physiotherapy should begin immediately. Corticosteroid therapy is often administered but is of no proven value, and may be positively harmful.

Chronic Neuropathies

In all patients with peripheral neuropathy full investigations for underlying causes must be undertaken and specific treatment provided when indicated. Physiotherapy is an important part of treatment. In severe cases, splints, callipers and other walking aids will be necessary and occasionally surgical corrective procedures will be required. A programme of rehabilitation should be commenced. In chronic relapsing demyelinating neuropathies, corticosteroid therapy may be helpful and some patients show a satisfactory response to immunosuppressive and cytotoxic drugs.

PLEXUS LESIONS

Herpes Zoster

Herpes zoster is an important cause of pain and muscle wasting in the elderly. The distribution of muscle wasting, which may be severe, is segmental and is due to involvement of anterior horn cells. However, the segmental distribution of the muscle wasting is not always identical to that of the herpetic eruptions.

Malignant Infiltration of the Brachial Plexus

The lower brachial plexus may be involved in apical carcinoma of the lung (Pancoast tumour), carcinoma of the breast and occasionally lymphoma. Pain in the medial aspect of the arm is often a feature and there is progressive weakness and wasting of intrinsic muscles of the hands and of forearm flexors. Sensory loss over the C8/T1 distribution may be detected and a Horner's syndrome is frequently present. Malignant infiltration of the brachial plexus may be difficult to distinguish from radiation neuropathy and entrapment of the brachial plexus due to lymphoedema after treatment of carcinoma of the breast (Thomas and Colby, 1972; Ganel et al., 1979).

Neuralgic Amyotrophy

Neuralgic amyotrophy (brachial neuralgia, paralytic brachial neuritis or brachial plexus neuropathy) is more common in young men but is occasionally seen in elderly patients (Devathasan and Tong, 1980). It may occur spontaneously or follow trauma to the shoulder or injections and vaccinations. The onset is acute with pain in the shoulder and arm. The condition may be localized to muscles of the shoulder girdle, such as the deltoid or supraspinatus, or it may be more generalized in the upper limbs. Pain usually abates but some muscle wasting and weakness generally persist (Turner and Parsonage, 1957).

Cervical Rib

Symptoms of cervical rib usually occur in young women and are rare in the elderly. There is insidious onset of weakness and wasting of the thenar muscles and other intrinsic muscles of the hand and forearm. Sensory loss, if present, is confined to the ulnar side of the hand and forearm (Gilliatt et al., 1970).

Lumbosacral Plexus Lesions

Lumbosacral plexus lesions usually result from malignant infiltration, often from carcinoma of the cervix or uterus, and sometimes from lymphomas. They must be distinguished from lumbar root lesions, femoral neuropathy and diabetic amyotrophy.

ENTRAPMENT NEUROPATHIES

Entrapment and compression neuropathies are common in elderly patients because underlying conditions, such as diabetes, rheumatoid arthritis and malnutrition render the nerve trunks more susceptible to damage and also because decreased mobility increases the risk of nerve compression (Hope, 1980).

Median Nerve

Carpal Tunnel Syndrome

The most common complaint is of pain and numbness in the hand and forearm which is worse at night. Examination may reveal no abnormality but in established cases there is wasting of the median-supplied thenar muscles and sensory loss over the median nerve distribution in the hand. The diagnosis can be confirmed by nerve conduction studies. Rheumatoid arthritis, diabetes, hypothyroidism and acromegaly should be excluded. Mild cases may respond to splinting of the wrist or local injections of hydrocortisone but in more severe cases surgical decompression of the median nerve at the wrist is necessary.

Median Nerve Entrapment in Forearm

The median nerve may also be compressed proximally near the elbow at the level of the pronator teres. The patients usually complain of pain in the forearm and there is weakness of the finger flexors as well as of the median-supplied thenar muscles. The anterior interosseous nerve may be entrapped in the forearm giving rise to weakness of finger flexion without sensory signs.

Ulnar Nerve

The ulnar nerve is commonly compressed at the level of the elbow giving rise to weakness and wasting of the interosseous muscles in the hand with sparing of the thenar muscles and sensory loss over the little and ulnar side of the ring finger. The diagnosis can be confirmed by nerve conduction studies demonstrating a localized lesion at the elbow. Conservative treatment, in which the patients are advised to avoid pressure on the elbow and to wear an elbow pad, should be tried initially. If this fails, surgical treatment by decompression and transposition of the nerve may be necessary.

The ulnar nerve may also be compressed at the level of the wrist, usually as a result of some repetitive manual activity. The deep palmar branch of the ulnar nerve is mainly affected giving rise to wasting of the interossei and sparing of the hypothenar muscles. The diagnosis may be confirmed by nerve conduction studies. Improvement usually occurs by avoiding trauma but surgical exploration may sometimes be required.

Radial Nerve

The most common site of compression of the radial nerve is at the lower end of the spiral groove in the upper arm giving rise to acute wrist drop with weakness of the brachioradialis, wrist and finger extensor muscles and sensory loss over the interdigital cleft between thumb and index finger. Improvement usually occurs with conservative management. The posterior interosseous nerve may be entrapped in the forearm giving rise to weakness of the extensors of the thumb and fingers with sparing of the wrist extensors and brachioradialis muscles and no sensory loss.

Sciatic Nerve

The sciatic nerve may be compressed in the buttock and it may also be injured by misplaced intramuscular injections. There is weakness of the hamstrings, anterior tibial, peroneal and calf muscles. Sensory loss occurs over the appropriate distribution and the ankle jerk is absent.

Lateral Popliteal Nerve

The lateral popliteal (peroneal nerve) is commonly damaged at the level of the neck of the fibula. The symptoms are footdrop and paraesthesiae over the dorsum and lateral aspects of the foot. There is weakness of dorsiflexion and eversion of the foot with preservation of plantar flexion and inversion. The ankle jerk is preserved. Diagnosis can be confirmed by nerve conduction studies and the treatment is nearly always conservative.

Lateral Cutaneous Nerve of the Thigh

Entrapment of the lateral cutaneous nerve of the thigh is common (meralgia paraesthetica). The patients, who are usually obese, complain of an unpleasant burning sensation over the lateral aspect of the thigh. The condition is caused by entrapment of the lateral cutaneous nerve beneath the inguinal ligament. Surgical treatment is rarely required.

Tarsal Tunnel Syndrome

The posterior tibial nerve may be compressed beneath the flexor retinaculum at the ankle giving rise to numbness, pain and burning sensations on the foot which are aggravated by standing and walking. The lesion may be localized by nerve conduction studies and the treatment is by surgical decompression.

MYOPATHIES

Myopathies usually present with proximal muscle weakness although this is not invariably the case. The first symptoms most commonly are weakness in the lower limbs with difficulty being experienced in rising from a chair or walking up hills or steps. Upper limb weakness may be manifested by difficulty in using the arms above the head to comb the hair or to dress and in hanging up washing on the line. Although increasing degrees of atrophy may be observed pathologically in the muscles after the age of 60 (Tomlinson et al., 1969) and there is a decline in measurable muscle strength (Burke et al., 1953), the muscles of healthy elderly subjects appear remarkably powerful when tested by the standard clinical techniques of the neurological examination (Andriola, 1978). Therefore if weakness of muscle groups is elicited by clinical testing, it probably has pathological significance; particular attention should be paid to the power of hip flexors and extensors.

Muscular dystrophies (genetically determined myopathies) very rarely present for the first time in elderly patients but some of the muscular dystrophies are compatible with a normal life-span and so may be seen occasionally in older subjects. Polymyositis is a relatively common cause of muscle pain and weakness and must be distinguished from polymalgia rheumatica. Other causes of muscle pain at rest include the myopathies of metabolic bone disease and acute rhabdomyolysis. Endocrine, toxic and drug-induced myopathies must always be considered in older patients with muscle weakness.

A brief discussion of some of the more common causes of myopathy follows but for more detailed accounts the reader is referred to more comprehensive descriptions of muscle disease (Walton, 1974; Bethlem, 1977; Griggs and Moxley, 1977).

Muscular Dystrophies

Facioscapulohumeral muscular dystrophy. This condition has an autosomal dominant mode of inheritance and usually a benign course. There is pronounced facial weakness, winging of the scapulae, weakness and wasting of biceps and triceps muscles with relative sparing of deltoids, weakness of hip flexors and often involvement of anterior tibial and peroneal muscles.

Limb-girdle muscular dystrophy has a variable age of onset and may not become apparent until late adult life. It has an autosomal recessive mode of inheritance. In the pelvifemoral form, weakness commences and is most pronounced in the pelvic girdle musculature, although mild shoulder girdle weakness and winging of the scapulae are usually present; in the scapulohumeral form, weakness and wasting predominate in the shoulder girdle musculature although the deltoids may be spared.

Scapuloperoneal muscular dystrophy has a dominant or X-linked mode of inheritance or may be sporadic. It usually presents in adult life with foot drop resulting from weakness of anterior tibial and peroneal muscles. The extensor digitorum brevis muscle is spared thus distinguishing the condition from anterior horn cell degenerations and peripheral neuropathies or root lesions. The scapulae are winged, and wasting may involve proximal and distal muscles in the upper limbs.

Ocular and oculopharnyngeal muscular dystrophies usually present in adult life with ptosis, progressive external ophthalmoplegia and sometimes dysphagia. Facial weakness and wasting of sternomastoid muscles may be present. Inheritance is usually autosomal dominant but sporadic cases occur.

Dystrophia myotonica which has an autosomal mode of inheritance is one of the most common forms of the adult muscular dystrophy. Patients have ptosis, marked facial weakness, wasted sternomastoid muscles, distal as well as proximal muscle weakness, frontal baldness, cataracts, testicular atrophy, and abnormalities of carbohydrate metabolism. Myotonia may be demonstrated by difficulty in relaxing the grip or by percussion of the tongue or muscles of the upper limbs. Clinical myotonia is not always apparent, but can nearly always be demonstrated by EMG.

Congenital myopathies, such as nemaline and centronuclear myopathy and central core disease, are very rare in late adult life.

Inherited metabolic myopathies. There are a number of different types of genetically determined metabolic myopathies including glycogen storage disease, disorders or lipid metabolism and mitochondrial myopathies. These disorders, and the familial periodic paralysis which are manifested by attacks of weakness associated with alteration in serum potassium levels, usually present in childhood or early adult life.

Polymyositis and Dermatomyositis

The inflammatory myopathies, polymyositis and dermatomyositis, are important and relatively common forms of muscle disease in the older age groups. Several clinical varieties are recognized: (i) uncomplicated polymyositis, (ii) dermatomyositis, (iii) polymyositis or dermatomyositis secondary to connective tissue diseases, such as polyarteritis, systemic lupus erythematosus, scleroderma and rheumatoid disease, (iv) polymyositis and dermatomyositis secondary to underlying malignancy.

Most commonly, polymyositis presents with progressive weakness affecting predominantly proximal muscles, but on examination a more diffuse muscle weakness may be apparent with weakness of neck flexors and occasionally pharyngeal muscles. Muscle pain and tenderness may be a feature but these symptoms are often absent. Deep tendon reflexes are usually preserved. In dermatomyositis, the typical skin rash in periorbital regions and butterfly area of the face and shoulders is usually present. Sometimes, the onset of the condition may be acute with fever, muscle and joint pain, rapidly progressive weakness and myoglobinuria. Malignancy is present in about 10–15 per cent of adult cases of polymositis and is more common in dermatomyositis and in the older age groups (Rose and Walton, 1966; de Vere and Bradley, 1975). The malignancy is usually carcinoma of the lung, ovary, breast, or gastrointestinal tract, but occasionally reticuloses and other malignancies may be present. About 10 per cent of adult cases are associated with connective tissue disease.

The diagnosis of polymositis depends upon the demonstration of an elevation of the serum creatine phosphokinase (CPK), abnormalities of the EMG and inflammatory changes on the muscle biopsy. In the appropriate clinical context, the diagnosis is established by abnormalities of two of these three investigations (Rose and Walton, 1966). The EMG usually reveals spontaneous fibrillation, and patchy abnormalities consistent with primary muscle disease. The muscle biopsy provides only a small sample of skeletal muscle for examination and the typical changes of necrosis, regeneration and infiltration with inflammatory cells may sometimes be missed. Contrary to popular belief, the erythrocyte sedimentation rate (ESR) is usually not elevated.

Polymyalgia Rheumatica

This is a disease of patients over the age of 50 and is frequently associated with temporal arteritis; giant-cell arteritis may be demonstrated on temporal artery biopsy in a significant proportion of patients with polymyalgia rheumatica (Douglas et al., 1979; Miller and Ferguson, 1979). The symptoms are those of muscle pain and stiffness, especially of the shoulder girdle muscles on àwakening, malaise, weight loss, fatigue and anaemia. The ESR is nearly always elevated above 40 mm/hour; CPK and EMG are normal. Muscle biopsy does not show the inflammatory changes and necrosis of polymositis but there may be atrophy of Type II fibres. The most grave complication is loss of vision due to underlying temporal arteritis. The response to steroids is usually excellent. Since rheumatoid arthritis may present with similar symptoms it should always be excluded (Dimant, 1979; Weinberger, 1980).

Endocrine Myopathies

Thyrotoxicosis, hypothyroidism, acromegaly, Cushing's disease and administration of steroids may all give rise to a proximal myopathy. The EMG shows myopathic changes and the CPK is usually normal. The muscle biopsy shows Type II atrophy in Cushing's disease and steroid myopathy. Hypokalaemia, secondary to purgatives, diuretics, carbenoxolone, and liquorice may cause an acute myopathy with elevated CPK levels.

Metabolic Bone Disease

Metabolic bone disease which may be secondary to hyperparathyroidism, malabsorption, vitamin D deficiency and chronic renal failure causes painful proximal myopathy affecting predominantly the lower limbs.

Sarcoidosis

Sarcoidosis may give rise to a long history of proximal myopathy mainly of the pelvic girdle musculature. Non-caseating granulomas may be seen in the muscle biopsy specimens (Gardner-Thorpe, 1972).

Toxic Myopathies

Alcohol

Excessive alcoholic intake may cause acute rhabdomyolosis with muscle pain, weakness, myoglobinuria and very high CPK levels. A chronic proximal myopathy may occasionally be seen in chronic alcoholism but myopathy is much less common than peripheral neuropathy.

Drugs

A number of drugs may cause an acute or subacute myopathy. They include chloroquine, vincristine, cimetidine, clofibrate, amphetamine, heroin, phencyclidine, emetine and propranolol (Lane and Mastaglia, 1978).

Management of Myopathies

Careful history taking, including details of family history, and physical examination are of prime importance. Details of alcoholic intake, drugs and other diseases should be obtained. Other musculoskeletal disorders which may mimic myopathy such as cervical and lumbar spondylosis, bursitis, supraspinatus tendinitis, osteoarthritis and rheumatoid arthritis should be excluded. Appropriate tests to exclude endocrine myopathies should be performed and a search for associated collagen vascular diseases and underlying malignancy should be carried out. Any underlying conditions to which the myopathy is secondary should be treated.

Polymyositis is best treated initially with prednisone, 60–80 mg per day, and when response has occurred this may be changed to alternate day therapy to reduce the side effects. When an adequate clinical response and fall in CPK levels has occurred the prednisone dosage may be gradually reduced but any sudden reduction in dosage may cause a relapse. Immunosuppressive agents, such as azathioprine, methotrexate and cyclophosphamide, should be administered if there is no improvement on steroid therapy.

MYASTHENIA GRAVIS

Myasthenia gravis is now known to be an autoimmune disorder in which there are circulating antibodies to the acetylcholine receptors on the muscle endplates (Drachman, 1978). It may present in elderly patients with a history of fatiguability relieved by rest and frequently diplopia due to involvement of ocular muscles (McQuillen, 1979). There is a higher incidence of thymic tumours in elderly patients. The diagnosis depends on the clinical history, confirmed by electrophysiological studies, response to edrophonium hydrochloride (Tensilon 5–10 mg i.v.) and the demonstration in the serum of anti-acetylcholine receptor antibodies. In elderly patients, thymectomy should only be considered when a thymoma is present. If a satisfactory response to anti-cholinesterase drugs does not occur, steroid therapy, commencing with small doses (5 mg a day) of prednisone and increasing slowly by 5–10 mg/week should be instigated. Ocular myasthenia often responds dramatically to steroid therapy. If myasthenia gravis does not respond to anticholinesteras or steroid therapy, immunosuppressive drugs may be helpful and plasmapheresis is often of temporary value in severe cases.

Occasionally, myasthenia may occur secondarily to administration of drugs, particularly antibiotics, lithium and anti-arrhythmic drugs.

A *myasthenic syndrome* may occur secondarily to underlying malignancy, particularly carcinoma of the lung. Weakness is usually proximal and temporarily improves with exercise although the fatigue and weakness return after a short period of time. In the myasthenic syndrome, deep tendon reflexes are frequently absent. In contrast to myasthenia gravis electrophysiological studies demonstrate an increase in the amplitude of the muscle action potential with repetitive stimulation. There is a presynaptic defect in the release of acetylcholine from the nerve terminals.

REFERENCES

Andriola M. J. (1978) *Geriatrics* **33** (June) 79.
Arnold M. and Harriman D. G. F. (1970) *J. Neurol. Neurosurg. Psychiatry* **33**, 55.
Asbury A. K. (1975). In: *Peripheral Neuropathy*. Dyck P. J., Thomas P. K. and Lambert E. H. (ed). Philadelphia, Saunders, p. 982.
Bethlem J. (1977) *Myopathies*. Amsterdam, North-Holland.
Burke W. E., Tuttle W. W., Thompson C. W. et al. (1953); *J. Appl. Physiol.* **5**, 628.
Critchley M. (1931) *Lancet* **1**, 1221.

Devathasan G. and Tong H. I. (1980) *Aust. NZ J. Med.* **10**, 188.
Dimant J. (1979) *J. Am. Geriatr. Soc.* **27**, 183
Douglas J. G., Ford M. J., Innes J. A. et al. (1979) *Eur. J. Clin. Invest.* **9**, 137
Drachman D. B. (1978) *N. Engl. J. Med.* **298**, 729
Dyck P. J. (1975) In: Dyck P. J., Thomas P. K. and Lambert E. H. (ed.) *Peripheral Neuropathy.* Philadelphia, Saunders, p. 465.
Dyck P. J., Lais A. C., Ohta M. et al. (1975) *Mayo Clin. Proc.* **50**, 621.
Dyck P. J. and Lambert E. H. (1968) *Arch. Neurol.* **18**, 603.
Dyck P. J., Thomas P. K. and Lambert E. H. (ed.) (1975) *Peripheral Neuropathy.* Philadelphia, Saunders, 2 vols.
Ganel A., Engel J., Sela M. et al. (1979) *Cancer* **44**, 2254.
Gardner-Thorpe C. (1972) *Neurology (Minn)* **22**, 917.
Gilliatt R. W., Le Quesne P. M., Logue V. et al. (1970) *J. Neurol. Neurosurg. Psychiatry* **33**, 615.
Griggs R. C. and Moxley R. T. (ed.) (1977) *Ad. Neurol.* Vol. *17*. New York, Raven Press.
Hope T. (1980) *Geriatrics* **35** (May) 79.
Howell H. E. (1949) *Br. Med. J.* **1**, 56.
Huang C-Y. (1981) *J. Am. Geratr. Soc.* **29**, 49.
Lane R. J. H. and Mastaglia F. L. (1978) *Lancet* **2**, 562.
Lascelles R. G. and Thomas P. K. (1966) *J. Neurol. Neurosurg. Psychiatry* **29**, 40.
Low P. A., McLeod J. G., Turtle J. R. et al. (1974). *Brain* **97**, 139.
McLeod J. G. (1975) In: Dyck P. J., Thomas P. K. and Lambert E. H. (ed.) *Peripheral Neuropathy.* Philadelphia, Saunders, p. 1301.
McLeod J. G., Prineas J. W., Walsh J. C. et al. (1976) *J. Neurol. Sci.* **27**, 145.
McLeod J. G. and Walsh J. C. (1975a) In: Dyck P. J., Thomas P. K. and Lambert E. H. (ed.) *Peripheral Neuropathy.* Philadelphia, Saunders, p. 1314.
McLeod J. G. and Walsh J. C. (1975b) In: Dyck P. J., Thomas P. K. and Lambert E. H. (ed.) *Peripheral Neuropathy.* Philadelphia, Saunders, p. 1012.
McQuillen M. P. (1979) *Geriatrics* **34** (May) 67.
Miller R. D. and Ferguson III E. C. (1979) *Postgrad. Med.* **66**, 177.
Newman H. and Corbin K. B. (1936) *Proc. Soc. Exp. Biol. Med.* **35**, 273.
Ochoa J. and Mair W. G. P. (1969) *Acta Neuropathol. Berl.* **13**, 217.
O'Sullivan D. J. and Swallow M. (1968) *J. Neurol. Neurosurg. Psychiatry*, **31**, 464.
Pallis C. A. and Scott J. R. (1965) *Br. Med. J.* **1**, 1141.
Prineas J. W. and McLeod J. G. (1976) *J. Neurol. Sci.* **27**, 427.
Rose A. L. and Walton J. N. (1966) *Brain* **89**, 747.
Swallow M. (1966) *J. Neurol. Neurosurg. Psychiatry*, **29**, 205.
Thomas J. E. and Colby M. Y. (1972) *J. Am. Med. Assoc.* **222**, 1392.
Thomas P. K. and King R. H. M. (1974) *Brain* **7**, 395.
Tohgi H., Tsukagoshi H. and Toyokura Y. (1977) *Acta Neuropathol. Berl.* **38**, 213.
Tomlinson B. E., Walton J. N. and Rebeiz J. J. (1969) *J. Neurol. Sci.* **9**, 321.
Turner J. W. A. and Parsonage M. J. (1957) *Lancet* **2**, 209.
De Vere R. and Bradley W. G. (1975) *Brain* **98**, 637
Victor M. (1975) In: Dyck P. J., Thomas P. K. and Lambert E. H. (ed.) *Peripheral Neuropathy.* Philadelphia, Saunders, p. 1030.
Walsh J. C. (1971a) *J. Neurol. Neurosurg. Psychiatry* **34**, 42.
Walsh J. C. (1979b) *Arch. Neurol.* **25**, 404.
Walsh J. C. and McLeod J. G. (1970) *J. Neurol. Sci.* **10**, 457.
Walton J. N. (1974) *Disorders of Voluntary Muscle.* 3rd ed. London, Churchill-Livingstone.
Weinberger K. A. (1980) *J. Am. Geriatr. Soc.* **28**, 523.

14. DISORDERS OF THE AUTONOMIC NERVOUS SYSTEM
A. N. Exton-Smith

Impairment of autonomic function produces a variety of clinical manifestations and the most important in old age are orthostatic hypotension and disturbances of thermoregulatory control. In addition, sweating abnormalities, gastrointestinal disturbances, bladder dysfunction and pupillary abnormalities may be present. In elderly subjects compared with young adults hypotension is more readily produced by change in body posture from the lying to the upright position, and lowering of deep body temperature is more likely to occur on exposure to mild or moderate degrees of cold stress. When in addition to this physiological impairment there are pathological processes involving the autonomic nervous system the clinical manifestations are even more marked and can be more readily provoked.

AGE CHANGES IN AUTONOMIC FUNCTION

Several studies in which old people living at home have been examined indicate that impairment of autonomic function is common in old age.

Cardiovascular Reflexes

Caird et al. (1973) found that the incidence of postural hypotension increases with age. A fall of 20 mmHg or more in systolic blood pressure was observed in 16 per cent of subjects aged 65–74 years and in 30 per cent of those aged 75 and over. They believe that autonomic dysfunction is the underlying cause and that this commonly interacts with other factors (*see* p. 187). Gross (1970) also found that impairment of circulatory reflexes increased in frequency with advancing age as manifested by abnormality of the blood pressure response to the Valsalva manoeuvre. Strandell (1964) observed the mean increase in heart rate on standing in middle-aged and elderly subjects was 10–15 beats per minute compared with approximately 20 beats per minute in young adults. Bristow and his colleagues (1969) recorded the reflex bradycardia produced by the rise in pressure following intravenous injection of phenylephrine (25–100 µg) and found a diminished baro-reflex sensitivity with increasing age. It was believed that this was due to decreased distensibility of the arterial wall at the baro-reflex site in old age.

Thermoregulatory Responses

Fox and his colleagues (1973) measured body temperatures in a random sample of 1020 people aged 65 and over living at home in Great Britain during the first three months of 1972. Lowering of deep body temperature as measured by the urine temperature was significantly correlated with advancing age. In 10 per cent of subjects the deep body temperature was less than 35·5 °C; these individuals were thought to have some degree of thermoregulatory failure as shown by an inability to maintain an adequate core–peripheral temperature gradient. The mean difference between the urine temperature and the hand temperature in this group was 2·9 °C compared with 4·6 °C for those in the normal temperature group, whose deep body temperatures were 36·0 °C and above. This was confirmed when a 15 per cent subsample of the 1000 participants in the Camden Survey (also conducted in the first three months of 1972) were submitted to thermoregulatory function

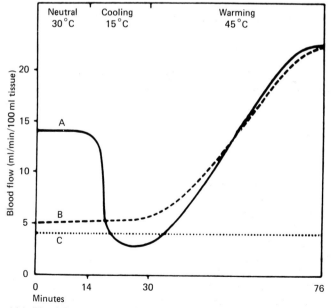

Fig. 14.1. Blood flow responses of (A) normal people; (B) non-constrictors; and (C) non-constrictor/non-dilators.

tests; these involved the measurement of physiological responses to a cycle of neutral, cool and warm environments created by a specially designed air-conditioned test bed. Shivering occurred during the cooling period in 12 per cent of the subjects as compared with 30 per cent of young adults. Sweating occurred in all the young subjects but only in about half the elderly during the period of warming. Abnormal peripheral blood flow patterns on cooling and warming (*Fig.* 14.1) were found in 56 per cent of the men and 45 per cent of the women. These abnormal patterns were rare in the young control subjects. When tests of thermoregulatory function were repeated four years later in 43 of the subjects a significantly higher proportion had low resting peripheral blood flow (less than 5 ml/100 ml hand tissue/min) and a higher proportion had a non-constrictor response on cooling (Collins et al., 1977). In the group with a normal peripheral blood flow pattern there was a significant increase in the deep body temperature required to initiate sweating on warming, compared with the level in the first study.

PATHOLOGICAL CONDITIONS AFFECTING AUTONOMIC FUNCTION

The autonomic nervous system may be involved in a number of pathological processes; the more important of these are listed in *Table* 14.1. The most widespread involvement occurs in the Shy–Drager

Table 14.1. Pathological conditions affecting autonomic function

Central disturbances	Autonomic neuropathy
Shy–Drager syndrome	Diabetes mellitus
Parkinsonism	Malignancy
Wernicke's encephalopathy	Amyloidosis
Cerebrovascular disease	Acute infective polyneuropathy
Tabes dorsalis	Vitamin B complex deficiency
Paraplegia	Chronic alcoholism
Chronic alcoholism	Peripheral acting drugs
Psychotropic drugs	

syndrome, and although this is a rare disease all the manifestations of autonomic failure are to be found in the clinical picture.

Shy–Drager Syndrome
Shy and Drager (1960) described 2 cases of a neurological syndrome associated with orthostatic hypotension, defective sweating and sphincter disturbances, with subsequent appearance of somatic neurological manifestations. The pathological changes included widespread degeneration in the medulla, the posterior hypothalamic region, the

cerebellum, the third nerve nuclei, the basal ganglia, the autonomic ganglia, the dorsal nucleus of the vagus and reduction in the number of cells in the anterolateral column of the spinal cord. Thomas and Schirger (1963) described 30 cases of the syndrome in which the presenting feature was orthostatic hypotension. The age range was from 42 to 74 years, and the condition was three times commoner in men than in women. The onset of the somatoneurological manifestations was usually insidious and followed the known onset of postural hypotension by 6 months to 20 years. Eleven patients had features resembling Parkinsonism.

Parkinsonism

Orthostatic hypotension can occur in patients with paralysis agitans. Aminoff and Wilcox (1971) described the clinical features of 11 Parkinsonian patients in whom autonomic dysfunction was present. Three were cases of the Shy–Drager syndrome in which autonomic symptoms preceded somatic neurological manifestations, while in 8 patients the autonomic symptoms succeeded the somatic manifestations. Investigation of autonomic function showed a resting blood pressure lower than expected for the patient's age and sex, orthostatic hypotension, increased sensitivity to noradrenaline, impairment of thermoregulatory function with patchy loss of sweating and abnormal bladder function. Gross et al. (1972) found that in 20 patients under the age of 63 with idiopathic Parkinsonism the Valsalva responses were normal but the percentage fall in mean blood pressure on passive tilting was significantly greater than in a control group of patients matched for age. Levodopa therapy of patients with uncomplicated Parkinsonism sometimes first reveals evidence of autonomic dysfunction, and it is possible that autonomic disturbances in paralysis agitans occur much more frequently than is generally recognized.

Wernicke's Encephalopathy

Birchfield (1964) found the following clinical features in 40 cases of Wernicke's disease: orthostatic hypotension (32), ophthalmoparesis (26), nystagmus (32), ataxia (in all of the 25 patients tested), peripheral neuropathy (29) and Korsakoff's psychosis (28). The condition is due to thiamine deficiency often associated with alcoholism. Characteristic petechial haemorrhages are to be found in the walls of the third ventricle, the hypothalamus and mammillary bodies. The hypothalamic lesions in Wernicke's encephalopathy can also lead to hypothermia (Philip and Smith, 1973). The disorder of temperature regulation is often overlooked. The response to thiamine administration in Wernicke's encephalopathy is usually dramatic.

Cerebrovascular Disease

Johnson and his colleagues (1965) found that a substantial proportion of the patients in a geriatric department in Oxford suffered from orthostatic hypotension: 17 per cent had a fall in systolic pressure of 20 mmHg or more after standing for 2 min. They attributed this to cerebrovascular disease. At autopsy ischaemic lesions were found at many sites in the brain but not in the spinal cord, hypothalamus or brain stem. Gross (1970) suggested that age and debility rather than cerebrovascular disease might be important factors. Orthostatic hypotension and impairment of thermoregulation may also be due to psychotropic drugs (especially phenothiazines) which are commonly prescribed for patients suffering from the effects of cerebrovascular disease.

Autonomic Neuropathy

Diabetes mellitus is the commonest cause of autonomic neuropathy associated with peripheral neuropathy. Malignancy, especially of the bronchus and pancreas is another important cause in old age. The other conditions listed in *Table* 14.1 are relatively uncommon. In diabetic autonomic neuropathy the symptoms include dizziness and faintness due to postural hypotension, intermittent nocturnal diarrhoea, intermittent vomiting, gastric fullness, dysuria, reduced sweating in the legs, and impairment of temperature regulation, leading to hypothermia. The incidence of peripheral neuropathy as a complication of diabetes is uncertain and the reported frequency varies from 4 to 93 per cent (Roberts, 1970). It is even more difficult to estimate the frequency of autonomic involvement. In one series (Rundles, 1945) 25–30 per cent of patients with sensory or motor neuropathy were considered to have autonomic involvement, and in another series (Odel et al., 1955) the frequency was greater than 75 per cent.

Sharpey-Schafer and Taylor (1960) investigated 337 patients attending a diabetic clinic and found that 69 had diabetic neuropathy. Thirty-five of these were studied fully. Seventeen showed complete absence of circulatory reflexes and 14 a diminution in response to the Valsalva manoeuvre, tipping, coughing, hyperventilation and mental arithmetic. Ewing et al. (1976) emphasized that this condition has a bad prognosis; the mortality in $2\frac{1}{2}$ years in a series of diabetic patients was twice as great when autonomic neuropathy was present as when tests of autonomic function were normal. The authors suggested that in diabetes with clinical features of neuropathy simple autonomic function tests provide a good guide to prognosis.

CLINICAL SYNDROMES

Orthostatic hypotension

Blood pressure regulation depends on cardiac output and peripheral resistance. The heart rate which influences cardiac output is controlled by baroreceptor reflexes originating from the carotid sinus; a fall in blood pressure leads to cardiac acceleration. Peripheral resistance is dependent on vasoconstrictor tone mediated by the sympathetic nervous system. Normally on standing after lying parasympathetic activity decreases, causing cardiac acceleration, and sympathetic activity increases, resulting in constriction of arterioles and veins. About 700 ml of blood leave the chest and are rapidly pooled in the venous reservoirs in the abdomen and legs. The pressure in the right atrium falls to or below the mean intrathoracic pressure and there is diminished return of blood to the right side of the heart. In a fit young adult systemic arterial pressure drops only transiently on standing, and within 15–30 s the pressure returns to the previous level or slightly above. In older people, however, homoeostasis is less well maintained; in an investigation of old people participating in a hypothermia survey 14 per cent were found to have orthostatic hypotension with a fall in systolic blood pressure of 20 mmHg or more on standing (Exton-Smith et al., 1975). In a follow-up survey 4 years later the proportion who had orthostatic hypotension was found to have increased (Collins et al., 1977).

Pathogenesis

Autonomic dysfunction leading to orthostatic hypotension may be due to impairment of the afferent part of the baroreceptor reflex arc (Sharpey-Schafer and Taylor, 1960), to lesions in the central structures (Appenzeller and Descarries, 1964) or to impairment of function in the effector system (Bannister et al., 1967), which is responsible for systemic arteriolar constriction and possibly constriction of venous reservoirs. The cause of the autonomic dysfunction leading to an increasing incidence of orthostatic hypotension with age include an age-related decline in physiological mechanisms and the presence of pathological conditions, some of which are listed in *Table* 14.1. Wilkins et al. (1951) have emphasized that failure to control the splanchnic vascular bed may play an important part in the development of orthostatic hypotension. In diabetic patients with evidence of peripheral neuropathy and presumed autonomic neuropathy demyelination of the greater splanchnic nerve (a major sympathetic pathway) has been demonstrated (Low et al., 1975).

The commonly used drugs which can cause orthostatic hypotension are hypotensive agents, diuretics, levodopa and the phenothiazines. In the Glasgow study (Caird et al., 1973) two or more of the following factors—varicose veins, urinary tract infection, anaemia, hyponatraemia, absent ankle jerks and the use of potentially hypotensive drugs—were present in 50 per cent of subjects with a fall in systolic pressure of 30 mmHg or more and in 17 per cent without orthostatic hypotension ($P < 0.01$). This suggests that orthostatic hypotension in relatively healthy old people has more than one cause.

Clinical Features

In many instances orthostatic hypotension is asymptomatic since autoregulation of the cerebral circulation is able to compensate for the fall in systemic arterial pressure. In other cases, when autoregulation fails, possibly as the result of cerebrovascular disease, or if the orthostatic fall in blood pressure is excessive, the patient complains of weakness, faintness, dizziness, loss of balance or blacking out, especially when rising from the lying position. A fall associated with orthostatic hypotension may lead to fracture or to accidental hypothermia when the old person is living in cold conditions. Whenever orthostatic hypotension is discovered a search should be made for somatic neurological involvement, including peripheral neuropathy, pyramidal tract lesions, olivopontocerebellar degeneration and Parkinsonism. Even in the absence of clinical signs of multiple system degeneration elsewhere in the nervous system it is possible that deterioration in autonomic function is associated with a physiological decline in somatic function. Thus Overstall and his colleagues (1977, 1978) have shown that body sway is greater in those old people with orthostatic hypotension compared with age-matched controls; this increase in sway is unrelated to the level of blood pressure.

Management

Drugs with potentially hypotensive action should be withheld and appropriate treatment should be given to those patients who are found to have a correctable cause of orthostatic hypotension. There are several approaches to the management of severe orthostatic hypotension but most have serious limitations. Pooling of blood on assuming the upright position may be prevented by mechanical means such as the wearing of an anti-gravity suit. Although successful this is not usually a practical measure in the elderly. To be effective elastic stockings have to be full length and used in combination with an elastic abdominal support, these measures, too, are not well tolerated by older patients. The expansion of circulating blood volume by the use of mineralocorticoid hormones is usually ineffective in severe cases. In moderate orthostatic hypotension it may be effective in large doses (fludrocortisone 0·5–2·0 mg/day) but these cause supine hypertension and carry the risk of precipitating cardiac failure or pulmonary oedema. Perkins and Lee (1978) have shown that severe orthostatic hypotension may respond to therapy with the prostaglandin synthetase inhibitor flurbiprofen (50 mg twice daily) combined with fludrocortisone. The patient they describe was able to lead a normal life after three months combined therapy whereas prior to treatment she was unable to stand owing to syncope associated with a fall in blood pressure to an unrecordable level. Recently, Man In't Veld and Schalekamp (1981) have shown that a beta-adrenoreceptor agonist, pindolol, is therapeutically effective in severe orthostatic hypotension. They described 3 patients who were bedridden before treatment; while taking pindolol (15 mg/day) they were able to walk and did not collapse when standing for 15 min. Although increase in supine blood pressure occurred this did not reach hypertensive levels. The use of this treatment requires further evaluation in the elderly since the patients they describe were all under the age of 65. Orthostatic drop in blood pressure still occurred but the autoregulation in the cerebral circulation was able to maintain cerebral perfusion.

Accidental Hypothermia

Homoeothermy, or the capacity to maintain a stable deep body temperature, is an evolutionary development found only in birds, man and other mammals. Ideally, all body tissues would be maintained at optimum temperature but this would be difficult to achieve and costly in energy production. Thus in man and other homoeothermic animals deep body or 'core' temperature is controlled and the superficial or body 'shell' is used as a variable insulator or heat sink. The heart and circulation act as a heat exchanger system. In a warm environment the blood flow to the skin is increased to promote the transfer of heat to the body surface. Under cool conditions the blood flow is reduced to conserve heat. This vasomotor regulation is capable of maintaining homoeothermy only over a limited range of environmental temperatures. As a protection against hyperthermia and hypothermia the additional mechanisms of sweating and shivering are brought into play.

In man, vasomotor control in the skin depends upon vasoconstrictor autonomic nerves and on a vasodilator mechanism. The vasoconstrictor mechanism predominates in the hands and the feet and is only weakly represented in the proximal parts of the limbs and the trunk. Under thermally neutral conditions the blood flow in the hand is within the range 4–10 ml/100 ml hand tissue/min. In a person who feels cold but who is not shivering blood flow is approximately 1 ml/100 ml hand tissue/min and when the body is heated it rises to over 40 ml. A stimulus to vasoconstriction arises mainly from the cold receptors in the skin. Within the vasomotor control zone hand blood flow is very sensitive to small changes in skin temperature in the rest of the body, marked vasoconstriction and vasodilatation being elicited by minor degrees of cooling and warming respectively. The way in which the vasodilator mechanisms operate is unknown. Active vasodilatation begins just before sweating is initiated and is the dominant mechanism for promoting heat loss by increasing transport of heat to the skin for evaporation by sweating.

Hypothermia is defined as 'a state of subnormal body temperature in which the deep body temperature falls below 35·0 °C'. It became recognized in Great Britain during the 1960s as a problem particularly affecting old people. The term 'accidental hypothermia' is used to imply that the lowering of deep body temperature is unintentional and it has to be distinguished from hypothermia which is induced therapeutically.

Incidence

Even up to fifteen years ago accidental hypothermia was thought to be a rare condition. It was known to occur in association with certain diseases, e.g. myxoedema, hypopituitarism and alcoholism. The British Medical Association's Committee on Accidental Hypothermia in the Elderly (1964) reviewed the descriptions of cases reported in the literature and concluded that there was no accurate information on the prevalence of the condition. Hospital reports indicated that very few cases were recognized clinically before admission and elderly people with hypothermia suffered a high mortality.

Duguid et al. (1961) described 23 cases occurring in Scotland. All were elderly and developed hypothermia indoors. Deep body temperatures on admission, as measured by a rectal thermometer, ranged from 22·8 to 31·9 °C. Rosin and Exton-Smith (1964) described 32 patients with hypothermia, half of whom were seen during the very cold winter of 1962–3. With the exception of one, aged 39 years, their ages ranged from 60 to 92 years. Although 10 patients were found lying on the floor, the others suffered from lesser degrees of exposure; 10 were in bed at home, 2 were sitting in a chair and one developed hypothermia in hospital. The Royal College of Physicians' Survey (1966) conducted in 10 hospital groups during the months of February, March and April (1965) established the incidence of hypothermia as 0·68 per cent of all patients admitted, of whom 42 per cent were over the age of 65. These results indicate that about 3800 elderly patients could have been admitted with hypothermia to hospitals in Great

Britain during these three winter months. Ten years later a second Royal College of Physicians' Survey conducted at two London Hospitals in January to April 1975 showed that 3·6 per cent of patients over the age of 65 admitted to hospital were hypothermic, a prevalence considerably higher than that of the previous College study (Goldman et al., 1977).

Aetiology

As in so many disorders of the elderly multiple factors are involved in the aetiology of accidental hypothermia in old people and the more important are shown in *Table* 14.2.

Table 14.2. Causes of accidental hypothermia in the elderly

1. *Exogenous*—cold exposure
2. *Endogenous*— a. Physiological
    i. Impaired thermoregulatory responses
    ii. Impaired temperature perception
    b. Pathological
    i. Endocrine: myxoedema, hypopituitarism, diabetes
    ii. Neurological: hemiplegia, Parkinsonism, Wernicke's encephalopathy
    iii. Locomotor: arthritis and other causes of immobility
    iv. Mental: confusional states, dementia
    v. Infections: bronchopneumonia, septicaemia
    vi. Circulatory: cardiac infarction, pulmonary embolism
    vii. Drugs: phenothiazines, hypnotics and tranquillizers, antidepressants, alcohol
    viii. Miscellaneous: exfoliative dermatitis, steatorrhoea

Exogenous Factors. Exposure to cold is an overriding cause, and the Royal College of Physicians' Survey (1966) showed a clear relationship between the incidence of hypothermia and a low environmental temperature. The number of cases rose considerably when the ambient temperature fell below 0 °C. Many elderly people living at home who develop hypothermia have some common characteristics; they usually live alone under cold conditions, their houses lack basic amenities, and they have a high incidence of impaired mobility, nocturia, insomnia and liability to falls (Fox et al., 1973; Collins et al., 1977; Exton-Smith, 1977; Goldman et al., 1977). A common story is of an old person who falls after attempting to get out of bed at night; he remains on the floor for several hours, often partly clad, and is discovered the next day by a neighbour or a home help. Thus the exposure is likely to be longer when the old person lives alone and is socially isolated.

In many cases, however, exposure is minimal, and in some cases elderly people develop hypothermia under mild weather conditions.

Such a patient may be found in bed apparently well covered with clothes. Although in these instances insufficient body heat is being generated, so that even good external insulation is ineffective, in the majority of cases endogenous factors are of greater importance.

Endogenous Factors. The high incidence of accidental hypothermia in old people can mainly be accounted for by the physiological decline in thermoregulatory function which has been clearly revealed in both cross-sectional and longitudinal studies. The impairment of thermoregulatory reflexes has also been demonstrated in the survivors of accidental hypothermia (Macmillan et al., 1967); on moderate cooling shivering was absent, the metabolic rate did not rise and there was defective vasoconstriction. As a result the deep body temperature fell abnormally and progressively. These patients are at risk of developing further attacks of hypothermia which may be precipitated by moderate cold exposure or by the use of small doses of drugs with a hypothermic action, such as the phenothiazines.

In addition to impaired thermoregulatory function, many old people have a diminished sensitivity to cold. Tests of digital thermosensation (Collins et al., 1977) show that young people perceive mean temperature differences of about $0.8\,°C$ whereas elderly subjects can discriminate only between mean temperature differences of $2.5\,°C$. Some are unable to perceive differences of $5\,°C$ or more. Moreover, it has been shown that when old people are given the opportunity of controlling their own thermal environment many of them are less precise in making the necessary temperature adjustments and take longer in attaining the optimum temperature for thermal comfort (Collins et al., 1981; Collins and Hoinville, 1981). It is likely that a lesser sensitivity to cold is one of the reasons for the relatively large numbers of old people who appear to be able to tolerate cold conditions without discomfort. Nevertheless such individuals may be at risk of overtaxing the heat-conserving capacity of a failing thermoregulatory system.

Although some old people admitted to hospital suffer from primary accidental hypothermia (i.e. hypothermia resulting from cold exposure and failing thermoregulation), in the majority pathological conditions are present. A stroke may be responsible for the initial fall and cold exposure, because the patient remains immobile on the floor. In a number of neurological and locomotor disorders immobility is a factor limiting the amount of heat generated, and in Parkinsonism there may be an additional factor of autonomic dysfunction. Patients with confusional states and dementia may be unaware of environmental hazards and there is some evidence for impairment of temperature regulation in dementia. The psychotropic drugs commonly prescribed for these conditions also affect thermoregulation. Bronchopneumonia can precipitate hypothermia, and it usually develops insidiously in those suffering from hypothermia due to other causes. Other severe infections, cardiac infarction, and pulmonary embolism can cause an acute derangement of thermoregulatory mechanisms.

Clinical Features

The patient usually has a grey colour due to a mixture of pallor and cyanosis. The skin is cold to the touch not only in exposed parts of the body but also in those parts normally covered, e.g. the axillae and abdominal wall. The puffy facial appearance, the slow cerebration and a husky voice may be mistaken for myxoedema. The diagnosis can be established by measurement of the rectal temperature using a low reading clinical thermometer, which should read down to 25 °C.

An acute confusional state is often a salient feature. Drowsiness is usually apparent when the deep body temperature falls below 32 °C. The lower the body temperature the more likely is the patient to be comatose. In the series described by Rosin and Exton-Smith (1964) three-quarters of those with a rectal temperature below 27 °C were unconscious.

As the body temperature falls the reflexes become progressively depressed, shivering is usually absent and becomes replaced by muscle hypertonus, which gives rise to neck stiffness simulating meningism, and to rigidity of the abdominal wall. An involuntary flapping tremor in the arms and legs has been observed in some patients (Rosin and Exton-Smith, 1964).

The heart rate slows in response to cold due to sinus bradycardia or slow atrial fibrillation. The electrocardiogram usually shows some degree of heart block with an increase in P–R interval (in patients with sinus rhythm), and there is delay in intraventricular conduction. A pathognomonic sign is the appearance of a J wave shown by a characteristic deflection at the junction of the QRS and ST segment (Osborn, 1953; Emslie-Smith, 1958). The size of the J wave varies from patient to patient and is not related to the severity of hypothermia; the J wave is often absent altogether even in severe hypothermia. In any one individual the height of the wave diminishes as the patient recovers and the deep body temperature rises. A fall in arterial blood pressure is an ominous sign.

In severe hypothermia respirations are slow and shallow; this can progress to apnoea. The arterial Po_2 is low and the oxygen dissociation curve is shifted so that less oxygen is given up to the tissues at a given partial pressure of oxygen. The effect is to produce tissue anoxia, and this may be an important adverse factor influencing prognosis (McNicol and Smith, 1964). When hypopnoea is marked the Pco_2 may be so greatly elevated as to give rise to respiratory failure. Broncho-pneumonia may be present without the usual clinical signs; the basal crepitations which are often present may be due to cold injury to the alveoli.

Gastric dilatation is common and gives rise to the risk of aspiration of gastric contents. Acute ulceration of the stomach can cause haematemesis. Acute pancreatitis is often found at post-mortem examination but during life it is usually overlooked since few of the typical signs are present in the hypothermic patient. It should be suspected if the patient winces when firm pressure is applied to the epigastrium. A rise in the serum amylase was found in 11 of the 15 cases tested by Duguid et al. (1961).

Renal blood flow and glomerular filtration rate are decreased and tubular function is impaired. Oliguria is common and acute tubular necrosis can occur. This may be due to a combination of ischaemia and the direct effect of cold on the kidneys.

Haemoglobin and haematocrit may be raised owing to a decrease in plasma volume. A moderate elevation of the white cell count often occurs but a normal or low white cell count does not exclude the possibility of an infection, such as bronchopneumonia. Thrombocytopenia is not uncommon and this has been attributed to sequestration of platelets in the liver and spleen; it can give rise to bleeding. Multiple infarcts may occur in the myocardium, viscera, limbs or pancreas (Duguid et al., 1961).

The blood urea is usually moderately raised and the pattern of serum electrolytes varies according to the degree of renal and respiratory failure. Blood sugar concentrations above 6·7 mmol/l are common; in the absence of diabetes mellitus blood sugar returns to normal as the patient's temperature rises. In the series reported by Mills (1973) none of the non-diabetic patients who subsequently survived and who had an initial blood sugar above 6·7 mmol/l was found to have developed diabetes mellitus. Occasionally profound hypoglycaemia occurs.

Raised serum levels of the muscle enzymes aspartate aminotransferase, hydroxybutyrate dehydrogenase and creatine kinase are often found. Very high levels of these enzymes should lead to the suspicion that hypothermia is secondary to myxoedema; the levels fall to normal and deep body temperature rises even before thyroid replacement is started (Maclean et al., 1968). When myxoedema is suspected to be an underlying cause of hypothermia the diagnosis of hypothyroidism should be confirmed by assay of serum levels of tri-iodothyronine and thyroxine and by measurement of the serum TSH levels. Low levels of T3 and T4 and raised TSH are typical of primary myxoedema but the extent to which the levels of these hormones are influenced by hypothermia in the absence of myxoedema is not known. Caution is thus required in the interpretation of the results of these assays. Moreover, it is known that serum T3 levels can be depressed in severely ill patients in the absence of hypothyroidism and hypothermia.

A raised level of plasma cortisol is frequently found in hypothermia and is a good indicator of the patient's prognosis (Maclean and Browning, 1975a). There is also evidence that cortisol utilization during hypothermia is often very poor or even absent (Maclean and Browning, 1975b).

Prognosis

There are several factors which influence the outcome of patients suffering from accidental hypothermia. Both surveys carried out on behalf of the Royal College of Physicians (Royal College of Physicians of London, 1966; Goldman et al., 1977) clearly showed an inverse relationship between the deep body temperature and mortality. In addition to the severity of hypothermia outcome is also influenced by its duration; the longer the period during which low deep body temperatures are maintained the greater the likelihood of serious metabolic disturbances and the development of irreversible complications. The nature of the underlying disease responsible for hypothermia has a considerable influence on outcome, especially in elderly patients in whom multiple pathological processes are present (Exton-Smith, 1973). Prognosis is better when the causal disease is reversible or can be reaily treated, e.g. when hypothermia is secondary to the administration of phenothiazines or if thiamine deficiency in Wernicke's encephalopathy is corrected.

Management

Ideally a rapid restoration of normal temperature would be the best method of treatment since it should avoid some of the complications resulting from a long duration of hypothermia. Although rapid active surface rewarming can be practised as standard management in fit young adults who suffer from primary hypothermia due to cold immersion or exposure, such a procedure is hazardous in the elderly and frequently leads to circulatory collapse and an 'after drop' in the core temperature, which may precipitate cardiac dysrhythmias. It is therefore generally advocated that there should be no active rewarming, the patient should be lightly covered on the ward at an ambient temperature of 25 °C, and the body temperature should be allowed to come up very slowly. One of the two therapeutic regimens summarized in *Table* 14.3 can be instituted according to the degree of hypothermia. The measures outlined in these two regimens can be regarded as standard for the majority of cases of accidental hypothermia. For the individual patient, however, more detailed consideration has to be given to the use of some of these measures.

The low arterial P_{O_2} levels which occur in hypothermia produce

Table 14.3. Management of accidental hypothermia

Mild Hypothermia (Deep body temperature 32–35 °C)
  i. Room temperature of cubicle 25–27 °C; deep body temperature allowed to rise at about 0·5 °C/h
 ii. Barrier nursing. Administration of a broad-spectrum antibiotic
iii. Controlled oxygen administration by means of a Venturi mask
 iv. Pulse and blood pressure monitoring; if there is a fall in the blood pressure during the treatment the patient is cooled again temporarily by lowering the room temperature
  v. Active measures for the prevention of pressure sores (e.g. large-cell ripple mattress)

Moderate to Severe Hypothermia (Deep body temperature < 32 °C)
Additional measures to above, requiring treatment in an Intensive Care Unit
  i. Institution of positive-pressure ventilation to correct hypoxia and to re-expand collapsed alveoli
 ii. Insertion of central venous catheter for measurement of pressure and administration of warm fluids
iii. Correction of dehydration and electrolyte disturbances
 iv. Loading dose of intravenous prophylactic antibiotic, e.g. ampicillin or cloxacillin
  v. Monitoring of deep body temperature either continuously, i.e. thermistor in external auditory meatus, or half-hourly (rectal thermometer)
 vi. ECG monitoring for cardiac dysrhythmias

---

tissue anoxia. For patients whose rewarming proceeds satisfactorily the administration of pure oxygen is usually successful in restoring arterial oxygen levels to normal. When there is severe depression of the respiratory centre especially in hypothermia secondary to psychotropic drugs, anoxia may be the only stimulus driving respiration. In these cases oxygen therapy alone causes apnoea and it is essential to institute artificial ventilation. Ledingham and Mone (1972) have reported good results from the use of intermittent positive-pressure ventilation in hypoxic hypothermic patients.

Severe alterations in fluid and electrolyte balance can occur in hypothermia, especially in seriously ill or comatose patients. Monitoring of central venous pressure is essential in order to minimize the risk of pulmonary oedema following intravenous fluid replacement. Abnormal water retention, haemodilution and very low serum electrolyte concentrations are also features of hypothermia associated with longstanding myxoedema or hypopituitarism. Treatment with intravenous hypertonic saline should be avoided since it may precipitate pulmonary oedema. It may be necessary to use high doses of fludrocortisone (0·5–2·0 mg/day) if there is no response to fluid restriction alone over a period of 2–3 days.

If present, hyperkalaemia presents a serious hazard and requires prompt treatment. It can be due to several causes, such as renal failure, glycogen depletion and skeletal muscle damage. The usual electrocardiographic signs are often obscured by the ECG changes due to hypothermia itself. Since hypothermia enhances the toxic effects of potassium, ventricular fibrillation may occur suddenly or with little warning (Maclean and Emslie-Smith, 1972). It is best treated through stimulating glycogen synthesis by the intravenous administration of soluble insulin and glucose.

In many hypothermic patients who die shortly after recovering normal body temperature, extensive bronchopneumonic changes unsuspected during life are found at post-mortem examination. Although in comatose patients the routine use of antibiotics to prevent infection is of doubtful value, occult infection is so often already present in hypothermia that it is advisable to use a wide-spectrum antibiotic, such as intravenous ampicillin (or ampicillin combined with cloxacillin) until the deep body temperature returns to normal levels.

Thyroid hormones should not be administered to hypothyroid patients. Only if there is a strong suspicion from the clinical history or laboratory evidence that hypothermia is due to myxoedema should triiodothyronine be given in small doses (10 μg 2–3 times a day).

It is now recognized that the routine use of hydrocortisone is not required for treatment of accidental hypothermia. Maclean and Emslie-Smith (1972) have shown that not only are plasma 11-OHCS levels elevated in most hypothermic patients but utilization of cortisol is impaired. They have also shown that hypotension in hypothermia is not usually associated with low cortisol levels.

TESTS OF AUTONOMIC FUNCTION

Many investigations of autonomic function which are commonly used in younger subjects are less suitable for the elderly; these include the measurements of cardiovascular responses to static work, apnoeic face immersion, the Valsalva manoeuvre and cold pressor tests. In the elderly, non-invasive techniques which require little physical or mental effort by the subject are more appropriate. Collins and his colleagues (1980) have reported the results of investigation of autonomic function by means of three tests: (a) beat-to-beat variation in heart rate during postural change, (b) vasomotor thermoregulatory function, and (c) lower body negative pressure.

Heart Rate Response to Standing

The heart rate responsiveness on standing is diminished with increasing age; in young adults the increase is reported to be nearly 20 beats per minute and in middle and old age, 10–15 beats per minute (Strandell, 1964). In young subjects Ewing et al. (1976) found that the most pronounced decrease in R–R interval occurred usually at the 15th beat, followed by a maximum increase in the interval at the 30th beat after standing. This response was consistent in young and older controls but was absent in diabetic patients with autonomic neuropathy. The '30:15' ratio may not, however, be a reliable estimate particularly as the presence of sinus arrhythmia can significantly influence the value of a pre-selected interbeat interval (Oliver, 1978). In the investigations by Collins et al. (1980) comparison of heart rate responses in 9 normal control subjects (mean age 24 years) with 11 healthy elderly without evidence of postural hypotension or sinus arrhythmia (mean age 75 years) showed a pronounced flattening of the response in the elderly (*Fig.* 14.2).

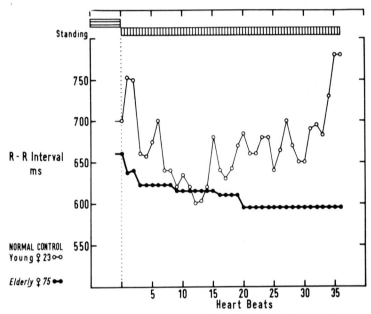

Fig. 14.2. The heart rate response on change from lying to standing position by R–R interval in a young subject and an elderly subject.

Vasomotor Thermoregulatory Function

A test of thermoregulatory function designed to study temperature control in the zone of vasomotor regulation, i.e. between the initiation of sweating or of shivering, has been developed for investigation of elderly patients. The test involves the measurement of physiological responses to a cycle of neutral, cool and warm environments created by an especially designed air-conditioned test bed (Fox, 1969) and has proved acceptable to the elderly. One-third of the elderly healthy subjects exhibited abnormal reflex blood flow responses of the hand mainly as the result of a poor vasoconstrictor response during cooling

(Collins et al., 1977, 1980). Forty-three per cent of those with abnormal motor responses to cooling and only 10 per cent of those with normal responses were found to have postural hypotension indicated by a fall in systolic blood pressure upon standing of 20 mmHg or more. In 3 elderly patients who had recovered from episodes of spontaneous hypothermia and in a patient with the Shy–Drager syndrome the constrictor response to cooling was considerably reduced and, in addition, there was a diminished vasodilator response on warming.

Lower Body Negative Pressure (LBNP)

Negative pressure applied to the lower body causes an increased pooling of blood in the lower extremities and the physiological responses include an increase in heart rate, decreased systolic and mean blood pressures, decreased pulse pressure, a reduction in peripheral and central blood flows and decreased cardiac output. A progressive LBNP

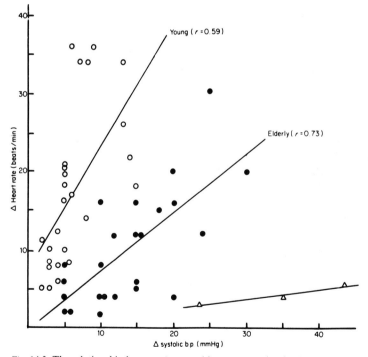

Fig. 14.3. The relationship between increased heart rate and reduction in systolic blood pressure in healthy elderly and young subjects during LBNP tets. (O) young adults (17–35 years), (●) elderly (66–85 years) and (△) a 70-year-old patient with Shy–Drager syndrome.

test is well tolerated by elderly people and avoids the practical difficulties inherent in postural tests on relatively immobile patients. Collins and his colleagues (1980) have studied the normal pattern of response in young and elderly subjects to a sequence of two-minute periods of LBNP (-10, -20, -30, -40 and -50 mmHg) separated by three-minute control intervals. Reduction in systolic blood pressure with little change in diastolic pressure and an increase in heart rate occurred earlier at smaller imposed negative pressures in the elderly than in the young (*Fig.* 14.3).

The regression of change in blood pressure with change in heart rate during LBNP shows a significant age-related difference in this haemodynamic relationship; a given fall in systolic blood pressure in the elderly is accompanied by a much smaller increment in heart rate (*Fig.* 14.3). In the extreme case of a 70-year-old woman with Shy–Drager syndrome there was virtually no change in heart rate although blood pressure fell precipitously with LBNP. Four elderly patients who were found to have an atonic bladder on urodynamic investigation also showed a marked intolerance to LBNP. On the other hand, those elderly patients whose urinary incontinence was due to detrusor instability were found to have normal blood pressure control for their age during the LBNP test.

REFERENCES

Aminoff M. J. and Wilcox C. S. (1971) *Br. Med. J.* **4**, 80.
Appenzeller O. and Descarries L. (1964) *N. Engl. J. Med.* **271**, 820.
Bannister R., Ardill L. and Fentem P. (1967) *Brain* **90**, 725.
Birchfield R. I. (1964) *Am. J. Med.* **36**, 404.
Bristow J. C., Gribbon B., Honour A. J. et al. (1969) *J. Physiol.* **202**, 45.
British Medical Association Memorandum (1964) *Br. Med. J.* **2**, 1255.
Caird F. I., Andrews G. R. and Kennedy R. D. (1973) *Br. Heart J.* **35**, 527.
Collins K. J., Doré C., Exton-Smith A. N. et al. (1977) *Br. Med. J.* **1**, 353.
Collins K. J., Exton-Smith A. N. and Doré C. (1981) *Br. Med. J.* **282**, 175.
Collins K. J., James M. H. et al. (1980) *Age Ageing* **9**, 17.
Collins K. J. and Hoinville E. (1981) *Bldg Serv. Engin. Res. & Tech.* **1**, 165.
Duguid H., Simpson R. G. and Stowers J. M. (1961) *Lancet* **2**, 1213.
Emslie-Smith D. (1958) *Lancet* **2**, 492.
Ewing D. J., Campbell I. W. and Clarke B. F. (1976) *Lancet* **1**, 601.
Exton-Smith A. N. (1973) *Br. Med. J.* **4**, 727.
Exton-Smith A. N. (1977) In: Exton-Smith A. N. and Grimley Evans J. (ed.) *Care of the Elderly: Meeting the Challenge of Dependency.* London, Academic Press.
Exton-Smith A. N., Green M. F. and Fox R. H. (1975) In: Proceedings of the 10th International Congress of Gerontology, Jerusalem.
Fox R. H. (1969) In: Weiner J. S. and Lurie J. A. (ed.) *Human Biology. A Guide to Field Methods.* Oxford, Blackwell. p. 359.
Fox R. H., Woodward P. M., Exton-Smith A. N. et al. (1973) *Br. Med. J.* **1**, 200.
Goldman A., Exton-Smith A. N., Francis G. et al. (1977) *J. Roy. Coll. Phys.* **11**, 291.
Gross M. (1970) *Clin. Sci.* **38**, 491.
Gross M., Bannister R. and Godwin-Austen R. (1972) *Lancet* **1**, 174.
Johnson R. H., Smith A. C., Spalding J. M. K. et al. (1965) *Lancet* **1**, 731.

Ledingham I. McA. and Mone J. G. (1972) *Lancet* **1**, 534.
Low P. A., Walsh J. C., Huang C. Y. et al. (1975) *Brain* **98**, 341.
Maclean D., Griffiths T. D. and Emslie-Smith D. (1968) *Lancet* **2**, 1266.
Maclean D. and Emslie-Smith D. (1972) *Accidental Hypothermia.* Oxford, Blackwell.
Maclean D. and Browning M. C. K. (1975a) *Resuscitation* **3**, 249.
Maclean D. and Browning M. C. K. (1975b) *Resuscitation* **3**, 257.
Macmillan A. L., Corbett J. L., Johnson R. H. et al. (1967) *Lancet* **2**, 165.
McNicol M. W. and Smith R. (1964) *Br. Med. J.* **1**, 19.
Man In't Veld A. J. and Schalekamp M. A. D. H. (1981) *Br. Med. J.* **282**, 929.
Mills G. (1973) *Br. J. Hosp. Med.* **9**, 691.
Odel M. H., Roth G. M. and Kealing F. R. (1955) *Diabetes* **4**, 92.
Oliver D. J. (1978) *Br. Med. J.* **1**, 1349.
Osborn J. J. (1953) *Am. J. Physiol.* **175**, 389.
Overstall P. W., Imms F. I., Exton-Smith A. N. et al. (1977) *Br. Med. J.* **1**, 261.
Overstall P. W., Johnson A. L. and Exton-Smith A. N. (1978) *Age Ageing* **7** (Suppl.), 92.
Perkins C. M. and Lee M. R. (1978) *Lancet* **2**, 1058.
Philip G. and Smith J. F. (1973) *Lancet* **2**, 122.
Roberts A. H. (1970) *Br. Med. J.* **1**, 33.
Rosin A. and Exton-Smith A. N. (1964) *Br. Med. J.* **1**, 16.
Royal College of Physicians of London (1966): Report of Committee on Accidental
    Hypothermia.
Rundles R. W. (1945) *Medicine* **24**, 111.
Sharpey-Schafer E. P. and Taylor P. J. (1960) *Lancet* **1**, 559.
Shy G. M. and Drager G. A. (1960) *Arch. Neurol.* **2**, 511.
Strandell T. (1964) *Acta Med. Scand.* **175**, Suppl. 414, 1.
Thomas J. E. and Schirger A. (1963) *Arch. Neurol.* **8**, 204.
Wilkins R. W., Culbertson J. W. and Ingelfinger F. L. (1951) *J. Clin. Invest.* **30**, 312.

15. HEAD INJURIES IN THE ELDERLY
Bryan Jennett

Head injury is a major cause of death and disability in westernized countries. It looms large as a cause of death in younger age groups, where there are now few competing causes. But head injury is quite a common event in the elderly, and older patients more often develop both intracranial and extracranial complications; the mortality rate after more severe head injuries is very much higher in the elderly. Chronic subdural haematoma is more frequently encountered in older people: it has many features that separate it from the problem posed by acute head injury, and it is therefore better discussed on its own at the end of the chapter.

Head injuries are widely dispersed throughout the health care system, but until recently most reports applied either to patients admitted to general hospitals or to those transferred to neurosurgeons. Comprehensive studies in Scotland have, however, included surveys of attenders at accident/emergency (A/E) departments (Strang et al., 1978), admissions to primary surgical wards (MacMillan et al., 1979), transfers to neurosurgical wards (Jennett, Murray et al., 1977) and fatalities that never reach hospital (Jennett and Carlin, 1978). Comparisons with England and Wales and with some other countries have provided a broad picture of the epidemiology of head injury (Jennett et al., 1977; Jennett and MacMillan, 1981). An international data bank of severe head injuries has also been established in Glasgow (Jennett, Teasdale et al., 1977), and a special study has been made of acute intracranial haematoma (Teasdale and Galbraith, 1981). This chapter is based on these various studies, and on the book on the management of head injuries recently published by the Glasgow school (Jennett and Teasdale, 1981).

FREQUENCY AND CAUSES OF INJURY

About a million newly head-injured patients attend accident/ emergency departments in Britain each year, and about 1 in 5 is admitted to hospital. Two-thirds of these are discharged within 48 hours whilst about 5 per cent are transferred to regional neurosurgical units because the initial injury has been severe or because complications are suspected.

Elderly patients (over 64 years) make up 6 per cent of attenders at accident/emergency departments after recent head injury, but 9 per cent of admissions—because a greater proportion of older patients are admitted to primary surgical wards, where they stay twice as long as younger patients. About 12 per cent of neurosurgical transfers and 13 per cent of acute intracranial haematomas in Glasgow are over 64 years of age as are 11 per cent of the several hundred severe injuries in the international data bank. The best guide to the incidence of injury is the population-based annual rate of attendance at accident/emergency departments. This is 829 per 10^5 population over the age of 64 years in Scotland, which is 70 per cent of the rate for the age group 25–64 years.

The causes of head injury vary according to the severity of injury, as well as with age and sex. Thus road accidents (at all ages) account for more than half the fatal and severe surviving head injuries, but for less than a fifth of attenders at accident/emergency departments. In the elderly falls are more common than road accidents as a cause of head injury: about half these falls are alcohol related. And elderly road accident victims are twice as often pedestrians as are younger adults. Assault is a very much less common cause of head injury in the elderly than in the age group 15–64.

PATHOLOGY OF BRAIN DAMAGE

A distinction must be made between damage sustained at the time of impact and that resulting from secondary processes (Adams et al., 1980). The most obvious impact lesions at autopsy are cortical contusions, but these are less important than the widespread microscopic disruption of fibres in the white matter. Indeed the most severely affected patients, in deep coma from the outset and either dying soon or surviving in a vegetative state, usually have such white matter lesions with few contusions and often no fracture. Secondary brain damage results either from raised intracranial pressure, or from systemic hypoxia or hypotension. The former may be due to an acute intracranial haematoma, or to brain swelling around contusions that spreads to involve a whole lobe, or one hemisphere or the whole brain. The latter (systemic insults to the brain) result from extracranial injuries or complications that cause blood loss, or from respiratory insufficiency (or both). The combined effect of raised intracranial pressure and of defective oxygen delivery to the head is to produce hypoxic/ischaemic brain damage. Widespread lesions of this kind are found in the brains of about 90 per cent of patients who die in hospital after head injury; the pattern of these lesions suggests patchy inadequacy of cerebral perfusion. Less common complications are meningitis and fat embolism.

About a third of patients who die in hospital after injury are known to have talked at some stage since injury, indicating that the initial impact damage was not very severe. This sequence of events is more common in elderly patients. In many of these patients who 'talked and died' one or more avoidable adverse events occurred that contributed to their death (Teasdale and Jennett, 1976). These avoidable factors include delay in the recognition or treatment of intracranial haematoma, inadequate treatment of extracranial injuries or their consequences (e.g. blood loss or pneumothorax) and inappropriate care of the airway in the unconscious patient. Most of these avoidable factors occur after the patient reaches hospital, and both mortality and morbidity could be reduced by making a concerted effort to minimize their frequency (Jennett and Carlin, 1978). Indeed this is the objective of the clinical management of the recently head injured patient. This is best considered separately for the patients who are and those who are not in coma.

STATE OF CONSCIOUSNESS AFTER HEAD INJURY

The most consistent and the most significant immediate biological sequel of injury to the head is alteration of consciousness. This reflects the effect on the brain as a whole of acceleration–deceleration forces, most often the result of the head hitting the ground—but it may be some other immovable object. In its most minor form the patient is no more than dazed or stunned momentarily; or he may be limp and unresponsive for a few minutes, but recover rapidly; or he may remain confused or in a coma for hours or days. Even when the patient begins to talk within a minute or so of impact he often remains confused for several minutes, and subsequently he will have no memory of events over a longer period—say half an hour or more. This phenomenon of post-traumatic amnesia (PTA) is important to recognize, and it applies also after more severe injuries; thus the patient who doesn't speak for, say, 6 hours after injury will likely have 24 hours or so of PTA, and this may extend over 3 or 4 weeks after injuries that resulted in several days of coma. During the latter part of the period of PTA the patient may appear to be fully recovered—and may perhaps be interviewed by the police about his accident; yet subsequently he will deny this, because no memory of it was laid down. For this reason patients need to be protected during this period. But PTA is also important because its duration provides a lasting guide to the severity of the *diffuse* brain damage sustained; evidence that is available to doctors who may first see the patient weeks or months after injury, when rehabilitation is the concern. Some of the elderly who sustain head injury will already have had impairment of short-memory before injury, and the assessment both of the degree of confusion immediately after injury, and subsequently of the duration of PTA, may be difficult.

Monitoring conscious level during the first few hours or days after injury is the main feature of observation—for which many patients are admitted briefly to hospital. This is because alterations in conscious level provide the most sensitive guide to recovery or to the development of intracranial complications, particularly those that demand urgent intervention (acute intracranial haematoma). The method now most widely used in many countries, both in general hospitals and in neurosurgical wards is the Glasgow Coma Scale (*Table* 15.1; *Fig.* 15.1).

Table 15.1. Glasgow Coma Scale

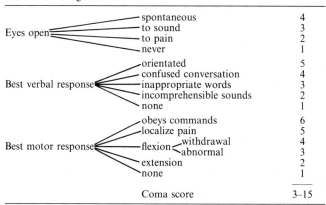

Eyes open	spontaneous	4
	to sound	3
	to pain	2
	never	1
Best verbal response	orientated	5
	confused conversation	4
	inappropriate words	3
	incomprehensible sounds	2
	none	1
Best motor response	obeys commands	6
	localize pain	5
	flexion withdrawal	4
	flexion abnormal	3
	extension	2
	none	1
	Coma score	3–15

This enables nurses to record the patient's conscious state graphically, and progress can be seen at a glance. The terms used in this scale have been evolved over several years to ensure that they have a low inter-observer error and can be readily understood by doctors and nurses who do not have specialized training (Teasdale and Jennett, 1976; Teasdale et al., 1978).

Using this scale coma is defined as no eye opening, not obeying commands and not uttering any understandable words. In such patients other aspects of brain activity have to be observed, in order to assess how deep is the coma and whether it is getting better or worse. These include the size and reaction of the pupils, and the movements of the eyes—both spontaneous and reflex; the latter in response to neck movements (oculocephalic or doll's eye movements), and to cold water irrigation of the ears (oculovestibular reaction). Also the pattern of movements in the four limbs, noting any asymmetry between the two sides which, like inequality of the pupils, may indicate a focal brain lesion (Jennett, Teasdale et al., 1977).

INSTITUTE OF NEUROLOGICAL SCIENCES, GLASGOW

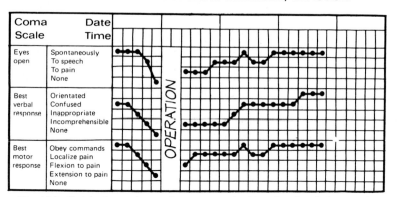

Fig. 15.1. Serial observations using coma scale. Deterioration before, and improvement after operation.

INVESTIGATIONS

Skull radiography is the most important investigation for the talking (often also walking) patient seen in the accident/emergency department—because the decision whether to admit such a patient or to send him home rests largely on whether or not there is a fracture (Jennett, 1980). If there is a linear fracture of the skull vault, the risk that an intracranial haematoma will develop is increased several fold, and the patient should be observed in hospital for 24–48 hours. If there is a scalp laceration, then a depressed fracture under this must be excluded—because simple suture would carry the risk of meningitis or even of intracranial abscess. Even in the patient who obviously has to come into hospital skull radiography should be done—the presence and site of a vault fracture will indicate the possibility of a haematoma developing, and its likely site; and the presence of a basal fracture, and/or the presence of intracranial air will declare the need for antibiotics to anticipate, and hopefully prevent meningitis, subsequent on a dural tear—which may also be evident from CSF rhinorrhoea or otorrhoea.

The *CT head scanner* is highly reliable in detecting intracranial haematoma and it is free of risk. It has transformed the management of the more serious injuries; in particular those in whom there is any suspicion of an acute haematoma. Indeed since its introduction it has become clear that many patients harbour a haematoma long before it is evident clinically; most such patients later deteriorate and often die, if the clot is not promptly removed. But to get a scan usually means transfer to a regional unit, and sensible selection is needed. In our view a scan is required for any patient whose conscious level deteriorates;

and for those who remain confused or comatose for several hours, especially if they have a vault fracture, unless they are obviously moribund, or are very old.

Within neurosurgical units intracranial pressure (ICP) monitoring is now sometimes used, particularly when a haematoma is found unexpectedly on CT scan in a patient who is still talking and not deteriorating; if ICP is raised then the clot requires surgical removal. It is also sometimes used in other circumstances to decide whether non-surgical measures to reduce pressure are required, and if so whether they are being effective. It requires skill to interpret pressure traces, and there is a small risk of infection.

MANAGEMENT OF THE PATIENT WHO IS TALKING

More than 90 per cent of patients are already talking by the time they reach hospital after recent head injury and the main problem for accident departments is how to deal with these patients. Many have scalp lacerations—and the importance of excluding an underlying depressed fracture has been mentioned. At present in Great Britain about 20 per cent of attenders after head injury are admitted, but it is 30 per cent for the over 64-year-olds. If the patient is confused he has to be admitted; compounding factors are alcohol and, in the elderly, the possibility that they were already confused before their injury. Some patients with minor head injuries have to be admitted because of major extracranial injuries; and some because no caring relative is available to take them home. When there is such a relative, and if a fracture has been excluded, it is reasonable to allow home even patients who have been briefly unconscious, if they have now recovered. The relatives must have clear instructions about contacting the hospital in the event of headaches or confusion developing over the next few days.

The development of persisting headache or of increasing confusion or drowsiness raises the question of an intracranial haematoma. Any trace of pupillary inequality, or unilateral limb weakness or the occurrence of a focal fit would increase this suspicion. These symptoms would call for careful clinical observation and consideration of the need for a scan. A fracture would still further increase the likelihood of a haematoma, but it is in the elderly (and in children) that this not infrequently occurs in the absence of skull fracture.

MANAGEMENT OF THE PATIENT IN COMA

Skilled nursing is needed to prevent complications of the unconscious state, in particular respiratory difficulties; and CT scanning is essential to identify remediable intracranial lesions. It is important to remember that only a minority of cases of haematoma have the classic sequence of a lucid interval following initial unconsciousness, followed by confusion and coma for the second time. A remediable haematoma is now quite often found in patients who have been confused or in coma from the beginning—although the prospects for good recovery are much less for such patients, particularly if they are elderly.

Various forms of aggressive non-surgical treatment have been advocated in the last decade or two for the patient still in coma several hours after head injury or as a result of complications, most of them directed at reducing intracranial pressure. These include steroid drugs (often in massive doses), osmotic agents, controlled ventilation and depressant drugs, such as barbiturates. Whilst there are some patients for whom some of these measures may be indicated there is no convincing evidence that their routine use, even in young patients, significantly improves mortality or morbidity (Jennett et al., 1981). In particular, several controlled trials have now failed to show any benefit from the use of high doses of steroids.

OUTCOME AFTER HEAD INJURY

After mild head injury patients frequently suffer somatic and mental symptoms for many weeks—headaches, postural vertigo, poor concentration, hyperacusis. It is now believed that these symptoms are organic in origin, and that only if they are ignored or evoke no sympathy may the patient develop an accident neurosis which aggravates and prolongs the symptoms. Treatment is reassurance, and dealing symptomatically with each aspect in turn.

Table 15.2. Glasgow Outcome Scale

Dead	
Persistent vegetative state	periods of eye opening non-sentient
Severely disabled	conscious but dependent*
Moderately disabled	independent but disabled
Good recovery	may have mild residual but capable of full normal activity

* Dependent defined as requiring the assistance of another person for some activity every day.

After severe injury outcome is now usually assessed on the Glasgow Outcome Scale (Table 15.2). About 90 per cent reach their final grade within 6 months of injury; although some improvement may continue for much longer; the amount of change is seldom enough to justify reclassification into a higher grade than that attained 6 months after injury.

The development of clearly defined scales for rating the initial severity of injury as well as the degree of recovery has enabled the

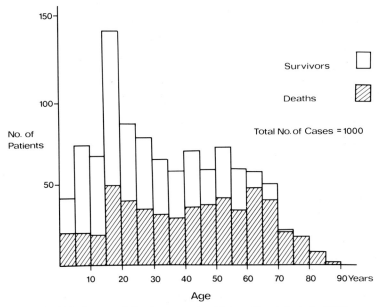

Fig. 15.2. Outcome following severe head injury (Teasdale et al., 1979).

relationship between the two to be explored statistically, using data from many hundreds of patients from several countries now stored on computer in Glasgow (Jennett et al., 1979). It had long been recognized that age was a crucial determinant of outcome after severe head injury, but these studies have enabled us to quantify this relationship more accurately (Teasdale et al., 1981). The pattern is of steadily increasing mortality with age (*Fig.* 15.2) and this applies both to patients who have had an acute intracranial haematoma removed and those who have not (*Table* 15.3). In a more recent analysis of our data we found that of 135 patients over the age of 64 years who were in coma for more than 6 hours less than 5 per cent became independent (moderately disabled or good recovery on the Glasgow Scale). The results in 71 elderly patients who had an acute intracranial haematoma

Table 15.3. Frequency of haematoma and influence on outcome at different ages

Age (years)	Total No. patients	% Dead or vegetative With haematoma	No haematoma
< 20	320	43	29
20–39	284	53	42
40–59	245	57	55
> 60	151	85	90

evacuated were better than this, about a quarter becoming independent; but of course strict selection limited surgery mainly to those considered likely to have a chance of recovery, usually because they were not yet in deep coma. A similar result has been reported for 94 patients with intracranial haematoma over the age of 60 years (Hernesniemi, 1979).

Clearly therefore the circumstances have to be very favourable before embarking on elaborate treatment, and particularly intracranial surgery, in elderly patients who remain in coma for several hours after head injury. In those still in coma after the first day there is little chance of survival, let alone of a reasonable recovery. The good results are mostly in patients whose initial injury was not severe but who then developed an extradural or subdural haematoma which was recognized and evacuated before marked deterioration had occurred.

DISABILITY IN SURVIVORS

Those who survive a severe head injury often suffer for many months from both physical and mental handicap; in some these last for the rest of their lives (Jennett et al., 1981). It is the mental changes that usually prove the most disabling and they interfere with rehabilitation from and adjustment to the physical deficits. These latter include hemiparesis and dysphasia; and cranial nerve palsies (especially anosmia, diplopia and deafness); and epilepsy. The mental effects are most consistently in personality and in memory; some patients also have marked improvement of reasoning capacity, as demonstrated on formal psychometric tests. In young patients the effect of head injury is often described as seeming to have prematurely aged them; in the elderly the effects of brain damage are added to those of pre-existing problems in the mental sphere in some cases, whilst there is obviously less reserve to call on at this age.

CHRONIC SUBDURAL HAEMATOMA

This condition remains somewhat of a mystery in regard to its pathogenesis and the way in which it produces symptoms. About half of the patients operated on are over the age of 64 years, but they do not differ markedly from the younger patients. Only in about half is a head injury identified, and then it has been trivial. Presentation is therefore seldom through accident departments or primary surgical wards, but usually from physicians, geriatricians or psychiatrists. About 40 per cent of patients complain of headache and a similar proportion have a mild hemiparesis. Personality change or 'dementia' is a feature of 30 per cent—with marked fluctuations in about a quarter of cases. Papilloedema occurs in only a fifth and epilepsy in only 10 per cent. The duration of symptoms is usually about 6 weeks, seldom more than 3 months.

A skull fracture occurs in less than 5 per cent and the main value of skull radiography is to show lateral shift of a calcified pineal—a usual finding in the elderly. Isotope scanning can be useful provided it is skilfully interpreted; the normal sagittal sinus frequently misleads the uninitiated into a false diagnosis of subdural haematoma. CT scanning is a reliable investigation, even if the haematoma is isodense. But in the words of a recent Editorial: 'The indiscriminate referral of every ageing and infirm patient with progressive or fluctuating dementia for CT scanning to exclude chronic subdural haematoma reflects both clinical and economic irresponsibility' (Editorial, 1979).

The results of evacuation of the always liquid haematoma by burr holes are excellent. In a recent series of 114 patients 93 per cent had a good result; 4 out of 5 deaths were over 65 years, but only 4 of the 8 who were unimproved after surgery were elderly (Cameron, 1978).

REFERENCES

Adams J. H., Graham D. I., Scott G. et al. (1980) *J. Clin. Path.* **33**, 1132.
Cameron M. M. (1978) *J. Neurol. Neurosurg. Psychiat.* **41**, 834.
Editorial (1979) *Br. Med. J.* **1**, 433.
Hernesniemi J. (1979) *Analysis of Outcome for Head Injured Patients with Poor Prognosis.* University of Helsinki.
Jennett B. (1980) *Clin. Radiol.* **31**, 463.
Jennett B. and Carlin J. (1978) *Injury* **10**, 31.
Jennett B. and MacMillan R. (1981) *Br. Med. J.* **282**, 101.
Jennett B., Murray A., Carlin J. et al. (1977) *Lancet* **11**, 696.
Jennett B., Snoek J., Bond M. R. and Brooks N. (1981) *J. Neurol. Neurosurg. Psychiatry* **44**, 285.
Jennett B. and Teasdale G. (1981) *Management of Head Injuries.* Philadelphia, Davies.
Jennett B., Teasdale G., Braakman R. et al. (1979) *Neurosurgery* **4**, 283.
Jennett B., Teasdale G., Galbraith S. et al. (1977) *J. Neurol. Neurosurg. Psychiatry* **40**, 292
MacMillan R., Strang I. and Jennett B. (1979) *Health Bull.* **37**, 75.
Strang I., MacMillan R. and Jennett B. (1978) *Injury* **10**, 154.
Teasdale G. and Galbraith S. (1981) In: Krayenbuhl H., Maspes P. E. and Sweet W. H. (ed.). *Progress in Neurological Surgery*, Vol. 10. Basel, Karger, p. 252.
Teasdale G. and Jennett B. (1976) *Acta Neurochir.* **34**, 45.
Teasdale G., Knill-Jones R. and Van der Sande J. (1978) *J. Neurol. Neurosurg. Psychiatry* **41**, 603.
Teasdale G., Skene A., Spiegelhalter D. et al. (1981) In: Grossman R. (ed.). *Seminars in Neurological Surgery.* Proceedings of 4th Chicago Conference. New York, Raven Press.
Teasdale G., Skene A., Parker L. et al. (1979) *Acta Neurochir.* Suppl. 28, 140.

16. SPINAL LESIONS
John S. Garfield

GENERAL PRINCIPLES

Physicians will be well aware of the general principles of clinical diagnosis of spinal cord lesions, and apart from a few special aspects, those principles generally apply in the elderly. However, any neural tissue in the elderly has fewer 'reserves' than in the younger patient, and therefore a severe neurological deficit in an elderly person, even 'though the cause may be relieved, is likely to have a particularly poor prognosis. This may lead to conflicting views when the management of an individual is being considered. Thus, the severity of the neurological deficit may be regarded too readily as irreversible simply because of age, and therefore attempts, and particularly surgical attempts, at treatment considered to be unjustified. Conversely, a relatively mild neurological deficit may lead to aggressive surgery without adequate consideration of the hazards and the natural history of the disease in the light of the patient's age.

Spinal cord lesions in the elderly pose particular problems which are in part ethical. The following are matters which the clinician must view *before* embarking upon investigations.

1. Quality of Life

The young paraplegic may achieve a reasonable existence, in part because supporting facilities and organization are generally available. For the elderly, paraplegia is a disaster in that support is often lacking, and other disabilities may prevent full use of the upper limbs, irrespective of the underlying neurological disease. Therefore, contrary to the clinician's initial reaction, age itself will strengthen the case for thorough investigation, especially of thoracic and lumbar lesions leading to paraparesis.

2. Mortality and Morbidity

For the elderly, mortality may be acceptable, but morbidity is not. Therefore, it is right that the approach to spinal disorders is aggressive, even if there is a significant surgical mortality. But if the results of increasing the neurological deficit are significant, as in the surgery of cervical spondylosis, the aggressive course is not acceptable.

3. Unrelated Disability

The presence of severe skeletal deformity and disability, as in rheumatoid or osteoarthritis, must temper the aggressive approach to spinal cord lesions. Few neurosurgeons could be prevailed upon to perform a decompressive thoracic laminectomy in an elderly patient totally confined to chair or bed by severe lower limb deformity. The argument that decompression is justifiable in such a patient simply to preserve cutaneous sensation and some bladder function is rarely persuasive, although on logical grounds it is reasonable if only to improve nursing care.

4. Assessment of Prospects of Survival

Anticipated survival for less than three months irrespective of the neurological lesion, is a reasonable contraindication to spinal surgery in the elderly. With spinal cord or cauda equina compression due to metastatic carcinoma of the breast, even with evidence of widespread bony and visceral metastases, the assessment of survival is often very difficult, especially in the elderly in whom metastases may lie dormant for many years. Therefore, even in the presence of histologically proven malignancy it is reasonable to relieve cord compression due to extradural metastases.

5. Intellectual State and 'the Will to Live'

These two inter-related aspects pose particular problems when dealing with spinal cord disorders and their possible surgical relief. Laminectomy, and especially cervical or extensive lumbar laminectomy, are 'severe' operations for the elderly, and surgical success depends to a considerable extent upon the postoperative intellectual state, determination to co-operate with the physiotherapist, and, perhaps even more, the determination to become self-sufficient at home. If those attributes are lacking balanced decisions about surgery will be weighted towards a conservative view. Particular early postoperative complications in addition to the general complications such as pulmonary embolism and pneumonia, include an acute paranoid state with delusions and illusions and a rejection of nursing and medical care; this is not due to analgesics or opiates, renal failure and pneumonia.

PROBLEMS OF CLINICAL DIAGNOSIS

The classic signs of spinal cord or cauda equina lesions, although familiar to clinicians, bear repetition because in the elderly these simple features may become obscured by other disabilities.

The **essential symptoms** are:

Weakness of the lower limbs or tetraparesis.

Pain of a segmental or root distribution at the level of the lesion.

Pain in the back, especially thoracic and lumbar.

Disturbance of micturition and defaecation.

The **essential signs** are:

Weakness of limbs.

Sensory loss at or below the level of the lesion.

A distended bladder.

It must be stressed that the initial and crucial steps in diagnosis, especially if paraplegia due to cord compression is to be averted, depend upon very simple clinical features and not upon the niceties of detailed neurological examination. Indeed in the elderly certain neurological findings may be misleading (*see below*) because they are often part of the normal process of ageing of the nervous and skeletal systems. The following paragraphs deal with some of the difficulties and pitfalls in clinical assessment.

Lower Limb Weakness

In the elderly a complaint of 'weak legs' is common and is usually due to skeletal rather than neurological disease. The two may coexist, the neurological symptoms and signs being obscured by the skeletal, and the opportunity for early diagnosis of a spinal cord lesion may be lost. (An alternative diagnostic trap is to mistake a fracture of the neck of the femur for osteoarthritis of the hip joint.) Formal testing of lower limb power is, therefore, essential and this can only be done when the patient is recumbent, so that limitation of range of movement at joints cannot mask weakness. An ancillary observation is that of gait, particularly when marked spasticity or foot drop are present, but it is the exception for these features to be obvious in the early stages of a spinal cord lesion.

Upper Limb Weakness

If the weakness is proximal (as in non-metastatic malignant syndromes) it is more readily detected than when distal. Severe rheumatoid arthritis causing profound muscle wasting in the hands may well obscure weakness due to lesions of the lower cervical cord segments or roots, which themselves may be due to cervical spondylosis in association with rheumatoid arthritis. Fortunately, diagnosis in these circumstances does not have the urgency of thoracic and lumbar lesions.

Tendon Reflexes

In the elderly abnormalities of the tendon reflexes may be of limited value in the diagnosis and localization of spinal lesions and in the traditional differentiation between upper and lower motor neurone lesions. With the ageing of the lumbar spine (*see* Degenerative Lumbar Spondylosis), compression of the lumbar roots is common and it is 'normal' for the ankle jerks, and less commonly the knee jerks, to be absent. This may obscure the hyper-reflexia of a cord lesion, and the absence of extensor plantar responses can never be relied upon to exclude such a lesion in those circumstances. Conversely, a mild cervical myelopathy may exist in the elderly without producing any significant deficit, but it may well produce hyper-reflexia. This is irrelevant and indeed confusing when a lumbar lesion is present, and misleading when there is both upper and lower limb hyper-reflexia despite the prime lesion being thoracic cord compression.

Sensory Loss

It is normal in the elderly for vibration sense to be lost in the lower limbs; similarly, but less strikingly, joint position sense may be impaired. Therefore, such findings in themselves are of limited value as evidence of cauda equina or conus lesions, whereas pinprick and light touch, which are usually preserved in the elderly, are of greater diagnostic value. Therefore differentiation between root or cord lesions and a peripheral neuropathy relies heavily upon changes in pinprick rather than upon the other modalities of sensation. These changes with ageing are rarer in the upper limbs. The most valuable abnormality is the trunk sensory level, detected most easily to pinprick, and which despite the confusion of other findings, provides the most accurate and reliable guide to a thoracic cord lesion, and its level.

Muscle Wasting

In the elderly the presence of muscle wasting is of limited value in neurological diagnosis. The 'guttering' of the hands, including the loss of bulk in the thenar and hypothenar eminences which is of such diagnostic value in the younger patient with a lower motor neurone cervical lesion, is most safely discounted in the elderly unless it is unilateral or strikingly asymmetrical. Rheumatoid arthritis weights the finding even more against a neurological origin. In the lower limbs, and especially below the knees, loss of muscle bulk is very common in the elderly, and is of little value even in the diagnosis of peroneal muscular atrophy. Conversely, a cauda equina lesion, such as that in association with degenerative lumbar spondylosis, causing severe pain and marked sensory loss, may produce relatively little wasting, even in the presence of obvious weakness.

Micturition

The detection and assessment of disorders of micturition in the elderly may be particularly difficult. As one of the cardinal symptoms of a cord lesion, and especially of thoracic cord compression, and as the symptom, almost above all others, which may demand immediate investigation and surgical action, this assessment becomes crucial. The pitfall in the male is to ascribe retention or incontinence (retention with overflow) to prostatic hypertrophy, which may indeed be present coincidentally with a spinal cord lesion. Neurological retention is usually painless, although in the early stages (when diagnosis is most desirable) it may be painful. Fortunately, disturbance of micturition is rarely the sole manifestation of a cord lesion, although it may be that of a central cauda equina or conus lesion (Garfield and Lytle, 1970).

In the elderly female assessment may be even more difficult. Incontinence being common, the effect of a cord lesion may pass unnoticed by patient and physician, especially as retention with overflow is usually painless. Therefore the clinical examination must include abdominal palpation and percussion *after voiding* in order to detect the full bladder. The triad of lower limb weakness, a distended bladder and a trunk sensory level to pinprick is sufficient for spinal investigation to be initiated without delay.

CERVICAL SPONDYLOSIS

Cervical spondylosis may be regarded as an exaggeration or acceleration of a normal process of ageing and, therefore, it may be difficult to decide when that process has become excessive and clinically significant in the elderly. A careful neurological examination in many elderly people will reveal signs of cervical myelopathy or a cervical root lesion, attributable to ageing of the cervical spine, in the absence of any functional disability. The *structural and pathological processes* in cervical spondylosis may be summarized as:

1. Osteophytic lipping of the margins of vertebral bodies; posterior osteophytes may compress the spinal cord; posterolateral osteophytes contribute to narrowing of the intervertebral foramina.

2. Degeneration and 'desiccation' of the intervertebral discs with narrowing of disc spaces.

3. Minor degrees of posterior or posterolateral bulging of the annulus fibrosus; the annulus becomes increasingly fibrotic and 'calcified' and merges with the contiguous marginal osteophytes to create 'bony bars' lying transversely which distort and compress the theca. True disc prolapse is rare.

4. Enlargement of the posterior (interlaminar, zygapophyseal) joints contributes to narrowing of the intervertebral foramina.

5. The ligamenta flava becomes thickened and buckled, and contributes to posterior compression of the theca and cord.

6. At the constricted intervertebral foramina there is compression of the emerging nerve roots, and also of the accompanying radicular arteries which make an essential contribution to the blood supply of the spinal cord. These radicular arteries are prominent at C4/5, 5/6 and 6/7, the levels at which spondylotic changes are usually most marked.

7. The blood supply of the spinal cord through the longitudinal systems (anterior and posterior spinal arteries) becomes tenuous in the elderly and is further compromised by the various changes causing narrowing and compression of the theca.

8. If the pre-existing sagittal diameter of the canal is constitutionally small, the effects of the 'spondylotic' changes will be accentuated (Burrows, 1963; Epstein et al., 1979).

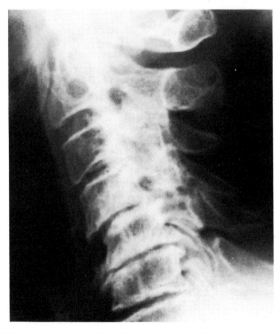

Fig. 16.1. Severe changes of cervical spondylosis with subluxation at C4/5.

9. The degenerative changes at the interlaminar joints and disc spaces may lead to degrees of subluxation and 'steps' in the alignment of vertebral bodies and laminae which produce further and often localized compression of the theca (*Fig.* 16.1). The effects of flexion and extension movements will be exaggerated at those levels.

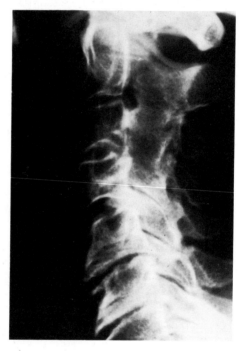

Fig. 16.2. Cervical spondylosis with fusion of laminae of C2, 3 and 4.

10. Relative fusion of vertebral bodies due to the changes at the disc spaces, or congenital fusion of laminae or vertebral bodies (e.g. Klippel–Feil syndrome) will exaggerate the effect of movement and compression at the levels where movement is structurally possible (*Figs.* 16.2 and 16.3).

Clinical Presentation

In the elderly these structural changes may produce radicular and myelopathic manifestations, and in the individual patient it is often difficult to establish which factor or combination of factors is significant (Nurick, 1972a, b). The problem may be one of neural compression, ischaemia, or abnormal movement. Furthermore, the struc-

Fig. 16.3. Same patient as in *Fig.* 16.2. Myelogram showing obstruction at junction between fused and normal laminae.

tural changes shown radiologically may be quite inconsistent with the severity or triviality of symptoms and signs.

1. *Myelopathy*

This presents the greatest problem of diagnosis in the elderly. The onset is insidious and may extend over many years with a gradually progressive spasticity in the lower limbs, rather than overt weakness. This leads to a disability of gait which because it is initially so mild and insidious is easily ascribed to coexistent skeletal disease. Furthermore, objective testing of power may remain normal until the disease is relatively advanced and spasticity severe. It is rare to detect a trunk sensory level, and loss of vibration sense in the lower limbs is no more than normal in the aged. Unlike thoracic cord and cauda equina lesions, disturbance of micturition may be absent or very mild when spasticity and the consequent ataxia are far advanced. Despite the apparent severity of the structural changes shown radiologically, pain in the neck may be trivial, and limitation of cervical movement no more than is usual in the elderly. Finally, a severe myelopathy may be present with little evidence of radiculopathy in the upper limbs despite the presence of gross constrictive changes affecting the cervical intervertebral foramina, and the hyper-reflexia extends as high as the biceps and pectoral jerks.

Differential diagnosis of the myelopathy is that of a very slowly advancing spastic paraparesis or quadriparesis, usually without any segmental level. Multiple sclerosis, a particularly misleading diagnosis, should be considered only to be dismissed on the grounds of lack of dissemination in time and space, age of onset and insidious progression. Ischaemic disease, which indeed may well be the mechanism of the myelopathy, is not acceptable as a primary structural or functional diagnosis. Vitamin B_{12} deficiency leading to subacute combined degeneration, is now very rare, at least in Western societies, and, like the intellectual, is usually accompanied by the general medical manifestations of that deficiency disease. Communicating or normal pressure hydrocephalus in the elderly may mimic cervical spondylosis, at least in its presenting disability of gait (Fischer, 1977). Although spasticity in hydrocephalus may be mild, and the disturbance of gait essentially akinesic or dyskinesic with a tendency to retropulsion, when the dementia of hydrocephalus is mild clinical differentiation may be difficult.

The most difficult differential diagnosis is that of cervical tumour, and it may well be impossible to differentiate clinically between the gradually progressive spasticity of cervical spondylosis and that of a cervical meningioma, or, less commonly, a neurofibroma (Schwannoma), or an intrinsic cord tumour. The diagnoses may coexist and indeed the spondylotic changes may aggravate the presentation of a tumour. The shorter the history the stronger the suspicion of tumour, the commonest in those circumstances being an extradural metastasis, and if destructive bone changes are visible on plain radiographs that diagnosis will be foremost. However, it may be difficult to differentiate radiologically between such changes and those of severe degenerative disease.

2. *Radiculopathy*

In the elderly, progressive weakness and wasting of the hands is the most disabling manifestation of cervical radiculopathy, often with weakness at the shoulder girdles, especially affecting abduction. If accompanied by myelopathy the diagnosis is not difficult, because cervical tumours rarely produce that particular combination of signs. Radiculopathy without obvious myelopathy may be confused with rheumatoid arthritis (and its neuropathy), and peripheral neuropathy, but the asymmetry and proximal findings in spondylotic radiculopathy usually clarify the diagnosis, especially if pain is a feature.

Management

The variety of views on the management of cervical spondylosis is testimony to the generally unsatisfactory methods of treatment, and especially surgery. A reasonable starting point is that any elderly patient becoming disabled due to spasticity (paraparesis or tetraparesis) should be investigated. If plain radiographs show severe degenerative changes in the cervical spine initial management should be immobilization in a well-fitting cervical support, which, ideally, should be worn day and night. A preliminary trial in a soft support is acceptable if the myelopathy is very mild, but cannot provide a reasonable trial of conservative treatment for a severe deficit. Throughout this period the diagnosis should be regarded as provisional. Fortunately, the majority of patients respond to these simple measures, which may be continued indefinitely, the support being worn later only at night. Immobilization in bed while wearing a cervical support may hasten the neurological improvement, but this gain has to be balanced against the ill effects of bed rest in the elderly.

If these simple measures fail after a trial of about 1 month, and there is progressive deterioration, myelography should be done first to exclude a cervical tumour, and second to determine the nature and extent of the spondylotic disease.

The indication for surgery is advancing disability, due to radiculopathy and myelopathy, despite a reasonable trial of immobilization in a well-fitting cervical support. In the elderly, results of surgery are often impossible to foretell in the individual; the hazards are significant in terms of worsening of especially the myelopathy, and the procedure is a very major one to which the patient may react unfavourably (*see* General Principles, p. 212). The technical objective is to decompress the theca posteriorly by a laminectomy, with removal of the thickened and buckled ligamenta flava. When the features of radiculopathy with pain are severe, the decompression is extended laterally to expose the appropriate nerve roots at the intervertebral foramina. In the past, attempts to improve the mobility of the cord by opening the dura and dividing dentate ligaments have been disappointing.

The alternative anterior approach with removal of intervertebral disc and inter-body fusion is more appropriate in the younger (middle-aged) patients where the compression is predominantly anterior and restricted to one or two intervertebral levels. In the elderly the factors in compression (*see* Structural and Pathological Processes, *above*) demand a posterior decompression over at least three segments, and more commonly from C2 to C7. The long-term results of surgery in one series in the age group of 61–70 were that 54 per cent achieved a fair result, 12 per cent a good result, in 16 per cent there was no change and in 16 per cent deterioration occurred (Guidetti and Fortuna, 1969). The results of anterior decompression for myelopathy remain unpredictable, and may be no better than with conservative management (Lunsford et al., 1980).

If subluxation is present a preoperative period of traction with stabilization in a halo-pelvic splint may be necessary, and at the time of decompressive laminectomy, posterior fusion by onlay tibial bone graft may be done.

RHEUMATOID ARTHRITIS

The presence of severe rheumatoid arthritis may aggravate the pathological changes and clinical effects of cervical spondylosis. Prolonged administration of steroids may increase the porotic changes in the

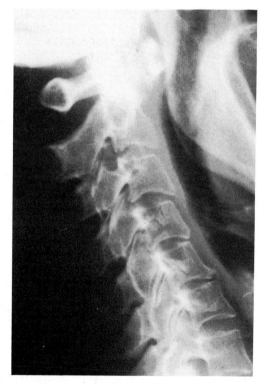

Fig. 16.4. Rheumatoid arthritis with atlanto-axial dislocation.

vertebral bodies, and when this affects the axis and the odontoid process, atlanto-axial dislocation with alarming forward movement of the axis may occur, similar to that seen in pathological fracture of the odontoid (*Fig.* 16.4). The spinal canal is abruptly narrowed between the arch of the atlas and the body of the axis with severe angulation and pinching of the theca. This deformity may contribute to a severe myelopathy.

Management is difficult. If it can be established that the deformity and deficit are progressive, and there is a clinical response to initial traction and reduction of the deformity, surgical stabilization by posterior wiring may be indicated.

SPINAL TUMOUR

The presentation and management of spinal tumours in the elderly does not differ significantly from that in younger patients. The problem of differentiation between cervical tumour and cervical spondylosis has been discussed (*see* Cervical Spondylosis) and attention drawn to the chronicity and very slow progression of spinal meningioma. Further comment will be made only upon the few lesions that pose particular problems in the elderly.

Extradural Spinal Metastasis

This is the most common spinal tumour, the main sites of the primary lesion in the elderly being breast, lung and prostate; myeloma is more frequent in the elderly than in the younger patient. Renal carcinoma may occasionally cause spinal metastases, but the alimentary tract very rarely. All these tumours may produce spinal cord compression without radiological evidence of collapse, deformity of the vertebral bodies, or change in bone texture; however, it is rare for prostatic cancer to produce cord compression without sclerotic and/or lytic bone changes. Therefore normal plain radiographs never exclude cord compression due to tumour.

Management

The problems of management in the elderly may be summarized as:

a. The presence of malignancy. In the absence of bone destruction the diagnosis of malignancy cannot be assumed unless there is positive pathological evidence elsewhere.

b. Carcinoma of the breast, primary and metastatic, may, especially in the elderly, remain dormant for many years. Therefore general prognosis may be very difficult to assess and in the absence of bony disease at the relevant neurological level, cord compression may be due to an unrelated benign tumour, or cervical spondylosis.

c. Carcinoma of the prostate in the elderly with bony spinal metastases may remain relatively static for many years, with or without vertebral collapse. If the diagnosis has already been established and if the evidence of cord compression is mild, initial treatment by local radiotherapy and stilboestrol is reasonable, thus avoiding lami- nectomy, provided the patient is closely observed for neurological deterioration.

d. The presence of collapse of vertebral bodies indicating anterior compression of the theca is an adverse factor, and, especially in the elderly militates against surgery.

e. Profound neurological deficit (e.g. total paraplegia and total sensory loss) carries a very poor prognosis in the elderly, and may be a contraindication to surgery and radiotherapy.

f. Myelography is necessary whenever there is clinical evidence of a cord lesion, especially to differentiate between extradural compression and an intradural extramedullary benign tumour (e.g. meningioma and Schwannoma), and to avoid radiotherapy for what may be a vascular

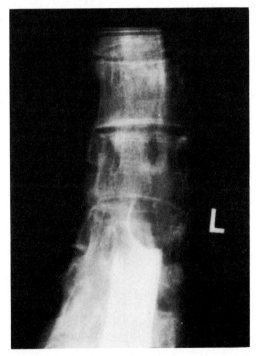

Fig. 16.5. Myelogram showing intradural tumour (meningioma) with scoliosis.

lesion without cord compression. However, if the cord lesion has been steadily progressive in the presence of bony disease at that level, it may be justifiable in the very frail and elderly patient to forego myelography and proceed with radiotherapy.

There has been continuing debate over the place of surgery (Brice and McKissock, 1965) versus radiotherapy in the treatment of extra-dural spinal metastases, a debate which is particularly relevant to the elderly (Dunn et al., 1980). Some authors have claimed that radio-therapy, provided it is given as a matter of urgency, is as effective, indeed more effective, than surgical decompression in relieving cord compression (Young et al., 1980). The case is not proven, but provided the diagnosis has been established, that course is reasonable, especially when vertebral body collapse is present.

Of the two important benign spinal tumours, Schwannoma (neuro-fibroma) and meningioma, the latter is more common in the elderly, 56

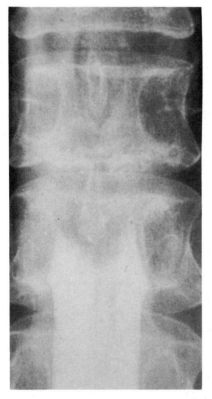

Fig. 16.6. Myelogram showing obstruction due to thoracic intervertebral disc. Clinical and radiological diagnosis of tumour.

per cent of meningiomas but only 37 per cent of Schwannomas occurring over the age of 50 (Sloof et al., 1964).

Meningiomas occur in the cervical region, where they mimic cervical spondylosis (*see above*), and in the thoracic region, but rarely in the lumbar. The features of cord compression may develop so gradually that the diagnosis may not be made until the neurological deficit is well advanced, especially when skeletal disease (e.g. osteoarthritis) of the lower limbs is present (*see* Problems of Clinical Diagnosis). However, the cord lesion is often relatively lateralized and a Brown-Séquard syndrome may be present. The chronicity in a frail elderly patient may tempt the clinician to make a diagnosis of 'spinal vascular disease' especially because pain in the back is not common (*Fig.* 16.5). Occasionally a thoracic disc protrusion may mimic clinically and radiologically an anteriorly placed thoracic meningioma (*Fig.* 16.6) (Carson et al., 1971).

SPINAL VASCULAR DISEASE

Apart from the vascular disturbances secondary to cervical and lumbar spondylosis, ischaemic disease of the spinal cord is rare. The clinical diagnosis of an acute ischaemic lesion, especially of the thoracic cord, can be rarely made confidently unless a profound neurological deficit was of very sudden onset. The classic anterior spinal artery syndrome of paraplegia with loss of pain and temperature sensation and relative sparing of posterior column sensation is rare, and more likely to be secondary to spinal cord compression than due to a primary ischaemic lesion. If there are symptoms and signs of dissection of the aorta, paraplegia may be reasonably ascribed to that cause, but in most cases the diagnosis of ischaemia can be made only by exclusion.

DEGENERATIVE LUMBAR SPONDYLOSIS

This common condition afflicts particularly the elderly, and is the cause of much suffering and distress which may be difficult to relieve. As in cervical spondylosis, the pathological factors are an exaggeration or acceleration of the normal ageing process which affects particularly the interlaminar joints (synonym: posterior, zygapophyseal), the intervertebral discs and the margins of the vertebral bodies. The changes have been clearly and fully described recently by Roberts (1980). The natural process of desiccation and shrinkage of the intervertebral discs with ageing, throws undue stress upon the interlaminar joints which show osteoarthritic changes; this includes marked enlargement of the articular processes, thereby producing a series of bony masses lying posterolaterally at each intervertebral level. The ligamenta flava which extend well laterally and into the lateral recesses of the spinal canal become thickened. Anteriorly the osteophytic lipping of the margins of the vertebral bodies and the hardening of the bulging annulus fibrosus produce hard transverse bars. These changes in combination produce narrowing of the spinal canal (spinal stenosis), especially in the sagittal diameter and a striking change in the cross-section of the canal from its normal triangular to a trefoil form. The posterolateral masses obliterate the lateral recesses of the canal and narrow the intervertebral foramina. The changes may be accentuated by pre-existing narrowing of the sagittal diameter of the canal.

The clinical presentation may be a combination of skeletal symptoms, especially pain in the back, symptoms and signs due to nerve root compression either within the spinal canal or at the intervertebral foramina, and compression of radicular arteries supplying the conus medullaris and cauda equina. The back pain, the most common symptom, is not in itself an indication for investigation beyond plain radiographs to exclude destructive bony disease. Analgesics, rest and a lumbar spinal support may bring some relief. The results of surgery are disappointing.

Nerve root compression produces lower limb pain of a radicular distribution, loosely described as 'sciatic', the pain being more striking than sensory loss or weakness. Although sensory loss affecting L4, 5 and S1 segments with absent tendon reflexes may mimic peripheral neuropathy, an accurate description of the distribution of pain should clarify the diagnosis. Disturbances of micturition, particularly in the female, may be the predominant or even the sole manifestation of cauda equina compression, and is more readily relieved by surgical decompression than other manifestations of the disease (Sharr et al., 1976). The main differential diagnoses include true prolapsed intervertebral disc, which is rare in the elderly, and spinal tumour which may occasionally present predominantly with disturbances of micturition (Garfield and Lytle, 1970).

Ischaemic disturbances secondary to degenerative lumbar spondylosis which characteristically lead to lower limb sensory symptoms and less commonly motor of an essentially root distribution provoked by walking and relieved rapidly by standing still are differentiated from intermittent claudication due to peripheral vascular disease by taking an accurate history (Verbiest, 1955; Blau and Logue, 1961; Hawkes and Roberts, 1980). However, the factors of stenosis of the spinal canal and the intervertebral foramina causing compression of the radicular arteries may be combined with arterial disease (atheroma) affecting the aortic and lumbar arteries (*Fig.* 16.7).

The indications for investigation are the severity of symptoms and the need to exclude a spinal tumour. Plain radiographs may demonstrate degenerative changes, especially sclerosis and hypertrophy of the interlaminar joints, and narrowing of the sagittal diameter of the canal.

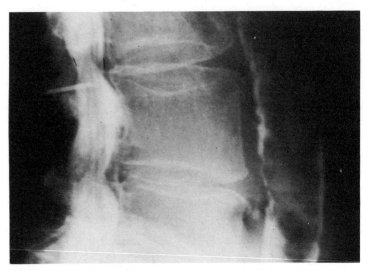

Fig. 16.7. Degenerative lumbar spondylosis. Compression of theca at multiple levels, and severe aortic calcification. Patient had symptoms of intermittent ischaemia of the cauda equina.

Myelography may show severe narrowing and 'waisting' of the theca and even complete obstruction (*Fig.* 16.8). The results of decompressive surgery are most favourable for bladder and ischaemic symptoms, and least so for skeletal symptoms, but operation is an extensive procedure for the elderly.

CONCLUSION

The differential diagnosis and management of spinal lesions in the elderly is similar to that in the middle-aged, but with an increasing incidence of the degenerative conditions of cervical and lumbar spondylosis. The difficulties of diagnosis are related more to the attitude and enthusiasm of the physician and the presence of unrelated skeletal disease, than to the neurological disorder. Successful management requires careful consideration of expectation and, above all, quality of life, provided that they are not used as a pretext for evading the need for investigation. With the degenerative conditions, and especially cervical spondylosis, the bias of management should be towards the conservative, but when cord compression by tumour, and especially benign tumour, is one of the differential diagnoses, the attitude should be one of aggression in the belief that it is better for the elderly to perish at surgery than to pass their remaining days, however few, paraplegic.

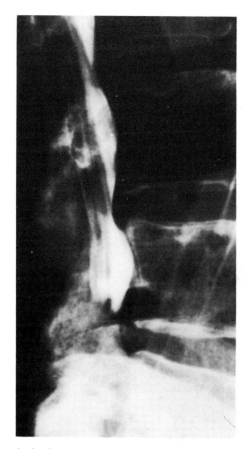

Fig. 16.8. Degenerative lumbar spondylosis causing complete myelographic block.

REFERENCES

Blau J. N. and Logue V. (1961) *Lancet* **1**, 1081.
Brice J. and McKissock W. (1965) *Br. Med. J.* **1**, 1341.
Burrows E. H. (1963) *Clin. Radiol.* **14**, 77.
Carson J., Gumpert J. and Jefferson A. (1971) *Neurol. Neurosurg. Psychiatry* **34**, 68.
Dunn R. C., Kelly, W. A. et al. (1980) *J. Neurosurg.* **52**, 47.
Epstein J. A., Carras R. et al. (1979) *J. Neurosurg.* **51**, 362.
Fischer C. M. (1977) *Clin. Neurosurg.* **24**, 270.
Garfield J. and Lytle S. N. (1970) *Br. J. Urol.* **42**, 551.
Guidetti B. and Fortuna A. (1969) *J. Neurosurg.* **30**, 714.
Hawkes C. H. and Roberts G. M. (1980) *Br. J. Hosp. Med.* **23**, 498.
Lunsford L. D., Bissonette P. A. C. and Zorub D. S. (1980) *J. Neurosurg.* **53**, 12.
Nurick S. (1972a) *Brain* **95**, 87.
Nurick S. (1972b) *Brain* **95**, 101.

Roberts G. (1980) MD Thesis, University of London.
Sharr M. M., Garfield J. S. and Jenkins J. D. (1976) *Br. Med. J.* **1**, 695.
Sloof J. L., Kernohan J. W. and MacCarty C. S. (1964) *Primary Intramedullary Tumours of the Spinal Cord and Filum Terminale.* Saunders, Philadelphia and London.
Verbiest H. (1955) *J. Bone Joint Surg.* **37B**, 576.
Young R. F., Post E. M. et al. (1980) *J. Neurosurg.* **53**, 741.

17. OTHER NEUROSURGICAL PROBLEMS
J. W. Turner and F. I. Caird

INTRACRANIAL TUMOUR

Although intracranial tumours are uncommon in the elderly in comparison with cerebral infarction and other neurological disorders (Twomey, 1978), they remain an important problem because their prognosis and management are very different. A minority of cases will benefit from curative surgical treatment, and many others should be treated with high-dose steroid therapy (Graham and Caird, 1978), from which they will benefit at least for some weeks or months. In others, rehabilitative effort will be less, and can be concentrated where it is more likely to be useful. Accurate diagnosis is thus essential if proper management is to be effective.

Table 17.1. Ninety-two intracranial tumours in elderly patients

	Age					Sex			
	<65	65–69	70–74	75–79	80+	M	F	Total	%
Primary malignant (astrocytoma)	1	11	15	5	3	19	15	34	37
Metastatic	3	9	14	6	3	26	9	35	38
Meningioma	2	1	2	5	3	3	10	13	14
Other	0	1	5	3	1	4	6	10*	11
Total	6	22	36	19	10	52	40	92	100

* Three pituitary adenomas; 3 lymphomas; 2 oligodendrogliomas; 1 gliosarcoma; 1 acoustic neuroma.

The present account is based in part on a study of 92 patients with intracranial tumour referred to the University Department of Geriatric Medicine at the Southern General Hospital, Glasgow, between 1972 and 1981 (*Table* 17.1).

Clinical Features

The main manifestations of intracranial tumour are signs and symptoms of raised intracranial pressure and of a focal intracranial lesion. Both signs and symptoms progress over a period of weeks or months,

231

though some meningiomas produce intermittent symptoms (Daly et al., 1961). About three-quarters of malignant tumours will have a history at the time of presentation of less than 6 months' duration, and three-quarters of benign tumours of longer than 6 months.

The symptoms of raised intracranial pressure in the elderly differ from those characteristic in young people. Headache has been recorded in approximately 50 per cent of cases in old age (Friedman and Odom, 1972; Cooney and Solitaire, 1974), but was much less common in the present series. Vomiting is also uncommon. These differences may be due to the age-related reduction in brain volume, and the consequent availability of more space within the cranium for tumour growth, whose main effect is thus distortion of the brain rather than increase in intracranial pressure. The symptoms attributable to raised intracranial pressure in the elderly are apathy, lethargy, confusion, and increasing immobility and incontinence; these are likely to be attributed in the first instance to a wide variety of other conditions. The signs of raised intracranial pressure are also few and non-specific. Apathy, slowness of response and drowsiness are characteristic. There may be neck stiffness, and there is often impairment of upward gaze (Pennybacker, 1949). Papilloedema is unusual; it was only certainly identified in 5 per cent of the present series, though Friedman and Odom (1972) and Cooney and Solitaire (1974) found it in up to 30 per cent. Though the finding of papilloedema is highly significant, its absence is of no diagnostic significance.

A hemiparesis due to tumour is likely to be attributed in the first instance to stroke, and this is much the commonest initial diagnosis (McLaurin and Helmer, 1962). In the great majority of patients with stroke, mental state and usually motor power improve over a period of days or weeks. If the focal lesion is due to tumour, there is no improvement, except in a small proportion of cases, especially with meningioma, but rather a steady worsening. Repeated review and careful assessment are thus necessary if the correct diagnosis is to be suspected.

Epileptic seizures are a feature of between 15 and 30 per cent of cases of hemisphere tumour in the elderly. Only 10–15 per cent of seizures of all types developing for the first time in old age are due to tumour (Roberts et al., 1982), but the proportion may be higher in the case of partial seizures.

Diagnosis

The essential diagnostic measures consist of establishing a possible primary site (bronchial carcinoma being the commonest (Friedman and Odom, 1972; *Table* 17.2)), with a scintiscan and an EEG. The scintiscan will be normal in only a small proportion of space-occupying lesions

(MacDonald, 1981), but is often abnormal in the first few weeks after a cerebral infarction. The EEG is also likely to be abnormal. The definitive investigation is the CT scan, which in the majority of cases can indicate the probable pathology (*see* pp. 54–7).

Verification of the pathology of intracranial tumour by biopsy remains important in the elderly, its principal purpose being to establish the diagnosis beyond doubt. Biopsy should be undertaken if there is uncertainty of combined clinical and CT scan grounds whether the lesion is a tumour (and not for instance an abscess), or any serious possibility that it may be benign, and so situated that surgical treatment is possible. Biopsy is less desirable if the tumour is in the dominant hemisphere, and dysphasia might be worsened. Biopsy is best carried out after at least 24 hours of steroid therapy (*see below*); this will lessen any surrounding oedema and render the procedure less immediately hazardous.

Table 17.2. Thirty-five metastatic intracranial tumours

Primary	M	F	Total
Lung, definite	16	2	23
Lung, probable	4	1	
Uncertain	3	3	6
Other	3*	3†	6
Total	26	9	35

*One each rectum, kidney, melanoma.
† One each breast, thyroid, melanoma.

Treatment

In most cases of benign intracranial tumour, partial or total removal should be undertaken, unless the tumour is so situated that this would carry undue risks, or the symptoms are minor and non-disabling. Three of the 13 meningiomas in the present series were incidental (cp. Moersch et al., 1941; Wood et al., 1957), and were certainly not responsible for the patient's symptoms.

Malignant intracranial tumours, whether primary or secondary, should be treated with high-dose steroid therapy. This is as beneficial in the elderly as in younger patients (Graham and Caird, 1978), and some 60 per cent may be expected to improve. In the present study 37 of the 61 patients so treated improved (61 per cent); this figure differed little between primary (17 of 27, 63 per cent) and secondary tumours (14 of 23, 61 per cent). Increased alertness and reduced motor disability are often evident within as little as 12 hours, and usually reach their maximum within 5 days, though improvement may continue to increase for several weeks. Improvement is due more to reduction in the mass effect of the oedema surrounding the tumour than of the tumour itself; it is thus the more likely the greater the oedema evident on the CT scan. A satisfactory policy is to begin treatment with dexamethasone 12 or 16 mg daily, to continue this dose for 5 days, and then to review the situation. If there has been no response, the dose should be rapidly reduced, and finally withdrawn after a further 7 days. If there has been a response, then the dose should be gradually reduced over 7–10 days to a level at which control of symptoms is maintained. A response is likely to continue for some weeks or months. When relapse occurs, it is usually best to withdraw steroids altogether; rapid and fatal deterioration is then likely over a period of a few days, for most of which the patient will be unaware.

Side effects attributable to steroids affect only some 5 per cent. Most are minor, such as insomnia and oral moniliasis. Frank steroid psychosis is much less common, as are diabetes, rapid increase in blood pressure, and perforation of a viscus. Weight gain and a Cushingoid facies may occur after some weeks. There can be no doubt that the benefits of treatment much outweigh its serious complications.

SURGERY OF PAIN AND TRIGEMINAL NEURALGIA

The elderly are more prone to certain painful conditions than younger people, e.g. paroxysmal trigeminal neuralgia, malignant disease, postherpetic neuralgia, and pain following stroke. The many painful degenerative musculoskeletal conditions which occur in the elderly seldom present for neurosurgical management, and will not be considered further.

As in other age groups, psychological factors are frequently important in the management of pain in elderly patients. Emotional aspects of personality may be particularly significant in the elderly, who are often increasingly lonely, having perhaps lost their spouse, and find themselves in a progressively contracting world and sphere of influence. Grief and loneliness are potent exacerbators of pain. The more anxious person and the depressive may become more aware of and reactive to pain with which they would previously have coped. Elderly patients frequently mention inability to cope with chronic pain. Secondary emotional changes become superimposed on the primary organic disorder (Merskey, 1974). A few patients depend on their pain in order to continue to receive attention; in these, relief of pain may be followed by other commanding but less easily definable and treatable symptoms.

Assessment

In the assessment of pain problems, it is useful to estimate the duration, type, quality, and amount of pain which the patient is suffering, and exacerbating and relieving factors should also be determined. The amount of pain may be assessed in several ways. The visual analogue scale may be useful. The 10 cm long scale represents pain ranging from nil to the most severe possible; the patient is asked to make a mark at the point on the scale which would fairly represent his pain at that particular time. If the test is repeated at specific times during the day, the scores can be charted and related to analgesics and other treatment. This method gives a good idea of how much pain the patient wishes the doctor to know about. A somewhat more objective method is algesiometry, in which increasing pressure is used to measure, first the pain perception threshold, and then a threshold for severe pain, for that patient at that time. A third figure can also be obtained, for the patient's average or most severe pain. These three figures may be related to various forms of treatment. Other tests, such as the tourniquet test (Sternbach et al., 1974), or the morphine test and the response to naloxone (Hosobuchi et al., 1981), may give useful information. In addition to these assessments, it is valuable to speak with relatives, particularly with a view to assessing previous personality, and to nurses, doctors, and other staff, to note the patient's reaction to pain.

Rationale of Surgical Treatment

Although its ability to explain all known facts has been doubted (Nathan, 1976), the gate control theory of pain (Melzack and Wall, 1965) has been a great stimulus to the management of pain problems. The theory suggests that, among other things, it is the relative balance of activity in large and small sensory fibres in the spinal cord that determines whether or not the transmission (T) cell is activated to give rise to the experience of pain. Large fibres act both on the T cell and on the small cells of the substantia gelatinosa of the cord, but it is the presynaptic inhibition from the latter, acting particularly on the small and also the large fibres, which constitutes the gating mechanism, and reduces input onto the T cell. Small fibre input, on the other hand, inhibits the substantia gelatinosa and allows the gate to open, so that the uninhibited small fibre activity acts upon the T cell, and results in the experience of pain.

There are three points which can be modified in an attempt to control pain. The small nociceptive fibres can be interrupted or damaged by surgical methods, thus reducing the input to the T cell and so the onward transmission of pain-producing impulses. Stimulation of large fibres increases inhibition from the substantia gelatinosa and closes the gate, so reducing the activity of the T cell and the experience of pain. Alteration of the central control mechanisms, and the powerful influences of personality and emotion, by drugs or stimulatory or destructive surgical treatment can alter the gain or bias in the system. A combined approach, employing more than one of these three forms of attack, would seem to be worthy of consideration in the management of chronic pain.

ABLATIVE TREATMENT

The small nociceptive fibres pass from the peripheral nerves through the dorsal sensory root, where they are surrounded by cerebrospinal fluid, into the dorsal aspect of the spinal cord. There they relay to fibres which cross anterior to the central canal and form the spinothalamic tract in the anterolateral quadrant of the cord, and pass to the thalamus and reticular nuclei of the brainstem (Bowsher, 1957). This so-called 'pain pathway' may be interrupted at any appropriate level. In peripheral nerves, surgical interruption of the small fibres may be accompanied by interruption of the large fibre system, which will in theory reduce the amount of presynaptic inhibition and so make firing of T cells more likely. Both sensory and motor loss will occur. The poor results expected of peripheral nerve section are borne out in practice, and surgical section and neurolytic agents rarely control pain for more than short periods. Cryoanalgesia (Lloyd, 1976) would appear to have a place in managing pain of relatively short duration.

Various agents may be introduced into the subarachnoid space, where they act upon the nerve rootlets. Intrathecal hypertonic saline introduced under general anaesthesia is effective in controlling pain in a reasonable proportion of cases, particularly those with bilateral pain of malignant origin (Hitchcock, 1973a). The risks of the procedure are few, but good results are of limited duration.

The prime site for neurosurgical intervention is the anterolateral quadrant of the spinal cord (Spiller and Martin, 1912; Nathan, 1963), with division of the spinothalamic tract. The pain pathway is fairly well isolated at this point, and interruption of the tract results in loss of pain (and temperature) sensation on the opposite side of the body extending two segments below the level of the section. Spinothalamic tractotomy may be performed percutaneously under local anaesthesia in the cervical region (Mullan et al., 1963; Rosomoff et al., 1965). It is of great value in controlling severe unilateral pain of malignant origin. Elderly patients usually tolerate the procedure well. It is particularly appreciated by those who have maintained a stoical attitude to severe malignant pain. In one group of patients (Turner and Bond, 1973) 43 per cent were suffering from pelvic malignancy (carcinoma of the rectum, cervix or bladder), with unilateral lower limb pain. A further 11 per cent suffered from carcinoma of the breast, and 23 per cent from carcinoma of the lung. Sixty-two per cent had pain in the lower trunk or lower limbs. The indications for cordotomy are intractable pain inadequately controlled by other methods, underlying malignant disease, and usually unilateral pain. Bilateral cordotomy carries a higher risk, than unilateral (Rosomoff, 1969). Contraindications are poor respiratory function (including diaphragmatic paralysis), or a terminal stage of the malignant disease. A heat lesion is made by radiofrequency current, which results in analgesia, usually beginning in the contralateral lower limb, and ascending as the size of the lesion is increased. The extent of the analgesia can often be tailored to the patient's needs. Early postoperative results are good, with satisfactory relief of pain in 87 per cent; this continues in 69 per cent (Turner and Bond, 1973). The reduction in analogue scale readings, and in analgesic requirements, and the change in pain thresholds were all considerable. Personality structures were restored towards normal, and anxiety reduced; there was no change in measures of introversion or extraversion.

The procedure of midline myelotomy divides the pain pathway from both sides of the spinal cord, and should therefore be suitable for patients with bilateral pain (Sourek, 1977). The technique has been used less often than it might, possibly because it entails open surgery, but probably because in the early days after operation dysaesthesiae develop in the limbs, probably because the probe or knife passes between the dorsal columns of the cord in order to reach the crossing of the pain pathways ventral to the central canal.

Other sites for ablative surgery are the brainstem (Hitchcock, 1973b), and the thalamus (Pagni, 1974), where the precision of stereotactic surgery is required. Suitable sites include the centromedianum and intralaminar nuclei of the thalamus. Although the elderly tolerate such interventions quite well, they are undoubtedly at increased risk compared with younger patients. There may, however, be few alternatives for patients suffering from cancer involving multiple cervical and cranial nerves. Pituitary ablation, including more recently by percutaneous alcohol injection (Moricca, 1974; Williams et al., 1980), has been used in the management of patients with malignant disease, and not only those with hormone-dependent tumours.

Trigeminal Neuralgia

The average age of patients with paroxysmal trigeminal neuralgia is 67. Women are more often affected than men in a ratio of 2:1. The relapsing and remitting pain, of a sharp, stabbing nature, is always in the distribution of the trigeminal nerve, most often in the nasolabial fold, where there is frequently a trigger spot, whose stimulation causes severe pain. Triggering may be produced by washing, eating, swallowing, talking, or even activities which transmit the slightest movement to the cheek, such as stretching an arm or even walking. Examination reveals no neurological abnormality. The pain virtually always responds to carbamazepine (200 mg t.d.s.), phenytoin (100 mg t.d.s.) or clonazepam (2 mg b.d.), but if side effects occur or the drugs become ineffective, surgical intervention is indicated.

Recent advances have enabled surgery to remove the pain without causing either total anaesthesia of the face or facial paralysis. Trigeminal thermocoagulation (Sweet and Wepsic, 1974) is very well suited to the elderly. Patients in the 8th and 9th decades tolerate the procedure well, though limited cooperation (including confusion or severe deafness) during the procedure will interfere with its success. The aim of trigeminal thermocoagulation is to create an area of analgesia (i.e. loss of pain sensation) or hypalgesia (i.e. partial loss of such sensation) covering the trigger area and the painful zone. A probe is passed through the cheek and foramen ovale towards the trigeminal rootlets lying between the trigeminal ganglion and the pons. Neuroradiological and functional control is necessary. Depending on the power passed through the nerve rootlets, radiofrequency thermocoagulation at the probe tip produces hypalgesia, analgesia, or anaesthesia (i.e. loss of all sensation). In one series (Turner, 1978), selective sensory depression was produced in the desired zone in 89 per cent; unintended corneal sensory loss occurred in only 3 per cent. Hypalgesia or analgesia without anaesthesia was achieved in 73 per cent. The success rate is not increased by producing total anaesthesia, and patients welcome residual touch sensation because they can feel the contact of food within the mouth and external objects on the cheek. The overall success rate of trigeminal thermocoagulation in this series was 92 per cent, a figure similar to that of others (Sweet and Wepsic, 1974; Apfelbaum, 1977; Siegfried, 1977). In a small but important minority of patients, anaesthesia or analgesia dolorosa developed; this consists of a most unpleasant burning or creeping sensation, rather than pain, in the numb area. Electrical stimulation and drugs are not always successful in relieving this sensation, which is particularly prone to develop in the ophthalmic division.

Microvascular decompression (Janetta, 1976) or limited rhizotomy have also been used in paroxysmal trigeminal neuralgia, but open operation with its associated risks is necessary. Although the elderly tolerate these procedures well, younger patients would seem more suitable. The older subtemporal approach to the trigeminal ganglion, with open operation and complete section of the retrogasserian rootlets, is seldom used, because it resulted in anaesthesia rather than analgesia. There was a risk of up to 10 per cent of facial paralysis. Neither of these problems is likely with modern surgery, and patients need to be reassured on these points at interview.

SENSORY STIMULATION

Following Melzack and Wall's description of the gate control theory, much interest focused on attempts to control pain by increasing the sensory input or deafferentation. For example, in phantom limb pain, electrical stimulation, and stimulation of peripheral nerves, spinal cord, and brain have been employed (Nashold, 1977). Transcutaneous stimulation is relatively simple and has few side effects; it can be stopped if necessary, and no permanent ablative lesion has been made. Small easily portable stimulators are available, which enable stimuli to be applied through various types of electrode to appropriate points on the skin, usually in the area of pain. The technique has been much used, particularly in those types of pain in which there is apparently loss of sensory input or deafferentation. For example, in phantom limb pain, Melzack (1974) has suggested that decreased sensory input into the brainstem reticular formation reduces the tonic inhibitory influence of the central biasing mechanism at all levels, and in particular on the spinal gating mechanism. This allows self-sustaining activity to be triggered repeatedly by remaining fibres, pain resulting when a critical level is exceeded. It is known that after amputation there is a marked reduction in the number of sensory fibres, and the remaining regenerating fibres tend to be of small diameter.

Elderly patients are particularly prone to develop post-herpetic neuralgia. The condition usually begins soon after the eruption of shingles has appeared, and although the pain usually fades rapidly, in some patients disabling burning pain persists for years, often worsened by contact between clothes and the scarred area when this is on the chest, or by exposure to cold when on the face. Examination of the area of scarring shows zones of hypalgesia, analgesia and of abnormal increased sensitivity. Histological examination shows a reduction in the number of large fibres. Treatment by transcutaneous stimulation can give significant relief to such patients (Nathan and Wall, 1974), particularly when combined with drugs, such as amitriptyline and perphenazine. Occasionally the patient is cured after only a short period of treatment, but more often alleviation rather than cure is obtained, particularly during the period of stimulation, with a carry-over effect lasting after stimulation has ceased. This method can also be used for phantom limb pain, pain following stroke, pain in multiple sclerosis, and pain from malignant disease.

Spinal cord stimulation (Shealy et al., 1970) aims at applying electrical stimuli more directly to the neural elements, and in particular the dorsal columns, of the spinal cord. A relatively straightforward percutaneous procedure under local anaesthesia places electrodes in the extradural space. It is still difficult to predict which patients will obtain relief, especially in the longer term, but pain of the chronic low back syndrome, terminal cancer, and the post-amputation syndrome have been successfully treated. Young (1978) reported that no patient followed for 4 years or more obtained complete relief. A trial period of external percutaneous stimulation may help to eliminate non-responders and improve the results (Miles et al., 1974; Urban and Nashold, 1978).

Direct electrical stimulation to deep brain structures may also be employed. Liebeskind et al. (1974) showed in animal experiments that stimulation of the central and periventricular grey matter showed an analgesic effect comparable to that of large doses of morphine, and reduced by the morphine antagonist, naloxone. Appropriate brain stimulation exerts a powerful attenuating effect on incoming pain by increasing inhibition at the spinal cord and other levels, closing the gate to pain. Stimulation-produced analgesia in man (Hosobuchi et al., 1981) appears to be closely related to the release of beta-endorphins, and is reversed by naloxone. The most effective site for stimulation to control pain was the ventrolateral periaqueductal grey matter.

CONCLUSION

In this review of some aspects of the surgical management of pain in elderly patients, other methods have necessarily been given scant or no reference. That is not to imply that they are not and have not already been fully utilized and combined with surgical treatments in patients in the groups described. While surgical methods are often considered to be the last resort, such an attitude should not be allowed to deprive patients of pain relief by surgery for too long (Editorial, 1981). Often pain cannot be cured, but it may frequently be alleviated by combined therapeutic approaches.

REFERENCES

Apfelbaum R. I. (1977) *Neurosurgery* 1, 16.
Bowsher D. (1957) *Brain* 80, 606.
Cooney L. M. and Solitaire G. B. (1974) *Modern Geriatrics* 4, 234.
Daly D. D., Svien, H. J. et al. (1961) *Arch. Neurol.* 5, 287.
Editorial (1981) *Br. Med. J.* 282, 1820.
Friedman H. and Odom G. L. (1972) *Geriatrics* 27 April, 105.
Graham K. and Caird F. I. (1978) *Age Ageing* 7, 146.
Hitchcock E. R. (1973a) *J. Neurosurg.* 39, 746.
Hitchcock E. R. (1973b) *Lancet* 1, 310.
Hosobuchi Y., Baskin D. S. et al. (1981) VIII Meeting of World Society for Stereotactic and Functional Neurosurgery. Zurich.
Janetta P. J. (1976) *Prog. Neurol. Surg.* 7, 180.
Liebeskind J. C., Mayer D. J. and Aki H. (1974) *Adv. Neurol.* 4, 261.
Lloyd J. W. (1976) *Lancet* 2, 932.

MacDonald J. B. (1981) In: Caird F. I. and Evans J. G. (ed.) *Advanced Geriatric Medicine*. London, Pitman Medical.
McLaurin R. L. and Helmer F. A. (1962) *JAMA* **180**, 1011.
Melzack R. (1974) *Adv. Neurol.* **4**, 319.
Melzack R. and Wall P. D. (1965) *Science* **150**, 971.
Merskey H. (1974) *Adv. Neurol.* **4**, 605.
Miles J., Lipton S., Hayward M. et al. (1974) *Lancet* **1**, 777.
Moersch F. P., Craig W. McK. and Kernohan J. W. (1941) *Arch. Neurol. Psychiatry* **45**, 235.
Moricca G. (1974) *Adv. Neurol.* **4**, 707.
Mullan S., Harper P. V., Hekmatpanah J. et al. (1963) *J. Neurosurg.* **20**, 931.
Nashold B. S. (1977) *Neurosurgery* **1**, 230.
Nathan P. W. (1963) *J. Neurol. Neurosurg. Psychiatry* **26**, 353.
Nathan P. W. (1976) *Brain* **99**, 123.
Nathan P. W. and Wall P. D. (1974) *Br. Med. J.* **3**, 645.
Pagni C. A. (1974) *Adv. Neurol.* **4**, 699.
Pennybacker J. (1949) *Edin. Med. J.* **56**, 590.
Roberts M. A., Godfrey J. W. and Caird F. I. (1982) *Age Ageing* **11**, 24.
Rosomoff H. L. (1969) *J. Neurosurg.* **31**, 41.
Rosomoff H. L., Carroll F., Brown J. et al. (1965) *J. Neurosurg.* **23**, 639.
Shealy C. N., Mortimer J. T. and Hagfors N. R. (1970) *J. Neurosurg.* **32**, 560.
Siegfried J. (1977) *Surg. Neurol.* **8**, 126.
Sourek K. (1977) *Prog. Neurol. Surg.* **8**, 15.
Spiller W. G. and Martin E. (1912) *JAMA* **58**, 1489.
Sternbach R. A., Murphy R. W., Timmermans G. et al. (1974) *Adv. Neurol.* **4**, 281.
Sweet W. H. and Wepsic J. C. (1974) *J. Neurosurg.* **40**, 143.
Turner J. W. (1978) *J. Neurol. Neurosurg. Psychiatry* **41**, 187.
Turner J. W. and Bond M. R. (1973) *J. Neurol. Neurosurg. Psychiatry* **36**, 889.
Twomey C. (1978) *Age Ageing* **7**, 138.
Urban B. J. and Nashold B. S. (1978) *J. Neurosurg.* **48**, 323.
Young R. F. (1978) *Neurosurgery* **3**, 363.
Williams N. E., Miles J. B., Lipton S. et al. (1980) *Ann. R. Coll. Surg. Engl.* **62**, 203.
Wood M. W., White R. J. and Kernohan J. W. (1957) *J. Neuropath. Exp. Neurol.* **16**, 337.

Index